APPLIED ENVIRONMENTAL GENOMICS

EDITORS: OLIVER F. BERRY, CLARE E. HOLLELEY AND SIMON N. JARMAN

CSIRO
PUBLISHING

CRC Press
Taylor & Francis Group
Boca Raton   London   New York

CRC Press is an imprint of the
Taylor & Francis Group, an **informa** business

A catalogue record for this book is available from the National Library of Australia.

ISBN: 9781486314928 (hbk)
ISBN: 9781486314935 (epdf)
ISBN: 9781486314942 (epub)

Published in print in Australia and New Zealand, and in all other formats throughout the world, by CSIRO Publishing.

CSIRO Publishing
Private Bag 10
Clayton South VIC 3169
Australia

Telephone: +61 3 9545 8400
Email: publishing.sales@csiro.au
Website: www.publish.csiro.au
Sign up to our email alerts: publish.csiro.au/earlyalert

Published in print only, throughout the world (except in Australia and New Zealand), by CRC Press, with ISBN 9781032584508.

CRC Press
6000 Broken Sound Parkway NW, Suite 300, Boca Raton, FL 33487-2742
and
4 Park Square, Milton Park, Abingdon, Oxon, OX14 4RN
Website: www.routledge.com

CRC Press is an imprint of Taylor & Francis Group, LLC

Cover illustration by Maya Edelman
Cover design by Cath Pirret
Typeset by Envisage Information Technology
Index by Master Indexing
Printed in China by Leo Paper Products Ltd

CSIRO Publishing publishes and distributes scientific, technical and health science books, magazines and journals from Australia to a worldwide audience and conducts these activities autonomously from the research activities of the Commonwealth Scientific and Industrial Research Organisation (CSIRO). The views expressed in this publication are those of the author(s) and do not necessarily represent those of, and should not be attributed to, the publisher or CSIRO. The copyright owner shall not be liable for technical or other errors or omissions contained herein. The reader/user accepts all risks and responsibility for losses, damages, costs and other consequences resulting directly or indirectly from using this information.

CSIRO acknowledges the Traditional Owners of the lands that we live and work on and pays its respect to Elders past and present. CSIRO recognises that Aboriginal and Torres Strait Islander peoples in Australia and other Indigenous peoples around the world have made and will continue to make extraordinary knowledge and science. The use of Western science in this publication should not be interpreted as diminishing the knowledge of plants, animals and environment from Indigenous ecological knowledge systems.

The paper this book is printed on is in accordance with the standards of the Forest Stewardship Council® and other controlled material. The FSC® promotes environmentally responsible, socially beneficial and economically viable management of the world's forests.

MIX
Paper | Supporting
responsible forestry
FSC® C020056
www.fsc.org

Contents

Acknowledgements

The editors thank our families for their support, and our many colleagues for shaping this exciting field.

OB and CH especially thank Andrew Young for his mentorship and unwavering enthusiasm for environmental genomics.

EDITORIAL ASSISTANT STAFF
Sarah Whiteley
Mark Wallace

REVIEWERS WHO VOLUNTEERED THEIR TIME
Alexander Schmidt-Lebuhn
Alyssa Budd
Andrea Wild
Arthur Georges
Austen Thomas
Benjamin Mayne
Caesar Li
Carlos Gonzalez Orozco
Catriona Campbell
Dan Bock
Eric Anderson
Hardip Patel
Haruko Ando
Jason Kennington
Karen Bell
Kristy Deiner and lab
Leo Joseph
Marina Alexander
Mark Haroldson
Max Lambert
Nic Rawlence
Pierre Feutry
Sam Andrew
Sam Banks
Sam Thomson
Stephen Sarre
Xavier Pochon

CSIRO PUBLISHING
Mark Hamilton
Tracey Kudis
Briana Melideo

List of contributors

Ostaizka Aizpurua
Center for Evolutionary Hologenomics, Globe Institute, University of Copenhagen, Copenhagen, Denmark

Antton Alberdi
Center for Evolutionary Hologenomics, Globe Institute, University of Copenhagen, Copenhagen, Denmark

Alana Alexander
Department of Anatomy, University of Otago, Dunedin, New Zealand

Fred W. Allendorf
Division of Biological Sciences, University of Montana, Missoula, USA

Jeremy J. Austin
Australian Centre for Ancient DNA (ACAD), School of Biological Sciences, The University of Adelaide, Adelaide, Australia

Andreas Bachler
National Research Collections Australia, CSIRO, Canberra, Australia; and Australian National University, Research School of Biology, Canberra, Australia

Katherine Belov
School of Life and Environmental Sciences, The University of Sydney, Sydney, Australia

Andrew Bissett
CSIRO Environment, Hobart, Australia

M. Teresa Boquete
Department of Evolutionary Ecology, Estación Biológica de Doñana, CSIC, Sevilla, Spain

Ángel Borja
AZTI, Marine Research, Basque Research and Technology Alliance (BRTA), Gipuzkoa, Spain

Mark V. Bravington
CSIRO, Hobart, Australia; and Estimark Research, Hobart, Australia

Georgina Brennan
Aquatic Ecology, Lund University, Lund, Sweden

Thibaut Capblancq
Department of Plant Biology, University of Vermont, Burlington, USA

Emma L. Carroll
Te Kura Mātauranga Koiora – School of Biological Sciences, Waipapa Taumata Rau – University of Auckland, Tāmaki Makaurau Auckland, Aotearoa New Zealand

Renee A. Catullo
School of Biological Sciences, University of Western Australia, Perth, Australia

Hugo Cayuela
Department of Ecology and Evolution, University of Lausanne, Lausanne, Switzerland; and Université Lyon 1, Laboratoire de Biométrie et Biologie Evolutive, Villeurbanne, France

Jackson Champer
Center for Bioinformatics, School of Life Sciences, Peking-Tsinghua Center for Life Sciences, Peking University, Beijing, China

Yuanyuan Cheng
School of Life and Environmental Sciences, The University of Sydney, Sydney, Australia

Anna C. Clark
Department of Anatomy, University of Otago, Dunedin, New Zealand

Joseph D. Clark
U.S. Geological Survey, Northern Rocky Mountain Science Center, University of Tennessee, Knoxville, USA

Jocelyn P. Colella
Biodiversity Institute and Department of Ecology and Evolutionary Biology, University of Kansas, Lawrence, USA

Joseph A. Cook
Museum of Southwestern Biology and Biology Department, University of New Mexico, Albuquerque, USA

Simon Creer
Molecular Ecology and Evolution Group at Bangor, School of Biological Sciences, Bangor University, Bangor, UK

Catherine Darst
U.S. Fish and Wildlife Service, Ventura, California, USA

Natasha de Vere
Natural History Museum of Denmark, University of Copenhagen, Copenhagen, Denmark

Bruce Deagle
Australian National Fish Collection, CSIRO, Hobart, Australia

Floriaan Devloo-Delva
National Research Collections Australia, CSIRO, Canberra, Australia

Rey Edison
Media Laboratory, Massachusetts Institute of Technology, Cambridge, USA

Raphael Eisenhofer
Center for Evolutionary Hologenomics, Globe Institute, University of Copenhagen, Copenhagen, Denmark

Francisco Encinas-Viso
Centre for Australian National Biodiversity Research, CSIRO, Canberra, Australia

Christopher Faulk
Department of Animal Science, University of Minnesota, St. Paul, USA

Brenna R. Forester
Department of Biology, Colorado State University, Fort Collins, USA

Neil J. Gemmell
Department of Anatomy, University of Otago, Dunedin, New Zealand

Paul George
Département de médecine moléculaire, Faculté de medicine, Université Laval, Quebec City, Canada

Arthur Georges
Institute for Applied Ecology, University of Canberra, Canberra, Australia

Tom Gibson
Molecular Ecology and Evolution Group at Bangor, School of Biological Sciences, Bangor University, Bangor, UK

Peter Gilchrist
Biodiversity, Environmental Protection, Saudi Aramco, Dhahran, Saudi Arabia

Alicia Grealy
The Australian National Herbarium, CSIRO, Canberra, Australia

Stephen E. Greiman
Department of Biology, Georgia Southern University, Statesboro, USA

Geoff Grossel
Australian Government Department of Agriculture, Fisheries & Forestry, Canberra, Australia

Carolyn J. Hogg
School of Life and Environmental Sciences, The University of Sydney, Sydney, Australia

Clare E. Holleley
National Research Collections Australia, CSIRO, Canberra, Australia

Luke Holman
Section for Evolutionary Genomics, Globe Institute, Faculty of Health and Medical Sciences, University of Copenhagen, Copenhagen, Denmark

Simon Jarman
School of Molecular and Life Sciences, Curtin University, Perth, Australia

Laura Jones
National Botanic Garden of Wales, Llanarthne, UK

Marty Kardos
Northwest Fisheries Science Center, National Marine Fisheries Service, USA

Mandira Katuwal
Department of Anatomy, University of Otago, Dunedin, New Zealand

Alexander Kopatz
Norwegian Institute for Nature Research, Trondheim, Norway

Susan Kutz
Faculty of Veterinary Medicine, University of Calgary, Calgary, Canada

Clayton Lamb
Department of Biology, University of British Columbia, Kelowna, Canada

Jesse R. Lasky
Department of Biology, Pennsylvania State University, University Park, USA

Tom Little
Institute of Ecology and Evolution, University of Edinburgh, Edinburgh, UK

Joshua Llinas
The Unusual Pet Vets Jindalee, Veterinary Services for Reptiles, Birds and Small Mammals, Australia

Abigail Lowe
National Botanic Garden of Wales, Llanarthne, UK

Holly L. Lutz
Department of Immunology and Microbiology, The Scripps Research Institute, La Jolla, USA

Benjamin Mayne
Environomics Future Science Platform, CSIRO, Crawley, Australia

Christiana McDonald-Spicer
Ecology & Evolution, Research School of Biology, Australian National University, Canberra, Australia

Julie McInnes
Institute for Marine and Antarctic Studies, University of Tasmania, Hobart, Australia

Sabrina M. McNew
Cornell Lab of Ornithology, Cornell University, Ithaca, USA; and Department of Ecology and Evolutionary Biology, Cornell University, Ithaca, USA

Alvine C. Mehinto
Toxicology, Southern California Coastal Water Research, Costa Mesa, USA

Liz Milla
Centre for Australian National Biodiversity Research, CSIRO, Canberra, Australia

Craig C. Moritz
Ecology & Evolution, Research School of Biology, Australian National University, Canberra, Australia

Garth Mowat
Fish and Wildlife Branch, BC Ministry of Forests, Nelson, Canada; and Department of Earth, Environmental and Geographic Sciences, University of British Columbia, Kelowna, Canada

Anita Norman
Department of Wildlife, Fish, and Environmental Studies, Swedish University of Agricultural Sciences, Umeå, Sweden

Iñaki Odriozola
Center for Evolutionary Hologenomics, Globe Institute, University of Copenhagen, Copenhagen, Denmark

Johan Pansu
ISEM, Université de Montpellier, Montpellier, France

Emma Peel
School of Life and Environmental Sciences, The University of Sydney, Sydney, Australia

William Bernard Perry
Water Institute, School of Biosciences, Cardiff University, Cardiff, UK; and Molecular Ecology and Evolution Group at Bangor, School of Biological Sciences, Bangor University, Bangor, UK

Kirthana Pillay
Molecular Ecology and Evolution Group at Bangor, School of Biological Sciences, Bangor University, Bangor, UK

Michael Proctor
Trans-border Grizzly Bear Project, British Columbia, Canada

Jérôme G. Prunier
Theoretical and Experimental Ecology Station, National Centre for Scientific Research, Paul Sabatier University, Moulis, France

Orly Razgour
Biosciences, University of Exeter, Exeter, UK

Christina L. Richards
Department of Integrative Biology, University of South Florida, Tampa, USA; and Plant Evolutionary Ecology Group, University of Tübingen, Tübingen, Germany

Lee A. Rollins
Evolution & Ecology Research Centre, School of Biological, Earth and Environmental Sciences, University of New South Wales, Sydney, Australia

Quentin Rougemont
CEFE, Université de Montpellier, Montpellier, France

Emily Roycroft
Division of Ecology and Evolution, Research School of Biology, The Australian National University, Canberra, Australia

Nils Ryman
Department of Zoology, University of Stockholm, Stockholm, Sweden

Michael Stat
School of Environmental and Life Sciences, University of Newcastle, Callaghan, Australia

Katarina C. Stuart
Evolution & Ecology Research Centre, School of Biological, Earth and Environmental Sciences, University of New South Wales, Sydney, Australia

Helen Taylor
Royal Zoological Society of Scotland, Edinburgh, Scotland

Michael Traugott
Department of Zoology, University of Innsbruck, Innsbruck, Austria

Jodie van de Kamp
CSIRO Environment, Hobart, Australia

Katrina West
CSIRO Australian National Fish Collection, National Research Collections Australia, CSIRO, Hobart, Australia

Lauren C. White
Arthur Rylah Institute for Environmental Research, Department of Environment, Land, Water and Planning, Heidelberg, Australia

Sarah L. Whiteley
National Research Collections Australia, CSIRO, Canberra, Australia; and Institute for Applied Ecology, University of Canberra, Canberra, Australia

Andrew P. Woolnough
Research, Innovation and Commercialisation, The University of Melbourne, Melbourne, Australia

Introduction to applied environmental genomics

THE CHALLENGE OF ENVIRONMENTAL MANAGEMENT

The economy is a wholly owned subsidiary of the environment, not the reverse.

— Herman E. Daly

Human life depends entirely on the goods and services provided by Earth's biological resources. The biosphere is our habitat, providing us the air we breathe, the plants and animals we eat, the fibres that clothe us, the clean water we drink, the pharmaceuticals that maintain our health, and the spiritual sustenance we experience in nature. Ironically, in the context of global climate change and its catastrophic impacts on biodiversity, even our carbon-based fuels have a biological origin. Economists estimate the value of global environmental services to be 125 trillion dollars annually (Almond *et al.* 2020). This sum is so vast it obscures meaning, but the reality is simple. Without a functioning environment, our economies, our societies, our cultures, and even our bodies cannot function.

It follows that purely from a self-interested perspective, care for the environment must be a core human responsibility since we control the biosphere more than any other species (Bar-On *et al.* 2018). Of course, many would argue that nature deserves respect and conservation independent of human interests. And yet, daily reminders point to virtually all indicators of environmental function going in the wrong direction. What is to be done?

Policies, efforts and actions - at every level - will only succeed ... when based on the best knowledge and evidence.

— Sir Robert Watson, Chair IPBES

Herein lies the central problem in managing ecosystems on their vast scales: a lack of information to support decision making. This situation is so familiar that it is regarded as unremarkable and is wholly normalised in scientific and political circles. Professor Graham Samuel in his recent critique of the fitness of Australia's Environmental Protection Biodiversity Conservation Act writes: 'Decision-makers, proponents and the community do not have access to the best available data, information and science' (Samuel 2020).

In a nutshell, we rarely have information at the scale, speed, and accuracy to make good decisions.

THE RELEVANCE OF GENOMICS

What is the relevance of genomics to this problem? We argue that genomics is relevant because it will be a part of the solution. Genomes encode biological identity, function and condition. Genomes and their products determine what organisms do, from the unique metabolic capabilities of microbes to the behaviour and interactions of large organisms with their environment. They regulate all manner of physiological responses to environmental stimuli. And finally, all levels of biological organisation can be distinguished by their unique DNA. Cells can be identified by transcriptional or epigenomic profiles, individuals can be identified by their genotype, and communities can be identified by the genetic signatures of the species within them. All these aspects – function, condition, and identity – have applications in environmental management. Our challenge is to access this information and make sense of it.

This challenge is within our capabilities. Capitalising on the rich information that genomes provide through advances in molecular biology, information sciences, and engineering, has transformed both medicine and agriculture in recent decades. Genomics has provided access to knowledge to treat human diseases, increase crop yields and more. A similar revolution in environmental science is possible. The massive budgets and engines of innovation in medicine and agriculture have fuelled the development of genomic technologies. The products of this are ripe for co-opting to environmental applications. The chapters of this book show that environmental genomics sits at a unique convergence where the need for better environmental management informed by science is very high, and mature genomic technologies are poised to provide this information.

Of course, the transfer of genomics technologies between medicine, agriculture, and environmental science builds on strong foundations, established over many decades. The methods used for genetic mark-recapture (Chapter 10) are equivalent to those used by forensic scientists for trace DNA collection. The direct genetic modification method provided by **CRISPR-Cas9** technology was developed for

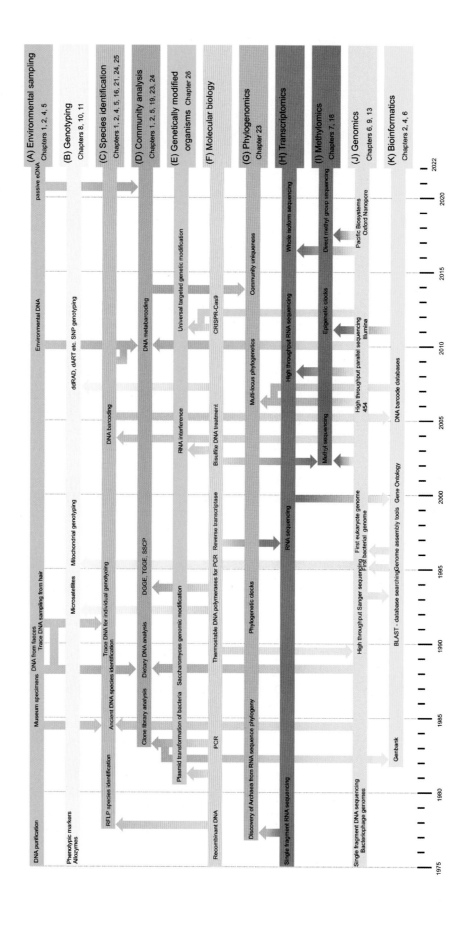

Fig. 1. Technological development in environmental genomics. Significant innovations in fields that contribute to environmental genomics are shown. Chapters in this book that relate to each field are indicated. (A) Nucleic acid extraction methods were initially for large samples from single species, but **polymerase chain reaction (PCR)** based methods enabled 'trace' DNA sampling such as the first **'ancient DNA'** study identifying a museum skin as an extinct Qagga species (Higuchi *et al.* 1984); and the first dietary analysis of food items from bear faeces in 1988 (Höss *et al.* 1992). eDNA sampling is the main field method for many chapters in this book, and new developments such as passive eDNA collection are transforming its capacity (Bessey *et al.* 2021). (B) Genotyping individuals was once generally done with morphological traits or allozymes until PCR enabled amplification of selected DNA regions. Microsatellite loci and **microsatellite DNA** sequencing were a mainstay of this area until High-throughput sequencing (HTS) was available. Methods for **Single nucleotide polymorphism (SNP)** genotyping such as ddRAD became cheap and powerful once HTS was available (Taberlet *et al.* 1999). (C) Species identification is now routinely DNA sequence based, with **DNA barcode** identification of samples from single species being commonplace. (D) Analysis of species diversity with DNA changed dramatically once HTS was available, as this allows mixed DNA pools to be sequenced with ease. When combined with PCR amplification of a **barcode,** this led to DNA **metabarcoding** (Taberlet *et al.* 2012). DNA metabarcoding replaced clone library analysis and methods based on DNA sequence conformation like DGGE and similar approaches. (E) Genetic modification of bacterial plasmids allowed production of bulk DNA before PCR, and bulk proteins if expression plasmids were constructed. Specific genomic modification methods were developed for a range of eukaryotes such as *Saccharomyces*, *Drosophila*, and multiple crop species. Gene knockout methods such as **RNA** interference technology worked on a wider range of species, but the more recent CRISPR-Cas9 technology provides a general approach for targeted gene modification in most organisms (Bak *et al.* 2018). (F) Molecular biology underpins all the research applications described in this book. The PCR transformed manipulation and detection of nucleic acids, especially once thermostable polymerases like *Taq* could be used. (G) The discovery of 'Archaea' by **phylogenetic** analysis of ribosomal RNA sequences overhauled our view of earth's biodiversity (Woese and Fox 1977). Phylogenomics became possible once large numbers of **genome assemblies** became available, and bioinformatic methods for selecting phylogenetically informative regions for comparison were developed. Affordable HTS now allows phylogenetic assessment of community uniqueness as a conservation metric. (H) RNA sequencing by cleavage was the earliest nucleic acid sequencing technology, but RNA sequencing was expensive and difficult until the reverse transcriptase enzyme was commercially available. This allowed RNA to be converted into 'complementary DNA' and sequenced by any DNA sequencing technology. HTS allowed the sequencing of all RNA transcripts in a sample and recent methods allow sequencing of whole, single RNA molecules. (I) Methylomics was enabled by bisulfite treatment of DNA, after which any HTS DNA sequencing platform can be used to determine CpG methylation levels. Newer long-read sequencing platforms can directly identify methylated cytosines and other modified bases. (J) Genomes of bacteriophages were assembled by manual alignment, the first being Φx174 in 1977. Bacterial and then yeast genomes were first sequenced from **Sanger** DNA sequencing data in the 1990s. High-throughput implementations of **Sanger sequencing** were used for the human genome project, initially completed in 2001. The high-throughput sequencing (HTS) era began with 454 'pyrosequencing' technology, which was sold as **'next generation sequencing' (NGS)**. HTS enabled complete genomes of any organism to be produced, with cost declining and quality of assembly improving with each iteration of HTS technologies. (K) Bioinformatics developed partly because of the abundant gene sequence data being deposited in nucleic acid sequence databases. Sequence alignment tools developed into database searching and genome assembly tools. Most chapters in this book involve some bioinformatic analysis, but those completely dependent on it are indicated.

medical applications but has environmental applications such as gene drives for population control of invasive animal species (Chapter 26) and the real-time monitoring or manipulation of population sex ratios in food production industries (Chapter 8). During the past few years, we have observed the applications of DNA and genomics to environmental science grow rapidly and diversify enormously (Fig. 1). In this book, we set out to capture a greater diversity of applications than typically are included in advanced texts by including applications scattered through the scientific journal literature. We present this exciting field in the words of the scientists leading this technological transformation, and the end users who are adopting new approaches to understanding and managing nature.

WHAT IS 'ENVIRONMENTAL GENOMICS'?

Genomes are connected to the environment of their host organism. The connections can be simple and direct, for example in species that can absorb metabolites directly through their cell wall. A classic example of this from formative research on genetics is the regulation of lactose metabolism by *Escherichia coli* bacteria. The *Lac* operon of the *E. coli* **genome** produces beta-galactosidase for digesting lactose at a rate determined by environmental levels of lactose (Jacob and Monod 1961). This research could now be called 'environmental genomics', although in the 1960s it would have been described as 'molecular biology' or 'functional genetics'. At that time, it was only possible to conduct genetic analysis one gene at a time and the term 'genomics' did not exist. Modern environmental genomic techniques allow the entire genomes, messenger RNAs and expressed proteins of whole bacterial communities to be studied in comprehensive detail from single environmental samples. With this information we can evaluate both long- and short-term changes to the environment in response to human and non-human actions. In many cases we can do it quickly, in detail and, increasingly, in the field without requiring a laboratory.

Environmental genomics is the use of information encoded in DNA or RNA to characterise and understand pattern and process in biological systems at a small or large scale. It encompasses studies of microbes, fungi, plants and animals. In the case of *applied* environmental genomics, the focus is on capture and provision of information relevant to natural resource management. This very broad definition spans sectors from water quality to wild harvest, biodiversity assessment and biosecurity monitoring. It includes such varied specific uses as bear counts in

landscapes, risk-assessment based on adaptive potential, synthetic biology for pest control, rapid biodiversity surveys, and more. These diverse applications are united because they take advantage of the rich information in genomes and the technological advances that provide rapid and detailed access to it.

Environmental genomics overlaps with research in related fields, partly because of shared scientific aims or methods, but also because terminology changes with time. For example, the fields of population genetics and molecular ecology were established before genomics methods were prevalent but could now be considered environmental genomics. As a rule of thumb, any environmental research that depends on high-throughput DNA sequencing (**HTS**), and the associated high-performance computing (HPC), likely falls under the umbrella of environmental genomics. Bioinformatic analysis is part of the workflow, and one hallmark of environmental genomics is that research in this field requires expertise in ecology, genomics, statistical analysis and bioinformatics.

WHAT IS IN THIS BOOK?

Our purpose is to introduce and synthesise the latest applications of genomic technologies for environmental science and management. We aim to emphasise the breadth of applications, highlighting real-world demonstrations, and to provide a one-stop-shop for advanced undergraduate students, postgraduate students and professionals.

We have focused on new applications of genomic technologies to environmental problems. The precise techniques used to study these problems will change with time, but we consider the chosen applications to have real value in solving current environmental issues. This book cannot provide comprehensive coverage of all aspects of environmental genomics. We chose not to cover several areas because they are so well covered by other publications. For example, molecular microbiology is a field of environmental genomics, but is thoroughly served by journals such as *Applied Environmental Ecology* and comprehensive, classic textbooks (e.g. Madigan *et al.* 2018). There are likewise new methods that are relevant to environmental genomics that are very well described in existing literature, for example spatially resolved transcriptomics (Larsson *et al.* 2021) and current genome assembly methods that recover **haplotype** phases (Kronenberg *et al.* 2021).

Each chapter of this book describes the application of genomic technologies to environmental problems or ecological research questions. We have asked experts to write chapters that are innovative, not well covered in other text-books, or that have had significant interest from environmental managers. Some of these environmental managers have written perspectives on how the genomic technologies have enabled them to undertake new or improved work. They are typically non-scientists whose daily work involves use of genomic-derived data to make decisions about the management of natural resources (Chapters 3, 9, 12, 15, 17, 20 and 27). This serves multiple aims. First, it illustrates that indeed genomics already has many and varied, very practical uses. Second, it points to the challenges sometimes faced in taking novel science out of the laboratory and into practical use. Finally, it emphasises the central importance of this translational step, since solving complex environmental problems requires much more than excellent science and innovation: it also requires commitment to partnering with the non-scientific world.

For convenience, we have organised the 27 chapters of this book into six themed sections, with each section framed around an area of application. Section A 'Biodiversity' focuses on characterisation of complex biological communities, say for biodiversity or biosecurity monitoring, and largely through DNA **metabarcoding** technologies, including the hot topic of environmental DNA 'eDNA'. The uptake of DNA metabarcoding by researchers, government and industry has been rapid, and this section emphasises the important subjects of sampling and survey design (Chapter 1), metrics for measurement of biodiversity in metabarcoding studies (Chapter 2), how to use metabarcoding to characterise trophic interactions among species through the analysis of diet (Chapter 4), and selection and use of metabarcoding assays appropriate to each biological question (Chapter 5).

Section B **'Life history** and population biology' focuses on development and use of biomarkers for ecological properties of individuals or populations. This includes the key attribute of abundance, which can be estimated through non-invasive sampling (Chapter 10) or analysis of kinship (Chapter 11). Demonstrating the versatility of genomics, those same samples can yield even more detailed insights, including an organism's age (Chapter 7), lifespan (Chapter 6) and sex (Chapter 8). Finally, Chapter 13 synthesises the fundamental links between evolutionary and ecological processes and their underpinning of population viability.

Section C 'Adaptation and change' expands the temporal frame to view current environments and species in historical and future contexts. This recognises that characterisation of evolutionary processes and past environmental changes can help predict future trajectories, evaluate

extinction risk, and guide decisions. Chapter 14 evaluates best practice for understanding the capacities of organisms to respond to environmental change through adaptation. Chapter 16 describes ancient DNA and 'museomics' applications to answer questions about extinct and extant organisms.

Section D 'Environmental molecular physiology' outlines the use of biomarkers for tracking the state and change of organisms or whole communities. Genomic methods provide the ability to rapidly characterise relative levels of nucleic acids with diverse functions. Analysis of the patterns of nucleic acids associated with physiological or community state provides a rapid means of identifying specific individual or community stress. Examples include evaluation of broad-scale epigenetic changes that relate to organismal physiological condition (Chapter 18), and at the other end of the scale, how the structure and metabolic behaviour of whole microbial communities can indicate broader ecosystem condition (Chapter 19).

Section E 'Spatial genomics' explores the use of genomics to track the movements of organisms from fine scale, short-term and individual level to the long-term species and population level. This includes the complex interactions between plants and the animals that pollinate them (Chapter 21), and landscape-scale movements of organisms and how they respond to features (Chapter 22). At a longer temporal scale, phylogenomic analysis of whole communities provides an objective means of comparing the evolutionary distinctiveness of communities, which is a useful measure for prioritising landscapes or communities for protection (Chapter 23).

Finally, Section F 'Biosecurity and disease monitoring' summarises leading directions in the use of genomics to track invasive species, including pathogens, and to manage them. This theme is not only of great environmental and economic significance, but also highly topical in this era of COVID-19 and other emerging zoonoses. Chapter 24 illustrates the versatility of genomics to support management of the four stages of invasion threat – prevention, eradication, containment and asset protection. Chapter 25 considers current genomic approaches for studying pathogenic organisms in their wildlife hosts. Chapter 26 is novel amongst all other chapters in this book because it discusses how genomes can be manipulated to offer levers for the control of invasive species. This is a challenging area of environmental genomics, not only technically, but also because social acceptance of these technologies is not universal.

Many technical terms are used in this book. Those in bold font are defined in the glossary section.

WHO IS THIS BOOK FOR?

Like the authors of this book, we anticipate that readers are individuals motivated to enact change in environmental science, and to understand and adopt new technologies that will make this possible. Readers will include advanced undergraduate students, postgraduate students, university lecturers and professionals working in natural resource management and policy. For the non-scientist, this text can be read as an introduction to a fast-moving field that undoubtedly is transforming the practice of environmental management with profound relevance to industry, government, and the public. It can also form the basis of a broad and advanced curriculum for university courses. To assist with teaching, authors of each chapter have provided a series of philosophical and practical questions designed to prompt readers to reflect on the chapter content.

Ultimately the goal of this book is to expose a wide audience to the real-world applications of genomics for environmental research. We hope that the discussions stimulated by these 20 focal areas of applied research will break down barriers that prevent successful implementation. It is only with a smooth translational pipeline and excellent communication that we as a community can together face the emerging and accelerating environmental challenges of the coming century.

There is reason for optimism that environmental genomics will catalyse real change in natural resource management, as innovation has consistently driven developments in the field for decades (Fig. 1). As editors it has been an enormous pleasure to work with a group of authors so committed to exposing this exciting and important field to a wider audience. We wish to express our sincere gratitude to them for their efforts, and to acknowledge the non-trivial time and effort they have devoted to this project when they have many competing responsibilities. We hope the result, which is much more than the sum of its parts, makes it worthwhile. Finally, to you the reader, we hope this text provides you with knowledge and confidence to use and extend the power of genomics for understanding and managing our environment.

Olly, Clare, Simon, August 2022

REFERENCES

Almond RE, Grooten M, Peterson T (2020) *Living Planet Report 2020-Bending the Curve of Biodiversity Loss*. World Wildlife Fund, Gland, Switzerland.

Bak RO, Gomez-Ospina N, Porteus MH (2018) Gene editing on center stage. *Trends in Genetics* 34(8), 600–611. doi:10.1016/j.tig.2018.05.004

Bar-On YM, Phillips R, Milo R (2018) The biomass distribution on Earth. *Proceedings of the National Academy of Sciences* 115(25), 6506–6511.

Bessey C, Jarman SN, Simpson T, Miller H, Stewart T, *et al.* (2021) Passive eDNA collection enhances aquatic biodiversity analysis. *Communications Biology* 4(1), 1–12. doi:10.1038/s42003-021-01760-8

Higuchi R, Bowman B, Freiberger M, Ryder OA, Wilson AC (1984) DNA sequences from the quagga, an extinct member of the horse family. *Nature* 312(5991), 282–284. doi:10.1038/312282a0

Höss M, Kohn M, Pääbo S, Knauer F, Schröder W (1992) Excrement analysis by PCR. *Nature* 359(6392), 199–199. doi:10.1038/359199a0

Jacob F, Monod J (1961) Genetic regulatory mechanisms in the synthesis of proteins. *Journal of Molecular Biology* 3(3), 318–356. doi:10.1016/S0022-2836(61)80072-7

Kronenberg ZN, Rhie A, Koren S, Concepcion GT, Peluso P, *et al.* (2021) Extended haplotype-phasing of long-read de novo genome assemblies using Hi-C. *Nature Communications* 12(1), 1935. doi:10.1038/s41467-020-20536-y

Larsson L, Frisén J, Lundeberg J (2021) Spatially resolved transcriptomics adds a new dimension to genomics. *Nature Methods* 18(1), 15–18. doi:10.1038/s41592-020-01038-7

Madigan M, Bender K, Buckley D, Sattley W, Stahl D (2018) *Brock Biology of Microorganisms*. 15th Global Edition. Benjamin Cummins, Boston, USA.

Samuel G (2020) Independent review of the EPBC Act: Interim report. Commonwealth of Australia, Canberra, Australia.

Taberlet P, Coissac E, Pompanon F, Brochmann C, Willerslev E (2012) Towards next-generation biodiversity assessment using DNA metabarcoding. *Molecular Ecology* 21(8), 2045–2050. doi:10.1111/j.1365-294X.2012.05470.x

Taberlet P, Waits LP, Luikart G (1999) Noninvasive genetic sampling: Look before you leap. *Trends in Ecology & Evolution* 14(8), 323–327. doi:10.1016/S0169-5347(99)01637-7

Woese CR, Fox GE (1977) Phylogenetic structure of the prokaryotic domain: The primary kingdoms. *Proceedings of the National Academy of Sciences* 74(11), 5088–5090. doi:10.1073/pnas.74.11.5088

SECTION A

BIODIVERSITY

1 Design considerations for eDNA metabarcoding surveys

*William Bernard Perry, Kirthana Pillay, Paul George,
Georgina Brennan, Abigail Lowe, Laura Jones, Luke Holman,
Tom Gibson, Natasha de Vere and Simon Creer*

ABSTRACT

There is a great diversity of eDNA metabarcoding studies in the literature and identifying how to design a survey to best suit your needs can be challenging. Design considerations are particularly important given that eDNA metabarcoding can be used to survey biodiversity across a breadth of environments and identifying taxa across the tree of life. Here, we highlight eight burgeoning areas of eDNA metabarcoding research: air, plant-pollinators, soil, diet, microbiome, freshwater, estuarine and marine. We highlight design considerations that are important for specific contexts, while also identifying common denominators across all eDNA metabarcoding surveys. In doing so, we hope to provide both a valuable introduction into eDNA metabarcoding survey design for beginners, gold standards of survey design, and fertile ground for collaboration between research areas which all fall under the umbrella of eDNA metabarcoding.

INTRODUCTION

At some point in our scientific lives, we may be fortunate enough to design an environmental DNA (eDNA) metabarcoding experiment. We refer to metabarcoding *sensu* (Taberlet, Coissac *et al.* 2012) and recommend readers review eDNA definitions and references therein according to Bohmann *et al.* (2014), Creer *et al.* (2016), Deiner *et al.* (2017). It can be an overwhelming challenge, but an intuitive puzzle to solve if you break the problem down into base principles in relation to your research questions. If performed correctly, the benefits will be large and immensely satisfying; alternatively, if some key decisions are not made correctly, the results may never materialise, or may be compromised. The aim of this chapter is to highlight some of the key design considerations to leverage high quality metabarcoding data that be effectively interpreted. Simultaneously, we will provide a range of contemporary, exemplar studies from diverse applications to inspire success for the next generation of biodiversity metabarcoding practitioners.

SAMPLING ENVIRONMENT

Air

While the collection of airborne eDNA is relatively new compared to aquatic eDNA, many organisations have been collecting particles from the air for decades, such as national pollen forecasts (Adams-Groom *et al.* 2002) or monitoring radioactive fallout (Karlsson *et al.* 2020; Söderström *et al.* 2002). More recently researchers have used molecular techniques to explore the airborne biodiversity of plants (Brennan *et al.* 2019), bacteria (Bowers *et al.* 2011), fungi (Ovaskainen *et al.* 2020), insects (Roger *et al.* 2021) and mammals (Clare *et al.* 2021; Lynggaard *et al.* 2021). Furthermore, patterns of airborne biodiversity have been linked with observations from terrestrial

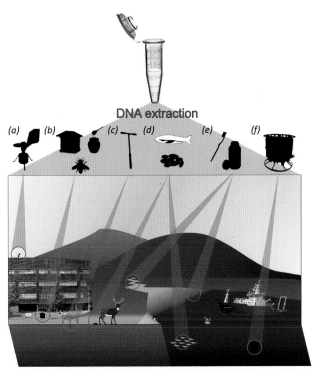

Fig. 1.1. A landscape view of the various environments sampled for eDNA and examples of equipment used in sampling them, including (a) Burkard Hirst design volumetric trap for sampling aerial DNA, (b) honey and pollen from insects for sampling DNA of flowering plants, (c) soil corer for sampling DNA of soil biota, (d) gastrointestinal and faecal samples for examining dietary and microbiome DNA, (e) toothbrush used for collecting biofilms and a bottle for collecting DNA in aqueous freshwater, estuarine and marine environments, and (f) a rosette sampler deployed from a research vessel for collecting DNA at different depths in the pelagic marine environment.

environments (Bowers *et al.* 2011; Brennan *et al.* 2019), allowing exploration of relationships between airborne communities and human health (Yamamoto *et al.* 2012; Rowney *et al.* 2021).

There are important considerations when designing an airborne eDNA survey that will influence biodiversity information recovered, including spatial and temporal elements, as well as the choice of sampling equipment. There is a variety of air sampling devices available, from passive samplers such as car cabin filters (Hurley *et al.* 2019), to targeted air samplers such as Burkard Hirst design volumetric traps (Kraaijeveld *et al.* 2015; Fig. 1.1a), Burkard Automatic Multi-Vial Cyclone Samplers (Brennan *et al.* 2019; Ovaskainen *et al.* 2020), SASS® 3100 Dry Air Samplers (typically used for microbes; Mbareche *et al.* 2018) and even handheld aerial samplers (de Weger *et al.* 2020). However, it is important to note that variations in the volume of air sampled and the material that captures particles will influence interpretation of data and downstream processing. For example, particles sampled into water (e.g. Coriolis Micro air sampler; Roger *et al.* 2021) require a further filtering step to prepare samples for DNA extraction (West and Kimber 2015).

Location and position of sampling devices (ground-level vs. building-top locations) and length of sampling time are directly relevant and influence our understanding of diversity and composition at local and regional scales, and across seasons. In addition, land-use, climatic and meteorological variables will directly influence the ecology of airborne eDNA (such as production and transport of eDNA; Bowers *et al.* 2011, 2013; Gandolfi *et al.* 2015; Brennan *et al.* 2019; Karlsson *et al.* 2020) and the importance of these variables in shaping the community composition will in turn be influenced by the same sampling decisions. Furthermore, modelling additional meteorological and climatic data will enable robust predictions on airborne community structure (Kurganskiy *et al.* 2021).

Plant-pollinators

Plant DNA metabarcoding can be used to gain an understanding of plant biodiversity which was not previously possible using morphological identification. It improves our ability to monitor biodiversity (Sjögren *et al.* 2017), detect rare species (Pornon *et al.* 2019), and explain community interactions (Thomsen and Sigsgaard 2019). In investigations of plant-pollinator interactions, metabarcoding has been used to uncover the foraging preferences of insects by using pollen from honey (De Vere *et al.* 2017), brood cells (Gresty *et al.* 2018), the bodies of insects (Potter *et al.* 2019) and pollen baskets (Richardson *et al.* 2015; Bänsch *et al.* 2020; Fig. 1.1b). Examples of application include revealing the changes in honeybee foraging over decadal timescales (Jones *et al.* 2021) and understanding levels of generalisation and specialisation within plant-hoverfly networks (Lucas *et al.* 2018), with implications for forage availability within the landscape and pollination.

However, it is important to consider the nature of the study system before designing a metabarcoding survey. For instance, honey, when contrasted with pollen on the bodies of individual bees, will represent the foraging effort of multiple individuals over a longer period of time (De Vere *et al.* 2017). This knowledge should influence decisions on the survey method (e.g. transects, timed observations) and how many individuals need to be collected to answer the study's aims. The survey methods are key to understanding the sampling universe, and what information on plant-pollinator interactions will be captured. The flight period of the insects and the flowering season of the plants, in addition to the maximum foraging distance, will affect the temporal and spatial scope of the survey. For example, while honeybees have been recorded as foraging up to 10 km in florally depauperate areas (Beekman and Ratnieks 2000), other bees such as *Lasioglossum* have been recorded foraging up to 1 km (Beil *et al.* 2008).

Metabarcoding, when compared with traditional pollinator survey methods, has an increased temporal range which can capture foraging information over a longer period of time (Arstingstall *et al.* 2021). Typically, for DNA analysis, insects are caught using a combination of nets and sterile tubes, with nets changed periodically and sterilised between surveys (Bell *et al.* 2017; Galliot *et al.* 2017; Lucas *et al.* 2018). For comparability, surveys should also account for meeting minimum weather conditions appropriate for the target group when sampling. In the laboratory, the insect bodies are washed in lysis buffer, to remove the pollen, and consideration should be given to whether the insect specimen requires morphological identification, which may affect processing strategies. Chapter 21 provides a comprehensive review of the design and implementation of DNA metabarcoding research on pollinators.

Soil

Advances in the use of eDNA have allowed researchers to rapidly expand our understanding of biodiversity in soils, especially unknown components of soil biodiversity and their response to change, with metabarcoding surveys having been conducted at national (Terrat *et al.* 2017; George *et al.* 2019) and continental scales (Tedersoo *et al.* 2014; Delgado-Baquerizo *et al.* 2018; Delgado-Baquerizo *et al.* 2018).

Soils are composed of a network of solid aggregates and gas- or water-filled habitable pore space (Ruamps *et al.* 2011; Totsche *et al.* 2018). Soil aggregates are formed by the adhesion of clay and soil organic matter (SOM), which progressively forms larger masses with the inclusion of more nutrients, material, and organic compounds over time (Amézketa 1999). SOM ranges from simple sugars to complex carbon structures like lignin (Romero-Olivares *et al.* 2017; Lehmann *et al.* 2020) and can strongly influence soil physical structure and microbial communities (Dungait *et al.* 2018). Some components of soil can interfere with DNA extraction, like humic acids that can bind with DNA (Sagova-Mareckova *et al.* 2008). To reduce inhibition, soil can be mixed with calcium carbonate (Sagova-Mareckova *et al.* 2008) or phosphate buffer solutions (Taberlet, Prud'Homme *et al.* 2012) prior to extraction to neutralise these acids.

For eDNA analyses, soil cores are taken from the organic-rich upper horizons (commonly the first 25 cm) using a soil sampler (Fig. 1.1c), as this is where the majority of microbes reside (Fierer *et al.* 2003). Both contemporary and older signals from soil animals (e.g. tardigrades, nematodes, annelids, and arthropods) can also be detected (George *et al.* 2019).

The distribution of aggregates, pore space, and nutrients creates diverse microhabitats within soil, and so very different local communities can be present in a small area. Therefore, it is critical that soil samples, or sub-samples, are aggregated and homogenised, to create a sample representative of the area in question (Taberlet *et al.* 2012). Considerations must also be made for the collection of metadata. pH (Tedersoo *et al.* 2014; Delgado-Baquerizo *et al.* 2018), carbon-to-nitrogen ratio (Griffiths *et al.* 2011; Tedersoo *et al.* 2014), soil bulk density, organic matter and macronutrients (e.g. phosphorus, sulphur, and nitrogen) can influence microbial communities. Soil architecture, including measures of porosity and available pore space can also be important, with Carson *et al.* (2010) highlighting that bacterial diversity increases with decreasing pore connectivity. However, these metrics are often much more difficult to analyse and require more specialised expertise.

Diet

Metabarcoding of diet is a cost-effective alternative to morphological identification of prey items (Elbrecht and Leese 2017, chapter 4) and commonly used when direct observation of feeding behaviours is not possible, especially in aquatic organisms (Sousa *et al.* 2019). Diet analysis provides insights into ecosystem functioning (Duffy *et al.* 2007), resource usage (Cristóbal-Azkarate and Arroyo-Rodríguez 2007), anthropogenic dietary change (Sousa *et al.* 2019) and species interactions (Ingala *et al.* 2021), all of which can be used for wildlife management (Kowalczyk *et al.* 2011) and conservation (De Barba *et al.* 2014).

Faecal material and stomach contents are widely used for dietary metabarcoding (Fig. 1.1d). Collection of faecal material is a non-invasive approach (Symondson 2002; Ando *et al.* 2020), but DNA quality can be poor compared to stomach contents, due to degradation from digestion. Contamination of faecal samples due to decomposition (Hawlitschek *et al.* 2018) is also common as samples are exposed to the environment, and can vary with humidity and temperature (Oehm *et al.* 2011). Decomposers such as bacteria, fungi and arthropods can be hard to discern from true diet content (McInnes *et al.* 2017), but can be removed bioinformatically if the system is well understood, or minimised by collecting fresh scat (Ando *et al.* 2018). Careful primer choice, as discussed in Chapter 5, and predator specific blocking primers (Vestheim and Jarman 2008), can also be used to prevent amplifying non-target species (Hawlitschek *et al.* 2018).

Stomach contents yield higher quality DNA as they are not completely degraded through digestion (Hawlitschek *et al.* 2018). Obtaining stomach contents by dissecting out the entire gastrointestinal tract is an invasive collection method that requires euthanising the individual. Stomach flushing is an alternative that does not involve euthanising and is more frequently used than forcefully expelling faeces. However, these invasive methods are not recommended when working with large or rare organisms.

Since diet is highly subjected to environmental variability, factors such as seasonality and changes in resource availability must be accounted for. Biological factors such as size and sex of individuals also affect dietary preferences (Lee *et al.* 2021). Finally, other diet analysis methods such as stable isotope analysis, which characterises long-term diet information, can be used to complement metabarcoding, which only provides a snapshot of current diet (Pompanon *et al.* 2012).

Microbiome

The gut microbiome has been at the centre of host-microbiome research due the volume and diversity of bacteria, and its functional role in digestion, metabolism and immune response (Cresci and Bawden 2015, chapter 2), with applications ranging from medicine (Cammarota *et al.* 2020) to aquaculture (Perry *et al.* 2020). It will therefore be the focus here; however, there is a variety of other host-associated microbiomes to explore.

Even within vertebrates, the gut microbiome shows considerable variation due to factors such as ecology and phylogeny (Colston and Jackson 2016). Variation can also be seen within host species, and within an individual gastrointestinal tract, both in time (Frazier and Chang 2020) and space (Chew *et al.* 2018). When designing a microbiome study, it is important to establish where samples should be taken (foregut, midgut or hindgut), and how often (hours, weeks, months). These questions will differ wildly between systems, but time series data are often neglected, and can be achieved by using non-invasive sampling of the same individual, or destructive sampling of clonal of familial siblings.

Collection of host metadata is also an important consideration. Factors such as age or life stage (Lim *et al.* 2019), sex (Sylvia *et al.* 2017) and social rank (Singh *et al.* 2019) can all impact host-environment interactions, host physiology and thus host microbiomes. The host's environment can also impact its microbiome (Kivistik *et al.* 2020), although it is often hard to tease apart interactions between environment, microbiome and host physiology. Controlling for environmental variables within an experiment can therefore be a powerful tool for focusing on host–microbe interactions. This can be achieved through translocation or common garden experimentation (Uren Webster *et al.* 2020) and laboratory studies where environmental parameters are tightly controlled (McCoy *et al.* 2017).

How you take microbiome samples is also an important consideration. Like diet analyses, extracting microbial DNA from a host can be prone to co-amplification of host organellar sequences (Fitzpatrick *et al.* 2018), however, unlike diet studies, differences in methylation between eukaryotes and prokaryotes can allow for separation (Feehery *et al.* 2013). Taking samples which minimise host tissue contamination, yet still sample intracellular and closely associated gut bacteria, is, however, the most cost-effective measure.

Finally, microbiome studies often focus on bacteria; however, there have been calls to assess a broader variety of microbes, including microbial eukaryotes (Laforest-Lapointe and Arrieta 2018) and viruses (Shkoporov et al. 2019), which also play important ecological roles.

Freshwater

Freshwater ecosystems are ecologically and topographically diverse, but freshwater population declines continue to outpace those in terrestrial and marine habitats (Reid et al. 2019), making effective eDNA metabarcoding surveys a vital tool for biomonitoring.

When designing a freshwater metabarcoding survey, it is first important to know if the system is lentic or lotic. Effective characterisation of eDNA in each of these habitat types may, for example, require different volumes of water to be filtered or sampling to take place at different times (Bedwell and Goldberg 2020). Sampling protocols should be based on how eDNA behaves in lentic and lotic systems, largely due to differences in transport and degradation.

In lotic systems, eDNA is transported downstream, sometimes for kilometres (Pont et al. 2018; Wacker et al. 2019), and therefore riverine dendritic networks are an important consideration. Transport of eDNA from other sources draining into a lentic system may also affect your results, for example lakes, an aquaculture facility pumping discharge into a local stream, or marine species contamination from wetland birds. However, eDNA transport will depend on a number of factors, including the source taxa, water parameters in the river as well as flow rates (Deiner and Altermatt 2014). To better understand transportation in your study system, it is worth including a positive control as part of your experimental design, which may consist of a species eDNA not found in the study system. Understanding eDNA transport can then inform sampling intervals along a river (e.g. every 100 m, 2 km, or just at the river's mouth), as identifying taxa location may be compromised at a finer scale due to eDNA transport.

Understanding eDNA transport, or dispersion, in lentic systems is complex, as it does not follow a linear direction as in rivers and streams. This is especially true in larger bodies of water and simply sampling from the shore may not be sufficient (Zhang et al. 2020). Vertebrate cage experiments have demonstrated eDNA detection declines sharply at a distance of 5–10 m (Dunker et al. 2016; Brys et al. 2021). eDNA may also become vertically stratified in larger water bodies, depending on abiotic factors linked with season, and so sampling regimes should examine a multitude of depths (Littlefair et al. 2021). In contrast, an issue with smaller water bodies, or the shallows of larger lakes, is that there may be horizontal barriers preventing the movement of eDNA, such as large mats of vegetation (Biggs et al. 2015). In these situations it is recommended that water is taken underneath or around potential eDNA dispersion barriers (Harper et al. 2018).

What eDNA sample you take is vital, both in lentic and lotic systems, as eDNA in the water, sediment, or even biofilms, are likely to reflect community composition in different ways (Sakata et al. 2020). Picking which of these sampling methods to use will depend on the questions you want to answer, and the taxa you want to identify. Finally, collecting metadata on the system alongside your sample will also be beneficial in understanding persistence of eDNA; for example, pH, UV and temperature can all be important explanatory variables (Strickler et al. 2015; Seymour et al. 2018).

Estuarine

Estuaries are highly dynamic environments which feature spatial and temporal gradients in their physical and chemical conditions, which in turn influence biota (McLusky 1993; McLusky and Elliott 2004). Sampling should therefore aim to capture, or account for, this spatio-temporal variability. The timing of sampling will influence the detection of species due to the changing contribution of eDNA transported from adjacent marine and freshwaters (Fig. 1.1e).

The relative importance of marine and freshwater influence varies with river flow, the state of the tide during each flood to ebb cycle and variation in tidal range during the spring to neap cycle (McLusky and Elliott 2004). There is also evidence that tidal state can influence eDNA assessments of biodiversity in a well-mixed meso/macrotidal estuary (Schwentner et al. 2021). Comparably, the effects of tidal flow have been shown to be minimal in a glacial fjord (Kelly et al. 2018). Sampling should therefore be standardised to specific points in the tidal cycle (Burgoa Cardás et al. 2020). The effects of river flow, like tide, are poorly studied in estuaries, but they can influence diversity, partially due to increased eDNA transport and dilution during high flow events (Milhau et al. 2021; Sales et al. 2021). Seasons with generally lower river flows could be favourable.

The spatial location of samples must also be considered. Despite the potential for eDNA transport homogenising community composition over space, distinct fish communities have been detected at the scale of hundreds of kilometres within an estuary (García-Machado et al. 2021). Therefore, estuarine sample sites should be positioned longitudinally, for example in the lower, middle and upper estuary. Depending on hydrography (McLusky and Elliott 2004), vertical transects may be necessary. Evidence from a fjord shows spatially specific eDNA signals can occur with depth across a halocline, in as little as 4 m (Jeunen *et al.* 2020). Finally, it is critical to contextualise the results by collecting environmental metadata, such as salinity, turbidity, dissolved oxygen and temperature (Hemingway and Elliot 2002).

Two technical issues present themselves when processing estuarine water samples. First, filters can rapidly clog as estuarine waters are often highly turbid. Many estuaries show a turbidity maxima in their middle and upper reaches, which can vary with tidal cycles (McLusky and Elliott 2004). Therefore, maintaining consistent sample volumes, which can influence species detection (Sigsgaard *et al.* 2017), may not be possible (Ahn *et al.* 2020). This can be remedied by using large pore sizes (Robson *et al.* 2016; Simpfendorfer *et al.* 2016), pre-filtration of samples (Robson *et al.* 2016; Stoeckle *et al.* 2017) and filtration of small water volumes (Kelly *et al.* 2018; Schwentner *et al.* 2021). Second, as with soils, estuarine waters feature high concentrations of humic compounds and potentially high levels of chemical pollutants which may inhibit PCR.

Marine

From the rocky shore to the deep sea, marine ecosystems are environmentally heterogenous and biologically diverse, and research has shown that many different types of eDNA sample are required to fully capture biodiversity (Holman *et al.* 2019; Antich *et al.* 2020). For example, Koziol *et al.* (2019) demonstrated that water, sediment, settlement plate and plankton trawl samples showed dramatic differences in their recovered community diversity and sensitivity to certain taxa.

Marine eDNA samples contain biodiversity information relevant to many scales of ecological investigation, demonstrating delineation of biological communities at 10–100s of metres (O'Donnell *et al.* 2017; West *et al.* 2020), between habitat types separated by kilometres (Jeunen *et al.* 2019) and across thousands of kilometres at biogeographic scales (Holman *et al.* 2021; West *et al.* 2021). Marine communities also change along depth gradients and studies have shown that eDNA can track and recover marine community changes across depth (Jeunen *et al.* 2020; Canals *et al.* 2021). Methods to collect marine eDNA vary in complexity depending on the community or species targeted. For example, it is simple to collect surface water from a pontoon using a plastic bottle or to collect sediment using a handheld corer or grab (Holman *et al.* 2019). In contrast, collecting eDNA from a remote deep-sea environment requires large expensive ocean-going vessels equipped with oceanographic deep-sea sampling instruments, such as rosettes or gravity corers.

Surveys using eDNA have previously captured seasonal changes in marine biodiversity (Rey *et al.* 2020; Stoeckle *et al.* 2021), demonstrating the importance of incorporating sampling across time in seasonal seas. Repeated sampling of eDNA can capture temporal changes in diversity, as eDNA samples represent a 'snap-shot' in time of the local biodiversity (Holman *et al.* 2021). A new approach is to use eDNA samplers that aggregate eDNA across time into a single sample, resulting in a time-integrated eDNA sample. Passive samplers can achieve this using existing eDNA diffusion in marine environments (Kirtane *et al.* 2020; Bessey *et al.* 2021), while natural samplers (such as sponges or scavenging organisms) have been shown to be enriched with eDNA from local biota (Mariani *et al.* 2019; Siegenthaler *et al.* 2019; Turon *et al.* 2020). However, it is still unclear what spatio-temporal scale eDNA collected from these sources represents and further work is required to understand what proportion of biodiversity these eDNA sources represent.

It is important to conduct pilot studies or examine the literature to ensure the type of marine eDNA sample taken has good sensitivity for the target taxa of interest. In addition, sampling schemes should account for the nested nature of eDNA samples to ensure inference at larger scales incorporates variance at lower sampling scales. For example, when sampling across a coastline, ensuring that all types of habitat, such as the intertidal and the neritic zone, are represented when the goal is to understand the biodiversity of the whole marine ecosystem. Finally, designs should incorporate temporal replicates when the study ecosystem is affected by seasonality or disturbance, for example in temperate seas or the intertidal.

IMPORTANT CONSIDERATIONS

We often get asked, 'how many samples/replicates should I analyse?'. In an ideal world, each ecological sample would feature multiple technical replicates (minimum of three subsamples extracted from a sample, with three PCR replicates per subsample, all of which are then sequenced) to achieve accurate representation of a complex DNA sample, as well as multiple ecological replicates, to represent ecological variation. A good summary of replicate types in metabarcoding studies is highlighted by Beentjes *et al.*

(2019) in their fig. 3. Ultimately, the number of replicates will depend on your hypotheses and will reflect the optimal level of work according to resource availability. To make the process easier, start with a simple multiplier table of factors such as sites, replicates, time points, types of sample, and number of markers. Care should also be taken in the design and statistical analysis of studies to avoid pseudo-replication of the ecological samples (Hurlbert 1984). Similarly, how many samples/markers should we multiplex on a single sequencing run, or at what depth should we sequence our eDNA samples? Assessing similar studies, or performing trial runs with lower throughput sequencing chemistries (e.g. Illumina MiSeq Nano) to test taxon accumulation asymptotes versus sequencing effort, are great routes to follow for efficient data collection. Importantly, if you predict comparatively low diversity, multiplexing more samples together with 10% PhiX will likely yield better results due to reduced risk of overclustering on Illumina platforms.

Technical considerations are also extremely valuable, such as negative controls taken at multiple stages of the practical work, for example during field collection, DNA extraction and PCR, which are sequenced along with the samples. Good negative controls and controls of taxa that do not feature in your study system will not only allow you to identify contamination or index hopping, but they can also allow you to bioinformatically filter out spurious taxa. Similarly, mock communities provide a valuable insight into how your metabarcoding pipeline may be skewing the taxa you are detecting. For example, in microbiome studies, a DNA extraction method may favour gram-negative bacteria (Ketchum *et al.* 2018), which would be detected by a good mock community. Finally, there has also been interest in synthetic amplicon spike-in controls, which are added to samples, and can help with the problem of tag jumping, sample mix-ups and cross-contamination (Tourlousse *et al.* 2018). With the knowledge these technical considerations provide, you are then able to interpret your results in a more informed manner, both statistically and conceptually.

CONCLUSIONS

Despite the breadth of sampling environments (Fig. 1.1) there are core principles of good metabarcoding survey design which minimise noise and maximise detection of ecological signals. In technical terms, this can be achieved by increasing the number of technical replicates or providing negative and mock community controls to later filter your metabarcoding dataset. However, a large proportion of noise within your dataset could come from sampling

strategy. In which case, it is important to minimise sampling noise by homogenising sampling campaigns according to your study system. Additionally, you can collect suites of metadata which can help statistically account for noise and confounding variables. Finally, two of the most common sources of sampling variation are time and space, and so it is important to establish adequate spatio-temporal sampling to leverage representative and powerful eDNA biodiversity data for accurate ecological synthesis.

DISCUSSION TOPICS

1. Imagine you are sampling an entirely new ecosystem. Examples might be the deep lithosphere from a mine shaft, or the atmosphere of a moon of Jupiter. What materials would you use to collect any eDNA, and how would you avoid contamination from DNA found in our familiar environment.
2. Environmental DNA metabarcoding is subject to many sources of sampling contamination. How would you design field sampling protocols that help to identify false positive eDNA identifications?
3. How would you compare DNA metabarcoding results for the same biological question, but with samples taken from different field material?
4. How can you be confident that a negative result for a species in an environmental sample means that the eDNA from that species is not really present?

REFERENCES

Adams-Groom B, Emberlin J, Corden J, Millington W, Mullins J (2002) Predicting the start of the birch pollen season at London, Derby and Cardiff, United Kingdom, using a multiple regression model, based on data from 1987 to 1997. *Aerobiologia* **18**, 117–123.

Ahn H, Kume M, Terashima Y, Ye F, Kameyama S, *et al.* (2020) Evaluation of fish biodiversity in estuaries using environmental DNA metabarcoding. *PLoS ONE* **15**(10), e0231127. doi:10.1371/journal.pone.0231127

Amézketa E (1999) Soil aggregate stability: A review. *Journal of Sustainable Agriculture* **14**(2–3), 83–151. doi:10.1300/J064v14n02_08

Ando H, Fujii C, Kawanabe M, Ao Y, Inoue T, *et al.* (2018) Evaluation of plant contamination in metabarcoding diet analysis of a herbivore. *Scientific Reports* **8**(1). doi:10.1038/s41598-018-32845-w

Ando H, Mukai H, Komura T, Dewi T, Ando M, *et al.* (2020) Methodological trends and perspectives of animal dietary studies by noninvasive fecal DNA metabarcoding. *Environmental DNA* **2**(4), 391–406. doi:10.1002/edn3.117

Antich A, Palacín C, Cebrian E, Golo R, Wangensteen OS, *et al.* (2020) Marine biomonitoring with eDNA: Can metabarcoding of water samples cut it as a tool for surveying benthic communities? *Molecular Ecology* **30**, 3175–3188. doi:10.1111/mec.15641

Arstingstall KA, DeBano SJ, Li X, Wooster DE, Rowland MM, *et al.* (2021) Capabilities and limitations of using DNA metabarcoding to study plant–pollinator interactions. *Molecular Ecology* **30**, 5266–5297. doi:10.1111/MEC.16112

Bänsch S, Tscharntke T, Wünschiers R, Netter L, Brenig B, *et al.* (2020) Using ITS2 metabarcoding and microscopy to analyse shifts in pollen diets of honey bees and bumble bees along a mass-flowering crop gradient. *Molecular Ecology* **29**, 5003–5018. doi:10.1111/mec.15675

De Barba M, Miquel C, Boyer F, Mercier C, Rioux D, *et al.* (2014) DNA metabarcoding multiplexing and validation of data accuracy for diet assessment: Application to omnivorous diet. *Molecular Ecology Resources* **14**(2), 306–323. doi:10.1111/1755-0998.12188

Bedwell ME, Goldberg CS (2020) Spatial and temporal patterns of environmental DNA detection to inform sampling protocols in lentic and lotic systems. *Ecology and Evolution* **10**(3), 1602–1612. doi:10.1002/ECE3.6014

Beekman M. Ratnieks FLW (2000) Long-range foraging by the honey-bee, *Apis mellifera L. Functional Ecology* **14**(4), 490–496. doi:10.1046/J.1365-2435.2000.00443.X

Beentjes KK, Speksnijder AG, Schilthuizen M, Hoogeveen M, van der Hoorn BB (2019) The effects of spatial and temporal replicate sampling on eDNA metabarcoding. *PeerJ* **7**(7), e7335. doi:10.7717/PEERJ.7335

Beil M, Horn H, Schwabe A (2008) Analysis of pollen loads in a wild bee community (Hymenoptera: Apidae) – a method for elucidating habitat use and foraging distances. *Apidologie* **39**(4), 456–467. doi:10.1051/APIDO:2008021

Bell KL, Fowler J, Burgess KS, Dobbs EK, Gruenewald D, *et al.* (2017) Applying pollen DNA metabarcoding to the study of plant–pollinator interactions. *Applications in Plant Sciences* **5**(6), 1600124. doi:10.3732/apps.1600124

Bessey C, Jarman SN, Simpson T, Miller H, Stewart T, *et al.* (2021) Passive eDNA collection enhances aquatic biodiversity analysis. *Communications Biology* **4**(1), 1–12. doi:10.1038/s42003-021-01760-8

Biggs J, Ewald N, Valentini A, Gaboriaud C, Dejean T, *et al.* (2015) Using eDNA to develop a national citizen science-based monitoring programme for the great crested newt (*Triturus cristatus*). *Biological Conservation* **183**, 19–28. doi:10.1016/J.BIOCON.2014.11.029

Bohmann K, Evans A, Gilbert MT, Carvalho GR, Creer S, *et al.* (2014) Environmental DNA for wildlife biology and biodiversity monitoring. *Trends in Ecology and Evolution* **29**(6), 358–367. doi:10.1016/j.tree.2014.04.003

Bowers RM, McLetchie S, Knight R, Fierer N. (2011) Spatial variability in airborne bacterial communities across land-use types and their relationship to the bacterial communities of potential source environments. *ISME Journal* **5**(4), 601–612. doi:10.1038/ismej.2010.167

Bowers RM, Clements N, Emerson JB, Wiedinmyer C, Hannigan MP, *et al.* (2013) Seasonal variability in bacterial and fungal diversity of the near-surface atmosphere. *Environmental Science and Technology* **47**(21), 12097–12106. doi:10.1021/es402970s

Brennan GL, Potter C, De Vere N, Griffith GW, Skjøth CA, *et al.* (2019) Temperate airborne grass pollen defined by spatio-temporal shifts in community composition. *Nature Ecology and Evolution* **3**(5), 750–754. doi:10.1038/s41559-019-0849-7

Brys R, Haegeman A, Halfmaerten D, Neyrinck S, Staelens A, *et al.* (2021) Monitoring of spatiotemporal occupancy patterns of fish and amphibian species in a lentic aquatic system using environmental DNA. *Molecular Ecology* **30**(13), 3097–3110. doi:10.1111/MEC.15742

Burgoa Cardás J, Deconinck D, Márquez I, Torre PP, Garcia-Vazquez E, *et al.* (2020) New eDNA based tool applied to the specific detection and monitoring of the endangered European eel. *Biological Conservation* **250**, 108750. doi:10.1016/j.biocon.2020.108750

Cammarota G, Ianiro G, Ahern A, Carbone C, Temko A, *et al.* (2020) Gut microbiome, big data and machine learning to promote precision medicine for cancer. *Nature Reviews Gastroenterology and Hepatology* **17**(10), 635–648. doi:10.1038/s41575-020-0327-3

Canals O, Mendibil I, Santos M, Irigoien X, Rodríguez-Ezpeleta N (2021) Vertical stratification of environmental DNA in the open ocean captures ecological patterns and behavior of deep-sea fishes. *Limnology and Oceanography* **6**, 339–347. doi:10.1101/2021.02.10.430594

Carson JK, Gonzalez-Quiñones V, Murphy DV, Hinz C, Shaw JA, *et al.* (2010) Low pore connectivity increases bacterial diversity in soil. *Applied and Environmental Microbiology* **76**(12), 3936–3942. doi:10.1128/AEM.03085-09

Chew YM, Lye S, Md. Salleh M, Yahya A (2018) 16S rRNA metagenomic analysis of the symbiotic community structures of bacteria in foregut, midgut, and hindgut of the wood-feeding termite Bulbitermes sp. *Symbiosis* **76**(2), 187–197. doi:10.1007/s13199-018-0544-5

Clare EL, Economou CK, Faulkes CG, Gilbert JD, Bennett F, *et al.* (2021) eDNAir: Proof of concept that animal DNA can be collected from air sampling. *PeerJ* **9**, e11030. doi:10.7717/peerj.11030

Colston TJ, Jackson CR (2016) Microbiome evolution along divergent branches of the vertebrate tree of life: what is known and unknown. *Molecular Ecology* **25**, 3776–3800. doi:10.1111/mec.13730

Creer S, Deiner K, Frey S, Porazinska D, Taberlet P, *et al.* (2016) The ecologist's field guide to sequence-based identification of biodiversity, *Methods in Ecology and Evolution* **7**, 1008–1018. doi:10.1111/2041-210X.12574

Cresci GA, Bawden E (2015) Gut microbiome: What we do and don't know. *Nutrition in Clinical Practice* **30**, 734–746. doi:10.1177/0884533615609899

Cristóbal-Azkarate J, Arroyo-Rodríguez V (2007) Diet and activity pattern of howler monkeys (*Alouatta palliata*) in Los Tuxtlas, Mexico: Effects of habitat fragmentation and implications for conservation. *American Journal of Primatology* **69**(9), 1013–1029. doi:10.1002/ajp.20420

Deiner K, Bik HM, Mächler E, Seymour M, Lacoursière-Roussel A, *et al.* (2017) Environmental DNA metabarcoding: Transforming how we survey animal and plant communities. *Molecular Ecology* **26**, 5872–5895. doi:10.1111/mec.14350

Deiner K, Altermatt F (2014) Transport distance of invertebrate environmental DNA in a natural river. *PLoS ONE* **9**(2), e88786. doi:10.1371/journal.pone.0088786

Delgado-Baquerizo M, Oliverio AM, Brewer TE, Benavent-González A, Eldridge DJ, et al. (2018) A global atlas of the dominant bacteria found in soil. *Science* **359**(6373), 320–325. doi:10.1126/science.aap9516

Delgado-Baquerizo M, Reith F, Dennis PG, Hamonts K, Powell JR, et al. (2018) Ecological drivers of soil microbial diversity and soil biological networks in the Southern Hemisphere. *Ecology* **99**(3), 583–596. doi:10.1002/ecy.2137

Duffy JE, Cardinale BJ, France KE, McIntyre PB, Thébault E, et al. (2007) The functional role of biodiversity in ecosystems: Incorporating trophic complexity. *Ecology Letters* **10**, 522–538. doi:10.1111/j.1461-0248.2007.01037.x

Dungait JAJ, Berhe AA, Gregory AS, Hopkins DW (2018) Physical protection and mean residence time of soil carbon. In *Soil and Climate*. (Eds R Lal, BA Stewart) pp. 171–182. CRC Press, Boca Raton, FL, USA. doi:10.1201/b21225-6

Dunker KJ, Sepulveda AJ, Massengill RL, Olsen JB, Russ OL, et al. (2016) Potential of environmental DNA to evaluate Northern Pike (*Esox lucius*) eradication efforts: An experimental test and case study. *PLoS One* **11**(9), 162277. doi:10.1371/journal.pone.0162277

Elbrecht V, Leese F (2017) Validation and development of COI metabarcoding primers for freshwater macroinvertebrate bioassessment. *Frontiers in Environmental Science* **5**(APR). doi:10.3389/fenvs.2017.00011

Feehery GR, Yigit E, Oyola SO, Langhorst BW, Schmidt VT, et al. (2013) A method for selectively enriching microbial DNA from contaminating vertebrate host DNA. *PLoS ONE* **8**(10), 76096. doi:10.1371/journal.pone.0076096

Fierer N, Schimel JP, Holden PA (2003) Variations in microbial community composition through two soil depth profiles. *Soil Biology and Biochemistry* **35**(1), 167–176. doi:10.1016/S0038-0717(02)00251-1

Fitzpatrick CR, Lu-Irving P, Copeland J, Guttman DS, Wang PW, et al. (2018) Chloroplast sequence variation and the efficacy of peptide nucleic acids for blocking host amplification in plant microbiome studies. *Microbiome* **6**(1), 1–10. doi:10.1186/s40168-018-0534-0

Frazier K, Chang EB (2020) Intersection of the Gut Microbiome and Circadian Rhythms in Metabolism. *Trends in Endocrinology and Metabolism* **31**, 25–36. doi:10.1016/j.tem.2019.08.013

Galliot J-N, Brunel D, Bérard A, Chauveau A, Blanchetête A, et al. (2017) Investigating a flower-insect forager network in a mountain grassland community using pollen DNA barcoding. *Journal of Insect Conservation* **21**, 827–837. doi:10.1007/s10841-017-0022-z

Gandolfi I, Bertolini V, Bestetti G, Ambrosini R, Innocente E, et al. (2015) Spatio-temporal variability of airborne bacterial communities and their correlation with particulate matter chemical composition across two urban areas. *Applied Microbiology and Biotechnology* **99**(11), 4867–4877. doi:10.1007/s00253-014-6348-5

García-Machado E, Laporte M, Normandeau E, Hernández C, Côté G, et al. (2021) Fish community shifts along a strong fluvial environmental gradient revealed by eDNA metabarcoding. *Environmental DNA* **4**, 117–134. doi:10.1002/edn3.221

George PBL, Lallias D, Creer S, Seaton FM, Kenny JG, et al. (2019) Divergent national-scale trends of microbial and animal biodiversity revealed across diverse temperate soil ecosystems. *Nature Communications* **10**(1), 1–11. doi:10.1038/s41467-019-09031-1

Gresty CEA, Clare E, Devey DS, Cowan RS, Csiba L, et al. (2018) Flower preferences and pollen transport networks for cavity-nesting solitary bees: Implications for the design of agri-environment schemes. *Ecology and Evolution* **8**(15), 7574–7587. doi:10.1002/ece3.4234

Griffiths RI, Thomson BC, James P, Bell T, Bailey M, et al. (2011) The bacterial biogeography of British soils. *Environmental Microbiology* **13**(6), 1642–1654. doi:10.1111/j.1462-2920.2011.02480.x

Harper LR, Buxton AS, Rees HC, Bruce K, Brys R, et al. (2018) Prospects and challenges of environmental DNA (eDNA) monitoring in freshwater ponds. *Hydrobiologia* **826**(1), 25–41. doi:10.1007/S10750-018-3750-5

Hawlitschek O , Fernandez-Gonzalez A, Balmori-de la Puente A, Castresana J (2018) A pipeline for metabarcoding and diet analysis from fecal samples developed for a small semi-aquatic mammal. *PLoS ONE* **13**(8). doi:10.1371/journal.pone.0201763

Hemingway KL Elliot M (2002) Field methods. In *Fishes in Estuaries*. (Eds K.L. Hemingway and M. Elliot) pp. 410–509. Blackwell Science Ltd, Oxford, UK.

Holman LE, de Bruyn M, Creer S, Carvalho G, Robidart J, et al. (2019) Detection of introduced and resident marine species using environmental DNA metabarcoding of sediment and water. *Scientific Reports* **9**(1), 1–10. doi:10.1038/s41598-019-47899-7

Holman LE, De Bruyn M, Creer S, Carvalho G, Robidart J, et al. (2021) Animals, protists and bacteria share marine biogeographic patterns. *Nature Ecology and Evolution* **5**(6), 738–746. doi:10.1038/s41559-021-01439-7

Hurlbert SH (1984) Pseudoreplication and the design of ecological field experiments. *Ecological Monographs* **54**(2), 187–211. doi:10.2307/1942661

Hurley KV, Wharton L, Wheeler MJ, Skjøth CA, Niles C, et al. (2019) Car cabin filters as sampling devices to study bioaerosols using eDNA and microbiological methods. *Aerobiologia* **35**(2), 215–225. doi:10.1007/S10453-018-09554-Y

Ingala MR, Simmons NB, Wultsch C, Krampis K, Provost KL, et al. (2021) Molecular diet analysis of neotropical bats based on fecal DNA metabarcoding. *Ecology and Evolution* **11**(12), 7474–7491. doi:10.1002/ECE3.7579

Jeunen G, Lamare MD, Knapp M, Spencer HG, Taylor HR, et al. (2020) Water stratification in the marine biome restricts vertical environmental DNA (eDNA) signal dispersal. *Environmental DNA* **2**(1), 99–111. doi:10.1002/edn3.49

Jeunen GJJ, Knapp M, Spencer HG, Lamare MD, Taylor HR, et al. (2019) Environmental DNA (eDNA) metabarcoding reveals strong discrimination among diverse marine habitats connected by water movement. *Molecular Ecology Resources* **19**(2), 426–438. doi:10.1111/1755-0998.12982

Jones L, Brennan GL, Lowe A, Creer S, Ford CR, et al. (2021) Shifts in honeybee foraging reveal historical changes in floral resources. *Communications Biology* **4**(1), 1–10. doi:10.1038/s42003-020-01562-4

Karlsson E, Johansson AM, Ahlinder J, Lundkvist MJ, Singh NJ, *et al.* (2020) Airborne microbial biodiversity and seasonality in Northern and Southern Sweden. *PeerJ* **2020**(1), 8424. doi:10.7717/peerj.8424

Kelly RP, Gallego R, Jacobs-Palme E (2018) The effect of tides on nearshore environmental DNA. *PeerJ* **2018**(3), e4521. doi:10.7717/peerj.4521

Ketchum RN, Smith EG, Vaughan GO, Phippen BL, McParland D, *et al.* (2018) DNA extraction method plays a significant role when defining bacterial community composition in the marine invertebrate *Echinometra mathaei*. *Frontiers in Marine Science* **5**(255). doi:10.3389/FMARS.2018.00255

Kirtane A, Atkinson JD, Sassoubre L (2020) Design and validation of passive environmental DNA samplers using granular activated carbon and montmorillonite clay. *Environmental Science & Technology* **54**(19). doi:10.1021/ACS.EST.0C01863

Kivistik C, Knobloch J, Käiro K, Tammert H, Kisand V, *et al.* (2020) Impact of salinity on the gastrointestinal bacterial community of *Theodoxus fluviatilis*. *Frontiers in Microbiology* **11**, 683. doi:10.3389/fmicb.2020.00683

Kowalczyk R, Taberlet P, Coissac E, Valentini A, Miquel C, *et al.* (2011) Influence of management practices on large herbivore diet-Case of European bison in Białowieza Primeval Forest (Poland). *Forest Ecology and Management* **261**(4), 821–828. doi:10.1016/j.foreco.2010.11.026

Koziol A, Stat M, Simpson T, Jarman S, DiBattista JD, *et al.* (2019) Environmental DNA metabarcoding studies are critically affected by substrate selection. *Molecular Ecology Resources* **19**(2), 366–376. doi:10.1111/1755-0998.12971

Kraaijeveld K, De Weger LA, Ventayol García M, Buermans H, Frank J, *et al.* (2015) Efficient and sensitive identification and quantification of airborne pollen using next-generation DNA sequencing. *Molecular Ecology Resources* **15**(1), 8–16. doi:10.1111/1755-0998.12288

Kurganskiy A, Creer S, De Vere N, Griffith GW, Osborne NJ, *et al.* (2021) Predicting the severity of the grass pollen season and the effect of climate change in Northwest Europe. *Science Advances* **7**(13), eabd7658. doi:10.1126/SCIADV.ABD7658

Laforest-Lapointe I, Arrieta M-C (2018) Microbial eukaryotes: A missing link in gut microbiome studies. *mSystems* **3**(2). doi:10.1128/msystems.00201-17

Lee C-I, Wang FY, Liu MY, Chou TK, Liao TY (2021) DNA metabarcoding for dietary analysis of Holland's carp (*Spinibarbus hollandi*) to evaluate the threat to native fishes in Taiwan. *Journal of Fish Biology* **99**, 1668–1676. doi:10.1111/JFB.14875

Lehmann J, Hansel CM, Kaiser C, Kleber M, Maher K, *et al.* (2020) Persistence of soil organic carbon caused by functional complexity. *Nature Geoscience* **13**(8), 529–534. doi:10.1038/s41561-020-0612-3

Lim MY, Song EJ, Kang KS, Nam YD (2019) Age-related compositional and functional changes in micro-pig gut microbiome. *GeroScience* **41**(6), 935–944. doi:10.1007/s11357-019-00121-y

Littlefair JE, Hrenchuk LE, Blanchfield PJ, Rennie MD, Cristescu ME (2021) Thermal stratification and fish thermal preference explain vertical eDNA distributions in lakes. *Molecular Ecology* **30**(13), 3083–3096. doi:10.1111/MEC.15623

Lucas A, Bodger O, Brosi BJ, Ford CR, Forman DW, *et al.* (2018) Floral resource partitioning by individuals within generalised hoverfly pollination networks revealed by DNA metabarcoding. *Scientific Reports* **8**(1), 5133. doi:10.1038/s41598-018-23103-0

Lucas A, Bodger O, Brosi BJ, Ford CR, Forman DW, *et al.* (2018) Generalisation and specialisation in hoverfly (Syrphidae) grassland pollen transport networks revealed by DNA metabarcoding. *Journal of Animal Ecology* **87**(4), 1008–1021. doi:10.1111/1365-2656.12828

Lynggaard C, Bertelsen MF, Jensen CV, Johnson MS, Frøslev TG, *et al.* (2021) Airborne environmental DNA for terrestrial vertebrate community monitoring. *Current Biology* **32**, 701–707. doi:10.1101/2021.07.16.452634

Mariani S, Baillie C, Colosimo G, Riesgo A. (2019) Sponges as natural environmental DNA samplers. *Current Biology* **29**(11), R401–R402. doi:10.1016/J.CUB.2019.04.031

Mbareche H, Veillette M, Bilodeau GJ, Duchaine C (2018) Bioaerosol sampler choice should consider efficiency and ability of samplers to cover microbial diversity. *Applied and Environmental Microbiology* **84**(23), 1589–1607. doi:10.1128/AEM.01589-18

McCoy KD, Geuking MB, Ronchi F (2017) Gut microbiome standardization in control and experimental mice. *Current Protocols in Immunology* **2017**(1), 23.1.1–23.1.13. doi:10.1002/cpim.25

McInnes JC, Alderman R, Deagle BE, Lea MA, Raymond B, *et al.* (2017) Optimised scat collection protocols for dietary DNA metabarcoding in vertebrates. *Methods in Ecology and Evolution* **8**(2), 192–202. doi:10.1111/2041-210X.12677

McLusky DS (1993) Marine and estuarine gradients – An overview. *Netherlands Journal of Aquatic Ecology* **27**(2–4), 489–493. doi:10.1007/BF02334809

McLusky DS, Elliott M (2004) *The Estuarine Ecosystem: Ecology, Threats, and Management.* 3rd edn. Oxford University Press, Oxford, UK. doi:10.1017/CBO9781107415324.004

Milhau T, Valentini A, Poulet N, Roset N, Jean P, *et al.* (2021) Seasonal dynamics of riverine fish communities using eDNA. *Journal of Fish Biology* **98**(2), 387–398. doi:10.1111/jfb.14190

O'Donnell JL, Kelly RP, Shelton AO, Samhouri JF, Lowell NC, *et al.* (2017) Spatial distribution of environmental DNA in a nearshore marine habitat. *PeerJ* **2017**(2), e3044. doi:10.7717/peerj.3044

Oehm J, Juen A, Nagiller K, Neuhauser S, Traugott M (2011) Molecular scatology: How to improve prey DNA detection success in avian faeces? *Molecular Ecology Resources* **11**(4), 620–628. doi:10.1111/j.1755-0998.2011.03001.x

Ovaskainen O, Abrego N, Somervuo P, Palorinne I, Hardwick B, *et al.* (2020) Monitoring fungal communities with the global spore sampling project. *Frontiers in Ecology and Evolution* **7**, 511. doi:10.3389/fevo.2019.00511

Perry WB, Lindsay E, Payne CJ, Brodie C, Kazlauskaite R (2020) The role of the gut microbiome in sustainable teleost aquaculture. *Proceedings of the Royal Society B: Biological Sciences* **287**(1926), 20200184. doi:10.1098/rspb.2020.0184

Pompanon F, Deagle BE, Symondson WO, Brown DS, Jarman SN, *et al.* (2012) Who is eating what: diet assessment using next generation sequencing. *Molecular Ecology* **21**(8), 1931–1950. doi:10.1111/J.1365-294X.2011.05403.X

Pont D, Rocle M, Valentini A, Civade R, Jean P, *et al.* (2018) Environmental DNA reveals quantitative patterns of fish biodiversity in large rivers despite its downstream transportation. *Scientific Reports* **8**(1), 1–13. doi:10.1038/s41598-018-28424-8

Pornon A, Baksay S, Escaravage N, Burrus M, Andalo C (2019) Pollinator specialization increases with a decrease in a mass-flowering plant in networks inferred from DNA metabarcoding. *Ecology and Evolution* **9**(24), 13650–13662. doi:10.1002/ECE3.5531

Potter C, De Vere N, Jones LE, Ford CR, Hegarty MJ, *et al.* (2019) Pollen metabarcoding reveals broad and species-specific resource use by urban bees. *PeerJ* **2019**(2), e5999. doi:10.7717/peerj.5999

Reid AJ, Carlson AK, Creed IF, Eliason EJ, Gell PA, *et al.* (2019) Emerging threats and persistent conservation challenges for freshwater biodiversity. *Biological Reviews* **94**(3), 849–873. doi:10.1111/BRV.12480

Rey A, Basurko OC, Rodriguez-Ezpeleta N (2020) Considerations for metabarcoding-based port biological baseline surveys aimed at marine nonindigenous species monitoring and risk assessments. *Ecology and Evolution* **10**(5), 2452–2465. doi:10.1002/ece3.6071

Richardson RT, Lin CH, Sponsler DB, Quijia JO, Goodell K, *et al.* (2015) Application of ITS2 Metabarcoding to Determine the Provenance of Pollen Collected by Honey Bees in an Agroecosystem. *Applications in Plant Sciences* **3**(1), 1400066. doi:10.3732/apps.1400066

Robson HLA, Noble TH, Saunders RJ, Robson SK, Burrows DW, *et al.* (2016) Fine-tuning for the tropics: Application of eDNA technology for invasive fish detection in tropical freshwater ecosystems. *Molecular Ecology Resources* **16**(4), 922–932. doi:10.1111/1755-0998.12505

Roger F, Ghanavi HR, Danielsson N, Wahlberg N, Löndahl J, *et al.* (2021) Airborne environmental DNA metabarcoding for the monitoring of terrestrial insects – a proof of concept. *bioRxiv*, 2021.07.26.453860. doi:10.1101/2021.07.26.453860

Romero-Olivares AL, Allison SD, Treseder KK (2017) Decomposition of recalcitrant carbon under experimental warming in boreal forest. *PLoS ONE* **12**(6), e0179674. doi:10.1371/journal.pone.0179674

Rowney FM, Brennan GL, Skjøth CA, Griffith GW, McInnes RN, *et al.* (2021) Environmental DNA reveals links between abundance and composition of airborne grass pollen and respiratory health. *Current Biology* **31**(9), 1995–2003.e4. doi:10.1016/j.cub.2021.02.019

Ruamps LS, Nunan N, Chenu C (2011) Microbial biogeography at the soil pore scale. *Soil Biology and Biochemistry* **43**(2), 280–286. doi:10.1016/j.soilbio.2010.10.010

Sagova-Mareckova M, Cermak L, Novotna J, Plhackova K, Forstova J, *et al.* (2008) Innovative methods for soil DNA purification tested in soils with widely differing characteristics. *Applied and Environmental Microbiology* **74**(9), 2902–2907. doi:10.1128/AEM.02161-07

Sakata MK, Watanabe T, Maki N, Ikeda K, Kosuge T, *et al.* (2020) Determining an effective sampling method for eDNA metabarcoding: A case study for fish biodiversity monitoring in a small, natural river. *Limnology* **22**(2), 221–235. doi:10.1007/S10201-020-00645-9

Sales NG, Wangensteen OS, Carvalho DC, Deiner K, Præbel K, *et al.* (2021) Space-time dynamics in monitoring neotropical fish communities using eDNA metabarcoding. *Science of the Total Environment* **754**, 142096. doi:10.1016/j.scitotenv.2020.142096

Schwentner M, Zahiri R, Yamamoto S, Husemann M, Kullmann B, *et al.* (2021) eDNA as a tool for non-invasive monitoring of the fauna of a turbid, well-mixed system, the Elbe estuary in Germany. *PLoS One* **16**(4 April), e0250452. doi:10.1371/journal.pone.0250452

Seymour M, Durance I, Cosby BJ, Ransom-Jones E, Deiner K, *et al.* (2018) Acidity promotes degradation of multi-species environmental DNA in lotic mesocosms. *Communications Biology* **1**(1), 1–8. doi:10.1038/s42003-017-0005-3

Shkoporov AN, Clooney AG, Sutton TD, Ryan FJ, Daly KM, *et al.* (2019) The human gut virome is highly diverse, stable, and individual specific. *Cell Host and Microbe* **26**(4), 527–541.e5. doi:10.1016/j.chom.2019.09.009

Siegenthaler A, Wangensteen OS, Soto AZ, Benvenuto C, Corrigan L, *et al.* (2019) Metabarcoding of shrimp stomach content: Harnessing a natural sampler for fish biodiversity monitoring. *Molecular Ecology Resources* **19**(1), 206–220. doi:10.1111/1755-0998.12956

Sigsgaard E, Nielsen IB, Carl H, Krag MA, Knudsen SW, *et al.* (2017) Seawater environmental DNA reflects seasonality of a coastal fish community. *Marine Biology* **164**(6), 128. doi:10.1007/s00227-017-3147-4

Simpfendorfer CA, Kyne PM, Noble TH, Goldsbury J, Basiita RK, *et al.* (2016) Environmental DNA detects Critically Endangered largetooth sawfish in the wild. *Endangered Species Research* **30**(1), 109–116. doi:10.3354/esr00731

Singh A, Faber-Hammond JJ, O'Rourke CF, Renn SC (2019) Gut microbial diversity increases with social rank in the African cichlid fish, *Astatotilapia burtoni. Animal Behaviour* **152**, 79–91. doi:10.1016/j.anbehav.2019.04.003

Sjögren P, Edwards ME, Gielly L, Langdon CT, Croudace IW, *et al.* (2017) Lake sedimentary DNA accurately records 20th Century introductions of exotic conifers in Scotland. *New Phytologist* **213**(2), 929–941. doi:10.1111/NPH.14199

Söderström C, Arntsing R, Lindh K (2002) *Quarterly report on measurements of radionuclides in ground level air in Sweden, Swedish Defence Research Agency.* Stockholm. https://inis.iaea.org/search/search.aspx?orig_q=RN:36108699

Sousa LL, Silva SM, Xavier R (2019) DNA metabarcoding in diet studies: Unveiling ecological aspects in aquatic and terrestrial ecosystems. *Environmental DNA* **1**(3), 199–214. doi:10.1002/edn3.27

Stoeckle MY, Adolf J, Charlop-Powers Z, Dunton KJ, Hinks G, *et al.* (2021) Trawl and eDNA assessment of marine fish diversity, seasonality, and relative abundance in coastal New Jersey, USA. *ICES Journal of Marine Science* **78**(1), 293–304. doi:10.1093/icesjms/fsaa225

Stoeckle MY, Soboleva L, Charlop-Powers Z (2017) Aquatic environmental DNA detects seasonal fish abundance and habitat preference in an urban estuary. *PLoS One* **12**(4), e0175186. doi:10.1371/journal.pone.0175186

Strickler KM, Fremier AK and Goldberg CS (2015) Quantifying effects of UV-B, temperature, and pH on eDNA degradation in aquatic microcosms. *Biological Conservation* **183**, 85–92. doi:10.1016/J.BIOCON.2014.11.038

Sylvia KE, Jewell CP, Rendon NM, John EA, Demas GE (2017) Sex-specific modulation of the gut microbiome and behavior in Siberian hamsters. *Brain, Behavior, and Immunity* **60**, 51–62. doi:10.1016/j.bbi.2016.10.023

Symondson WOC (2002) Molecular identification of prey in predator diets. *Molecular Ecology* **11**(4), 627–641. doi:10.1046/j.1365-294x.2002.01471.x

Taberlet P, Prud'Homme SM, Campione E, Roy J, Miquel C, *et al.* (2012) Soil sampling and isolation of extracellular DNA from large amount of starting material suitable for metabarcoding studies. *Molecular Ecology* **21**(8), 1816–1820. doi:10.1111/j.1365-294X.2011.05317.x

Taberlet P, Coissac E, Pompanon F, Brochmann C, Willerslev E (2012) Towards next-generation biodiversity assessment using DNA metabarcoding. *Molecular Ecology* **21**(8), 2045–2050. doi:10.1111/j.1365-294X.2012.05470.x

Tedersoo L, Bahram M, Põlme S, Kõljalg U, Yorou NS, *et al.* (2014) Global diversity and geography of soil fungi. *Science* **346**(6213), 1256688. doi:10.1126/science.1256688

Terrat S, Horrigue W, Dequietd S, Saby NP, Lelièvre M, *et al.* (2017) Mapping and predictive variations of soil bacterial richness across France. *PLoS ONE* **12**(10), e0186766. doi:10.1371/journal.pone.0186766

Thomsen PF, Sigsgaard EE (2019) Environmental DNA metabarcoding of wild flowers reveals diverse communities of terrestrial arthropods. *Ecology and Evolution* **9**(4), 1665–1679. doi:10.1002/ECE3.4809

Totsche KU, Amelung W, Gerzabek MH, Guggenberger G, Klumpp E, *et al.* (2018) Microaggregates in soils. *Journal of Plant Nutrition and Soil Science* **181**(1), 104–136. doi:10.1002/jpln.201600451

Tourlousse D, Ohashi A, Sekiguchi Y (2018) Sample tracking in microbiome community profiling assays using synthetic 16S rRNA gene spike-in controls. *Scientific Reports* **8**(9095). doi:10.1038/S41598-018-27314-3

Turon M, Angulo-Preckler C, Antich A, Præbel K, Wangensteen OS (2020) More than expected from old sponge samples: A natural sampler DNA metabarcoding assessment of marine fish diversity in Nha Trang Bay (Vietnam). *Frontiers in Marine Science* **7**, 1042. doi:10.3389/FMARS.2020.605148

Uren Webster TM, Rodriguez-Barreto D, Castaldo G, Gough P, Consuegra S, *et al.* (2020) Environmental plasticity and colonisation history in the Atlantic salmon microbiome: A translocation experiment. *Molecular Ecology* **29**(5), 886–898. doi:10.1111/mec.15369

De Vere N, Jones LE, Gilmore T, Moscrop J, Lowe A, *et al.* (2017) Using DNA metabarcoding to investigate honey bee foraging reveals limited flower use despite high floral availability. *Scientific Reports* **7**(1), 1–10. doi:10.1038/srep42838

Vestheim H, Jarman SN (2008) Blocking primers to enhance PCR amplification of rare sequences in mixed samples – a case study on prey DNA in Antarctic krill stomachs. *Frontiers in Zoology* **5**(1), 1–11. doi:10.1186/1742-9994-5-12

Wacker S, Fossøy F, Larsen BM, Brandsegg H, Sivertsgård R, *et al.* (2019) Downstream transport and seasonal variation in freshwater pearl mussel (*Margaritifera margaritifera*) eDNA concentration. *Environmental DNA* **1**(1), 64–73. doi:10.1002/EDN3.10

de Weger LA, Molster F, de Raat K, den Haan J, Romein J, *et al.* (2020) A new portable sampler to monitor pollen at street level in the environment of patients. *Science of The Total Environment* **741**, 140404. doi:10.1016/J.SCITOTENV.2020.140404

West JS, Kimber RBE (2015) Innovations in air sampling to detect plant pathogens. *Annals of Applied Biology* **166**(1), 4–17. doi:10.1111/aab.12191

West K, Travers MJ, Stat M, Harvey ES, Richards ZT, *et al.* (2021) Large-scale eDNA metabarcoding survey reveals marine biogeographic break and transitions over tropical north-western Australia. *Diversity and Distributions* **00**, 1–16. doi:10.1111/ddi.13228

West KM, Stat M, Harvey ES, Skepper CL, DiBattista JD, *et al.* (2020) eDNA metabarcoding survey reveals fine-scale coral reef community variation across a remote, tropical island ecosystem. *Molecular Ecology* **29**(6), 1069–1086. doi:10.1111/mec.15382

Yamamoto N, Bibby K, Qian J, Hospodsky D, Rismani-Yazdi H, *et al.* (2012) Particle-size distributions and seasonal diversity of allergenic and pathogenic fungi in outdoor air. *ISME Journal* **6**(10), 1801–1811. doi:10.1038/ismej.2012.30

Zhang S, Lu Q, Wang Y, Wang X, Zhao J, *et al.* (2020) Assessment of fish communities using environmental DNA: Effect of spatial sampling design in lentic systems of different sizes. *Molecular Ecology Resources* **20**(1), 242–255. doi:10.1111/1755-0998.13105

2 Measuring biodiversity with eDNA metabarcoding

Antton Alberdi, Iñaki Odriozola, Raphael Eisenhofer and Ostaizka Aizpurua

ABSTRACT

DNA metabarcoding is a powerful tool that is increasingly employed to detect and quantify the diversity of macro- and microorganisms in environmental samples. While it enables recovery of biological information with higher levels of **taxonomic resolution** and throughput than traditional methods, the molecular study of environmental DNA (eDNA) can yield distorted results if the basic features of the methodology and the studied system are not accounted for in the analysis. In this chapter, we provide an overview of the post-sequencing analysis of eDNA data, highlight potential sources of technical and biological distortion, and discuss strategies to minimise the impact of such biases in the final results. Overall, we aim to provide researchers with tools to critically revise their methods and results to ensure conclusions are driven by the biological signal rather than by technical and analytical artefacts.

SEARCHING FOR A UNIVERSAL METHOD FOR MEASURING BIODIVERSITY

DNA metabarcoding of environmental samples (eDNA metabarcoding) has become a preferred approach to detect and measure biodiversity in a wide range of biological systems, ranging from individual organisms to ecosystems (Bohmann *et al.* 2014; Thomsen and Willerslev 2015; Taberlet *et al.* 2018). eDNA metabarcoding is broadly used to characterise structure of microbial communities in soil

(Bahram *et al.* 2018), invertebrate communities in water (Kuntke *et al.* 2020), and dietary items in faecal samples (Alberdi *et al.* 2020) (see Chapters 1 and 4). This technique relies on the standardisation of taxonomically informative genetic markers that differentiate between biologically relevant units, such as species (Blaxter *et al.* 2005). Genetic markers are amplified from pools of total DNA extracted from environmental samples using PCR, and subsequently sequenced using high-throughput sequencing platforms (Taberlet *et al.* 2012). The real power of DNA metabarcoding is based on its high parallelisation capacity, as multiplexing strategies enable hundreds of samples to be processed and sequenced at once, thus generating vast amounts of information (Coissac *et al.* 2012).

The data generation process is not error-proof, however, and the high-throughput nature of the technique renders it impossible to manually curate each of the bits of information generated. The errors that accumulate during the steps prior to the bioinformatic processing of data introduce noise that can distort the characterisation of the targeted system (Alberdi *et al.* 2018, 2019). Hence, it is critical to implement bioinformatic pipelines that account for such potential errors and biases, to avoid the generated data creating a distorted vision of reality.

In this chapter, we will navigate through the process of generating, curating, and analysing eDNA metabarcoding data to address a variety of research questions. To illustrate the explanations, we will rely on two case studies (Box 2.1), which span a wide landscape of features, and aim at showcasing key decision-making steps, and how these can vary depending on the type of system and study aims.

Typical bioinformatic and analytical pipeline

There are multiple strategies to generate and analyse eDNA metabarcoding data, each of them with their strengths and weaknesses. However, the analysis of sequencing reads can seldom correct the limitations of inappropriate decisions regarding study design and marker choice. There are many considerations researchers must address before jumping into data analysis (Table 2.1), to ensure that the bioinformatic and analytical pipeline explained below will yield the expected results.

Data pre-processing

The typical bioinformatic pipeline starts with several data pre-processing steps that aim at preparing the raw sequencing reads for downstream analyses (Fig. 2.1A). The first of these steps is **demultiplexing.** eDNA metabarcoding data are generally produced by pooling DNA molecules belonging to multiple samples, each identified with a unique tag, into a single or multiple sequencing runs. Thus, it is necessary to first separate the sequence reads belonging to each

tagged sample (Binladen *et al.* 2007). Depending on the **sequencing library** preparation strategy employed (Bohmann *et al.* 2021), this step might be done by the sequencing platform, or might require action from the researcher.

Once the data files are separated by sample, sequencing reads are usually quality-filtered. Due to various features of DNA sequencing (Hu *et al.* 2021), the quality of the sequencing information varies across reads and sections within reads. Quality is defined as probability of an incorrect base call at a site in the read, which is typically expressed using logarithmic **Phred quality scores** (e.g. score of 10 = 10% chance of incorrect base, score of 20 = 1% chance). For example, in paired-end sequencing, the reverse reads tend to exhibit lower quality scores than forward reads, and the quality of sequencing reads decline towards the end of the sequence (Tan *et al.* 2019). It is therefore common practice to discard low quality sequences and to trim reads to remove low-quality tails (Callahan *et al.* 2016). This approach maintains only the reads that have a high enough Phred score (Edgar and Flyvbjerg 2015).

At this stage, reads can still contain the sequences of the primers and sequencing adapters that have been used to amplify and sequence the selected molecular marker. These

Table 2.1.   Some of the major design considerations that should be addressed before data analysis to achieve sound results.

Issues	Considerations	References
Study design: how should I design the study based on intrinsic features of the system and the technique?	- What is the expected biomass and related detectability of the biological units of interest? - What is the expected spatio-temporal variability of the biological units of interest?	Erickson *et al.* 2019; Carraro *et al.* 2021
Marker choice: how good does the selected marker capture the desired information?	- Should a single or multiple markers be used? - How long is the selected marker, and how does it fit with the considered sequencing strategy? - What is the resolution provided by the marker? - How taxonomically specific is the molecular marker chosen? - How complete are the reference databases to be employed for taxonomic annotation for the selected marker? - Should I rely on available public databases or create my own reference database?	Ghyselinck *et al.* 2013; Freeland 2017; Alberdi *et al.* 2018; Stoeckle *et al.* 2020; Ramakodi 2022
Reliability of data: how well do the data reflect the biological system of interest?	- How many biological or PCR replicates should be used? - Should the replicates be merged before sequencing? - Should the replicates be used to filter out sequences?	Alberdi *et al.* 2018; McLaren *et al.* 2019
Batch effects: how should samples be organised for processing?	- How should samples be randomised to minimise batch effects?	Gibbons *et al.* 2018
Contamination: how should I avoid spurious DNA sequences?	- Which measures should I take to minimise external contamination? - Which measures should I take to minimise cross-contamination? - Which strategy should I implement to detect and quantify contamination?	Davis *et al.* 2018; Eisenhofer *et al.* 2019; Minich *et al.* 2019
Sequencing depth: how much should be sequenced?	- How much **sequencing depth** is required to recover the desired diversity signal?	Grey *et al.* 2018; Shirazi *et al.* 2021

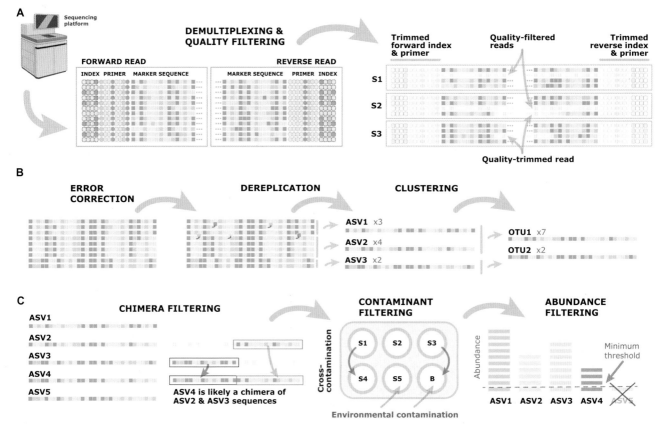

Fig. 2.1. Overview of a typical bioinformatic pipeline to process amplicon sequencing data, including (A) data pre-processing, (B) denoising and clustering and (C) data curation.

are clipped before further analysis, but can play an essential role for the correct processing of data if libraries have been built based on adapter-ligation (Carøe and Bohmann 2020). While PCR-based libraries are directional (e.g. all DNA molecules are sequenced in one direction, from **Forward primer** to **Reverse primer**), when using ligation-based libraries, half of the DNA molecules will be sequenced in the opposite direction (e.g. from Reverse primer to Forward primer). Hence, unless these primers are properly removed and sequences are flipped, they can distort downstream analyses, such as the generation of phylogenetic trees, because 50% of the sequences will not align with the other 50%, thus producing erroneous phylogenies. In consequence, understanding the library preparation strategy employed in the lab is essential for the correct processing of the data (Bohmann et al. 2021). Finally, depending on the downstream data processing strategy, paired reads may be merged during this pre-processing stage.

Denoising and clustering

The core procedures of eDNA metabarcoding data processing occur when **denoising** and clustering sequencing reads

(Fig. 2.1B), as without these steps, sequence errors obtained during DNA sequencing would artificially inflate diversity. Denoising aims to detect and correct spurious sequences derived from PCR amplification and DNA sequencing (Antich et al. 2021). There are multiple software packages that perform this operation using a variety of analytical approaches, such as DADA2 (Callahan et al. 2016), UNOISE3 (Edgar 2016) and Deblur (Amir et al. 2017), which use different nomenclature to refer to the denoised sequences: **ASV** (DADA2), zero radius operational taxonomic unit (zOTU) (UNOISE3) and sub-operational taxonomic unit (sOTU) (Deblur). The choice of the denoising strategy is not a trivial one for two reasons. First, it will determine the upstream steps to prepare the required input (e.g. DADA2 requires unmerged reads while UNOISE3 requires merged reads), as well as downstream steps based on the features of each algorithm. Second, the choice of the denoising approach can determine the resulting dataset of denoised reads (O'Rourke et al. 2020).

Similar DNA sequences can then be clustered together, usually during or following the denoising process. Historically, DNA sequence clustering has had two objectives: reduce noise (e.g. PCR and sequencing errors) and obtain meaningful biological entities. In the initial stages of eDNA metabarcoding, there were no algorithms that enabled erroneous sequences to be corrected, so researchers relied on clustering to group similar sequences (i.e. within a % threshold of nucleotide identity), and assign one representative sequence (typically the most abundant one) to the entire group, known as (Molecular) Operational Taxonomic Unit (MOTU or **OTU**) (Blaxter *et al.* 2005). With the development of denoising algorithms, this has become redundant (Callahan *et al.* 2017). However, in certain cases, high-resolution molecular data can inflate diversity through capturing intra-genomic variation (e.g. distinct 16S rRNA sequences within a single bacterial genome (Schloss 2021)), and in some other cases the intra-specific variation captured within the molecular marker could blur detection of the desired biological signal. Clustering also reduces the dimensionality of the dataset, and therefore still plays a central role in eDNA metabarcoding studies (Brandt *et al.* 2021). Clustering can be performed using similarity thresholds (e.g. UPARSE, VSEARCH), Bayesian methods (e.g. CROP), or methods based on single-linkage-clustering (e.g. SWARM), among others. Of note, denoised sequences represent biological features (e.g. DNA sequences), and are thus comparable between studies if processed in the same way. In contrast, clustering is dependent on the total sequence diversity being analysed, so for studies to be compared they need to be clustered together.

Data curation

eDNA datasets require further curation after denoising and clustering steps to ensure the final output is representative of the studied system (Fig. 2.1C). One of the most important of such data curation steps is removal of chimeric sequences (Alberdi *et al.* 2018). Chimeras are spurious constructs typically formed during PCR amplification when the DNA fragment resulting from an aborted extension acts as a primer in downstream PCR cycles, thus creating artificial sequences derived from two (or more) templates (Kopczynski *et al.* 1994). Chimera formation may be reduced experimentally by optimising PCR conditions and carefully selecting the polymerase enzyme (Gury *et al.* 2008; Ahn *et al.* 2012; Stevens *et al.* 2013), yet no specific method fully prevents chimera generation (Smyth *et al.* 2010). As a result, a number of algorithms have been developed to detect and filter out chimeric sequences, some of which are now included in the most popular bioinformatic pipelines.

The other critical step is to detect and identify DNA sequences derived from contamination and cross-contamination across samples (Eisenhofer *et al.* 2019). In addition to the contamination that can occur in the field, reagents and plasticware employed in the laboratory often contain living organisms or their DNA remains, which can also be amplified and sequenced during a DNA metabarcoding study. This is especially critical for studies that target bacteria and fungi, because many reagents can get easily contaminated by such microorganisms. Additionally, if DNA extraction and library preparation are not physically separated, and strategies for minimising contamination (e.g. efficient cleaning routines, use of laminar flow-hoods) are not implemented, DNA amplified in previous batches can also be re-amplified and sequenced (Sefers and Schmitz 2018). The high-throughput nature of DNA metabarcoding entails that many samples (often entire plates of 96 samples) are processed together, which increases the risk of cross-contamination. If these sources of false-positives are not accounted for and minimised, it is very probable that diversity estimations will be inflated, and it has been shown that DNA contamination can lead to erroneous biological conclusions (Salter *et al.* 2014). Dedicated software has been developed to identify DNA contamination from sequences found in negative control samples (Davis *et al.* 2018; Minich *et al.* 2019).

Abundance-filtering is another important step that researchers can apply to further curate datasets (Alberdi *et al.* 2018). Researchers can opt for removing DNA sequences whose relative abundance within samples or prevalence across samples is below a certain threshold. Such filters might aim at removing potentially spurious sequences to avoid false-positives (Reitmeier *et al.* 2021) or to handle a lighter dataset focused on the most abundant taxa. The decision to filter sequences based on their representation in the studied dataset will depend on the importance researchers attribute to false-positives and false-negatives (Alberdi *et al.* 2018). A **false-positive** is the detection of a biological unit that was not present in the studied system or sample, while a **false-negative** is the omission of a biological unit that was present in the system or sample but that the researchers were unable to detect.

Taxonomic annotation and phylogenetic information

Although taxonomic annotation is not compulsory for quantifying diversity from metabarcoding data, bioinformatic pipelines usually employ a step for the taxonomic annotation of DNA sequences (Mächler *et al.* 2021). This is achieved by aligning the reads against a reference database of sequences with well-known taxonomic annotation, and assigning the most probable taxon based on the similarity between the query and reference sequences (Hleap *et al.*

2021). The success of taxonomic annotation is dependent on the comprehensiveness of the reference database, which is highly variable depending on the employed molecular marker and targeted taxa (Machida *et al.* 2017; Gold *et al.* 2021). The reliability of the taxonomic assignments can also be database-dependent, since databases can have different levels of curation. Therefore, taxonomy assignment based on different reference databases might lead to different results (Balvočiūtė and Huson 2017; O'Rourke *et al.* 2020), and the resolution of the taxonomic assignment can depend on how well the detected taxa are represented in each of these databases.

Lastly, DNA sequences enable building phylogenetic trees to establish relationships between the detected sequences, which is relevant to account for relatedness when computing diversity (Chao *et al.* 2010). Phylogenetic trees can be built *de novo* from the recovered DNA sequences, yet it is important to note that the short markers employed for eDNA metabarcoding usually exhibit poor phylogenetic signal (Douady *et al.* 2003). Strategies to account for the high level of phylogenetic uncertainty of metabarcoding markers in biodiversity measurement have been proposed (Alberdi and Gilbert 2019), yet such trees should not be used for high-resolution phylogenetic inference. Long-read sequencing platforms now enable longer markers (e.g. full-length ITS or rRNA genes) to be sequenced from eDNA, which improves the recovery of phylogenetic signal, although this doesn't overcome the inherent limitations of single-gene based phylogenies (Heeger *et al.* 2018; Tedersoo *et al.* 2018). An alternative approach that can be used when complete databases are available is to rely on phylogenetic placement, which establishes the phylogenetic identity of the DNA sequences by means of a given phylogenetic reference tree (Barbera *et al.* 2021; Czech *et al.* 2022).

Statistical analyses and modelling

All the aforementioned steps are necessary to reach the stage at which data can be used for measuring, comparing and modelling biological diversity. These analyses are typically conducted on four data units, which can be separated or be part of a single data object (e.g. phyloseq (McMurdie and Holmes 2013)): 1) a count table in which the quantitative relationship between samples (*x*-axis) and unique DNA sequences (*y*-axis) is shown, 2) a sample metadata table that specifies the features and relationships among samples, 3) a taxonomy table that indicates the taxonomic annotations of the DNA sequences, and 4) a phylogenetic tree or distance matrix that establishes phylogenetic, functional or phenotypic relationships across DNA sequences. In the following

two sections, we will delve into diversity measurement and modelling based on such data.

MEASURING DIVERSITY

The bioinformatic pipeline outlined above shows that the eDNA metabarcoding data generation is not a trivial process. Decisions made on the steps listed above can impact the qualitative and quantitative features of the data that will be used for measuring biodiversity; thus researchers must not assume that the data generated using DNA metabarcoding techniques is a neat reproduction of the biological reality of the studied system (Deiner *et al.* 2017; Alberdi *et al.* 2019). In consequence, diversity measurement based on eDNA data will need to account for the many choices outlined above to yield representative results. In the following, we discuss some of the most relevant considerations when measuring biological diversity based on eDNA metabarcoding data, which deals with the resolution of the data, strategy to quantify diversity, considered components of diversity, and other core aspects that researchers must be aware of.

Resolution of the data

Defining the biological unit upon which diversity will be measured (namely, the type) is a critical decision for any quantitative inference of diversity. When working with eDNA metabarcoding data, the definition of types can be either based on taxonomy or on DNA sequence features.

Taxonomy-based type definition

Taxonomy-based definition of types requires the taxonomic annotation of DNA sequences. The main advantage of this approach is that it provides information that resembles the traditional methods for measuring biodiversity. Researchers can choose which taxonomic resolution they want to use, and aggregate read counts accordingly. As mentioned above, taxonomic annotation is completely dependent on the reference databases, which although ever-increasing in size and resolution, still exhibit large completeness biases depending on the taxa (Marques *et al.* 2021). In addition, not all molecular markers provide species-level resolution. In consequence, only a fraction of DNA sequences is generally taxonomically annotated at the species or genus levels. This might force researchers to select higher taxonomic levels, thus losing resolution. For these reasons, taxonomy-based approaches do not make the most of the information provided by molecular techniques.

Taxonomy-free type definition

Taxonomy-free approaches provide more flexibility and enable making the most of the molecular information, yet also require deeper understanding of the molecular structure of biological elements and employed techniques. The finest resolution that a researcher can aim for is defined by the selected molecular marker, and the bioinformatic strategy employed to process the data. Recovering ASVs entails considering the highest possible resolution provided by the molecular data. The two main advantages of this strategy are: 1) it recovers the entire genetic diversity that a given molecular marker can capture; and 2) it provides the least manipulated vision of the data, thus enabling higher reproducibility and comparability across studies. However, genetic diversity might not reflect species diversity, which is often the resolution of interest in biodiversity inventories (Antich *et al.* 2021). Besides, it is important to note that the information on genetic diversity is limited to a single short molecular marker, and that the degree of average variation for that given marker can differ across taxa (Alberdi *et al.* 2018; Elbrecht *et al.* 2018). Hence, the recovered diversity might not be representative of the actual genetic diversity of a given taxa, thus potentially leading to biased estimations. Finally, this approach comes with increased computational cost, so researchers need to assess carefully whether ASVs should be clustered into broader types, broadly known as OTUs. While often useful, one main disadvantage is that their definition is usually study-specific and often based on arbitrary thresholds (Callahan *et al.* 2017).

Incidence- vs. abundance-based measurement of diversity

Another major decision that researchers need to make when measuring diversity is whether the analysis will be based on incidence or abundance data (Deagle *et al.* 2019). Although the default output of eDNA metabarcoding is read-abundance data, most genetic markers exhibit amplification biases that can distort the real distribution of DNA molecules in the sample (Elbrecht and Leese 2015). Furthermore, the copy number of molecular markers does not generally correlate with biomass, except in specific circumstances (Matesanz *et al.* 2019; Lavrinienko *et al.* 2021; Garrido-Sanz and Senar 2022). Hence, many authors opt for skipping abundance data and relying only on presence or absence of any given type in each sample.

Abundance data can easily be transformed into presence/absence data by replacing any non-zero value by one. While often considered more conservative, this choice is not exempt from issues (Deagle *et al.* 2019). First, incidence data

do not completely solve the primer amplification bias issue, since some taxa present in the sample might not be amplified at all. Second, incidence data are extremely dependent on the copy number thresholds established to discard low-copy reads (e.g. discarding singletons). Third, types that exhibit drastically different read abundance data (e.g. 10 reads vs. 100 000 reads) are assigned the same value (= presence), which can also introduce considerable biases mainly when sample sizes are low. Hence, an increasing number of authors opt for analysing the results using both incidence and abundance approaches, as they can provide complementary information (Deagle *et al.* 2019). When using abundance data, it should be noted that the datasets generated from high-throughput sequencing platforms are compositional because they have an arbitrary total imposed by the technique (Gloor *et al.* 2017). Moreover, the observed total count in the output is not necessarily associated with the absolute number of molecules in the input sample (Gloor *et al.* 2017). Consequently, the abundance of a type in a sample can only be interpreted in relation to the abundances of the other types in the same sample. Currently, there is no consensus in the literature on how to deal with the compositional nature of high-throughput sequencing data in the downstream statistical analyses (see e.g. McMurdie and Holmes 2014; Gloor *et al.* 2017; Weiss *et al.* 2017; Deagle *et al.* 2019), but this inherent characteristic of the data should be considered.

Whatever the choice between incidence- or abundance-based approaches, it is important to bear in mind that, although identical diversity metrics might be applied, these two strategies measure different things. In the incidence-based approach, the units used to compute diversity are the **samples** in which a type (e.g. ASV, OTU) is present, while in the abundance-based approach, the units used to compute diversity are the **DNA sequences** assigned to each type (Alberdi and Gilbert 2019).

Accounting for different components of diversity

Diversity can be measured using a myriad of different metrics, each with its own features and peculiarities (Tuomisto 2010). It is important to bear in mind that these indices and metrics can actually measure different things. For example, the Shannon index computes a value of entropy, while the Simpson index provides a probability value (Chao *et al.* 2014). For this reason, it is not always straightforward to assign biological meaning to the obtained quantitative values. Furthermore, biological diversity is a complex feature that can be decomposed into different components, including richness, evenness and regularity, and not all diversity metrics account for the same components of diversity (Jost 2010; Alberdi and Gilbert 2019). As each of these components measure different properties of the diversity, and can be shaped by different ecological forces (Wilsey and Stirling 2007), it is useful to compare metrics that account for different components of diversity (Alberdi *et al.* 2021). This can be done easily through Hill numbers (Hill 1973; Jost 2006), which unify many of the diversity metrics broadly employed in ecology within a single mathematical framework that enables accounting for, and modifying the weight of, components of diversity in a straightforward way (Alberdi and Gilbert 2019).

Among the aforementioned components of diversity, richness is the simplest measure of diversity, as it only measures whether types are present or not (McIntosh 1967). This is the **baseline** upon which more components of diversity can be considered. When using richness, abundant and rare types are given the same weight for the computation of diversity. As types present in a system are seldom distributed evenly, richness alone is rarely the best approach to measure the diversity of a system.

Evenness is the component of diversity that measures the balance of the relative representation of types. When types in a system exhibit very similar relative abundances, the evenness component is high, while when relative abundances are skewed towards a few types, the evenness component drops. Hill numbers enable controlling the evenness component through modifying the so-called order of diversity or q-value, that regulates the weight given to relative abundance data (Jost 2010). Two popular diversity indices that account for richness and evenness components are the Shannon and Simpson indices, whose respective Hill numbers respond to q-values of 1 and 2.

The third component of diversity is regularity, which accounts for the degree of similarity across types. Richness, Shannon index and Simpson index treat types as independent elements, thus overlooking that in most biological systems types tend to be functionally, phylogenetically or ecologically correlated (Chao *et al.* 2021). Considering the regularity component enables accounting for such functional, phylogenetic or ecological features when measuring the diversity of the system. For instance, Faith's PD considers richness and regularity components, while Allen's H and Rao's Q account for the three components of diversity. Each of the mentioned metrics have their respective Hill number, which accounts for the source of regularity indicated by the researcher (Alberdi and Gilbert 2019). For instance, the homogeneity of the spatial distribution and hunting flexibility of bats is correlated with dietary breadth, yet only if the phylogenetic relations between prey are accounted for when measuring dietary breadth (Alberdi *et al.* 2020).

Measuring observed vs. estimated diversity

Despite the availability of dozens of metrics, estimating the diversity of a given sample is not as trivial as it may seem, because the capacity to detect the presence of a type in a given sample depends on the effort. The number of birds visually identified in a large pond will depend on the time spent staring at the lake using binoculars, while when characterising samples using molecular tools, it will depend on the depth of sequencing (how many sequencing reads are generated). If the employed sequencing is not deep enough to recover the full diversity within a sample, any diversity metric measured will yield a skewed result. The feature that measures the relative proportion of the estimated diversity actually captured in the studied sample is known as completeness (Hsieh *et al.* 2016). The R package iNEXT incorporated Hill numbers-based estimators for q-values 0, 1 and 2 (Hsieh *et al.* 2016), and the iNEXT.3D expanded these estimators to Hill numbers incorporating regularity components such as phylogenetic and functional relationships across types (Chao *et al.* 2021). Using these estimators, it is possible to ascertain what the completeness level of a sample is, as well as to estimate what would be the expected diversity if the sample were characterised properly (i.e. 100% completeness) or at any other lower level of completeness. Completeness could theoretically be improved by sequencing samples deeper, yet it is important to note that depth of sequencing alone cannot recover the diversity of a sample if the sample has not been appropriately collected in the field and processed in the lab (Deiner *et al.* 2017; Alberdi *et al.* 2019). Deeper sequencing can also lead to an accumulation of sequencing errors (Alberdi *et al.* 2018). It is also important to bear in mind that the estimators will highly depend on the strategies employed to generate, curate and filter eDNA metabarcoding data.

Diversity partitioning and compositional dissimilarity

The study of diversity is often not limited to measuring and comparing diversity values of individual samples. Researchers often want to measure dissimilarities across samples, or to compare diversity levels across multiple hierarchies. These two types of analyses are based on the partitioning of diversity into **alpha** (local), **beta** and **gamma** (regional) components (Whittaker 1960). The relationship between these components can be established in different ways depending on the mathematical framework employed (Tuomisto 2010); however, within the aforementioned Hill numbers framework, diversity partitioning follows a multiplicative definition, i.e. alpha × beta = gamma (Chao *et al.* 2012). This offers multiple advantages that have been discussed elsewhere (Alberdi and Gilbert 2019). Partitioning diversity does not only enable ascertaining the hierarchical structure of diversity within a system, but is also the basis for quantifying (dis)similarity between subsystems. (Dis)similarity measurements are often used in ecology to address scientific questions, and they are a necessary step to conduct popular statistical methods such as NMDS or ANOSIM. While traditionally calculated through pairwise comparisons, the Hill numbers framework enables overall (dis)similarities to be computed for multiple samples, based on the **beta diversity** value derived from the aforementioned multiplicative definition of diversity partitioning (Chao *et al.* 2014, 2019; Chiu *et al.* 2014).

MODELLING DIVERSITY

Measurement or estimation of diversity should not be the endpoint of eDNA metabarcoding studies, but a stepping stone on the way to generate statistical models that enable researchers to understand how biological processes work or to predict specific outcomes. Statistical modelling can be conducted by relating diversity measurements with explanatory variables, aimed at explaining the observed variation across characterised samples. As with any other type of response variable, it is essential to consider several aspects of the data when deciding which statistical analyses will be implemented to model diversity.

Univariate vs. multivariate responses

Diversity modelling can be conducted using univariate or multivariate responses. Univariate responses might include incidence or abundance data of a single type, or a diversity metric (i.e. Hill numbers) of a given system, among others. To analyse this kind of data, robust and flexible statistical methods are available. Generalised linear mixed models (GLMM) enable applying linear models to complex study design, while generalised additive mixed models (GAMM) enable accounting for complex non-linear relationships between explanatory and response variables (Zuur *et al.* 2009; Wood 2017). **Machine learning** algorithms, such as random forests (RF), multivariate adaptive regression splines (MARS), and artificial neural networks (ANN) are also becoming increasingly popular. Although these methods produce more accurate predictions in many circumstances, interpreting complex machine learning models can be very challenging.

Instead of targeting a single type or using a diversity metric, researchers might also be interested in modelling an entire community. Such a multivariate approach (in the sense of accepting multiple response variables) has been traditionally addressed using ordination-based methods, either unconstrained or constrained. Some popular unconstrained ordination methods are the principal component analysis (PCA), the closely related principal coordinate analysis (PCoA), the correspondence analysis (CA) and the non-metric multidimensional scaling (NMDS) (Borcard *et al.* 2018). These methods are used to reflect the main axes of variation of the response data, yet they do not allow the inclusion of explanatory variables. In contrast, constrained ordinations enable hypotheses on the relationships between the communities and explanatory variables to be formally tested. Constrained methods usually work by applying a regression between the response community and the explanatory variables, and subsequently applying an ordination on the fitted values. Some popular constrained ordination methods include canonical correspondence analysis (CCA), and direct and distance-based redundancy analysis (RDA) (Borcard *et al.* 2018). Another highly popular approach related to constrained ordination methods is the permutational multivariate analysis of variance (PERMANOVA) (Anderson 2001), which statistically tests the differences in community (dis)similarity between groups of sampling units. The choice of standardisation and transformation of the community matrix, as well as the selection of the dissimilarity index (for the cases where the analysis is performed on a dissimilarity matrix) are crucial steps in the above analyses, since different choices can heavily influence the outcomes of the analyses (Borcard *et al.* 2018).

Finally, there are other model-based approaches that have been specifically developed to do differential abundance analysis based on high-throughput sequencing data. These methods include, for example, the edgeR (Robinson *et al.* 2010), DESeq2 (Love *et al.* 2014) or ANCOM (Lin and Peddada 2020) methods, which can be used to test which types are differentially abundant between specific experimental treatments. A limitation of these methods is that they are suitable for only relatively simple experimental setups. In recent years, there have been promising developments in joint species distribution modelling (JSDM) (Warton *et al.* 2015) that allows for robust model-based statistical methods that are suitable for complex experimental and observational study designs (Ovaskainen and Abrego 2020).

Box 2.1: Case studies with contrasting experimental, biological and technical features

In the following, aimed at showcasing the diversity of options and choices eDNA analyses can encompass, we outline two examples of research studies relying on biodiversity analyses of eDNA with contrasting properties (Table 2.2). Note that the listed decisions are not compulsory, but an attempt to highlight the range of options within eDNA biodiversity studies.

Case study 1: Hierarchical structure of fish diversity in streams and rivers within a basin

Freshwater fish are valuable indicators of the biological and ecological status of fresh waters and are commonly used for evaluating the functioning of these ecosystems and the quality of their habitats (Radinger *et al.* 2019). Understanding how spatial scale influences biodiversity is a crucial step in the application of management strategies that can facilitate conservation of regional species diversity and maximise the health of ecosystems. Metabarcoding conducted on DNA filtered from water samples can help researchers and managers to increase the resolution and throughput of biodiversity assessment, and in doing so improve the monitoring and management of freshwater fish communities (Boivin-Delisle *et al.* 2021). We set out a case study that aims to assess how fish biodiversity is partitioned across primary and secondary streams and rivers within a basin (Fig. 2.2).

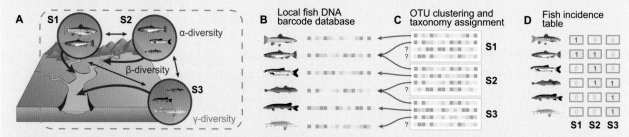

Fig. 2.2. Study design and methodological highlights of the case study about hierarchical structure of fish diversity in streams and rivers within a basin. (A) Overview of study design with partitioning of diversity across streams in a basin. (B) A local reference DNA **barcode** library is used for accurate taxonomic assignment. (C) Sequencing reads are clustered into OTUs to account for population-level species-specific marker variability, and OTUs that do not match any reference are overlooked. (D) An incidence table on the detection of each fish in each sample is used for statistical analyses.

Table 2.2. Overview of technical choices made for each case study.

	Case study 1	Case study 2
Marker gene	**COI**, because it is the gene that was standardised as the primary DNA barcode in eukaryotic organisms.	**16S rRNA**, because it is the gene that was standardised as the primary DNA barcode in bacteria and archaea.
Type resolution	**OTU**, because strain-level resolution is not required, and results should be as close as possible to traditional methods that considered the species as the unit of study.	**ASV**, because much of the diversity of bacteria and archaea is embedded within strain-level variation.
Data type	**Incidence-based**, because the aim is at detecting specific fish taxa, rather than estimating their abundances.	**Abundance-based**, because the aim is to identify relative abundance changes of microbial taxa.
Taxonomic annotation	**Specific database**, because not all target fish species might be represented in public databases.	**Public database**, because human-associated bacteria have been intensively surveyed and recorded in reference databases.
Type of diversity assessment	**Taxonomy-based**, because for management strategies the biological species is most meaningful resolution to be used as the type for diversity measurement.	**Taxonomy-free**, because diversity metrics can capture the desired diversity shifts without relying on taxonomy.
Type of diversity metrics	**Neutral metrics**, because phylogenetic information is not considered especially relevant.	**Phylogenetic metrics**, because phylogeny explains a large fraction of variation in microbial communities.
Objectives of statistical analyses	Partitioning diversity into primary streams, secondary rivers and the entire basin.	Detecting differential abundance of microbes between groups.

Case study 2: Gut bacterial diversity in a control-treatment study in humans

Research over the past few decades has demonstrated that microorganisms living in the gastrointestinal tract (gut microbiota) can profoundly influence host health (Gilbert *et al.* 2018). Food additives, such as **probiotics**, **prebiotics**, and **synbiotics**, are being continuously tested as potential treatments to modulate the gut microbiota (Gibson *et al.* 2017). Metabarcoding of the bacterial/archaeal 16S rRNA gene can be used to accurately measure shifts of diversity and composition of the gut microbiota induced by the additives. The case study we set out aims to measure differences in microbiota between groups of people who received a probiotic product and those who did not (Fig. 2.3).

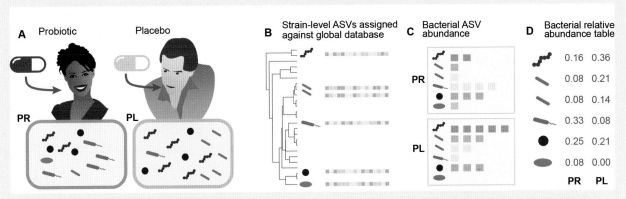

Fig. 2.3. Study design and methodological highlights of the case study about gut bacterial diversity in a randomised controlled trial study in humans. (A) Overview of a simplified study design in which the gut microbiota of two groups of individuals who received different treatments are compared. (B) Strain-level ASVs are annotated using a global database, and the phylogenetic distances among bacteria are calculated. (C) Bacterial abundances are estimated based on the number of copies of each ASV. (D) A relative abundance table of each bacterial strain is used for statistical analyses.

Appropriate data models for each data type

The response variables generated through eDNA metabarcoding may belong to different data types. While a linear regression assuming the normal model may be a reasonable starting point to model continuous variables such as a diversity metric (e.g. Hill numbers), alternative data models are required to analyse count data or binary data. GLM provides a robust framework to analyse the data types that we can generate with eDNA metabarcoding. A binomial GLM is suitable to analyse binary (e.g. presence/absence of an organism in a sample) and proportional data (e.g. proportion of animals infected with a parasite in a farm). A Poisson GLM may be appropriate to model count data (e.g. type richness or sequence counts of a type in a sample); however, count data in biological samples are usually overdispersed (meaning that the variance of the counts increases faster than the mean) so the negative binomial GLM or the log-normal Poisson GLM may be necessary to analyse such data. Sequencing data are also usually zero inflated (they contain more zeros than expected under the negative binomial or log-normal Poisson distributions) so zero inflated or hurdle GLM models may be required (Zuur *et al.* 2009). All these data models have also been implemented in several JSDMs and are available to analyse multivariate

response data, e.g. BORAL (Hui 2016), Hmsc (Tikhonov *et al.* 2020).

Accounting for the study design

Studies using eDNA metabarcoding often involve complex designs that induce dependencies among sampling units. These include hierarchical study designs where several sampling units are taken from a higher level of organisation: for example, streams within a basin, host individuals within a population. Data points coming from the same streams or host individuals are expected to resemble each other more than data points coming from different ones. In such cases, random effects, which can be implemented using GLMMs (Zuur *et al.* 2009), are needed to account for dependencies between data points. In the case of spatially continuous study designs, sampling units coming from close by locations are expected to resemble each other more than those from distant locations, because of a phenomenon called spatial autocorrelation. A similar phenomenon occurs in temporal study designs, where sampling units collected in a short time interval will be more similar than sampling units separated by a long-time interval. Spatially and temporally explicit models can be fitted to those kinds of datasets using generalised least squares (GLS) or GLMMs (if a combination of hierarchical and spatiotemporal random effects are required) (Zuur *et al.* 2009). Since basic GLMs and most other methods assume the independence of model residuals, ignoring those dependencies is considered a form of pseudoreplication (Hulbert 1984). Hence, inferences made from such models may be biased (Beale *et al.* 2007; Dormann 2007). For multivariate analyses, the Hmsc package has unique flexibility to account for complex study designs, since multiple random effects can be adjusted together to account for residual hierarchical, spatial or temporal autocorrelation, both in species occurrences (or abundances) and co-occurrences (or associations) (Ovaskainen and Abrego 2020).

CONCLUSIONS

The estimation of biodiversity through eDNA involves multiple steps, many of which require decisions to be made depending on the design and goals of the study. While there is no one-size-fits-all approach for eDNA analyses, we hope that the topics, concepts, and tools covered in this chapter will empower researchers to tailor their analytical methods to meet the needs of each research activity. Only a critical perspective on the generated data and employed techniques will enable researchers to accurately capture biodiversity patterns through eDNA metabarcoding, and in doing so contribute to increasing our understanding of fundamental natural processes.

DISCUSSION TOPICS

1. What are the differences between what Simpson's and Shannon's diversity indices?
2. What is the relationship between diversity indices and species abundance distributions?
3. How do diversity indices assist statistical analyses of environmental DNA metabarcoding data?

ACKNOWLEDGEMENTS

We thank Matthew Heydenrych for a constructive review of this chapter. We also acknowledge the University of Maryland Center for Environmental Science (http://ian. umces.edu/symbols/) for the use of their vector images in the figures.

REFERENCES

Ahn JH, Kim BY, Song J, Weon HY (2012) Effects of PCR cycle number and DNA polymerase type on the 16S rRNA gene pyrosequencing analysis of bacterial communities. *Journal of Microbiology* **50**, 1071–1074.

Alberdi A, Aizpurua O, Bohmann K, Gopalakrishnan S, Lynggaard C, et al. (2019) Promises and pitfalls of using high-throughput sequencing for diet analysis. *Molecular Ecology Resources* **19**, 327–348.

Alberdi A, Aizpurua O, Gilbert MTP, Bohmann K (2018) Scrutinizing key steps for reliable metabarcoding of environmental samples. *Methods in Ecology and Evolution* **9**, 134–147.

Alberdi A, Gilbert MTP (2019) A guide to the application of Hill numbers to DNA based diversity analyses. *Molecular Ecology Resources* **19**, 804–817.

Alberdi A, Martin Bideguren G, Aizpurua O (2021) Diversity and compositional changes in the gut microbiota of wild and captive vertebrates: a meta-analysis. *Scientific Reports* **11**, 22660.

Alberdi A, Razgour O, Aizpurua O, Novella-Fernandez R, Aihartza J, et al. (2020) DNA metabarcoding and spatial modelling link diet diversification with distribution homogeneity in European bats. *Nature Communications* **11**, 1154.

Amir A, McDonald D, Navas-Molina JA, Kopylova E, Morton JT, et al. (2017) Deblur rapidly resolves single-nucleotide community sequence patterns. *mSystems*, **2**, e00191-16.

Anderson MJ (2001) A new method for non-parametric multivariate analysis of variance. *Austral Ecology* **26**, 32–46.

Antich A, Palacin C, Wangensteen OS, Turon X (2021) To denoise or to cluster, that is not the question: Optimizing pipelines for COI metabarcoding and metaphylogeography. *BMC Bioinformatics* **22**, 177.

Bahram M, Hildebrand F, Forslund SK, Anderson JL, Soudzilovskaia NA, et al. (2018) Structure and function of the global topsoil microbiome. *Nature* **560**, 233–237.

Balvočiūtė M, Huson DH (2017) SILVA, RDP, Greengenes, NCBI and OTT - how do these taxonomies compare? *BMC Genomics* **18**, 114.

Barbera P, Czech L, Lutteropp S, Stamatakis A (2021) SCRAPP: A tool to assess the diversity of microbial samples from phylogenetic placements. *Molecular Ecology Resources* **21**, 340–349.

Beale CM, Lennon JJ, Elston DA, Brewer MJ, Yearsley JM (2007) Red herrings remain in geographical ecology: A reply to Hawkins et al. (2007). *Ecography* **30**, 845–847.

Binladen J, Gilbert MTP, Bollback JP, Panitz F, Bendixen C, et al. (2007) The use of coded PCR primers enables high-throughput sequencing of multiple homolog amplification products by 454 parallel sequencing. *PLoS One* **2**, e197.

Blaxter M, Mann J, Chapman T, Thomas F, Whitton C, et al. (2005) Defining operational taxonomic units using DNA barcode data. *Philosophical Transactions of the Royal Society B: Biological Sciences* **360**, 1935–1943.

Bohmann K, Elbrecht V, Carøe C, Bista I, Leese F, et al. (2021) Strategies for sample labelling and library preparation in DNA metabarcoding studies. *Molecular Ecology Resources* **22**, 1231–1246.

Bohmann K, Evans A, Gilbert MTP, Carvalho GR, Creer S, Knapp M, et al. (2014) Environmental DNA for wildlife biology and biodiversity monitoring. *Trends in Ecology & Evolution* **29**, 358–367.

Boivin-Delisle D, Laporte M, Burton F, Dion R, Normandeau E et al. (2021) Using environmental DNA for biomonitoring of freshwater fish communities: Comparison with established gillnet surveys in a boreal hydroelectric impoundment. *Environmental DNA* **3**, 105–120.

Borcard D, Gillet F, Legendre P (2018) Spatial analysis of ecological data. In *Numerical Ecology with R.* (Eds D Borcard, F Gillet, P Legendre) pp. 299–367. Springer International Publishing, Cham.

Brandt MI, Trouche B, Quintric L, Günther B, Wincker P, *et al.* (2021) Bioinformatic pipelines combining denoising and clustering tools allow for more comprehensive prokaryotic and eukaryotic metabarcoding. *Molecular Ecology Resources* **21**, 1904–1921.

Callahan BJ, McMurdie PJ, Holmes SP (2017) Exact sequence variants should replace operational taxonomic units in marker-gene data analysis. *The ISME Journal* **11**, 2639–2643.

Callahan BJ, McMurdie PJ, Rosen MJ, Han AW, Johnson AJA, *et al.* (2016) DADA2: High-resolution sample inference from Illumina amplicon data. *Nature Methods* **13**, 581–583.

Carøe C, Bohmann K (2020) Tagsteady: A metabarcoding library preparation protocol to avoid false assignment of sequences to samples. *Molecular Ecology Resources* **20**, 1620–1631.

Carraro L, Stauffer JB, Altermatt F (2021) How to design optimal eDNA sampling strategies for biomonitoring in river networks. *Environmental DNA* **3**, 157–172.

Chao A, Chiu C-H, Hsieh TC (2012) Proposing a resolution to debates on diversity partitioning. *Ecology* **93**, 2037–2051.

Chao A, Chiu C-H, Jost L (2010) Phylogenetic diversity measures based on Hill numbers. *Philosophical Transactions of the Royal Society B: Biological Sciences* **365**, 3599–3609.

Chao A, Chiu C-H, Jost L (2014) Unifying species diversity, phylogenetic diversity, functional diversity, and related similarity and differentiation measures through Hill Numbers. *Annual Review of Ecology, Evolution, and Systematics* **45**, 297–324.

Chao A, Chiu C, Villéger S, Sun I, Thorn S, *et al.* (2019) An attribute-diversity approach to functional diversity, functional beta diversity, and related (dis)similarity measures. *Ecological Monographs* **89**, e01343.

Chao A, Henderson PA, Chiu C-H, Moyes F, Hu K-H, *et al.* (2021) Measuring temporal change in alpha diversity: A framework integrating taxonomic, phyloletic and functional diversity and the iNEXT.3D standardization. *Methods in Ecology and Evolution* **12**, 1926–1940.

Chiu C-H, Jost L, Chao A (2014) Phylogenetic beta diversity, similarity, and differentiation measures based on Hill numbers. *Ecological Monographs* **84**, 21–44.

Coissac E, Riaz T, Puillandre N (2012) Bioinformatic challenges for DNA metabarcoding of plants and animals. *Molecular Ecology* **21**, 1834–1847.

Czech L, Stamatakis A, Dunthorn M, Barbera P (2022) Metagenomic analysis using phylogenetic placement – a review of the first decade. *Frontiers in Bioinformatics* **2**. doi:10.3389/fbinf.2022.871393

Davis NM, Proctor DM, Holmes SP, Relman DA, Callahan BJ (2018) Simple statistical identification and removal of contaminant sequences in marker-gene and metagenomics data. *Microbiome* **6**, 226.

Deagle BE, Thomas AC, McInnes JC, Clarke LJ, Vesterinen EJ, *et al.* (2019) Counting with DNA in metabarcoding studies: How should we convert sequence reads to dietary data? *Molecular Ecology* **28**, 391–406.

Deiner K, Bik HM, Mächler E, Seymour M, Lacoursière-Roussel A, *et al.* (2017) Environmental DNA metabarcoding: Transforming how we survey animal and plant communities. *Molecular Ecology* **26**, 5872–5895.

Dormann CF (2007) Effects of incorporating spatial autocorrelation into the analysis of species distribution data. *Global Ecology and Biogeography* **16**, 129–138.

Douady CJ, Delsuc F, Boucher Y, Doolittle WF, Douzery EJP (2003) Comparison of Bayesian and maximum likelihood bootstrap measures of phylogenetic reliability. *Molecular Biology and Evolution* **20**, 248–254.

Edgar RC (2016) UNOISE2: improved error-correction for Illumina 16S and ITS amplicon sequencing. bioRxiv. doi:10.1101/081257

Edgar RC, Flyvbjerg H (2015) Error filtering, pair assembly and error correction for next-generation sequencing reads. *Bioinformatics* **31**, 3476–3482.

Eisenhofer R, Minich JJ, Marotz C, Cooper A, Knight R *et al.* (2019) Contamination in low microbial biomass microbiome studies: Issues and recommendations. *Trends in Microbiology* **27**, 105–117.

Elbrecht V, Leese F (2015) Can DNA-Based ecosystem assessments quantify species abundance? Testing primer bias and biomass–sequence relationships with an innovative metabarcoding protocol. *PLoS One* **10**, e0130324.

Elbrecht V, Vamos EE, Steinke D, Leese F (2018) Estimating intraspecific genetic diversity from community DNA metabarcoding data. *PeerJ* **6**, e4644.

Erickson RA, Merkes CM, Mize EL (2019) Sampling designs for landscape-level eDNA monitoring programs. *Integrated Environmental Assessment and Management* **15**, 760–771.

Freeland JR (2017) The importance of molecular markers and primer design when characterizing biodiversity from environmental DNA. *Genome* **60**, 358–374.

Garrido-Sanz L, Senar MÀ (2022) Relative species abundance estimation in artificial mixtures of insects using mito-metagenomics and a correction factor for the mitochondrial DNA copy number. *Molecular Ecology Resources* **22**, 153–167.

Ghyselinck J, Pfeiffer S, Heylen K, Sessitsch A, De Vos P (2013) The effect of primer choice and short read sequences on the outcome of 16S rRNA gene based diversity studies. *PLoS One* **8**, e71360.

Gibbons SM, Duvallet C, Alm EJ (2018) Correcting for batch effects in case-control microbiome studies. *PLOS Computational Biology* **14**, e1006102.

Gibson GR, Hutkins R, Sanders ME, Prescott SL, Reimer RA, *et al.* (2017) Expert consensus document: The International Scientific Association for Probiotics and Prebiotics (ISAPP) consensus statement on the definition and scope of prebiotics. *Nature Reviews Gastroenterology & Hepatology* **14**, 491–502.

Gilbert JA, Blaser MJ, Caporaso JG, Jansson JK, Lynch SV (2018) Current understanding of the human microbiome. *Nature Medicine* **24**, 392–400.

Gloor GB, Macklaim JM, Pawlowsky-Glahn V, Egozcue JJ (2017) Microbiome datasets are compositional: And this is not optional. *Frontiers in Microbiology* **8**, 2224.

Gold Z, Curd EE, Goodwin KD, Choi ES, Frable BW, *et al.* (2021) Improving metabarcoding taxonomic assignment: A case study of fishes in a large marine ecosystem. *Molecular Ecology Resources* **21**, 2546–2564.

Grey EK, Bernatchez L, Cassey P, Deiner K, Deveney M, *et al.* (2018) Effects of sampling effort on biodiversity patterns estimated from environmental DNA metabarcoding surveys. *Scientific Reports* **8**, 8843.

Gury J, Zinger L, Gielly L, Taberlet P, Geremia RA (2008) Exonuclease activity of proofreading DNA polymerases is at the origin of artifacts in molecular profiling studies. *Electrophoresis* **29**, 2437–2444.

Heeger F, Bourne EC, Baschien C, Yurkov A, Bunk B, *et al.* (2018) Long-read DNA metabarcoding of ribosomal RNA in the analysis of fungi from aquatic environments. *Molecular Ecology Resources* **18**, 1500–1514.

Hill MO (1973) Diversity and evenness: A unifying notation and its consequences. *Ecology* **54**, 427–432.

Hleap JS, Littlefair JE, Steinke D, Hebert PDN, Cristescu ME (2021) Assessment of current taxonomic assignment strategies for metabarcoding eukaryotes. *Molecular Ecology Resources* **21**, 2190–2203.

Hsieh TC, Ma KH, Chao A (2016) iNEXT: an R package for rarefaction and extrapolation of species diversity (Hill numbers). *Methods in Ecology and Evolution* **7**, 1451–1456.

Hui FKC (2016) boral – Bayesian ordination and regression analysis of multivariate Abundance data in r. *Methods in Ecology and Evolution* **7**, 744–750.

Hulbert JH (1984) Pseudoreplication and the design of field experiments in ecology. *Ecological Monographs* **54**, 187–211.

Hu T, Chitnis N, Monos D, Dinh A (2021) Next-generation sequencing technologies: An overview. *Human Immunology* **82**, 801–811.

Jost L (2006) Entropy and diversity. *Oikos* **113**, 363–375.

Jost L (2010) The relation between evenness and diversity. *Diversity* **2**, 207–232.

Kopczynski ED, Bateson MM, Ward DM (1994) Recognition of chimeric small-subunit ribosomal DNAs composed of genes from uncultivated microorganisms. *Applied and Environmental Microbiology* **60**, 746–748.

Kuntke F, de Jonge N, Hesselsøe M, Lund Nielsen J (2020) Stream water quality assessment by metabarcoding of invertebrates. *Ecological Indicators* **111**, 105982.

Lavrinienko A, Jernfors T, Koskimäki JJ, Pirttilä AM, Watts PC (2021) Does intraspecific variation in rDNA copy number affect analysis of microbial communities? *Trends in Microbiology* **29**, 19–27.

Lin H, Peddada SD (2020) Analysis of compositions of microbiomes with bias correction. *Nature Communications* **11**, 3514.

Love MI, Huber W, Anders S (2014) Moderated estimation of fold change and dispersion for RNA-seq data with DESeq2. *Genome Biology* **15**, 550.

Machida RJ, Leray M, Ho S-L, Knowlton N (2017) Metazoan mitochondrial gene sequence reference datasets for taxonomic assignment of environmental samples. *Scientific Data* **4**, 170027.

Mächler E, Walser J-C, Altermatt F (2021) Decision-making and best practices for taxonomy-free environmental DNA metabarcoding in biomonitoring using Hill numbers. *Molecular Ecology* **30**, 3326–3339.

Marques V, Milhau T, Albouy C, Dejean T, Manel S, *et al.* (2021) GAPeDNA: Assessing and mapping global species gaps in genetic databases for eDNA metabarcoding. *Diversity and Distributions* **27**, 1880–1892.

Matesanz S, Pescador DS, Pías B, Sánchez AM, Chacón-Labella J, *et al.* (2019) Estimating belowground plant abundance with DNA metabarcoding. *Molecular Ecology Resources* **19**, 1265–1277.

McIntosh RP (1967) An index of diversity and the relation of certain concepts to diversity. *Ecology* **48**, 392–404.

McLaren MR, Willis AD, Callahan BJ (2019) Consistent and correctable bias in metagenomic sequencing experiments. *eLife* **8**, e46923.

McMurdie PJ, Holmes S (2013) phyloseq: An R package for reproducible interactive analysis and graphics of microbiome census data. *PLoS One* **8**, e61217.

McMurdie PJ, Holmes S (2014) Waste not, want not: Why rarefying microbiome data is inadmissible. *PLOS Computational Biology* **10**, e1003531.

Minich JJ, Sanders JG, Amir A, Humphrey G, Gilbert JA, *et al.* (2019) Quantifying and understanding well-to-well contamination in microbiome research. *mSystems* **4**, e00186-19.

O'Rourke DR, Bokulich NA, Jusino MA, MacManes MD, Foster JT (2020) A total crapshoot? Evaluating bioinformatic decisions in animal diet metabarcoding analyses. *Ecology and Evolution* **10**, 9721–9739.

Ovaskainen O, Abrego N (2020) *Joint Species Distribution Modelling: With Applications in R.* Cambridge University Press, Cambridge, UK.

Radinger J, Britton JR, Carlson SM, Magurran AE, Alcaraz-Hernández JD, *et al.* (2019) Effective monitoring of freshwater fish. *Fish and Fisheries* **20**, 729–747.

Ramakodi MP (2022) Influence of 16S rRNA reference databases in amplicon-based environmental microbiome research. *Biotechnology Letters* **44**, 523–533.

Reitmeier S, Hitch TCA, Treichel N, Fikas N, Hausmann B, *et al.* (2021) Handling of spurious sequences affects the outcome of high-throughput 16S rRNA gene amplicon profiling. *ISME Communications* **1**, 1–12.

Robinson MD, McCarthy DJ, Smyth GK (2010) edgeR: A Bioconductor package for differential expression analysis of digital gene expression data. *Bioinformatics* **26**, 139–140.

Salter SJ, Cox MJ, Turek EM, Calus ST, Cookson WO, *et al.* (2014) Reagent and laboratory contamination can critically impact sequence-based microbiome analyses. *BMC Biology* **12**, 87.

Schloss PD (2021) Amplicon sequence variants artificially split bacterial genomes into separate clusters. *mSphere* **6**, e0019121.

Sefers S, Schmitz JE (2018) Molecular contamination and amplification product inactivation. In *Advanced Techniques in Diagnostic Microbiology: Volume 1: Techniques.* (Eds Y-W Tang, C.W. Stratton) pp. 505–526. Springer International Publishing, Cham.

Shirazi S, Meyer RS, Shapiro B (2021) Revisiting the effect of PCR replication and sequencing depth on biodiversity metrics in environmental DNA metabarcoding. *Ecology and Evolution* **11**, 15766–15779.

Smyth RP, Schlub TE, Grimm A, Venturi V, Chopra A, *et al.* (2010) Reducing chimera formation during PCR amplification to ensure accurate genotyping. *Gene* **469**, 45–51.

Stevens JL, Jackson RL, Olson JB (2013) Slowing PCR ramp speed reduces chimera formation from environmental samples. *Journal of Microbiological Methods* **93**, 203–205.

Stoeckle MY, Das Mishu M, Charlop-Powers Z (2020) Improved environmental DNA reference library detects overlooked marine fishes in New Jersey, United States. *Frontiers in Marine Science* **7**, 1–12.

Taberlet P, Bonin A, Zinger L, Coissac E (2018) *Environmental DNA: For Biodiversity Research and Monitoring*. Oxford University Press, Oxford, UK.

Taberlet P, Coissac E, Pompanon F, Brochmann C, Willerslev E (2012) Towards next-generation biodiversity assessment using DNA metabarcoding. *Molecular Ecology* **21**, 2045–2050.

Tan G, Opitz L, Schlapbach R, Rehrauer H (2019) Long fragments achieve lower base quality in Illumina paired-end sequencing. *Scientific Reports* **9**, 2856.

Tedersoo L, Tooming-Klunderud A, Anslan S (2018) PacBio metabarcoding of Fungi and other eukaryotes: Errors, biases and perspectives. *New Phytologist* **217**, 1370–1385.

Thomsen PF, Willerslev E (2015) Environmental DNA – An emerging tool in conservation for monitoring past and present biodiversity. *Biological Conservation* **183**, 4–18.

Tikhonov G, Opedal ØH, Abrego N, Lehikoinen A, de Jonge MMJ, et al. (2020) Joint species distribution modelling with the r-package Hmsc. *Methods in Ecology and Evolution* **11**, 442–447.

Tuomisto H (2010) A diversity of beta diversities: straightening up a concept gone awry. Part 1. Defining beta diversity as a function of alpha and gamma diversity. *Ecography* **33**, 2–22.

Warton DI, Blanchet FG, O'Hara RB, Ovaskainen O, Taskinen S, et al. (2015) So many variables: Joint modeling in community ecology. *Trends in Ecology & Evolution* **30**, 766–779.

Weiss S, Xu ZZ, Peddada S, Amir A, Bittinger K, et al. (2017) Normalization and microbial differential abundance strategies depend upon data characteristics. *Microbiome* **5**, 27.

Whittaker RH (1960) Vegetation of the Siskiyou Mountains, Oregon and California. *Ecological Monographs* **30**, 279–338.

Wilsey B, Stirling G (2007) Species richness and evenness respond in a different manner to propagule density in developing prairie microcosm communities. *Plant Ecology* **190**, 259–273.

Wood SN (2017) *Generalized Additive Models: An Introduction with R*. 2nd edn. CRC Press. Boca Raton, FL, USA.

Zuur AF, Ieno EN, Walker N, Saveliev AA, Smith GM (2009) *Mixed Effects Models and Extensions in Ecology with R*. Springer, New York, NY.

3   Perspective – eDNA and metagenomics: a story of a disruptive technology for biodiversity monitoring

Peter Gilchrist, Biodiversity, Environmental Protection, Saudi Aramco, Dhahran, Saudi Arabia

I remember being blown away by a conference presentation by a recently graduated PhD student back in 2013. They had presented a typical multi-variate experimental design looking at different treatments for restoring lowland heath in the United Kingdom, a habitat with a high conservation priority. What was groundbreaking was that instead of using plant species and their cover as the biodiversity metrics, they had used a metagenomics approach to collect soil biota data from the experiment. These data were used to demonstrate the success of the different restoration treatments and how the soil communities developed towards a reference site's soil community … amazing.

These type of data for these taxa had been beyond the reach of science using traditional soil faunal extraction and identification techniques. It was just too expensive and time-consuming to ever have applied this approach in a research setting, never mind commercially. An added challenge would be finding the taxonomic experts for the soil taxa and to get them together to work on a project.

What really excited me was the avenues that eDNA, metagenomics, high throughput sequencing technology and bioinformatics could lead to in terms of biodiversity monitoring and new approaches in big-data analysis of ecological systems and the insights and solutions it could provide.

The commercial breakthrough came in 2014 with the UK regulators accepting eDNA presence/absence survey data for the European protected amphibian, the great

crested newt (*Triturus cristatus*) when considering applications for development licenses. In one stroke the technology was head-to-head with traditional ecological surveys and on all fronts seemed to be better. It was cheaper, quicker, and safer than having ecologists repeatedly visiting the same water body to do surveys. Also, the collection of the field data didn't require specialists: an important consideration with declining tertiary degree programs in taxonomy and ecological field studies leading to skill shortages in biological sciences and reflected in the decline of STEM graduates.

However, the regulator acceptance immediately caused a capacity issue in the sector. Once clients heard that survey costs were 70% cheaper than traditional methods, they all wanted the eDNA service. At the time there was only one commercial lab providing the service to the UK and that was based in France. By the second field season there were six companies offering the service. This rapid capacity building immediately caused quality issues and people started to query the validity of the results from the technique.

In a perfect mirror of the Gartner Hype Cycle for disruptive digital technology, eDNA hit a trough of disillusionment with another challenge. The original data that convinced acceptance by regulators had been collected by a citizen science protocol. This methodology had been specified in the regulatory protocol and, coupled with the commercialisation of the technique, meant that there was no flexibility in its application. So, when 'manufactured' eDNA was used as a positive control rather than 'live' eDNA swabbed from newts, the protocol was compromised by the concentrations and the smaller fragments of DNA in the artificial control DNA. The qPCR process was picking up and amplifying these tiny fragments of DNA which would aerosolise as soon as the packaging was opened, causing false-positive results throughout the labs providing the service. Some companies explained their issues, but others tried bravado to mask their false-positive results, further leading to mistrust of the technology. The issue was further compounded by the rigidity of the protocol in the regulations, which led to the lack of flexibility in adapting the methodology. This meant a simple fix of using a different area of the newt's genome to use as the positive identifier, which the artificial eDNA didn't represent, couldn't be used.

Fortunately, the issues were resolved and the presence/absence test for great crested newts is now accepted as a tried and tested methodology in the UK. There are also other eDNA and applied genome surveys which are used to support the evidence base for decision makers. However, to date there have been no other eDNA tests for protected species fully accepted by regulators and this is a missed opportunity.

Incremental innovations make small changes to existing technologies, breakthrough innovations make significant changes to technology, radical innovations, which take place more rarely, combine technology and business innovation to create major new industries with the potential for exponential growth. eDNA, metabarcoding and metagenomics coupled with bioinformatics technology should be just such an innovation.

The reasons for why there has been a reticence in regulatory acceptance and commercialisation are many-fold. There is ambiguity within the science and academic debate around what the results mean, which protocol to adopt and the limitations of the techniques. All of these lead to a lack of regulatory acceptance and in business no one likes to be first as it carries both commercial failure and reputational risks.

There are solutions for these issues, and organisations such as DNAqua-net in Europe, the eDNA Society in Japan, and the Southern eDNA Society in Australia and New Zealand are working hard to develop the applications and protocols to gain wider acceptance.

I am an advocate for applied genomics. I have used the technology for a wide sector of clients and on a variety of projects including monitoring ancient and restored woodland soils (following on the work I saw presented when I first became aware of the technique), presence/absence surveys for a variety of cryptic, protected, or endangered species, ecological trophic relationship mapping, investigating ecosystem recovery, biosecurity protocols and ecosystem services monitoring establishment around the globe.

As applied genomics and its evidence base continues to develop, the biodiversity data captured and bioinformatics to help analyse these data enable new questions to be asked and new understanding to be developed that simply would have been inaccessible without the technology. It leads to exciting new approaches to surveying and monitoring whole communities rapidly and relatively cheaply and opens up biodiversity information to the whole realm of big data analytics. In the current biodiversity extinction crisis, it is an invaluable tool in providing a rapid inventory of what we have, identifying issues and providing solutions and helping to ensure that biodiversity is given due consideration in decision making. And the PhD student I saw back in 2013 … she started her own applied genomics company and is working with IUCN to develop the eBioAtlas to map global freshwater and inland biodiversity using environmental DNA.

4 Revealing animal diet and food webs through DNA metabarcoding

Bruce E. Deagle, Johan Pansu, Julie McInnes and Michael Traugott

ABSTRACT

Knowledge of animal diet is an important part of many fundamental and applied ecological studies. The use of DNA-based methods to identify food remains in stomach contents or faeces has now been applied to study the diet of a wide range of animal species from crustaceans and insects to antelope and whales. In this chapter, we present a brief history of the research field and outline how dietary DNA metabarcoding (i.e. the simultaneous identification of species through amplification of DNA markers and high-throughput sequencing of food DNA in diet samples) is employed to study the diet of animals. Moreover, we identify important technical challenges that researchers may face when carrying out a dietary DNA metabarcoding study, such as unique sampling considerations and dominance of non-target DNA. We also highlight some of the critical questions that need to be considered during study design and data interpretation. Based on our experiences, we describe a few studies that illustrate the diversity of approaches and ecological questions that can be addressed. Overall, we hope to provide a clear view of the complexities associated with this approach as well as a sense of excitement around the large number of opportunities that exist in using DNA metabarcoding to study animal diet.

DETERMINING ANIMAL DIET IS A KEY PART OF UNDERSTANDING THEIR ECOLOGY, BUT CAN BE CHALLENGING

Studying animal diet has been a long-standing focus in ecology, but when a group of prominent ecologists put together a list of fundamental unanswered questions, details about what animals eat was a key piece of missing information required to answer many of them:

> *How does the structure of ecological interaction networks affect ecosystem functioning and stability? What are the indirect effects of harvesting on ecosystem structure and dynamics? How can we use species' traits as proxies to predict trophic interaction strength? What is the relative importance of trophic and non-trophic interactions in determining the composition of communities? To what extent will climate change uncouple trophic links due to phenological change?*
>
> — Sutherland *et al.* (2013)

This ongoing focus on diet reflects the central role trophic interactions have in shaping biological communities. It also reflects the fact that we do not have detailed data on these connections in most ecosystems. Diet data that are accessible usually have only broad taxonomic resolution and are rarely well resolved in space and time (Pringle and Hutchinson 2020). Beyond fundamental ecology, dietary information is also a critical component of many applied ecological studies. For example, diet information is needed to determine the effectiveness of biological control in agricultural systems (González-Chang *et al.* 2016; Staudacher *et al.* 2018), or when implementing ecosystem-based conservation and fisheries management programs (Ando *et al.* 2013; Guyton *et al.* 2020; Ratcliffe *et al.* 2021).

Methods for determining diets are varied and none of them is applicable to all questions, species or study systems (Nielsen *et al.* 2018). Even in humans, dietary intake is notoriously difficult to capture. An analysis of dietary questionnaire data from a 40-year US study found that due to inconsistent reporting, two-thirds of the participants did not appear to be consuming enough calories to survive (Archer *et al.* 2013). For wild animals, a wide range of approaches has been used to examine what they eat: observations of feeding behaviour is possible in some situations (Balme *et al.* 2020), but is often impractical or lacks taxonomic resolution. Chemical signatures from food that are incorporated into tissue or faeces of consumers such as stable isotope ratio or fatty acid signatures can be analysed to infer the trophic level of the consumer (Quinby *et al.* 2020) based on the diet integrated over long time periods (Jones *et al.* 2020). However, these approaches typically do not provide detailed taxonomic information on the food items consumed (Traugott *et al.* 2013).

Morphological identification of food remains in gut contents and faeces has been the mainstay method used for dietary analysis. In some cases, this provides high taxonomic resolution data, but there is a bias towards digestion-resistant food items and identification requires food with identifiable diagnostic parts (such as bones or seeds) and specialist taxonomic expertise. DNA-based identification methods can be applied to these same diet samples to obtain high taxonomic resolution data even from biological material without identifiable macroremains. The increased sensitivity of DNA methods opens many new opportunities: diet of tiny organisms (e.g. terrestrial invertebrates) can be studied without isolating microscopic food, diet of larger species (e.g. mammals, seabirds) can be studied less invasively through prey DNA in amorphous faeces rather than capture or stomach flushing, and even diet of liquid-feeding species can be examined (Clare 2014).

In this chapter, we present a brief history of DNA-based diet analysis and provide an overview of current approaches.

Focusing on DNA metabarcoding, we discuss the challenges unique to this approach that researchers may face in diet studies. We also highlight important considerations for study design and outline applications where food DNA metabarcoding has allowed us to obtain new insights into the feeding ecology of animals.

HISTORY AND VARIETY OF DNA-BASED APPROACHES USED TO STUDY DIET

Limitations in methodological approaches used to study diet have led to an extensive body of research on new methodology and refinements. The development of DNA methods in diet studies has been closely linked to advances in genetic technology which allowed increasingly sophisticated DNA-based taxonomic identification. The first application emerged not long after the invention of PCR when a study amplified a plant DNA barcode marker from bear faecal material (Höss *et al.* 1992). There was an initial lull, but by the end of the 1990s it had been shown that food DNA could be detected in everything from whole beetles (Agustí *et al.* 1999; Zaidi *et al.* 1999) to prey remains isolated from fish stomachs (Asahida *et al.* 1997) and even **coprolites** (Poinar *et al.* 1998). Interest then intensified and a range of DNA-diet studies were published using methods adopted from microbial ecologists, **ancient DNA** researchers and the emerging DNA barcoding initiative. Many of these early studies relied on diagnostic PCR where taxon-specific primers were used to screen dietary samples (Harper *et al.* 2005). Other studies laboriously cloned and sequenced DNA molecules present in DNA mixtures (Jarman *et al.* 2004) or identified isolated food remains using single-species DNA barcoding (Kvitrud *et al.* 2005; Clare *et al.* 2009). A major turning point occurred with the first applications of high-throughput sequencing (Deagle *et al.* 2009; Valentini *et al.* 2009), after which the dietary DNA metabarcoding approach we commonly use today became widely accessible and the number of studies increased exponentially (Ando *et al.* 2020).

Currently a range of different approaches are applied in DNA-based diet studies (Table 4.1). Diagnostic PCR is a useful option for many studies when a smaller number of diet items need to be identified, and this method involves relatively straightforward laboratory and data analysis procedures (see Box 4.1). DNA metabarcoding involves PCR amplification of food DNA using group-specific primers followed by high-throughput sequencing to identify taxa present. This approach allows taxonomic identification of

Table 4.1.   Comparison of different DNA-based approaches for diet studies.

	Diagnostic PCR	**DNA barcoding**	**DNA metabarcoding**	**Metagenomics**
Definition	Detection of taxa in a sample using PCR assays designed to amplify DNA only from a specific species or taxonomic group	PCR amplification of a barcode marker using DNA extracted from a single specimen, followed by sequencing to identify the species	PCR amplification of barcode marker(s) in a complex sample containing DNA from many taxa, followed by high-throughput sequencing to identify all amplified taxa	Direct high-throughput sequencing of all DNA in a complex sample containing DNA from many taxa, with no enrichment of specific barcode markers
Applications	*A priori* detection of one or a few functionally important food taxa (e.g. pests or endangered species)	Identification of individual macroremains isolated from dietary samples	Diet composition of the entire prey spectrum, resource partitioning, trophic network structure, etc.	Potentially whole diet composition coupled with gut microbiome, parasites, etc.
***A priori* knowledge of consumer diet**	Yes	Some required	Some required	No
Laboratory method development	Variable, often requires development of specific PCR assays, but assays are available for some taxa	Minimal	Variable, can require development of PCR markers but markers for many taxonomic groups are available	Minimal
Type of samples	Whole, faecal, regurgitate or gut sample	Isolated macroremains from diet sample	Whole, faecal, regurgitate or gut sample	Whole, faecal, regurgitate or gut sample
Cost per sample	Low	Medium	Medium to high	Very high
Time	In the lab: Low Data analysis: Low	In the lab: High Data analysis: Medium	In the lab: Medium-high Data analysis: High	In the lab: Low Data analysis: Very high
Suitability for large sample numbers	High	Low	Medium	Low
PCR/enrichment method	PCR, qPCR or ddPCR with taxon-specific primers	PCR of macroremains (i.e. single species templates) with group-specific primers	PCR (or capture) of a complex sample with broad or group-specific primers	None
Sequencing	No	Sanger or high-throughput sequencing	High-throughput sequencing	High-throughput sequencing
Bioinformatics complexity	None	Low	High	Very high
Potential quantitative information	Number of prey DNA copies within diet sample measured with qPCR	Mass or number of DNA-identified macroremains	Relative read abundance after sequencing (with caution due to PCR and other biological/technical biases)	Relative read abundance after sequencing (no PCR bias) still potential biological biases
Taxonomic resolution	High Controlled by specificity of primers used	Medium-high Depends on barcode marker used	Medium-high Depends on barcode marker used,	Potentially high Currently limited by low number of full genomes reference sequences available
Sensitivity	High-very high Depends on assay characteristics such as primers, reagents, thermocycling protocol	Medium Not all food survives digestion; contaminating DNA from other food items can sometimes interfere	Medium-high Subject to PCR amplification biases; common DNA may mask rare DNA present in sample	Low-high Low currently since few reads match references even with very large sequencing depth

complex DNA mixtures. It has proven useful in a huge variety of diet studies (see reviews by Pompanon *et al.* 2012; Clare 2014; Alberdi *et al.* 2019; Deagle *et al.* 2019; Ando *et al.* 2020; Traugott *et al.* 2021). However, as will become apparent later in the chapter, the methodology can be complex, both in the laboratory and the bioinformatics, and for most situations there is no simple off-the-shelf protocol that can be followed.

Box 4.1: Diagnostic PCR in diet analyses

When the goal of a study is to identify a small set of food taxa that we can *a priori* expect to find in the consumer's diet, diagnostic PCR tests with high specificity and sensitivity can often be more useful than DNA metabarcoding. Diagnostic PCR typically is used for assessing food/prey which is deemed functionally important. Taxon-specific PCR primers can be designed to the required taxonomic level of detection (e.g. species, genus or family level). Primers can be applied to one food taxon in singleplex PCR, or different food targets can be simultaneously detected within one multiplexed reaction typically covering not more than 10 taxa in one assay (Sint *et al.* 2012). The identity of the different food taxa in multiplexed PCR can be determined by differences in amplicon length when endpoint PCR and electrophoresis are used or, in the case of qPCR, by either melting curve analysis or the use of primers which are labelled with taxon-specific fluorescent dyes. Different PCR formats, including endpoint PCR coupled with gel or capillary electrophoresis, real-time/quantitative PCR, and droplet digital PCR, are used for diagnostic food detection. Depending on the type of PCR employed, relative or absolute quantification of target DNA in the diet sample is possible.

There are several advantages of diagnostic PCR approaches over food metabarcoding due to its methodological simplicity (see also Table 4.1). Results are immediately available after molecular testing and no additional bioinformatic analysis is required. Diagnostic PCR is suited to screen large numbers of diet samples time- and cost-effectively. The diagnostic approach is less prone to methodological variation as the molecular procedures are less complex and therefore are easier to control and standardise. Diagnostic approaches have also been used as an effective means to assess feeding interactions between closely related predators and prey. In addition, quantitative PCR techniques allow for the amount of food DNA present in a sample to be estimated, although, like quantitative metabarcoding approaches, interpretation can be challenging (e.g. Greenstone *et al.* 2014).

The major disadvantage of diagnostic PCR is that consumers can only be screened for a predefined and restricted set of food taxa (see also Table 4.1). Therefore, this approach requires a certain level of knowledge of the species' diet and cannot be used for describing the entire diet spectrum. Combined and nested multiplex PCR approaches have been employed covering up to 20 (Sint *et al.* 2019) and 35 (Thalinger *et al.* 2016) prey taxa, respectively. Another limitation is that sequences of the amplified food are not recovered, so extra care needs to be taken to verify the specificity of the assays. Developing and validating highly sensitive and specific assays can also be time-consuming, especially in the case of multiplex formats.

HOW IS DIETARY DNA METABARCODING DIFFERENT FROM OTHER ENVIRONMENTAL DNA METABARCODING?

Sampling in dietary DNA metabarcoding studies

One unique aspect of DNA dietary studies compared to other applications presented in this book concerns the nature of samples and sampling methods. Analysis can be carried out on DNA extracted from faeces, gut contents, whole consumers (mainly for small invertebrates) or individually isolated food remains. There is often more DNA available in dietary samples compared to other eDNA samples (e.g. soil, water, sediment) and, in some cases, samples can be reliably collected and are of consistent quality (e.g. large mammal faecal samples, fresh regurgitates of insects). The choice of samples depends not just on the research question, but also on the taxa studied and ethical considerations (i.e. invasive vs. non-invasive sampling). Gut contents can be collected by dissection (e.g. for fish), as regurgitates (e.g. for birds, beetles), or through analysis of whole organisms (King *et al.* 2008). Faecal samples are usually collected using non-invasive approaches for larger organisms, but may involve capture of the animal to obtain faeces produced by smaller animals such as arthropods (e.g. Guillerault *et al.* 2017; Pringle *et al.* 2019). Different sample types may have better quality DNA or be detectable for longer times post-feeding (Oehm *et al.* 2017; Alberdi *et al.* 2019). For example, in a study on ground beetles, whole animals and regurgitates enabled longer post-feeding DNA detection and a higher detection success than faeces (Kamenova *et al.* 2018). In the case of faecal samples, they should be collected fresh where possible to avoid the risk of DNA degradation (e.g. from UV and rain) and contamination with non-target DNA (e.g. fungi, vegetation, insect eggs; Oehm *et al.* 2011; Ando *et al.* 2013; McInnes, Alderman, Deagle *et al.* 2017). As the detection probability of food DNA decreases significantly with time post-feeding (Oehm *et al.* 2011; Greenstone *et al.* 2014; McInnes, Alderman, Deagle *et al.* 2017; Kamenova *et al.* 2018), it is important to understand the physiology, ecology and behaviour of the animal prior to sample collection to avoid issues such as fasting periods, or collection of samples from young animals that are not feeding directly on the prey. Also, it can be important to record environmental variables which can affect post-feeding detection intervals (e.g. temperature, time of the day) to account for their impact on the molecular trophic data. Often a substantial proportion of samples contain little or no food DNA, so collecting extra samples is recommended. Finally, when designing experiments, one should keep in mind that molecular diet analysis provides a snapshot of recently consumed prey, and does not reflect long-term feeding behaviour.

Given what we know about the presence of DNA in the environment, it is not surprising that there is a very real risk of contamination during sample collection and discriminating real food DNA from contamination can be challenging in some cases. For example, in a study of Bryde's whale diet where faeces were collected with nets, the background plankton diversity in the sampled water needed to be considered to draw conclusions about the origin of the zooplankton detected in the sample (Carroll *et al.* 2019). Other examples where problems could arise include the collection of plant material along with herbivore faeces, external material on whole animal samples (e.g. Remén *et al.* 2010), or the deposition of insect eggs in insectivore faeces. Even when environmental contamination is unlikely to be confused with diet, contaminating DNA may make up a large proportion of recovered sequences and mask the signal from diet items (e.g. albatross faecal collections can contain a lot of plant DNA from the nesting area; McInnes, Alderman, Deagle *et al.* 2017). Methods to reduce contamination include washing the exterior of sampled arthropods with sodium hypochlorite ('*bleach*') before grinding them up, putting sheets under nests or along foraging routes for faecal collections, collection of fresh samples soon after defecation, and avoiding collection of any part of the sample in contact with the ground substrate or surrounding living organisms such as plants (e.g. Vesterinen *et al.* 2016; Briem *et al.* 2018; Cavallo *et al.* 2018). In any study, careful consideration is needed prior to sample collection to ensure the amount of food DNA is maximised, contamination minimised, and that there is consistency in sampling for comparability.

Dominance of non-target DNA in diet samples and what to do about it

Once samples are collected, one of the biggest challenges in a dietary DNA metabarcoding study is the potential dominance of non-target DNA from the consumer and/or parasites in the samples (O'Rorke *et al.* 2012; Fig. 4.1A and 4.1B). The extent of the issue varies between consumers and sample types. Even if non-target DNA is dominant in samples, it is not necessarily a problem; for example, most eDNA samples are dominated by microbe DNA, but taxa in the remaining fraction can still be characterised with PCR primers that will amplify only taxa of interest. A similar approach can be applied in some dietary studies where it is possible to use PCR markers that amplify solely the food groups of interest, but not the consumer. An example of this is seen in most studies of herbivores where a plant-specific marker can be amplified, excluding consumer DNA from downstream analysis (Fig. 4.1C). Similarly, for strictly insectivorous mammals (e.g. many bats) it is possible to use insect-specific DNA metabarcoding markers. Diagnostic PCRs could also be used to focus directly on one or a few food species of interest and circumvent the problem of excessive cross-amplification of non-target DNA (Traugott *et al.* 2021; Box 4.1).

Difficulties arise when the consumer (and potentially parasites) in a study is phylogenetically embedded within the range of food taxa one is interested in characterising. Examples include mammalian predators that eat other mammals (Shehzad *et al.* 2012), terrestrial arthropods which consume other arthropods, and seabirds which eat other vertebrates (e.g. fish) as well as invertebrates (e.g. crustaceans and squid; see Fig. 4.1D). In these cases, if PCR primers are conserved among all food items, then the non-target DNA will also be amplified and sequences of food DNA will often be swamped (McInnes, Alderman, Deagle *et al.* 2017; Fig. 4.1). For studies focusing on a restricted set of potential food items, diagnostic PCR can be used to avoid the amplification of non-target DNA (Box 4.1). However, if the objective is to investigate the entire prey spectrum using DNA metabarcoding, there are two primary ways to deal with problematic non-target DNA once samples have been collected. The first is to design multiple group-specific primers that focus only on taxonomically restricted and cohesive food groups (Fig. 4.1D). This increases the complexity of the study considerably; using multiple markers requires optimisation of several protocols, and possibly distinct bioinformatic pipelines and reference databases. Constructing overall diet is also difficult because each marker provides a blinkered view, and the relative contribution of the different groups is difficult to establish. This is a major impediment to studying the diet of omnivores as the plant and animal components often need to be considered separately. In some cases broad coverage markers sequenced in more depth can provide an overall view of diet despite the background DNA (Piñol *et al.* 2014). This broad approach can be combined with

What DNA is in a diet sample?

Most DNA in diet samples comes from bacteria, the consumer or from parts of the food genomes that are not taxonomically informative; this is exemplified by metagenomics studies. When metabarcoding with broad ('universal') markers, sequences from the consumer (penguin in example below) or non-targeted groups (e.g. parasites) may be prevalent.

(A) Overall view from metagenomic sequencing of wood grouse faeces
(data from Chua et al. 2021)

(B) Proportional data from a metabarcoding analysis of penguin faeces using a broad eukaryote marker (each bar is a separate sample) (data from Ratcliffe *et al*. 2021)

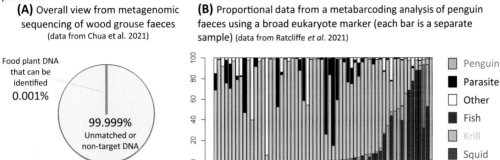

Ways to improve food DNA detection

Group-specific markers avoid non-target DNA. Food taxa sometimes represents a distinct **lineage** from the consumer (simple situation). Often several markers are needed to cover the whole diet when the consumer is phylogenetically embedded within the range of prey taxa (complex situation), and the comparisons between separate datasets are challenging.

(C) Simple (e.g. Herbivore)

(D) Complex (e.g. penguin)

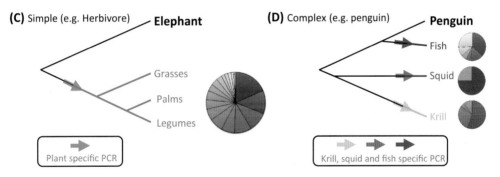

Selective blocking prevents amplification of a specific DNA lineage. This can allow effective use of markers which amplify DNA from both food and the consumer. The figures below show an increase in prey diversity obtained from leopard cat faeces with predator specific blocking (data from Shezad *et al*. 2012).

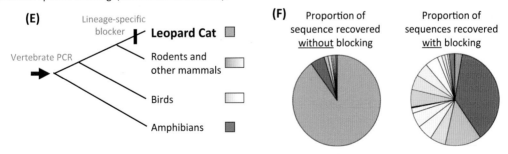

Fig. 4.1. The view of what DNA is present in a dietary sample depends on the protocol used and the reference database coverage. **(A)** Metagenomic sequencing does not enrich any fraction and provides the most realistic view of the DNA in a sample. Unfortunately, without the focus on standard barcode markers only a tiny component of sequence match those in current reference databases. **(B)** Broad eukaryote primers highlight the dominance of consumer DNA in many diet samples. **(C and D)** Group-specific markers allow the focus to be directed to the food component of a sample and can be relatively simple in some cases, but when food is closely related to the consumer and/or comes from diverse phylogenetic groups, several markers may be required. **(E and F)** Blocking amplification of consumer DNA can allow the detection of more food taxa.

group-specific markers to get better taxonomic resolution of different dietary components (Takahashi *et al.* 2020).

The other option to minimise the amplification of consumer DNA is to use primers that target a broad range of taxa but selectively remove consumer DNA from the analysis (Fig. 4.1E and F). Most often this is done by adding a 'blocking oligonucleotide' into the PCR mix which specifically binds to unwanted non-target DNA and limits its amplification (Vestheim and Jarman 2008; Leray *et al.* 2013). Alternatively, restriction enzymes can be used to cleave unwanted DNA (Dunshea 2009). The time and expense required to develop these approaches mean they are only an option when studies are on a single or few consumers. These approaches may also have some unexpected effects on the recovery of food DNA (i.e. some food DNA may inadvertently be excluded).

DNA quality, variable digestion, secondary predation and scavenging

All samples used in diet studies are digested to some degree by the consumer. In faecal samples, much of the food DNA is highly fragmented (i.e. more small DNA fragments than large ones; Box 4.2). Choosing shorter PCR markers can

therefore provide a more sensitive assay for the digested food component but often at the expense of taxonomic resolution (see Box 4.2). DNA quality can also be highly variable between different components because less digested material is present (e.g. woody material in large herbivore faeces, or hard insect exoskeletons in bat faeces). In some cases, the undigested remains in faeces can be screened out of faecal samples to provide a signal that is less influenced by these macroremains (Thomas *et al.* 2017). In stomach contents, differential degradation of food is almost always found and is related to the type of tissue and the time since consumption; digestion rates for different food species being consumed have been measured in some cases (Greenstone *et al.* 2014). An analogous situation happens with eDNA in soil/water when recently deposited versus older eDNA is present, and the persistence of eDNA differs between species. These features make the inference of quantitative data particularly challenging, especially for stomach contents (see also Box 4.3).

Another issue to consider is secondary predation/consumption, where material in the digestive tract of the food species is detected and is difficult to distinguish from food of the consumers' primary diet, leading to so-called false

---

Box 4.2: Markers for DNA diet analysis?

Selection of markers for dietary DNA metabarcoding follows the same general principles outlined by Stat and West (Chapter 5). The core gene regions used for broad eukaryote assays are the conserved nuclear ribosomal RNA genes (usually 18s); for land plants, a portion of the chloroplast genome (*trn*L intron) or sequences in ribosomal RNA genes (ITS); and for animals, mitochondrial ribosomal RNA genes (16S and 12S) or cytochrome c oxidase subunit I (COI). Despite its excellent reference database, COI is not used as often as one might expect since this protein coding gene has less conserved primer binding sites (Deagle *et al.* 2014). A variety of other markers are employed to increase taxonomic resolution or improve marker recovery for a particular consumer, but these often require development of a custom reference database. Many diet studies design their own PCR primers to meet additional requirements, such as group-specific primers which avoid consumer/parasite DNA (see main text) and primers that keeping the length of marker as short as feasible to increase the detectability of small fragments (which are more abundant than large fragments due to DNA degradation) (Fig. 4.2).

With the wide variety of markers that have proliferated, it is strongly advised to carry out *in silico* assessment to examine the coverage in the reference database and taxonomic resolution of the marker in potential dietary taxa (Taberlet *et al.* 2018). Even when adopting markers used in similar studies, they should be evaluated for specific systems.

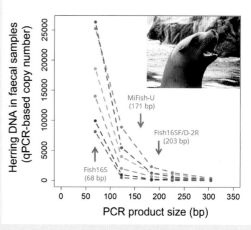

Fig. 4.2. DNA fragment size distribution of herring DNA in six sea lion faecal samples based on quantitative PCR of five different sized amplicons (data from Deagle *et al.* 2006). Data show an exponential decline in the amount of the digested herring DNA. Also shown are the size of some amplicons for fish-specific markers that could potentially be used in dietary metabarcoding studies (marker information taken from Zhang *et al.* 2020).

trophic links and food web errors (King *et al.* 2008). Empirical evaluations can be made to estimate the importance of this phenomenon. Using feeding experiments with insects, Guenay *et al.* (2021) have suggested secondarily consumed food produces a relatively weak signal. Similar results were obtained for marine fish by evaluating the food DNA component coming from guts of ingested prey removed from fish stomachs (Clarke *et al.* 2020). However, secondary predation can be a significant issue in other systems. A study on puffin diet (Bowser *et al.* 2013) found that several potential food species detected in faecal samples were not realistically prey for the birds, but these taxa were found in the stomach contents of herring (the main puffin prey). It is also likely that secondary predation will be commonly detected in omnivores since plant tissue could be from direct consumption or from the guts of herbivore prey, which are likely to contain food due to continuously feeding of many herbivores (Tercel *et al.* 2021).

Like most diet determination methods, DNA-based methods alone cannot distinguish between scavenging and consumption of fresh prey. This can be important where active predation needs to be distinguished from feeding on carrion, such as in studies on biological control of pests (e.g. Foltan *et al.* 2005; Juen and Traugott 2005). One approach to get a proxy for the significance of scavenging versus active predation is the assessment of the availability of carrion prey in each habitat and/or the screening of obligate scavengers for the prey of interest. Recent findings which assessed prey DNA and prey RNA within a diet sample have shown that it is possible to differentiate between the consumption of fresh and carrion prey as the amount of prey RNA is greatly reduced in the carrion prey compared to freshly consumed prey (Neidel *et al.* in press).

DIETARY DNA METABARCODING STUDY DESIGN AND DATA INTERPRETATION

The potential power and deceptively simple concept of using DNA in diet studies needs to be tempered with the real complexity of study design and implementation (Zinger *et al.* 2019). There are many aspects of the approach that should be questioned at the start of a diet study to ensure researchers know what to expect. Many of these questions also arise in eDNA metabarcoding studies more generally, and the answers will often be unique to a particular study. Rather than trying to provide answers, we outline some of the issues that we feel are important to consider. The first obvious question is whether DNA methods are best suited to your objectives (Nielsen *et al.* 2018). If

DNA methods are useful, but is DNA metabarcoding the best approach or are other genetic methods more suited (Table 4.1, Box 4.1; Alberdi *et al.* 2019; Traugott *et al.* 2021)? If DNA metabarcoding is appropriate, there are still many factors to consider (see reviews by Alberdi *et al.* 2019; Ando *et al.* 2020), some of which include: What is the best sample type and collection method to use? Can appropriate sample numbers and representative samples (spatially and/or temporally) be collected? What is the cost of analysing samples (time and money) and what laboratory/computer equipment is needed? What is the best choice of marker(s)? Is non-target DNA likely to be a problem? How will potential laboratory contamination be controlled? What kind of controls/replicates are needed to assess biological, environmental and methodological variation (Alberdi *et al.* 2018; Mata *et al.* 2019)?

It is also important to think about aspects of data analysis at an early stage of the study. The availability of reference sequences and the level of taxonomic assignment possible for your chosen marker and study system need to be assessed (Taberlet *et al.* 2018). Downloading and exploring relevant sequence data from potential taxa of interest from public sequence repositories such as GenBank or BOLD (Meiklejohn *et al.* 2019) is a good starting point. It is also important to consider the taxa that are missing from these databases to provide a level of certainty or caveats around taxonomic assignment. For example, in a situation where three closely related food species are present in the region but only one is represented in the reference database, a good match to the database sequence does not conclusively exclude the other two species (without data it is not known how distinct these other species are). Taxonomic assignment may only be possible if additional reference samples are obtained. It is often necessary (and always recommended) to produce custom reference sequences from local voucher specimens, and make it as exhaustive as possible, to have confidence in taxonomic assignments. Making sure there is a suitable bioinformatic pipeline for analysing DNA-based diet data from high-throughput sequencing, and having an understanding of the process and the consequences of the choice of parameters at each step of the pipeline, is also critical (Alberdi *et al.* 2018). Another consideration is how quantitative the data need to be for the researcher's purposes (see Box 4.3). This is a complex question since all methods of diet analysis provide imperfect estimates and true diets are unknown. Before launching a DNA diet study, preliminary work in the form of a pilot study or a feeding trial may be useful to get some baseline technical information to aid in interpretation of results

Box 4.3: Challenges of quantitative DNA metabarcoding diet analysis

One of the first questions likely to be raised by ecologists when discussing approaches to studying diet is whether quantitative data can be obtained. The short answer is that all diet determination methods only approximate the true diet, so users need to carefully consider their requirements and examine options for their study system.

With DNA metabarcoding there are two general ways to get quantitative diet estimates at the population level. The first is referred to as frequency of occurrence (FOO) and counts the number of detections of each food item across samples. The other is the relative read abundance (RRA) and uses the relative amount of amplified DNA sequences (i.e. sequence counts) from different food items in each sample and is averaged across the population to provide a mean RRA for each food item.

$$FOO_i = \frac{1}{S}\sum_{k=1}^{S} I_{i,k}$$

FOO for food item i where S is the number of samples, and I is an indicator function such that $I_{i,k} = 1$ if food item i is present in sample k, and 0 if not.

$$RRA_i = \frac{1}{S}\sum_{k=1}^{S} \frac{n_{i,k}}{\sum_{i=1}^{T} n_{i,k}}$$

RRA for food item i where S is the number of samples, T is the number of food items (taxa) and $n_{i,k}$ is the number of amplified sequences of food item i in sample k.

Unfortunately, both methods have pervasive biases (see Deagle *et al.* 2019).

FOO overestimates the contribution of minor diet items (potentially magnifying impact from secondary predation and low-level contamination). This metric is also sensitive to the threshold of number of sequences used to define a presence.

For RRA the relative number of sequences will not accurately reflect relative biomass of food items due to both biological (e.g. difference in DNA density between species, or differential digestion) and technical (e.g. variable primer binding) biases (Pompanon *et al.* 2012). Despite the certainty of biases in RRA, using counts to weight food contributions can still improve diet estimates in many cases (Deagle *et al.* 2019). Another complication with RRA is that data are proportional, not absolute, and therefore require special statistical consideration (e.g. Quinn *et al.* 2017).

There are several ways to circumvent the challenges of producing quantitative data. The first is framing science questions so they are robust to these errors. This could be done by focusing on diet diversity, or relative dietary changes over time. It is also possible to increase confidence in DNA-based results through preliminary experiments (e.g. feeding trials) that evaluate, and potentially correct, biases in a particular system (Thomas *et al.* 2016). If independent diet determination methods are available, they will ideally be used in parallel to give additional confidence in conclusions.

from a larger study (Deagle *et al.* 2010; Wallinger *et al.* 2013; Schattanek *et al.* 2021).

Given the considerable number of technical questions to consider when dietary DNA metabarcoding is being applied in a new system, it is important to have experienced molecular ecologists involved during planning stages. Another option is to engage one of the increasing numbers of commercial service providers. These companies can help in study design, conduct the laboratory analysis, and perform the bioinformatics. In theory this is a good system, where experts in a particular aspect of the workflow focus on producing the best datasets. However, this approach moves one group of scientists away from the fascinating technological complexity of the methods and another group of scientists away from having a comprehensive understanding of the study system. There are many situations where this can work, but often the best studies will be from truly

collaborative research where scientists actively share a larger view of the overall study.

APPLICATION EXAMPLES

There are now hundreds of dietary DNA applications in the literature. We highlight a few examples here based mainly on studies we have been involved in. The aim is to illustrate the types of questions that can be addressed, the diversity of approaches being used, some of the challenges, and the unique opportunities that DNA-based diet analysis offer.

Diet of invertebrates

DNA-based analysis of trophic interactions has been particularly useful for assessing what food invertebrates consume since diet samples are usually very small and the prey items are often completely macerated or pre-digested (e.g. spiders), leaving no visually identifiable remains in their gut contents. One example where conventional approaches of diet analysis are unsuitable concerns soil-living invertebrates with pre-oral digestion, such as the larvae of *Agriotes* click beetles (Coleoptera: Elateridae). These generalist plant feeders live in highly diverse plant-root environments and little is known about their dietary choices. To assess how the level of plant diversity affects the consumption of different plants throughout the season in a maize crop system, Staudacher *et al.* (2013) employed a combination of stable isotope analysis and DNA-based gut content analysis of *Agriotes* larvae. Stable isotope analysis showed how much carbon ingested by the larvae was derived from the maize crop compared to the other plants, while DNA-based diet analysis allowed for the identification of exactly which plant species were preferred or avoided, and how preferences changed throughout the season.

Even more complex feeding interactions were examined by Sint *et al.* (2019) who investigated arthropod predator food webs in early and late pioneer sites of glacier forelands in the Austrian Alps. Due to close relatedness of the taxa examined and the associated problems of cross-amplification of consumer and prey DNA, a series of multiplex PCR assays was employed to allow detection of 20 prey groups (this included intraguild prey, where the predator is eating other competing predators, and extraguild prey). Dietary information derived from over 1800 individual spiders and beetles collected in three glacier forelands was used to construct semi-quantitative intraguild-extraguild food webs for early and late pioneer sites (Fig. 4.2 and Box 4.4). These food webs revealed that although pronounced changes between invertebrate community composition was observed between valleys and successional stages, the identity of the predator was the strongest factor determining its prey choice, and even closely related beetles and

---

Box 4.4: DNA can help untangle complex food webs

Food webs are schematic networks that show feeding interactions, or patterns of energy flow, within a community. Food webs start with diet descriptions of individuals and populations, then ideally build larger networks until they encompass a large set of trophic interactions in the system under study. From these trophic network models, we can examine coupling between taxa to infer general structural properties of the community that help us unravel which mechanisms drive changes in populations and communities (Pimm 2002). Understanding these complex interactions is a unifying goal in ecology, but major knowledge gaps remain (Fulton *et al.* 2019; Pringle 2020).

Several barriers have hampered the reconstruction of accurate food webs; some of these can be overcome using DNA-based dietary datasets (Roslin and Majaneva 2016; Pringle and Hutchinson 2020):

1. **Increased taxonomic resolution**. Traditional diet data (identification of digested remains or chemical tracers) tends to lump groups of species together and misses the presence of cryptic species (either consumer or food). This conflates linkages in food webs and can lead to misleading interpretations. DNA-based methods can provide species-level identification in dietary samples and discriminate cryptic species.
2. **Revealing otherwise invisible trophic interactions.** DNA can uncover new trophic linkages in a whole range of ecosystems (see examples in the chapter).
3. **Increased sample size.** Representations of even modest food webs requires analysis of many samples. DNA methods have the potential to provide larger datasets, although as emphasised in the main text, having high capacity to sequence DNA does not equate to easily obtainable diet information.
4. **Standardisation of datasets**. Methods of studying diet often vary between different trophic levels and/or ecosystems. Since each method comes with unique biases, comparisons are difficult. Using DNA as a common biomarker can provide a standard, comparable currency to reconstruct multi-trophic networks and allow to the investigation of variations in networks structure through space and time.

Due to the complexity of food web research, much of the empirical work has focused on relatively simple specialised systems (e.g. host-parasite or plant–insect pollinator trophic networks). DNA-based approaches have been applied in these model systems (e.g. Pornon *et al.* 2017) and many more complex food webs (e.g. Casey *et al.* 2019; Pansu *et al.* 2019; Sint *et al.* 2019). While broader food web studies have been carried out using DNA approaches, there remains a gap between the mathematically focused field of food web ecology and the detailed genetic diet datasets that molecular ecologists can now produce. Integration of these field will undoubtedly continue and produce some more exciting breakthroughs in our understanding of community ecology.

spider species occupied clearly definable trophic niches (Fig. 4.3). The valley of origin had a smaller, albeit statistically significant, effect and the successional stage an even smaller effect. This study also resolved the 'predator first paradox', which is the paradoxical observation that early successional arthropod communities on bare ground surrounded by intact ecosystems are often dominated by arthropod predators. It showed that roughly two-thirds of the prey consumed by these predators was derived from distant (allochthonous) sources (i.e. flying insects) and intraguild predation; only one-third was derived from local autochthonous productivity (e.g. collembolans).

Vertebrate predators

Traditionally, diet studies of vertebrate predators have used morphological examination of faeces or stomach contents; this creates a strong bias towards the detection of food remains that resist digestion and can be identified visually. DNA dietary analysis can reveal previously undetected prey even in consumers where diet is thought to be well understood. In marine ecosystems, new DNA-based detections of soft-bodied food have facilitated a paradigm shift in the importance of gelatinous plankton (jellyfish) in food webs (Hays *et al.* 2018). In a global diet study on black-browed albatross using DNA metabarcoding, jellyfish DNA was present in 42% of samples overall and up to 80% of samples at some sites (Fig. 4.3; McInnes, Alderman, Lea *et al.* 2017). Jellyfish was the only DNA detected in many samples, ruling out secondary ingestion. Similarly, jellyfish DNA has been detected in fish stomachs (Lamb *et al.* 2017; Günther *et al.* 2021) and penguin faeces (Jarman *et al.* 2013; Cavallo *et al.* 2018). These results have forced a rethink about what seabirds choose to eat (Thiebot and McInnes 2020).

Data from DNA diet studies often provide unique insight into a study system but also require a considerable amount of study-specific technical development. This was the case for a DNA metabarcoding diet study conducted in north-western Australia that examined dietary partitioning of two closely related fish species (red snappers) that are morphologically indistinguishable as juveniles (Takahashi *et al.* 2020). The authors examined intestinal contents from adults and juvenile snappers (juveniles were distinguished using DNA barcoding) and obtained high resolution diet data; 57% of recovered prey were identified to species level and 19% to genus. The study was complex in that it used a broad eukaryotic marker (targeting 18S rDNA) and three group-specific markers (cephalopods, crustaceans, bony fish). A range of fish prey was revealed but only after development of 'host-specific blocking primer' for each of the snapper species being studied (Takahashi *et al.* 2020). The initial investment in developing exhaustive methodology to perform a detailed study like this can be quite high and needs to be considered before initiating DNA diet work.

Vertebrate herbivores

Species coexistence in hyperdiverse tropical ecosystems has attracted scientists' interest for a long time (Moreau 1948). DNA metabarcoding continues to shed light on fine-scale mechanisms of resource partitioning supporting such coexistence among large ungulates in Kenyan and Mozambican savannas (e.g. Kartzinel *et al.* 2015; Pansu *et al.* 2019). In these ecosystems, the analysis of herbivore diet has long been hampered by the difficulty of visual observation of feeding, or identification of dietary plant macro-remains in faecal samples. Therefore, their diet has traditionally been discriminated along a grazer (grass-eater) – browser (non-grass eater) continuum. DNA-based methods now allow the reconstruction of fine-scale (and often cryptic) plant–herbivore interactions in species-rich food webs (see also Box 4.4). Focusing on DNA extracted from freshly collected faecal samples, these studies demonstrated that sympatric populations of large herbivores tend to eat a different suite of plant taxa in differing proportion, showing evidence that resource partitioning occurs not only in space and time (e.g. selection of different patches) or by plant type (browser and grazer) but also at the level of plant species. In Mozambique, relative abundance diet data were recently combined with plant trait data to further identify key plant traits that underpin this dietary niche partitioning (Potter *et al.* 2022) and to infer inter-individual differences in diet composition and quality (Fig. 4.3; Atkins *et al.* 2019; Becker *et al.* 2021).

These African herbivore studies were primarily based on a plant-specific marker to amplify DNA, the P6 loop of the *trn*L intron (Taberlet *et al.* 2007). This marker offers broad taxonomic coverage but, due to its short length, exhibits an unequal taxonomic resolution between groups. To circumvent this issue, other studies on terrestrial herbivores combined several markers. Goldberg *et al.* (2020) detect 30% more plant taxa in the diet of the northern Idaho ground squirrel using two additional markers (from the ITS region) along with the *trn*L marker (Goldberg *et al.* 2020). As the number of plant markers used for herbivore diet studies increase, the comparability of multiple markers will need to be assessed as will the reliability of quantitative data interpretation.

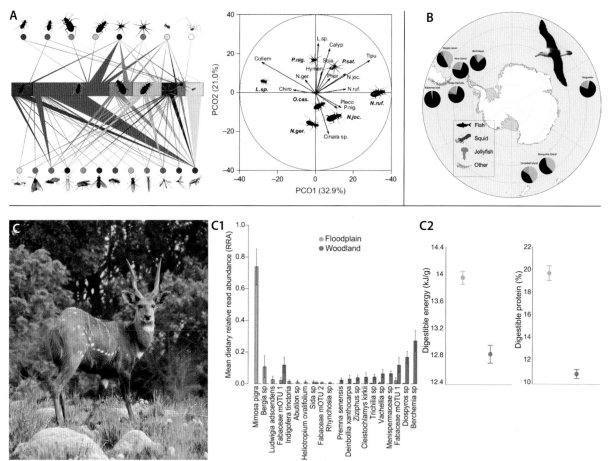

Fig. 4.3. (A) Semi-quantitative food web (left panel) and ordination of prey composition (right panel) of beetle and spider predators collected in three glacier forelands in Austria. Food web depicts in the middle section four species of predatory carabid beetles (red to yellow), two species of lycosid spiders (dark and medium grey) and several species of linyphiid spiders (light grey) with bar with indicating the relative abundance of each species. Width of the links to extraguild (bottom) and intraguild (top) prey are proportional to the DNA-detection frequency of the respective prey taxa. The food web represents the data collected in three glacier forelands at early successional stages. Ordination of prey composition is based on principal coordinates analysis on Bray–Curtis similarity where predators are pictured at centroids with bold labels and prey indicated as arrows indicating correlations with axis referenced to the unit circle drawn. Figure adapted from Sint *et al.* (2019). (B) DNA from diet items in faecal sample of black-browed albatross from across their circumpolar breeding range reveal the importance of jellyfish predation. Pie charts show proportions of sequences (based on relative read abundance) of fish (black), squid (blue), jellyfish (green) and other food items such as krill (grey). Figure adapted from McInnes, Alderman, Lea *et al.* (2017). (C) Variation in diet composition and quality between two sympatric sub-groups of bushbucks (*Tragelaphus scriptus*, a forest African antelope) foraging in two different habitats (floodplain in orange and wooded savannas in blue). This species is a closed-habitat specialist, however in Gorongosa National Park (Mozambique), because of the low predation pressure, some individuals forage in more risky open habitats. These results show that these individuals feeding in the floodplain have access to a higher quality diet than those foraging only in wooded areas. (C1) The mean relative read abundance of the 10 most abundant food plant taxa for the two sub-groups. (C2) Estimated mean digestible energy and protein contents of the diet. These data were inferred from faecal DNA metabarcoding using relative read abundance data, coupled with nutritional quality data of the surrounding vegetation. Figure adapted from Atkins *et al.* (2019).

FUTURE DIRECTIONS AND OUTSTANDING QUESTIONS

The field of DNA diet analysis will continue to change with advances in genetic technology and bioinformatics. For the DNA metabarcoding approach, finding better ways to selectively reduce PCR amplification from non-target DNA is an area where improvements are possible. For example, there has been progress using genome editing technology

(CRISPR/Cas9) to selectively deplete abundant sequences and increase the signal to noise ratio coming from DNA mixtures (Gu *et al.* 2016). There has also been considerable interest in analytical approaches which move away from the reliance on PCR amplification (due to PCR biases and primer design challenges, discussed above and in other chapters). One way to do this is through the use of non-PCR target enrichment approaches such as DNA hybrid capture techniques (Wilcox *et al.* 2018), but reliable concentrations of target DNA might be hard to obtain. Another potential avenue that is being actively researched are metagenomics approaches where all DNA in a sample is sequenced without targeted marker enrichment (Srivathsan *et al.* 2015; Chua *et al.* 2021). The prevalence of bacterial and consumer DNA, combined with lack of genomic reference sequences, currently limit the effectiveness of this approach, but in the future, it may become a powerful method of diet analysis.

Genome sequencing, or genome skimming of DNA from reference specimens to obtain multicopy mitochondrial and chloroplast genome sequences (Bohmann *et al.* 2020), will drastically expand available DNA metabarcoding marker choices and improve both DNA metabarcoding and metagenomic approaches. For the most benefit, the expansion of reference sequence databases needs to emphasise accurate taxonomy, and there should be parallel improvements in bioinformatic methods used for taxonomic assignment. The implementation of analyses that use prey RNA along with prey DNA is another topic where methodological improvements may increase the information which can be derived from diet samples, such as whether food was actively predated or scavenged. Finally, focusing on how variables outside the laboratory (biological and environmental) affect food DNA detection is another area that needs continued investigation to allow for more powerful inferences in study systems.

While innovations in methodology is welcome, continued focus on developing technical aspects arguably distracts from the ecological questions the methods are designed to address. Using established methodology in creative applications and large-scale research initiatives is undoubtably where the most exciting research will emerge. This includes topics such as the implementation of standardised methods in long-term monitoring programs (Jarman *et al.* 2013), insights from large-scale food-web studies (Roslin and Majaneva 2016), using food web ecology to improve environmental management and conservation (Staudacher *et al.* 2018), addressing questions about climate change impacts (Holland *et al.* 2021) and addressing fundamental ecological questions in model systems (Pringle *et al.* 2019). Combining dietary DNA metabarcoding methods with other related genetic analyses can also provide unique new insights about, for example, interactions between diet and microbiome (Kartzinel *et al.* 2019) and prevalence of parasites (de Vos *et al.* 2018; Tombak *et al.* 2021). As outlined at the start of the chapter, there are many unanswered ecological questions that require dietary information – DNA-based approaches will be an integral part of providing the answers.

DISCUSSION TOPICS

You've been asked to carry out a diet study on a species of insectivorous bat using DNA metabarcoding of faecal samples to unravel how their diet changes between seasons.

1. What is some of the key information you would want to know about the study system? (Hint: there are a lot of potential answers.)
2. What type of research questions could you potentially answer with dietary DNA metabarcoding? What questions might be better answered with diagnostic PCR?
3. What are some of the limitations of DNA as a dietary biomarker you might need to consider?
4. What factors might you consider before collecting the samples and how could you minimise environmental contamination?
5. How would your answers to the above questions be different if the study were on a black bear (an omnivore eating a range of plants and animals) or a predatory beetle preying on other beetle species?

ACKNOWLEDGEMENTS

We thank our colleagues for the many informative discussions, and the large number of scientists that contribute to the ongoing research in this field.

REFERENCES

Agustí N, De Vicente M, Gabarra R (1999) Development of sequence amplified characterized region (SCAR) markers of *Helicoverpa armigera*: a new polymerase chain reaction-based technique for predator gut analysis. *Molecular Ecology* **8**, 1467–1474.

Alberdi A, Aizpurua O, Bohmann K, Gopalakrishnan S, Lynggaard C, *et al.* (2019) Promises and pitfalls of using high-throughput sequencing for diet analysis. *Molecular Ecology Resources* **19**, 327–348.

Alberdi A, Aizpurua O, Gilbert MTP, Bohmann K (2018) Scrutinizing key steps for reliable metabarcoding of environmental samples. *Methods in Ecology and Evolution* **9**, 134–147.

Ando H, Mukai H, Komura T, Dewi T, Ando M, *et al.* (2020) Methodological trends and perspectives of animal dietary studies by noninvasive fecal DNA metabarcoding. *Environmental DNA* **2**, 391–406.

Ando H, Setsuko S, Horikoshi K, Suzuki H, Umehara S, *et al.* (2013) Diet analysis by next-generation sequencing indicates the frequent consumption of introduced plants by the critically endangered red-headed wood pigeon (*Columba janthina nitens*) in oceanic island habitats. *Ecology and Evolution* **3**, 4057–4069.

Archer E, Hand GA, Blair SN (2013) Validity of U.S. nutritional surveillance: National health and nutrition examination survey caloric energy intake data, 1971–2010. *PLoS One* **8**, e76632.

Asahida T, Yamashita Y, Kobayashi T (1997) Identification of consumed stone flounder, *Kareius bicoloratus* (Basilewsky), from the stomach contents of sand shrimp, *Crangon affinis* (De Haan) using mitochondrial DNA analysis. *Journal of Experimental Marine Biology* **217**, 153–163.

Atkins JL, Long RA, Pansu J, Daskin JH, Potter AB, *et al.* (2019) Cascading impacts of large-carnivore extirpation in an African ecosystem. *Science* **364**, 173–177.

Balme GA, le Roex N, Rogan MS, Hunter LT (2020) Ecological opportunity drives individual dietary specialization in leopards. *Journal of Animal Ecology* **89**, 589–600.

Becker JA, Hutchinson MC, Potter AB, Park S, Guyton JA, *et al.* (2021) Ecological and behavioral mechanisms of density-dependent habitat expansion in a recovering African ungulate population. *Ecological Monographs* **91**, e01476.

Bohmann K, Mirarab S, Bafna V, Gilbert MTP (2020) Beyond DNA barcoding: The unrealized potential of genome skim data in sample identification. *Molecular Ecology* **29**, 2521–2534.

Bowser AK, Diamond AW, Addison, JA (2013) From puffins to plankton: A DNA-based analysis of a seabird food chain in the northern Gulf of Maine. *PLoS One* **8**, e83152.

Briem F, Zeisler C, Guenay Y, Staudacher K, Vogt H, *et al.* (2018) Identifying plant DNA in the sponging–feeding insect pest *Drosophila suzukii*. *Journal of Pest Science* **91**, 985–994.

Carroll E, Gallego R, Sewell M, Zeldis J, Ranjard L, *et al.* (2019) Multi-locus DNA metabarcoding of zooplankton communities and scat reveal trophic interactions of a generalist predator. *Scientific Reports* **9**, 1–14.

Casey JM, Meyer CP, Morat F, Brandl SJ, Planes S, *et al.* (2019) Reconstructing hyperdiverse food webs: Gut content metabarcoding as a tool to disentangle trophic interactions on coral reefs. *Methods in Ecology and Evolution* **10**, 1157–1170.

Cavallo C, Chiaradia A, Deagle BE, McInnes JC, Sanchez S, *et al.* (2018) Molecular analysis of predator scats reveals role of salps in temperate inshore food webs. *Frontiers in Marine Science* **5**, 381.

Chua PY, Crampton-Platt A, Lammers Y, Alsos IG, Boessenkool S, *et la.* (2021) Metagenomics: A viable tool for reconstructing herbivore diet. *Molecular Ecology Resources* **21**, 2249–2263.

Clare EL (2014) Molecular detection of trophic interactions: emerging trends, distinct advantages, significant considerations and conservation applications. *Evolutionary Applications* **7**, 1144–1157.

Clare EL, Fraser EE, Braid HE, Fenton MB, Hebert PD (2009) Species on the menu of a generalist predator, the eastern red bat (*Lasiurus borealis*): Using a molecular approach to detect arthropod prey. *Molecular Ecology* **18**, 2532–2542.

Clarke LJ, Trebilco R, Walters A, Polanowski AM, Deagle BE (2020) DNA-based diet analysis of mesopelagic fish from the southern Kerguelen Axis. *Deep Sea Research Part II: Topical Studies in Oceanography* **174**, 1–9.

de Vos A, Faux CE, Marthick J, Dickinson J, Jarman Jarman SN (2018) New determination of prey and parasite species for northern Indian Ocean Blue Whales. **5**, 104.

Deagle BE, Chiaradia A, McInnes J, Jarman SN (2010) Pyrosequencing faecal DNA to determine diet of little penguins: Is what goes in what comes out? *Conservation Genetics* **11**, 2039–2048.

Deagle BE, Eveson JP, Jarman SN (2006) Quantification of damage in DNA recovered from highly degraded samples–a case study on DNA in faeces. *Frontiers in Zoology* **3**, 1–10.

Deagle BE, Jarman SN, Coissac E, Pompanon F Taberlet P (2014) DNA metabarcoding and the cytochrome c oxidase subunit I marker: Not a perfect match. *Biology Letters* **10**, 20140562.

Deagle BE, Kirkwood R, Jarman SN (2009) Analysis of Australian fur seal diet by pyrosequencing prey DNA in faeces. *Molecular Ecology* **18**, 2022–2038.

Deagle BE, Thomas AC, McInnes JC, Clarke LJ, Vesterinen EJ, *et al.* (2019) Counting with DNA in metabarcoding studies: How should we convert sequence reads to dietary data? *Molecular Ecology* **28**, 391–406.

Dunshea G (2009) DNA-based diet analysis for any predator. *PLoS One* **4**, e5252.

Foltan P, Sheppard S, Konvicka M, Symondson WO (2005) The significance of facultative scavenging in generalist predator nutrition: detecting decayed prey in the guts of predators using PCR. *Molecular Ecology* **14**, 4147–4158.

Fulton EA, Blanchard JL, Melbourne-Thomas J, Plagányi ÉE, Tulloch VJ (2019) Where the ecological gaps remain, a modelers' perspective. *Frontiers in Ecology and Evolution* **7**, 424.

Goldberg AR, Conway CJ, Tank DC, Andrews KR, Gour DS, *et al.* (2020) Diet of a rare herbivore based on DNA metabarcoding of feces: Selection, seasonality, and survival. *Ecology and Evolution* **10**, 7627–7643.

González-Chang M, Wratten SD, Lefort M-C, Boyer S (2016) Food webs and biological control: A review of molecular tools used to reveal trophic interactions in agricultural systems. *Food Webs* **9**, 4–11.

Greenstone MH, Payton ME, Weber DC, Simmons AM (2014) The detectability half-life in arthropod predator–prey research: What it is, why we need it, how to measure it, and how to use it. *Molecular Ecology* **23**, 3799–3813.

Gu W, Crawford ED, O'Donovan B, Wilson MR, Chow ED, *et al.* (2016) Depletion of Abundant Sequences by Hybridization (DASH): Using Cas9 to remove unwanted high-abundance species in sequencing libraries and molecular counting applications. *Genome Biology* **17**, 1–13.

Guenay Y, Trager H, Glarcher I, Traugott M, Wallinger C (2021) Limited detection of secondarily consumed plant food by DNA-based diet analysis of omnivorous carabid beetles. *Environmental DNA* **3**, 426–434.

Guillerault N, Bouletreau S, Iribar A, Valentini A, Santoul F (2017) Application of DNA metabarcoding on faeces to identify European catfish Silurus glanis diet. *Journal of Fish Biology* **90**, 2214–2219.

Günther B, Fromentin J-M, Metral L, Arnaud-Haond S (2021) Metabarcoding confirms the opportunistic foraging behaviour of Atlantic bluefin tuna and reveals the importance of gelatinous prey. *PeerJ* **9**, e11757.

Guyton JA, Pansu J, Hutchinson MC, Kartzinel TR, Potter AB, *et al.* (2020) Trophic rewilding revives biotic resistance to shrub invasion. *Nature Ecology and Evolution* **4**, 712–724.

Harper GL, King RA, Dodd C, Harwood JD, Glen D, *et al.* (2005) Rapid screening of invertebrate predators for multiple prey DNA targets. *Molecular Ecology* **14**, 819–827.

Hays GC, Doyle TK, Houghton JDJTiE, Evolution (2018) A paradigm shift in the trophic importance of jellyfish? *Trends in Ecology and Evolution* **33**, 874–884.

Holland OJ, Young MA, Sherman CDH, Tan MH, Gorfine H, *et al.* (2021) Ocean warming threatens key trophic interactions supporting a commercial fishery in a climate change hotspot. *Global Change Biology* **27**, 6498–6511.

Höss M, Kohn M, Pääbo S, Knauer F, Schröder W (1992) Excrement analysis by PCR. *Nature* **359**, 199–199.

Jarman S, Deagle B, Gales N (2004) Group-specific polymerase chain reaction for DNA-based analysis of species diversity and identity in dietary samples. *Molecular Ecology* **13**, 1313–1322.

Jarman SN, McInnes JC, Faux C, Polanowski AM, Marthick J, *et al.* (2013) Adélie penguin population diet monitoring by analysis of food DNA in scats. *PLoS One* **8**, e82227.

Jones KA, Baylis AM, Orben RA, Ratcliffe N, Votier SC, *et al.* (2020) Stable isotope values in South American fur seal pup whiskers as proxies of year-round maternal foraging ecology. *Marine Biology* **167**, 1–11.

Juen A, Traugott M (2005) Detecting predation and scavenging by DNA gut-content analysis: a case study using a soil insect predator-prey system. *Oecologia* **142**, 344–352.

Kamenova S, Mayer R, Rubbmark OR, Coissac E, Plantegenest M, *et al.* (2018) Comparing three types of dietary samples for prey DNA decay in an insect generalist predator. *Molecular Ecology Resources* **18**, 966–973.

Kartzinel TR, Chen PA, Coverdale TC, Erickson DL, Kress WJ, *et al.* (2015) DNA metabarcoding illuminates dietary niche partitioning by African large herbivores. *Proceedings of the National Academy of Sciences* **112**, 8019–8024.

Kartzinel TR, Hsing JC, Musili PM, Brown BR, Pringle RM (2019) Covariation of diet and gut microbiome in African megafauna. *Proceedings of the National Academy of Sciences* **116**, 23588–23593.

King R, Read D, Traugott M, Symondson WOC (2008) INVITED REVIEW: Molecular analysis of predation: a review of best practice for DNA-based approaches. *Molecular Ecology* **17**, 947–963.

Kvitrud M, Riemer S, Brown R, Bellinger M, Banks M (2005) Pacific harbor seals (Phoca vitulina) and salmon: genetics presents hard numbers for elucidating predator-prey dynamics. *Marine Biology* **147**, 1459–1466.

Lamb PD, Hunter E, Pinnegar JK, Creer S, Davies RG, *et al.* (2017) Jellyfish on the menu: mtDNA assay reveals scyphozoan predation in the Irish Sea. *Royal Society Open Science* **4**, 171421.

Leray M, Agudelo N, Mills SC, Meyer CP (2013) Effectiveness of annealing blocking primers versus restriction enzymes for characterization of generalist diets: unexpected prey revealed in the gut contents of two coral reef fish species. *PLoS One* **8**, e58076.

Mata VA, Rebelo H, Amorim F, McCracken GF, Jarman S, *et al.* (2019) How much is enough? Effects of technical and biological replication on metabarcoding dietary analysis. *Molecular Ecology* **28**, 165–175.

McInnes JC, Alderman R, Deagle BE, Lea MA, Raymond B, *et al.* (2017) Optimised scat collection protocols for dietary DNA metabarcoding in vertebrates. *Methods in Ecology and Evolution* **8**, 192–202.

McInnes JC, Alderman R, Lea MA, Raymond B, Deagle BE, *et al.* (2017) High occurrence of jellyfish predation by black-browed and Campbell albatross identified by DNA metabarcoding. *Molecular Ecology* **26**, 4831–4845.

Meiklejohn KA, Damaso N, Robertson JM (2019) Assessment of BOLD and GenBank–Their accuracy and reliability for the identification of biological materials. *PLoS One* **14**, e0217084.

Moreau RE (1948) Ecological isolation in a rich tropical avifauna. *Journal of Animal Ecology* **17**, 113–126.

Neidel V, Wallinger C, Traugott M (in press) Secondary predation by omnivores: Cereal aphid consumption bears no risk of misinterpretation in DNA-based diet analysis. *Journal of Applied Entomology.*

Nielsen JM, Clare EL, Hayden B, Brett MT, Kratina P (2018) Diet tracing in ecology: Method comparison and selection. *Methods in Ecology and Evolution* **9**, 278–291.

O'Rorke R, Lavery S, Jeffs A (2012) PCR enrichment techniques to identify the diet of predators. *Molecular Ecology Resources* **12**, 5–17.

Oehm J, Juen A, Nagiller K, Neuhauser S, Traugott M (2011) Molecular scatology: How to improve prey DNA detection success in avian faeces? *Molecular Ecology Resources* **11**, 620–628.

Oehm J, Thalinger B, Eisenkölbl S, Traugott M (2017) Diet analysis in piscivorous birds: What can the addition of molecular tools offer? *Ecology and Evolution* **7**, 1984–1995.

Pansu J, Guyton JA, Potter AB, Atkins JL, Daskin JH, *et al.* (2019) Trophic ecology of large herbivores in a reassembling African ecosystem. *Journal of Ecology* **107**, 1355–1376.

Pimm SL (2002) *Food Webs.* University of Chicago Press, Chicago, IL, USA.

Piñol J, San Andrés V, Clare E, Mir G, Symondson W (2014) A pragmatic approach to the analysis of diets of generalist predators: The use of next-generation sequencing with no blocking probes. *Molecular Ecology Resources* **14**, 18–26.

Poinar HN, Hofreiter M, Spaulding WG, Martin PS, Stankiewicz BA, *et al.* (1998) Molecular coproscopy: dung and diet of the extinct ground sloth Nothrotheriops shastensis. *Science* **281**, 402–406.

Pompanon F, Deagle BE, Symondson WO, Brown DS, Jarman SN, *et al.* (2012) Who is eating what: diet assessment using next generation sequencing. *Molecular Ecology* **21**, 1931–1950.

Pornon A, Andalo C, Burrus M, Escaravage NJSR (2017) DNA metabarcoding data unveils invisible pollination networks. *Scientific Reports* **7**, 1–11.

Potter AB, Hutchinson MC, Pansu J, Wursten B, Long RA, *et al.* (2022) Mechanisms of dietary resource partitioning in large-herbivore assemblages: A plant-trait-based approach. *Journal of Ecology* **110**(4), 817–832.

Pringle RM (2020) Untangling food webs. In *Unsolved Problems in Ecology.* (Eds A Dobson, D Tilman, RD Holt) pp. 225–238. Princeton University Press, Princeton, NJ, USA.

Pringle RM, Hutchinson MC (2020) Resolving food-web structure. *Annual Review of Ecology, Evolution, and Systematics* **51**, 55–80.

Pringle RM, Kartzinel TR, Palmer TM, Thurman TJ, Fox-Dobbs K, *et al.* (2019) Predator-induced collapse of niche structure and species coexistence. *Nature* **570**, 58–64.

Quinby BM, Creighton JC, Flaherty EA (2020) Stable isotope ecology in insects: A review. *Ecological Entomology* **45**, 1231–1246.

Quinn TP, Richardson MF, Lovell D, Crowley TM (2017) propr: An R-package for Identifying Proportionally Abundant Features Using Compositional Data Analysis. *Scientific Reports* **7**, 16252.

Ratcliffe N, Deagle B, Love K, Polanowski A, Fielding S, et al. (2021) Changes in prey fields increase the potential for spatial overlap between gentoo penguins and a krill fishery within a marine protected area. *Diversity and Distributions* **27**, 552–563.

Remén C, Krüger M, Cassel-Lundhagen A (2010) Successful analysis of gut contents in fungal-feeding oribatid mites by combining body-surface washing and PCR. *Soil Biology and Biochemistry* **42**, 1952–1957.

Roslin T, Majaneva S (2016) The use of DNA barcodes in food web construction–terrestrial and aquatic ecologists unite! *Genome Biology* **59**, 603–628.

Schattanek P, Riccabona SA, Rennstam Rubbmark O, Traugott M (2021) Detection of prey DNA in bat feces: Effects of time since feeding, meal size, and prey identity. *Environmental DNA* **3**, 959–969.

Shehzad W, McCarthy TM, Pompanon F, Purevjav L, Coissac E, et al. (2012) Prey preference of snow leopard (Panthera uncia) in South Gobi, Mongolia. *PLoS One* **7**, e32104.

Sint D, Kaufmann R, Mayer R, Traugott M (2019) Resolving the predator first paradox: Arthropod predator food webs in pioneer sites of glacier forelands. *Molecular Ecology* **28**, 336–347.

Sint D, Raso L, Traugott M (2012) Advances in multiplex PCR: balancing primer efficiencies and improving detection success. *Methods in Ecology and Evolution* **3**, 898–905.

Srivathsan A, Sha JC, Vogler AP, Meier R (2015) Comparing the effectiveness of metagenomics and metabarcoding for diet analysis of a leaf-feeding monkey (P ygathrix nemaeus). *Molecular Ecology Resources* **15**, 250–261.

Staudacher K, Rennstam Rubbmark O, Birkhofer K, Malsher G, Sint D, et al. (2018) Habitat heterogeneity induces rapid changes in the feeding behaviour of generalist arthropod predators. *Functional Ecology* **32**, 809–819.

Staudacher K, Schallhart N, Thalinger B, Wallinger C, Juen A, et al. (2013) Plant diversity affects behavior of generalist root herbivores, reduces crop damage, and enhances crop yield. *Ecological Applications* **23**, 1135–1145.

Sutherland WJ, Freckleton RP, Godfray HCJ, Beissinger SR, Benton T, et al. (2013) Identification of 100 fundamental ecological questions. *Journal of Ecology* **101**, 58–67.

Taberlet P, Bonin A, Zinger L, Coissac E (2018) *Environmental DNA: For Biodiversity Research and Monitoring.* Oxford University Press, Oxford, UK.

Taberlet P, Coissac E, Pompanon F, Gielly L, Miquel C, et al. (2007) Power and limitations of the chloroplast trn L (UAA) intron for plant DNA barcoding. *Nucleic Acids Research* **35**, e14–e14.

Takahashi M, DiBattista JD, Jarman S, Newman SJ, Wakefield CB, et al. (2020) Partitioning of diet between species and life history stages of sympatric and cryptic snappers (Lutjanidae) based on DNA metabarcoding. *Scientific Reports* **10**, 1–13.

Tercel MPTG, Symondson WOC, Cuff JP (2021) The problem of omnivory: A synthesis on omnivory and DNA metabarcoding. *Molecular Ecology* **30**, 2199–2206.

Thalinger B, Oehm J, Mayr H, Obwexer A, Zeisler C et al. (2016) Molecular prey identification in Central European piscivores. *Molecular Ecology Resources* **16**, 123–137.

Thiebot J-B, McInnes JC (2020) Why do marine endotherms eat gelatinous prey? *ICES Journal of Marine Science* **77**, 58–71.

Thomas AC, Deagle BE, Eveson JP, Harsch CH, Trites AW (2016) Quantitative DNA metabarcoding: Improved estimates of species proportional biomass using correction factors derived from control material. *Molecular Ecology Resources* **16**, 714–726.

Thomas AC, Nelson BW, Lance MM, Deagle BE, Trites AW (2017) Harbour seals target juvenile salmon of conservation concern. *Canadian Journal of Fisheries* **74**, 907–921.

Tombak KJ, Hansen CB, Kinsella JM, Pansu J, Pringle RM et al. (2021) The gastrointestinal nematodes of plains and Grevy's zebras: Phylogenetic relationships and host specificity. *International Journal for Parasitology: Parasites and Wildlife* **16**, 228–235.

Traugott M, Kamenova S, Ruess L, Seeber J, Plantegenest M (2013) Empirically characterising trophic networks: what emerging DNA-based methods, stable isotope and fatty acid analyses can offer. *Advances in Ecological Research* **49**, 177–224.

Traugott M, Thalinger B, Wallinger C, Sint D (2021) Fish as predators and prey: DNA-based assessment of their role in food webs. *Journal of Fish Biology* **98**, 367–382.

Valentini A, Miquel C, Nawaz MA, Bellemain E, Coissac E, et al. (2009) New perspectives in diet analysis based on DNA barcoding and parallel pyrosequencing: The *trn*L approach. *Molecular Ecology Resources* **9**, 51–60.

Vesterinen EJ, Ruokolainen L, Wahlberg N, Peña C, Roslin T, et al. (2016) What you need is what you eat? Prey selection by the bat Myotis daubentonii. *Molecular Ecology* **25**, 1581–1594.

Vestheim H, Jarman SN (2008) Blocking primers to enhance PCR amplification of rare sequences in mixed samples–a case study on prey DNA in Antarctic krill stomachs. *Frontiers in Zoology* **5**, 1–11.

Wallinger C, Staudacher K, Schallhart N, Peter E, Dresch P, et al. (2013) The effect of plant identity and the level of plant decay on molecular gut content analysis in a herbivorous soil insect. *Molecular Ecology Resources* **13**, 75–83.

Wilcox TM, Zarn KE, Piggott MP, Young MK, McKelvey KS, et al. (2018) Capture enrichment of aquatic environmental DNA: A first proof of concept. *Molecular Ecology Resources* **18**, 1392–1401.

Zaidi R, Jaal Z, Hawkes N, Hemingway J, Symondson W (1999) Can multiple-copy sequences of prey DNA be detected amongst the gut contents of invertebrate predators? *Molecular Ecology* **8**, 2081–2087.

Zhang S, Zhao J, Yao M (2020) A comprehensive and comparative evaluation of primers for metabarcoding eDNA from fish. *Methods in Ecology and Evolution* **11**, 1609–1625.

Zinger L, Bonin A, Alsos IG, Bálint M, Bik H, et al. (2019) DNA metabarcoding–Need for robust experimental designs to draw sound ecological conclusions. *Molecular Ecology* **28**, 1857–1862.

5 Approaching ecological questions using DNA barcodes

Michael Stat and Katrina West

ABSTRACT

The range of ecological questions that can be addressed using DNA barcodes extracted from the environment is diverse. In the design of any specific project however, robust conclusions are dependent on targeting relevant taxa. For community analyses, species that span a broad taxonomic range are required, whereas a surveillance study may be restricted to the distribution of a single species. In approaching ecological questions using DNA barcodes, several methodological considerations become relevant, notably those that will affect the resolution and taxonomic range recovered with DNA barcodes. Careful selection of the PCR assays that target DNA barcodes from the environment is therefore critical. What can be achieved with environmental DNA today is remarkable, yet with future improvements in DNA sequencing technology and reduced cost, effective monitoring of all biota within an ecosystem will provide a powerful tool for managing and protecting the natural world.

INTRODUCTION

The field of ecology is diverse, encompassing the myriad of species found on earth and their interaction with the environment. Unsurprisingly then, the number of ecological questions that can be pursued is similarly vast. For example, a phycologist may be concerned with the community composition of microscopic algae in extreme environments like the Antarctic, whereas the diet of the endangered chimpanzee could be the focus of research for a terrestrial conservationist (Ugalde *et al.* 2016; Bugir *et al.* 2021). While different, both studies are similarly focused on characterising biodiversity to advance our understanding of ecology.

The study of environmental DNA (eDNA), through the recovery and analysis of DNA barcodes from the environment, is changing the way in which we can audit biological communities (Taberlet *et al.* 2012; Cristescu 2014). However, unlike traditional barcoding that targets the COI gene from single-source (tissue) DNA to resolve an animal species, approaching ecological questions involves greater thought over the choice and number of DNA barcodes to use (Hebert *et al.* 2003). With this in mind, one must first define the research question of interest, taking particular care to identify the target species (i.e. microscopic algae or the prey of chimpanzee in the example above) and the environment to be sampled (i.e. Antarctic waters, or the stomach contents or faeces of chimpanzee). Using current environmental genomic approaches, notably eDNA metabarcoding, such inquiry leads to an initial assessment of the species diversity expected in the sample and how best to extract the most informative biodiversity data. This is crucial, as the outcomes of an eDNA research project are greatly influenced by several methodological choices and it is important to understand how these may impact your results and any conclusions reached.

While there are several elements that need to be considered in an eDNA metabarcoding study that contribute towards biodiversity recovery, this chapter focuses on the methodological factors contributing to barcode selection in the context of a given ecological question. One key aspect is the choice of primers that are used to amplify DNA barcodes from an eDNA sample, as these will determine what taxa you can identify. Therefore, which DNA barcodes (and how many) to target with what primers requires careful thought in the design of any ecological project that utilises eDNA.

METHODOLOGICAL CONSIDERATIONS AND BARCODE SELECTION

There are many methodological aspects of metabarcoding that need to be considered prior to application, as they will, inevitably, affect the detection sensitivity, efficiency, reproducibility and resolution of the data. In the design of an eDNA research project and selection of appropriate DNA primers however, it is first important to have a well-defined question and at least some prior knowledge of what the target taxa are and what the most appropriate material to sample would be (Chapter 1). DNA is everywhere in the environment, yet the likelihood of retrieving DNA of any particular species is predominantly based on their ecology. Collecting DNA from a given substrate may be obvious in addressing certain questions, such as the faeces of a particular animal for its diet (Chapter 4), honey or wildflowers for insects (Chapter 21), soil for terrestrial vertebrates, or seawater for marine taxa (Bohmann *et al.* 2014). In other instances, however, further consideration of the environment to sample may increase the likelihood of detecting taxa important to the study. In the ocean environment, for example, a different community of marine taxa is recovered depending on whether the seawater, sediment, or biological material scraped from a settlement plate or scooped into a plankton tow net is collected (Koziol *et al.* 2019). Furthermore, depth within the water column also influences what marine taxa is detected (Jeunen *et al.* 2019). Ultimately, as the habitat more specific to a certain species is more thoroughly sampled, the chance of detecting that organism increases against the backdrop of DNA from other taxa. Lastly, the taxa detected will be influenced by the diversity of the community present and each species' DNA shedding rate, which has been shown to be variable, even within a specific lineage such as fish (Sassoubre *et al.* 2016; Andruszkiewicz Allan *et al.* 2020). Therefore, choosing the appropriate primer for the target species of a project needs to be assessed in the context of various biological and ecological factors.

Template complexity

An environmental sample contains a myriad of DNA from various species, and thus a 'template' sample can be quite diverse. The sensitivity of an applied assay/s in detecting target taxa can, under certain circumstances, be influenced by the broader composition of the mixed template sample. For example, in targeting rare, small and/or low-abundant taxa that subsequently represent a low percentage (e.g. <1%) of the total DNA captured as template, the target DNA signal may become obscured by higher-abundant DNA fragments from other organisms (Chandler *et al.* 1997; Green and Minz 2005; Vestheim and Jarman 2008; Bylemans *et al.* 2018). This can inhibit PCR amplification efficiency and the ability to detect taxa relevant to the study. This is particularly prominent when applying universal metabarcoding assays designed to simultaneously amplify large taxonomic groups as outlined below (Lacoursière-Roussel *et al.* 2016; Harper *et al.* 2018; Bylemans *et al.* 2019; Nester *et al.* 2020). Inevitably, DNA fragments that are in higher abundance and those that are also more readily able to bind to primers ('**Primer biases**') will be preferentially amplified. One can increase the chance of amplifying and detecting the target taxa by increasing the level of biological sampling, PCR replication and sequencing, but also limiting contamination of trace eDNA samples with highly abundant DNA sources. The application of multiple PCR assays to amplify multiple barcodes can average out PCR and primer biases, thus providing a more representative taxonomic assemblage that includes low-abundant taxa. This approach can also help limit the occurrence of false-positives and false-negatives as the use of multiple barcodes can cross-validate and provide more certainty in the detection of invasive or critically endangered species.

Universal vs. taxon-specific assays

In choosing the most appropriate primer set to use (i.e. the assay type), the taxonomic range and coverage required become important. A representation of what diversity can be expected from an eDNA study based on the assay/s selected is presented in Fig. 5.1. A broad **phylogenetic diversity** of taxa is attainable using a universal assay (e.g. Chariton *et al.* 2010). There are numerous 'universal' primers that target a common barcode region of all eukaryotes, such as the *18S ribosomal DNA*, which can recover a taxonomically diverse range of species (e.g. Pochon *et al.* 2013). What is evident with universal primers, however, is a lack of specificity towards many DNA templates. Mismatches in the template binding region of the primers cause an inability to

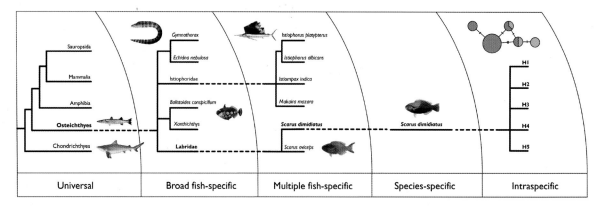

ASSAY TYPE

Fig. 5.1. Phylogenetic diversity and resolution achieved using DNA barcodes. Detection of phylogenetic diversity is greatest when employing a universal assay (left), but comes at the cost of low taxonomic resolution and high false-negative detection rates. As the specificity of an assay increases, so does the taxonomic resolution of the targeted taxa, in conjunction with a decrease in false-negative detection rates (left to right). The use of multiple fish-specific assays (for example) can further improve both the taxonomic resolution and extent of fish detections. Intraspecific assays that target a hypervariable gene region in a single species can also provide population-level data (far right). Fish images © CSIRO Australian National Fish Collection.

detect many species in any given taxonomic group (Elbrecht and Leese 2015; Pinol *et al.* 2015). To overcome such 'blind spots', multiple universal assays that target the same or a different barcode can be employed and will increase the overall diversity recovered, as described above for overcoming template complexity (Zhang *et al.* 2018). Therefore, one must consider whether a 'snapshot' of biodiversity recovered using universal primers is sufficient to address the ecological aims of the project, whereby many species within a given taxonomic group may go undetected. Alternatively, one may decide to select more specific primers that target a particular taxonomic group or species that will provide more biotic information relevant to the study (Deagle *et al.* 2014).

Whilst a broad snapshot of biodiversity is appropriate for many studies, others may be more narrowly focused. For example, a project may be centred on fish communities, and even though the taxa may be detected using universal assays, employing a fish-specific assay will increase the diversity of fish recovered as compared to universal assays (e.g. Stat *et al.* 2017). If multiple taxon-specific assays are utilised in a study (i.e. one for fish, crustaceans, plants, bacteria etc.) and the biotic information are combined, an impressive audit across the entire tree of life is achievable, as demonstrated for both the marine and terrestrial biomes (Drummond *et al.* 2015; Stat *et al.* 2017). In such studies, the diversity recovered using multiple assays and barcodes far exceeds what is achievable with any single assay alone. The application of multiple assays will also detect a higher diversity of any specific group of taxa, as blind spots may still be present within the range of taxa targeted by any group-specific assay, as observed when using universal

assays. If we continue with using fish diversity as an example, studies have shown that using a different fish-specific assay (up to four) recovers a different composition of fish (Nester *et al.* 2020; Cole *et al.* 2021). When combined, information from all assays provides a much more comprehensive picture of the fish diversity present in the sampled environment. Hence, multi-marker metabarcoding should be employed for any biodiversity study, whether the goal is to audit the entire tree of life or a much narrower taxonomic range, providing the budget and time allows for it.

Barcode size

The length and relative abundance of targeted barcodes may also influence the ability to readily amplify target taxa in a mixed template. DNA degradation in the environment e.g. through microbial activity, UV exposure, temperature, and acidity, will fragment and constrain the length of barcodes that can be amplified post-shedding (Deagle *et al.* 2006; Barnes *et al.* 2014; Strickler *et al.* 2015). The majority of eDNA studies, therefore, opt for barcodes ranging between 70–500 bp. This not only facilitates amplification of fragmented eDNA, but also allows for direct, high-throughput sequencing of short-reads on next-generation platforms e.g. Illumina, Roche, Life Technologies and BGI, although developing third-generation platforms, such as from Pacific Biosciences, Oxford Nanopore, Quantapore and Stratos, are now pushing sequencing length capabilities. While it may seem logical to target the smallest barcodes, e.g. 100 bp, to maximise amplification of fragmented eDNA, there can be a substantial trade-off between barcode length and resolution (see 'Resolution' in Glossary).

Typically, a longer DNA sequence provides more opportunity for the accumulation of nucleotide polymorphisms, used to distinguish metabarcoding sequences and provide, with increasing certainty, a higher-level taxonomic assignment (e.g. species, genus). However, given post-shedding degradation processes where longer DNA sequences are less abundant to amplify, a compromise is to target short-medium length barcodes with an elevated mutation rate (Deagle *et al.* 2006).

Barcode regions

Mitochondrial DNA (mtDNA) barcodes have been widely targeted in metabarcoding studies, reflecting a relative ease in amplification, high cellular abundance, absence of recombination, hypermutability to delineate species, and public access to a wealth of reference barcodes from population genetic and phylogenetic research (Rees *et al.* 2014; Harrison *et al.* 2019). Across eukaryotes, mtDNA differs in genome size, gene content, and gene-specific mutation rates. Variation in mutational rates of point substitutions and deletions have produced an alternating structure of variable and conserved regions across the mitochondrial genome (Ladoukakis and Zouros 2017). This alternating structure is ideal for both DNA barcoding and metabarcoding purposes, as conserved regions facilitate the binding of 'universal' or 'broad taxonomic' primers to flank and amplify adjacent variable barcodes.

The mtDNA control region is a long, non-coding, hypervariable region considered to have the highest level of nucleotide polymorphism in the mitochondrial genome (Stoneking *et al.* 1991). However, the existence of several repeats in this non-coding region has complicated PCR amplification and sequencing of this region for some species (Bronstein *et al.* 2018). As a result, many phylogenetics, barcoding and subsequent metabarcoding studies target other comparatively less variable but still highly distinguishable regions such as the *cytochrome c oxidase subunit 1 (COI)*, the *cytochrome B (Cyt b)*, the *16S ribosomal RNA (16S)*, and the *12S ribosomal RNA (12S)* genes (Aylagas *et al.* 2016). Notably however, gene regions can also vary in their mutation rates between taxonomic groups. For example, whilst mtDNA is widely observed to mutate faster than nuclear DNA (nuDNA) overall, this can vary drastically with a mutation rate ratio of mtDNA to nuDNA (μ_{mit}/μ_{nuc}) of 0.57 in corals, 3.1 in arachnids, 11.6 in bony fish, and 26.4 in scaled reptiles (Lynch *et al.* 2006; Allio *et al.* 2017). Nuclear markers that are multi-copy, such as variable internal transcribed spacers (*ITS1* and *ITS2*), *18S ribosomal RNA (18S)* and *28S ribosomal RNA (28S)* genes are

therefore routinely used for coral, fungi and plants (Schmidt *et al.* 2013; Fujise *et al.* 2021), the latter also utilising several plastid genes such as the *ribulose 1,5-bisphosphate carboxylase (rbcL)* and the *maturase K (matK)* genes. For many targeted metabarcoding studies, marker choice is often based on what has previously been determined to have a high level of taxonomic resolution from phylogenetic and barcode approaches. Resolving barcode identities to species level, and differentiating the target from closely related congenerics, is of primary importance when targeting species of interest. Intraspecific diversity and population-level analyses may also be achievable with certain barcodes that display variation within a single species (Sigsgaard *et al.* 2016; Stat *et al.* 2017; Tsuji *et al.* 2020). Therefore, in choosing an appropriate short–medium length barcode we must consider variation in mutational rates across both genes and targeted taxonomic groups to acquire high taxonomic resolution, in addition to ensuring accessibility to reference material and/or sequences.

FUTURE DIRECTIONS OF MULTI-MARKER METABARCODING

Growing global pressures on natural ecosystems, economic and social processes are contributing to shortfalls in conservation and management resources. Conservation resources are costly, sometimes scarce, and typically only directed towards species and/or ecosystems when they decline below a critical threshold or are assigned statutory protection; that is, a conservation triage approach (Bottrill *et al.* 2008). However, with escalating global biodiversity loss and mounting extinction rates, it is argued that implementing a proactive conservation approach, focused on rapid, large-scale, multi-taxa monitoring methods that address data-deficiencies, will identify early population declines and avoid costly, near-extinction species recovery plans (Walls 2018). Multi-marker eDNA metabarcoding provides a genetic avenue to whole-ecosystem surveying, whereby environmental samples could be screened with multiple, high-resolution targeted assays and provide an extensive ecosystem profile ranging from bacteria to plants, fungi, protists, vertebrates, and invertebrates (Stat *et al.* 2017). Notably, this approach only relies on specialised taxonomic expertise for initial reference barcoding and not for conducting the whole-ecosystem survey itself, omitting the need for specialists to morphologically identify each taxonomic group. This multi-marker approach has been preliminarily demonstrated in marine, estuarine and terrestrial ecosystems, simultaneously profiling several taxonomic groups such as bony fish, elasmobranchs, crustaceans, insects, molluscs, mammals, birds and plants (Drummond *et al.* 2015; Stat *et al.* 2017; West *et al.* 2020; Zhang *et al.* 2020; van der Heyde *et al.* 2020; Saenz-Agudelo *et al.* 2021). At present, however, we are only scratching the surface in the potential of multi-marker metabarcoding for whole-ecosystem surveying.

Advancements in the high-throughput capabilities of next-generation sequencing have facilitated the development of eDNA metabarcoding technologies over the last decade. The uptake of these technologies, is in part, attributed to the decreasing cost of sequencing, from US$10 000 per genome in 2011 to US$1000–2000 per genome today (Wetterstrand 2020). Further cost reductions are anticipated to increase the affordability of multi-marker approaches that typically require a high sequencing depth. At present, the estimated cost of metagenomic sequencing is US$18 per metabarcoding assay/per sample on an Illumina MiSeq platform in 2021 once the DNA has been extracted. Third-generation sequencing, that is, of single DNA molecules through single molecule real-time (SMRT) and nanopore sequencing, is currently under active development, but holds considerable potential for high-throughput multiplexed sequencing of longer eDNA fragments and amplicons, and also for conducting rapid eDNA applications in remote locations (Truelove *et al.* 2019).

There is also a move towards the use of metagenomic approaches for eukaryotic environmental surveying, including metazoans, whereby extracted eDNA is directly sequenced at low coverage, that is, shotgun sequencing and genome skimming, on either next- or third-generation sequencing platforms (Krehenwinkel *et al.* 2019). The promise of these approaches is that they avoid some of the biases introduced by PCR-based assays. The omission of PCR removes the need for universal and/or multi-marker assays to target various taxonomic groups altogether, subsequently removing downstream effects of template-primer mismatches and unlocking unbiased quantification of relative species abundance. However, it can be difficult to capture and sequence low abundance DNA (without PCR or a target capture approach) in environmental samples that overwhelmingly have a high bacterial DNA load (i.e. approximately 95% of the template; Stat *et al.* 2017). As such, metagenomic applications to target eukaryotic eDNA require incredibly high sequencing depth, storage and computing for the analysis of such large datasets. This is currently cost-prohibitive for routine eukaryotic monitoring but is anticipated to become more feasible with the decreasing cost of sequencing, developing high-performance computing resources, tools and pipelines, genome databases and centralised data storage (Cherkashin *et al.* 2019; Pearman *et al.* 2020).

DISCUSSION TOPICS

1. Imagine you have been approached by a council manager who is interested in using eDNA to study all animals living in the council precinct. How would you go about developing this project and what limitations of the approach would you discuss with the manager?

2. An invasive goby species has been identified in a river system. How could molecular ecologists use eDNA to determine the distribution of this species and its competition with native species in the surrounding ecosystem?

3. How might the mutation rate of different barcodes affect the ability to provide robust, species-level assignments?

4. How can molecular ecologists prevent false-positive and false-negative eDNA detections of invasive or critically endangered species?

ACKNOWLEDGEMENTS

The authors thank Sam Thompson for a constructive review of this chapter.

REFERENCES

Andruszkiewicz Allan E, Zhang WG, Lavery A, Govindarajan A (2020) Environmental DNA shedding and decay rates from diverse animal forms and thermal regimes. *Environmental DNA* **3**(2), 492–514. doi:10.1002/edn3.141

Allio R, Donega S, Galtier N, Nabholz B (2017) Large variation in the ratio of mitochondrial to nuclear mutation rate across animals: implications for genetic diversity and the use of mitochondrial DNA as a molecular marker. *Molecular Biology and Evolution* **34**(11), 2762–2772.

Aylagas E, Borja Á, Irigoien X, Rodríguez-Ezpeleta N (2016) Benchmarking DNA metabarcoding for biodiversity-based monitoring and assessment. *Frontiers in Marine Science* **3**, 96.

Barnes MA, Turner CR, Jerde CL, Renshaw MA, Chadderton WL, *et al.* (2014) Environmental conditions influence eDNA persistence in aquatic systems. *Environmental Science & Technology* **48**(3), 1819–1827.

Bohmann K, Evans A, Gilbert MT, Carvalho GR, Creer S, *et al.* (2014) Environmental DNA for wildlife biology and biodiversity monitoring. *Trends in Ecology & Evolution* **29**(6), 358–367. doi:10.1016/j.tree.2014.04.003

Bottrill MC, Joseph LN, Carwardine J, Bode M, Cook C, *et al.* (2008) Is conservation triage just smart decision making? *Trends in Ecology & Evolution* **23**(12), 649–654.

Bronstein O, Kroh A, Haring E (2018) Mind the gap! The mitochondrial control region and its power as a phylogenetic marker in echinoids. *BMC Evolutionary Biology* **18**(1), 1–15.

Bugir CK, Butynski TM, Hayward MW (2021) Prey preferences of the chimpanzee (Pan troglodytes). *Ecology & Evolution* **11**(12), 7138–7146.

Bylemans J, Gleeson DM, Duncan RP, Hardy CM, Furlan EM (2019) A performance evaluation of targeted eDNA and eDNA metabarcoding analyses for freshwater fishes. *Environmental DNA* **1**(4), 402–414.

Bylemans J, Gleeson DM, Hardy CM, Furlan E (2018) Toward an ecoregion scale evaluation of eDNA metabarcoding primers: A case study for the freshwater fish biodiversity of the Murray-Darling Basin (Australia). *Ecology and Evolution* **8**(17), 8697–8712. doi:10.1002/ece3.4387

Chandler DP, Fredrickson JK, Brockman FJ (1997) Effect of PCR template concentration on the composition and distribution of total community 16S rDNA clone libraries. *Molecular Ecology* **6**(5), 475–482.

Chariton AA, Court LN, Hartley DM, Colloff MJ, Hardy CM (2010) Ecological assessment of estuarine sediments by pyrosequencing eukaryotic ribosomal DNA. *Frontiers in Ecology and the Environment* **8**(5), 233–238. doi:10.1890/090115

Cherkashin E, Shigarov A, Malkov F, Morozov A (2019) An instrumental environment for metagenomic analysis. In *Information Technologies in the Research of Biodiversity.* pp. 151–158. Springer, Cham.

Cole VJ, Harasti D, Lines R, Stat M (2021) Estuarine fishes associated with intertidal oyster reefs characterized using environmental DNA and baited remote underwater video. *Environmental DNA* **4**, 50–62. doi:10.1002/edn3.190

Cristescu ME (2014) From barcoding single individuals to metabarcoding biological communities: Towards an integrative approach to the study of global biodiversity. *Trends in Ecology & Evolution* **29**(10), 566–571.

Deagle BE, Eveson JP, Jarman SN (2006) Quantification of damage in DNA recovered from highly degraded samples–a case study on DNA in faeces. *Frontiers in Zoology* **3**(1), 1–10.

Deagle BE, Jarman SN, Cossiac E, Pompanon F, Taberlet P (2014) DNA metabarcoding and the cytochrome c oxidase subunit I marker: not a perfect match. *Biology Letters* **10**(9), 1–10.

Drummond AJ, Newcomb RD, Buckley TR, Xie D, Dopheide A, *et al.* (2015) Evaluating a multigene environmental DNA approach for biodiversity assessment. *Gigascience* **4**, 46. doi:10.1186/s13742-015-0086-1

Elbrecht V, Leese F (2015) Can DNA-Based ecosystem assessments quantify species abundance? Testing primer bias and biomass-sequence relationships with an innovative metabarcoding protocol. *PLoS One* **10**(7), e0130324. doi:10.1371/journal.pone.0130324

Fujise L, Suggett DJ, Stat M, Kahlke T, Bunce M, Gardner SG, Nitschke MR (2021) Unlocking the phylogenetic diversity, primary habitats, and abundances of free-living Symbiodiniaceae on a coral reef. *Molecular Ecology* **30**(1), 343–360.

Green SJ, Minz D (2005) Suicide polymerase endonuclease restriction, a novel technique for enhancing PCR amplification of minor DNA templates. *Applied and Environmental Microbiology* **71**(8), 4721–4727.

Harper LR, Lawson Handley L, Hahn C, Boonham N, Rees HC, *et al.* (2018) Needle in a haystack? A comparison of eDNA metabarcoding and targeted qPCR for detection of the great crested newt (*Triturus cristatus*). *Ecology and Evolution* **8**(12), 6330–6341.

Harrison JB, Sunday JM, Rogers SM (2019) Predicting the fate of eDNA in the environment and implications for studying biodiversity. *Proceedings of the Royal Society B* **286**(1915), 20191409.

Hebert PD, Cywinska A, Ball SL, DeWaard JR (2003) Biological identifications through DNA barcodes. *Proceedings of the Royal Society of London* **270**(1512), 313–321.

Jeuen GJ, Lamare MD, Knapp M, Spencer HG, Taylor HR, *et al.* (2019) Water stratification in the marine biome restricts vertical environmental DNA (eDNA) signal dispersal. *Environmental DNA* **2**(1), 99–111. doi:10.1002/edn3.49

Koziol A, Stat M, Simpson T, Jarman S, DiBattista JD, *et al.* (2019) Environmental DNA metabarcoding studies are critically affected by substrate selection. *Molecular Ecology Resources* **19**(2), 366–376. doi:10.1111/1755-0998.12971

Krehenwinkel H, Pomerantz A, Prost S (2019) Genetic biomonitoring and biodiversity assessment using portable sequencing technologies: current uses and future directions. *Genes* **10**(11), 858.

Lacoursière-Roussel A, Dubois Y, Normandeau E, Bernatchez L (2016) Improving herpetological surveys in eastern North America using the environmental DNA method. *Genome* **59**(11), 991–1007.

Ladoukakis ED, Zouros E (2017) Evolution and inheritance of animal mitochondrial DNA: rules and exceptions. *Journal of Biological Research-Thessaloniki* **24**(1), 1–7.

Lynch M, Koskella B, Schaack S (2006) Mutation pressure and the evolution of organelle genomic architecture. *Science* **311**(5768), 1727–1730.

Nester GM, De Brauwer M, Koziol A, West KM, DiBattista JD, *et al.* (2020) Development and evaluation of fish eDNA metabarcoding assays facilitate the detection of cryptic seahorse taxa (family: Syngnathidae). *Environmental DNA* **2**(4), 614–626.

Pearman WS, Freed NE, Silander OK (2020) Testing the advantages and disadvantages of short-and long-read eukaryotic metagenomics using simulated reads. *BMC Bioinformatics* **21**, 1–15.

Pinol J, Mir G, Gomez-Polo P, Agusti N (2015) Universal and blocking primer mismatches limit the use of high-throughput DNA sequencing for the quantitative metabarcoding of arthropods. *Molecular Ecology Resources* **15**(4), 819–830.

Pochon X, Bott NJ, Smith KF, Wood SA (2013) Evaluating detection limits of next-generation sequencing for the surveillance and monitoring of international marine pests. *PLoS One* **8**(9), e73935.

Rees HC, Maddison BC, Middleditch DJ, Patmore JR, Gough KC (2014) The detection of aquatic animal species using environmental DNA–a review of eDNA as a survey tool in ecology. *Journal of Applied Ecology* **51**(5), 1450–1459.

Saenz-Agudelo P, Delrieu-Trottin E, DiBattista JD, Martínez-Rincon D, Morales-González S, *et al.* (2021) Monitoring vertebrate biodiversity of a protected coastal wetland using eDNA metabarcoding. *Environmental DNA* **4**, 77–92.

Sassoubre LM, Yamahara KM, Gardner LD, Block BA, Boehm AB (2016) Quantification of Environmental DNA (eDNA) shedding and decay rates for three marine fish. *Environmental Science & Technology* **50**(19), 10456–10464. doi:10.1021/acs.est.6b03114

Schmidt PA, Bálint M, Greshake B, Bandow C, Römbke J, *et al.* (2013) Illumina metabarcoding of a soil fungal community. *Soil Biology and Biochemistry* **65**, 128–132.

Sigsgaard EE, Nielsen IB, Bach SS, Lorenzen ED, Robinson DP, Knudsen SW, Thomsen PF (2016) Population characteristics of a large whale shark aggregation inferred from seawater environmental DNA. *Nature Ecology & Evolution* **1**(1), 0004.

Stat M, Huggett MJ, Bernasconi R, DiBattista JD, Berry TE, *et al.* (2017) Ecosystem biomonitoring with eDNA: metabarcoding across the tree of life in a tropical marine environment. *Scientific Reports* **7**(1), 1–11.

Stoneking M, Hedgecock D, Higuchi RG, Vigilant L, Erlich HA (1991) Population variation of human mtDNA control region sequences detected by enzymatic amplification and sequence-specific oligonucleotide probes. *American journal of human genetics* **48**(2), 370.

Strickler KM, Fremier AK, Goldberg CS (2015) Quantifying effects of UV-B, temperature, and pH on eDNA degradation in aquatic microcosms. *Biological Conservation* **183**, 85–92.

Taberlet P, Coissac E, Hajibabaei M, Rieseberg LH (2012) Environmental DNA. *Molecular Ecology* **21**, 1789–1793.

Truelove NK, Andruszkiewicz EA, Block BA (2019) A rapid environmental DNA method for detecting white sharks in the open ocean. *Methods in Ecology and Evolution* **10**(8), 1128–1135.

Tsuji S, Maruyama A, Miya M, Ushio M, Sato H (2020) Environmental DNA analysis shows high potential as a tool for estimating intraspecific genetic diversity in a wild fish population. *Molecular Ecology Resources* **20**(5), 1248–1258. doi:10.1111/1755-0998.13165

Ugalde SC, Westwood KJ, van den Enden R, McMinn A, Meiners KM (2016) Characteristics and primary productivity of East Antarctic pack ice during the winter-spring transition. *Deep Sea Research Part II*: Topical Studies in Oceanography **131**, 123–139.

van der Heyde M, Bunce M, Wardell-Johnson G, Fernandes K, White NE, *et al.* (2020) Testing multiple substrates for terrestrial biodiversity monitoring using environmental DNA metabarcoding. *Molecular Ecology Resources* **20**(3), 732–745.

Vestheim H, Jarman SN (2008) Blocking primers to enhance PCR amplification of rare sequences in mixed samples–a case study on prey DNA in Antarctic krill stomachs. *Frontiers in Zoology* **5**(1), 1–11.

Walls SC (2018) Coping with constraints: Achieving effective conservation with limited resources. *Frontiers in Ecology and Evolution* **6**, 24.

West KM, Stat M, Harvey ES, Skepper CL, DiBattista JD, *et al.* (2020) eDNA metabarcoding survey reveals fine-scale coral reef community variation across a remote, tropical island ecosystem. *Molecular Ecology* **29**(6), 1069–1086.

West KM, Adam AA, White N, Robbins WD, Barrow D, *et al.* (2021) The applicability of eDNA metabarcoding approaches for sessile benthic surveying in the Kimberley region, northwestern Australia. *Environmental DNA* **4**, 63–76.

Wetterstrand KA (2020) DNA Sequencing Costs: Data from the NHGRI Genome Sequencing Program (GSP). <www.genome.gov/sequencingcostsdata>. Accessed 22/08/2021.

Zhang GK, Chain FJJ, Abbott CL, Cristescu ME (2018) Metabarcoding using multiplexed markers increases species detection in complex zooplankton communities. *Evolutionary Applications* **11**(10), 1901–1914. doi:10.1111/eva.12694

Zhang Y, Pavlovska M, Stoica E, Prekrasna I, Yang J, *et al.* (2020) Holistic pelagic biodiversity monitoring of the Black Sea via eDNA metabarcoding approach: From bacteria to marine mammals. *Environment International* **135**, 105307.

LIFE HISTORY AND POPULATION BIOLOGY

6   Lifespan estimation from genomic analysis

Benjamin Mayne and Christopher Faulk

ABSTRACT

Lifespan is a fundamental parameter of population biology and central to wildlife management. Lifespan limits individual reproductive capacity, probability of mortality, population growth rates, dispersal capacity, and viability. The lifespan of most species is unknown and this limits objective wildlife management. On a genomic level it has been shown the CpG density in gene promoters is both associated and predictive of lifespan. In this chapter, we discuss the development of lifespan clocks that produce estimates of animal lifespans from genome sequences. We also discuss the biological and evolutionary mechanisms of CpG density and lifespan. DNA can be readily obtained from species and a lifespan prediction may provide life-history traits. Knowing the lifespan of a species can provide better resources for wildlife management. Our research shows the benefit of using DNA to predict the lifespan of species, such as in predicting lifespan in species that outlive researchers or are extinct. It also provides insight into the evolutionary mechanism of the variability of species lifespan.

INTRODUCTION

Maximum lifespan is a fundamental parameter for management of any wild animal species. Maximum lifespan can be used to assess both extinction risk and the spread of **invasive species** (IUCN 2008; Tabak *et al.* 2018). Unfortunately, lifespan for most species is either unknown or is estimated from a limited number of individuals. In many cases, the individuals have been kept captive and this may lead to lifespans that are artificially extended beyond the normal wild limit. The problem is intensified with long-lived species as they may outlive a generation of researchers. The lack of lifespan information makes it difficult for wildlife managers to decide on appropriate management for most species.

Mortality rates, life expectancy, and longevity (life expectancy at birth) are all determined by maximum lifespan (Hsieh 1991). These parameters are used in a broad spectrum of population biology analyses and minute changes can influence wildlife management. It is imperative the appropriate value for maximum lifespan is used as it can potentially impact the management of a species. For example, in fisheries catch limits are highly dependent upon natural mortality rates. Catch limits can be difficult to determine when mortality rates are poorly defined (Then *et al.* 2014; Kenchington 2014). The orange roughy (*Hoplostethus atlanticus*) population collapsed due to a poorly defined lifespan and consequent excess harvesting (Boyer *et al.* 2001; Clark 2001). Mortality rates can be determined using lifespan, preventing similar situations in the future (Hoenig 2005). A rapid approach for calculating fundamental parameters of life history is critical to better manage populations in a rapidly changing global environment with more species to manage than can be resourced (Healy *et al.* 2019).

Of the many characteristics of the genome, cytosine-phosphate-guanine (CpG) density is one of the less explored (Box 6.1). There are four nucleotide letters used in DNA, and 16 possible combinations of pairs. Within vertebrate genomes, **CpG sites** are the fastest evolving dinucleotides, and their density proximal to genes is under strong evolutionary selection. Similarly, lifespan is a trait that evolves under unusual selective pressure with wide variability in vertebrates and is of great interest in both ecological contexts and human health regarding ageing.

In this chapter, we demonstrate the lifespan clock as a predictor of lifespan in vertebrates (Mayne *et al.* 2020). This chapter focuses on the construction of the first lifespan clock and gives example applications to bowhead whales and marine turtles. We also discuss potential future directions of the work presented and how the reader can develop their own lifespan clock on species not covered in this chapter. This may include non-vertebrate animal groups. We also discuss some of the evolutionary aspects and other genomic features associated with lifespan.

Box 6.1: The evolution of CpG sites

Many of the intrinsic factors that determine the lifespans of species are genomic (Kenyon 2010). CpG sites in the genome host epigenetic **DNA methylation** that changes with age unlike nucleotide sequence (see Chapter 7). In other words, the 'C' within a CpG site can be either methylated or unmethylated, and the state of methylation changes over the lifespan of an individual (Kanherkar *et al.* 2014). DNA methylation suppresses gene expression, so intergenic regions and parts of the genome that must be silenced are highly methylated in vertebrates. In contrast, parts of the genome that must be active often have very low levels of DNA methylation, most notably in promoter **CpG islands**. CpG islands exhibit both genetic and epigenetic conservation across the vertebrate radiation. In fact, experiments have shown that CpG density alone is predictive of methylation level (Long *et al.* 2016). This epigenetic mark also has evolutionary consequences. A methylated C can become deaminated over evolutionary time and transition to T, creating a TpG site. Comparative genomics reveals that CpG sites mutate away at a higher rate than any other dinucleotide because of the high frequency of methylated CpG sites in the genome. The result is that the CpG dinucleotide has the lowest observed vs. expected frequency within vertebrate genomes (Fig. 6.1). The case for the outsize importance of the CpG sites is illustrated in humans and our nearest relative, the chimpanzee. The genetic difference between us and chimps averages 0.92% per base pair across the genome; however, at CpG sites that rate jumps to over 15%. In other words, between us and chimps, there is 1 SNP out of a 100 bases on average, but that rises to 1 out of 7 at CpG sites. Because CpG sites mutate rapidly and host DNA methylation that ultimately governs gene expression, they are the both a primary cause of genetic variation and the substrate for both epigenetic and gene regulatory changes (Antequera 2003; Deaton and Bird 2011; Bell *et al.* 2012).

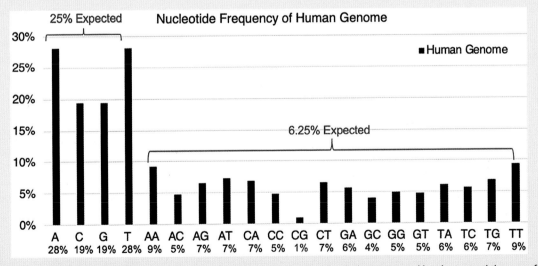

Fig. 6.1. Mutation rate isn't equal for every type of base. The genome is less GC rich than expected by chance and there are fewer CpG sites than any other pair of nucleotides.

APPLICATION

The construction of the lifespan clock builds upon two domains of research. The first is the work by McLain & Faulk (McLain and Faulk 2018). McLain & Faulk drew upon multiple databases including the Eukaryotic Promoter Database (EPD), a source of promoter sequences (Dreos *et al.* 2017), the National Center for Biotechnology Information (NCBI) genomes database (https://www.ncbi.nlm.nih.gov/genome/); and the Animal Ageing and Longevity Database (AnAge), a source of lifespans of species (Tacutu *et al.* 2018). McLain & Faulk found the CpG density in 5% of all promoters significantly correlated with lifespan in mammals.

The second research domain is the methodology commonly used with **epigenetic clocks** (Chapter 7). Epigenetic clocks have been developed for a wide variety of vertebrates and can predict age from the DNA methylation levels of selected CpG sites (De Paoli-Iseppi *et al.* 2017). One of the common methods of developing an epigenetic clock is using an **elastic net regression** model (Friedman*et al.* 2010). Briefly, as it is outside the scope of this chapter, an elastic net regression model can fit a linear model and identify the minimum number of predictors required to predict an outcome. In the case of the lifespan clock the predictors are CpG densities in promoter sequences and the outcome is lifespan. The elastic net regression model is ideal for handling the data presented in this chapter as it can work with many predictors and small sample size. The model of Mayne *et al.* identified 42 promoters conserved across vertebrates as the minimum number of markers required for accurate prediction of lifespan (Mayne *et al.* 2019). These 42 promoters encompass what is referred to as the lifespan clock.

Example: Lifespan prediction of the bowhead whale by genomic analysis

The wildlife management of long-lived species that do not have known lifespan benefits greatly from the lifespan clock. Although it is ideal to use the lifespan clock with reference genomes (see Chapter 9), it is possible to predict lifespan using basic molecular approaches. In this chapter we give an example of how to predict lifespan with and without a **reference genome**.

Table 6.1. The coefficients to be inputted into the lifespan prediction equation for each vertebrate class.

Class	a	b
Aves	-0.90323	2.14857
Fish	2.14632	-6.58228
Mammalia	-0.92888	2.33508
Reptilia	-0.48958	1.17281

Bowhead whales are thought to be the longest-lived mammal (Keane *et al.* 2015). The oldest aged bowhead whale was found to be 211 years old (George *et al.* 1999). This 211-year-old individual showed no pathological features of age-related diseases, suggesting they could potentially live longer (George *et al.* 1999). The bowhead whale has a reference genome that can be used for lifespan prediction (Keane *et al.* 2015). Lifespan prediction with a reference genome can occur in three main steps. First, the 42 unique promoter sequences are identified using a Basic Local Alignment Search Tool (**BLAST**). BLAST can rapidly identify similar sequences within the genome. The sequences of the promoters used by BLAST are found in the link within the Resources section of this chapter. The second step involves calculating the CpG density. CpG density is the total number of CpG sites divided by the length of the BLAST hit. The final step is to input the CpG densities into the lifespan prediction equation, shown below.

$$ln\,(maximum\;lifespan) = -4.38996 + 2.57328x + ax + b$$

where x is the raw summed CpG density weight per sample and a and b are coefficients relating to the vertebrate class (Table 6.1).

For each promoter the CpG density is multiplied by a unique coefficient that was calculated during the model development. These coefficients can be found in a link within the Resources section. The sum of the product of the CpG densities and coefficients are represented in the equation by x. For the bowhead whale $x = 4.65$. We can then input x and the mammalian specific coefficients (Table 6.1) into the lifespan equation.

$$ln\,(maximum\;lifespan) = -4.38996 + (2.57328{\times}4.65) + (-0.92888{\times}4.65) + 2.33508$$

$$maximum\;lifespan = e^{5.59158} = 268\;years$$

As demonstrated with the bowhead whale, a reference genome can provide a straightforward approach to predict lifespan. BLAST is a common bioinformatic tool used to search for similar sequences. CpG densities can be readily calculated once the promoter sequences have been identified and using basic algebraic methods, lifespan can be predicted using the equation above.

Example: Marine turtle lifespan

Marine turtles are both slow growing and long-lived, with the potential to outlive a generation of researchers (Musick and Limpus 1997). Lifespan values for marine turtle species have the potential to provide better predictions for population growth, survival probabilities, and risk of extinction (Hoenig 2005). In this example the lifespans of marine turtles that occur in Australian waters, but lacking a reference genome, was predicted (Mayne *et al.* 2020). First, tissue from each marine turtle was collected for DNA extraction. Any tissue from a somatic cell can be used for lifespan estimation. Of the six marine turtles occurring in Australian waters only the Green sea turtle (*Chelonia mydas*) has a reference genome and lifespan estimate in the AnAge database (Wang *et al.* 2013; Tacutu *et al.* 2018).

The green sea turtle genome was used to BLAST the lifespan promoters and to design PCR primers. Primers were then optimised using DNA from each marine turtle species. By optimising primers for closely related species negates the need to have a reference genome for each species. PCR was used to amplify the promoters of the marine turtles that were then subject to Sanger sequencing. Sanger sequencing enables to calculate the CpG density of each promoter. Once the CpG density has been determined for each promoter the process above can be used without deviation. Table 6.2 details the lifespan prediction for each marine turtle species. In this chapter we have shown how lifespan can be predicted with and without a reference genome. The bowhead whale and marine turtles are examples of long-lived species where access to estimates of their lifespan can contribute significantly to their management.

FUTURE DIRECTIONS

Lifespan prediction from genomics has many future directions with implications that could benefit the management of wildlife. The lifespan clock was developed with five classes of vertebrate species. Multiple lifespan clocks can be developed for specific taxonomic groups (Box 6.2). Lifespan clocks calibrated to taxonomic groups of interest may increase the accuracy of clock predictions for species within these groups. One of the challenges of developing lifespan clocks for a broader range of species is the lack of reliable lifespan data for calibration. Lifespans are often difficult to obtain due to the longevity of long-lived species. A workaround may be to develop a lifespan clock on short-lived species that can be held in captivity. The subsequent clock that is developed could potentially be extrapolated to long-lived species. Granted, extrapolating any model beyond the confines of the training can result in false-positives and false-negatives (Forbes *et al.* 2008). It should be noted that the purpose of any model is to provide guidance to a challenge or problem. A lifespan clock may not be able to provide the exact number of years a species can live to but may be able to provide potential brackets or ranges.

So far in this chapter, the reader has had to have significant bioinformatic and machine learning knowledge to determine lifespan for their species of interest. However, it should be acknowledged that most researchers may not have the time or expertise to carry out the analysis. A future project for this work is to automate the method, through a web-based upload. Here, users could upload the reference genome and receive a species lifespan prediction. This would provide simple efficient method alternative to performing the bioinformatic analysis by oneself.

Table 6.2. The lifespan predictions of marine turtles using sanger sequencing to determine CpG density.

Species	Prediction
Leatherback sea turtle (*Dermochelys coriacea*)	90.4
Loggerhead sea turtle (*Caretta caretta*)	62.8
Olive Ridley sea turtle (*Lepidochelys olivacea*)	54.3
Hawksbill sea turtle (*Eretmochelys imbricata*)	53.2
Flatback sea turtle (*Natator depressus*)	50.4

Box 6.2: How to develop a novel lifespan clock

Step 1: Assemble a dataset of known lifespan species with reference genomes.
   There are three components that are required to develop a novel lifespan clock: reference genomes; well-defined lifespans, most likely to be obtained from sources such as AnAge (Tacutu *et al.* 2018), promoter sequences of the group of species that will be used to determine CpG density. Some examples of promoter databases include EPD and the Ensembl genome database (Hubbard *et al.* 2002; Tacutu *et al.* 2018).
Step 2: Determine promoter CpG density.
   Once the list of species with reference genomes and well-defined lifespans has been collated, the next step is to determine the CpG density of the promoters for each species. This can be done using software such as BLAST. In the

original studies, a BLAST hit was considered with an identity of identity >70% (McLain and Faulk 2018; Mayne *et al.* 2019). Once the BLAST hit sequences have been determined, CpG density can be calculated by dividing the frequency of CpG sites by the BLAST hit length. This part is the most computationally expensive as it requires the download of potentially large genomes and creating temporary BLAST databases to search for promoter sequences.

Step 3: Machine learning to develop a lifespan clock

The final part to develop a lifespan predictor is to calibrate and test the model. Typically, 70% of the samples should be randomly assigned to a training dataset and the remaining to a validation dataset. Since lifespan is a continuous outcome, a regression algorithm can be used. In the original study, an elastic net regression, implemented in the glmnet R package was used to develop the lifespan predictor (Friedman *et al.* 2010; Mayne *et al.* 2019).

This method is first applied to the training dataset to identify the promoters that can predict lifespan. These promoters are then tested on the validation data. The performance of the model can be assessed by comparing the known and predicted lifespans with Pearson correlations, absolute and relative error rates. It is important to ensure the model is not overfitted. This can be done by comparing the correlations, absolute and relative error rates between the training and validation data. Ideally, no difference should be observed. The method described here can be carried out on any taxonomic group to develop novel lifespan clocks.

DISCUSSION

Can a lifespan clock be developed for invertebrates?

CpG methylation is sparse within invertebrate genomes, despite their overall greater genome wide CpG density. To understand why, it is helpful to examine mutation in the context of evolutionary pressure. The ancestral animal genome, prior to the divergence of Chordata from other phyla, probably had CpG sites in similar frequency to all other dinucleotides (Fig. 6.2) Within the newly evolved vertebrate clade, DNA methylation also evolved as a means of gene control and transposon suppression (Box 6.3).

Therefore, most CpG sites became methylated, except for ones in the promoter regions nearby genes since that would have suppressed important gene expression, CpG sites near genes remained unmethylated and were spared from deamination mutations. Over time, the methylated CpG sites outside of promoters mutated rapidly away leaving the present pattern of CpG islands within vertebrates. Thus, the accumulation of CpG islands was a consequence, not a cause, of evolution (Sharif *et al.* 2010). For this reason, it is unlikely that a 'lifespan clock' could be built for species with very sparse DNA methylation using CpG density.

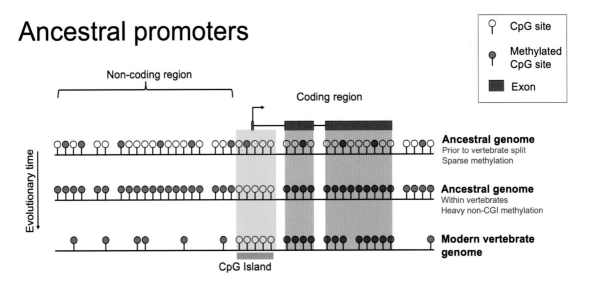

Fig. 6.2. Ancestral animal genomes had sparse methylation with no deviation in expected CpG site frequency. During vertebrate evolution, heavy DNA methylation became standard at CpG sites. Due to rapid mutation of methylated CpGs, the genome lost most CpG sites outside of promoter CpG islands where they are generally unmethylated. Note that CpG sites within coding regions are under negative selective pressure to avoid coding substitutions in amino acids.

Box 6.3: The ageing epigenome

As animals age, the strongly defined epigenetic pattern of DNA methylation degrades, with most highly methylated CpG sites gradually becoming demethylated, while relatively unmethylated CpG islands increase in methylation. In fact, this pattern is predictable enough that careful selection of CpG sites has allowed the development of epigenetic clocks to measure the ageing process by the change in methylation over chronological time (Wagner 2017). Since the methylation of CpG sites increases as an animal ages, the evolution of CpG sites becomes crucial to understanding ageing. Within mammals, coding regions of genomes are quite similar, yet lifespan varies widely. The epigenetic clock ticks according to longevity. Evidence supporting this case has been shown with mice carrying a complete copy of human chromosome 21. When epigenetic 'clock sites' on hum_chr21 were assessed, the human chromosome aged at the rate of the host mouse, suggesting that trans-factors govern ageing rate (Lowe et al. 2018). Similarly, dog epigenomes age at drastically different rates depending on the lifespan of the breed, despite being extremely genetically similar overall. Therefore, strong evidence indicates that ageing-associated methylation marks are a dynamic molecular readout of lifespan variation among different mammalian species.

What is the role of CpG density with lifespan?

Very CpG dense promoter regions tend to be hypomethylated and resist the natural increase in DNA methylation as we age. We hypothesise that CpG density itself is under selective pressure in some genes to maintain expression stability for a long life, in effect 'guarding' genes necessary for the continued homeostasis of organisms during their extended lifespan (Gardiner-Garden and Frommer 1987; Antequera 2003; Mayne et al. 2019). Ultimately, CpG density links both genetic and epigenetic variation across both evolutionary time across species and within the lifespan of a single individual.

What other genomic features are associated with lifespan?

The clustering of genomic features in general has been understudied with respect to lifespan. For example, CpG density itself has only recently been examined in relation to gene function. A recent paper by Boukas et al. demonstrated that CpG density is highest in genes most intolerant to **loss of function (LOF) mutations** (Boukas et al. 2020). They conclude that 'high CpG density is not merely a generic feature of human promoters but is preferentially encountered at the promoters of the most selectively constrained genes, calling into question the prevailing view that CpG islands are not subject to selection'.

Similarly, other genomic features besides coding regions should be assessed for their roles in the evolution of lifespan. The best example of this is the activity and consequences of transposons. While animals all have in the range of 10 to 20 thousand genes, the number of transposons in humans and mice is on the order of 4 million, or about 40–50% of the genome (Canapa et al. 2015). Interestingly, though most animals have about the same proportion of transposons, it appears that each clade has a unique expansion and complement of transposons (Platt et al. 2018). They also cluster in the genome in non-random ways and affect nearby gene expression, and are understudied in terms of lifespan due to difficulty in sequence mapping. Other features under natural selection for density have been studied but not in the context of lifespan include transcription factor motifs, SNP density in molecular evolution, target motifs for iron-binding proteins, and even olfactory receptor DNA binding motifs (Zhao et al. 2003; Sonntag et al. 2004; Kim et al. 2007; Faulk and Kim 2009).

CONCLUDING REMARKS

Rapid prediction of lifespan has the potential to advance many aspects of wildlife management. A lifespan clock reduces the need to monitor species from birth to death to obtain a lifespan estimate. Therefore, parameters relating to population dynamics can be immediately determined and evaluations of populations more accurately assessed. Advancements in lifespan clocks are still required, including expanding into invertebrates and increasing automation. In addition, more work is required to better understand the evolutionary aspects and basic biology relating lifespan and the genome.

DISCUSSION TOPICS

1. What is maximum lifespan? Discuss the definitions of lifespan, and how different definitions may affect interpretation of the estimates provided by lifespan-predicting models.
2. What considerations need to be made when assembling genomes and lifespan data for calibration of a lifespan prediction model?

3. Lifespan is one life history characteristic that can be estimated from genome sequence analysis. What other life history parameters do you expect might be predictable from similar models?

RESOURCES

Promoter sequences and coefficients to predict lifespan:
https://static-content.springer.com/esm/art%3A10.1038%2Fs41598-019-54447-w/MediaObjects/41598_2019_54447_MOESM3_ESM.xlsx

REFERENCES

Antequera F (2003) Structure, function and evolution of CpG island promoters. *Cellular and Molecular Life Sciences CMLS* **60**(8), 1647–1658. doi:10.1007/s00018-003-3088-6

Bell CG, Wilson GA, Butcher LM, Roos C, Walter L, et al. (2012) Human-specific CpG 'beacons' identify loci associated with human-specific traits and disease. *Epigenetics* **7**(10), 1188–1199. doi:10.4161/epi.22127

Bjornsson HT, Hansen KD (2020) Promoter CpG density predicts downstream gene loss-of-function intolerance. *The American Journal of Human Genetics* **107**(3), 487–498. doi:10.1016/j.ajhg.2020.07.014

Boyer D, Kirchner CH, McAllister MK, Staby A, Staalesen BI (2001) The orange roughy fishery of Namibia: lessons to be learned about managing a developing fishery. *South African Journal of Marine Science* **23**(1), 205–221.

Canapa A, Barucca M, Biscotti MA, Forconi M, Olmo E (2015) Transposons, genome size, and evolutionary insights in animals. *Cytogenetic and Genome Research* **147**(4), 217–239. doi:10.1159/000444429

Clark M (2001) Are deepwater Fisheries sustainable? – the example of orange roughy (*Hoplostethus atlanticus*) in New Zealand. *Fisheries Research* **51**, 123–135.

Deaton AM, Bird A (2011) CpG islands and the regulation of transcription. *Genes & Development* **25**(10), 1010–1022. doi:10.1101/gad.2037511

Dreos R, Ambrosini G, Groux R, Cavin Périer R, Bucher P (2017) The eukaryotic promoter database in its 30th year: focus on non-vertebrate organisms. *Nucleic Acids Research* **45**, D51–D55. doi:10.1093/nar/gkw1069

Faulk CD, Kim J (2009) YY1's DNA-Binding motifs in mammalian olfactory receptor genes. *BMC Genomics* **10**(1), 576. doi:10.1186/1471-2164-10-576

Forbes VE, Calow P, Sibly RM (2008) The extrapolation problem and how population modeling can help. *Environmental Toxicology and Chemistry* **27**(10), 1987–1994. doi:10.1897/08-029.1

Friedman J, Hastie T, Tibshirani R (2010) Regularization paths for generalized linear models via coordinate descent. *Journal of Statistical Software* **33**(1), 1–22.

Gardiner-Garden M, Frommer M (1987) CpG islands in vertebrate genomes. *Journal of Molecular Biology* **196**(2), 261–282. doi:10.1016/0022-2836(87)90689-9

George J, Bada J, Zeh J, Scott L, Brown SE, et al. (1999) Age and growth estimates of bowhead whales (*Balaena mysticetus*) via aspartic acid racemization. *Canada Journal of Zoology* **77**(4), 571–580.

Healy K, Ezard TH, Jones OR, Salguero-Gómez R, Buckley YM (2019) Animal life history is shaped by the pace of life and the distribution of age-specific mortality and reproduction. *Nature Ecology & Evolution* **3**(8), 1217–1224. doi:10.1038/s41559-019-0938-7

Hoenig J (2005) Empirical use of longevity data to estimate mortality rates. SEDAR33RD17. SEDAR, North Charleston, SC, USA.

Hsieh JJ (1991) A general theory of life table construction and a precise abridged life table method. *Biometrical journal, Biometrische Zeitschrift* **33**(2), 143–162. doi:10.1002/bimj.4710330204

Hubbard T, Barker D, Birney E, Cameron G, Chen Y, et al. (2002) The Ensembl genome database project. *Nucleic Acids Research* **30**(1), 38–41. doi:10.1093/nar/30.1.38

IUCN (2008) *Strategic Planning for Species Conservation: A Handbook, The Species Conservation Planning Task Force.* IUCN Species Survival Commission, Gland.

Kanherkar RR, Bhatia-Dey N, Csoka AB (2014) Epigenetics across the human lifespan. *Frontiers in Cell and Developmental Biology* **2**, 49. doi:10.3389/fcell.2014.00049

Keane M, Semeiks J, Webb AE, Li YI, Quesada V, et al. (2015) Insights into the evolution of longevity from the bowhead whale genome. *Cell Reports* **10**(1), 112–122. doi:10.1016/j.celrep.2014.12.008

Kenchington TJ (2014) Natural mortality estimators for information-limited fisheries. *Fish and Fisheries* **15**(4), 533–562. doi:10.1111/faf.12027.

Kenyon CJ (2010) The genetics of ageing. *Nature* **464**(7288), 504–512. doi:10.1038/nature08980

Kim JD, Faulk C, Kim J (2007) Retroposition and evolution of the DNA-binding motifs of YY1, YY2 and REX1. *Nucleic Acids Research* **35**(10), 3442–3452. doi:10.1093/nar/gkm235

Long HK, King HW, Patient RK, Odom DT, Klose RJ (2016) Protection of CpG islands from DNA methylation is DNA-encoded and evolutionarily conserved. *Nucleic Acids Research* **44**(14), 6693–6706. doi:10.1093/nar/gkw258

Lowe R, Barton C, Jenkins CA, Ernst C, Forman O, et al. (2018) Ageing-associated DNA methylation dynamics are a molecular readout of lifespan variation among mammalian species. *Genome Biology* **19**, 1. doi:10.1186/s13059-018-1397-1

Mayne B, Berry O, Davies C, Farley J, Jarman S, (2019) A genomic predictor of lifespan in vertebrates. *Scientific Reports* **9**(1), 17866. doi:10.1038/s41598-019-54447-w

Mayne B, Tucker AD, Berry O, Jarman S, (2020) Lifespan estimation in marine turtles using genomic promoter CpG density. *PLoS One* **15**, 7. doi:10.1371/journal.pone.0236888

McLain AT, Faulk C (2018) The evolution of CpG density and lifespan in conserved primate and mammalian promoters. *Aging (Albany NY)* **10**(4), 561–572. doi:10.18632/aging.101413

Musick JA, Limpus CJ (1997) Habitat utilization and migration in juvenile sea turtles. In *The Biology of Sea Turtles, Boca Raton.* pp. 137–163, CRC Press, Costa Rica.

De Paoli-Iseppi R, Deagle BE, McMahon CR, Hindell MA, Dickinson JL, et al. (2017) Measuring animal age with DNA methylation: From humans to wild animals. *Frontiers in Genetics* **8**, 106. doi:10.3389/fgene.2017.00106

Platt RN, Vandewege MW, Ray DA (2018) Mammalian transposable elements and their impacts on genome evolution. *Chromosome Research* **26**(1–2), 25–43. doi:10.1007/s10577-017-9570-z

Sharif J, Endo TA, Toyoda T, Koseki H, (2010) Divergence of CpG island promoters: a consequence or cause of evolution? *Development, Growth & Differentiation* **52**(6), 545–554. doi:10.1111/j.1440-169X.2010.01193.x

Sonntag DM, de Boer J, Medvedovic M, Baxter CS, LeMasters G, *et al.* (2004) Mutational biases associated with potential iron-binding DNA motifs in rodent lacI and human p53 mutational databases. *Mutation Research/Fundamental and Molecular Mechanisms of Mutagenesis* **550**(1–2), 73–88. doi:10.1016/j.mrfmmm.2004.02.004

Tabak MA, Webb CT, Miller RS (2018) Propagule size and structure, life history, and environmental conditions affect establishment success of an invasive species. *Scientific Reports* **8**(1), 10313. doi:10.1038/s41598-018-28654-w

Tacutu R, Thornton D, Johnson E, Budovsky A, Barardo D, *et al.* (2018) Human Ageing Genomic Resources: new and updated databases. *Nucleic Acids Research* **46**, 1083–1090. doi:10.1093/nar/gkx1042.

Then AY, Hoenig JM, Hall NG, Hewitt DA, Jardim HeE (2014) Evaluating the predictive performance of empirical estimators of natural mortality rate using information on over 200 fish species. *ICES Journal of Marine Science* **72**(1), 82–92. doi:10.1093/icesjms/fsu136

Wagner W (2017) Epigenetic aging clocks in mice and men. *Genome Biology* **18**(1), 107. doi:10.1186/s13059-017-1245-8

Wang Z, Pascual-Anaya J, Zadissa A, Li W, Niimura Y, *et al.* (2013) The draft genomes of soft-shell turtle and green sea turtle yield insights into the development and evolution of the turtle-specific body plan. *Nature Genetics* **45**, 701. doi:10.1038/ng.2615

Zhao Z, Fu YX, Hewett-Emmett D, Boerwinkle E (2003) Investigating single nucleotide polymorphism (SNP) density in the human genome and its implications for molecular evolution. *Gene* **312**, 207–213. doi:10.1016/s0378-1119(03)00670-x

7 Development of epigenetic clocks

Simon Jarman, Benjamin Mayne and Tom Little

ABSTRACT

Age is a fundamental feature of individual and population ecology. Many species do not have morphological characters that allow their age to be determined. For those that do, measurement often requires capture of the animal or dissection of deceased animals. Many of these methods are impractical to apply in species that are not being killed for harvest or management purposes. Genomic methods enable age estimation with tissue samples from live animals. We describe current methods for developing 'epigenetic clocks', which predict age based on the degree of methylation at specific CpG sites. Epigenetic clock development depends on samples of known age animals to calibrate the clock, which should be from the same tissue type that will be collected for age analysis in the wild population. The clock development process involves choosing a genomic method to identify highly age-related CpG sites from amongst all those in the genome of that species. A lower-cost genomic method for measuring CpG methylation in test samples should also be chosen. We discuss the process of developing epigenetic clocks for a new target animal species. The range of genomic methods for implementing epigenetic clocks has increased recently, and there is evidence is emerging that epigenetic clocks may be useful in animal clades other than vertebrates.

ANIMAL AGE ESTIMATION

The value of age information in animal ecology

The age of an animal is the strongest predictor of its developmental and life cycle stage (Healy *et al.* 2019). These age-related stages determine many aspects of physiological state, including size, reproductive potential, and trophic requirements (Havenhand 1995). Age is also a significant determinant of mortality and fecundity rates throughout lifespan (Keyfitz and Caswell 2005; Jones *et al.* 2014). The strong effects of age on these most fundamental traits of life history makes age measurement of great value for studying any individual animal's ecology (Hu and Barrett 2017; Heydenrych *et al.* 2021).

Population biology is also strongly influenced by age distributions and their effects on fecundity, mortality, and population growth rates. 'Life tables' list the number of individuals of different age classes in an animal population, and are used to calculate the probability of an individual in one age class surviving to the next one (Begon and Townsend 2020). In populations with a stable age distribution, life table analysis allows prediction of a range of secondary parameters from age data, including life expectancy, reproductive potential, and population growth rate. Life tables are frequently restricted to **cohort** analysis where individuals must be marked when young and tracked through their lifespan. In **'longitudinal studies'**, individuals of some

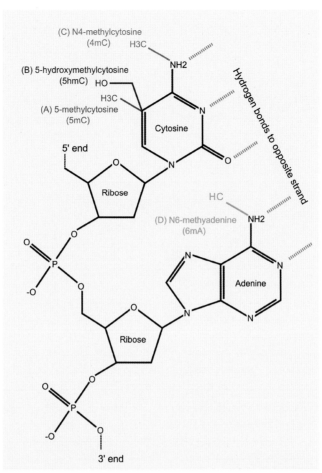

Fig. 7.1. DNA methylation. Methylation is one of the most common chemical modifications of biological molecules. In DNA, four main modifications have been studied: methylation of cytosine to 5-methylcytosine (5mC) (A), hydroxymethylcytosine (B), and N4-methylcytosine (4mC) (C) (Ratel *et al.* 2006). Hydroxymethylcytosine has a different genomic regulatory role to 5mC, and can also be an intermediary between 5mC and unmodified cytosine (de Mendoza *et al.* 2019). Adenine can also be methylated to make N6-methyladenine (6mA) (D). 6mA occurs in throughout the domains of life, but is most abundant and best studied in Eubacteria and Archaea where its function is to protect DNA from cleavage by endogenous endonucleases. Determining the functions of 6mA in eukaryotes is still in progress (Iyer *et al.* 2016).

species can be identified by persistent natural markings such as the spot patterns of whale sharks (Arzoumanian *et al.* 2005). However, most species require artificial marks, such as leg bands or radio-frequency identification tags commonly used in bird studies (Bonter and Bridge 2011). Genetic mark-recapture is a clear alternative if animals have been sampled near birth and can be genotyped when re-encountered (Chapter 10).

Static life tables, however, are based on a sample of ages found in a population at one time in 'cross-sectional' studies. They do not require such long research programs and can be applied in in a broader range of situations. As an example, cross-sectional ageing would be the only option for the study of age structure in putative populations of invasive species (see Chapter 24). The age structure of recently invasive populations would be biased towards younger individuals, whereas established populations have

a more even age structure (Hansen *et al.* 2016). Traditional cross-sectional age studies are possible in some species with features that change in specific time increments, such as annual growth rings in the otolith ear bones of fishes that enable integer estimates of age (Campana 2001). Continuous variables such as overall length or size of a morphological feature can often be related to age by various growth models (Ogle and Isermann 2017). However, many species do not have age-informative morphology, or only have informative features that necessitate killing or capturing the individual to determine its age.

The lack of cross-sectional ageing options for most animal species has motivated research on developing a range of chemical and genomic age estimating methods (Jarman *et al.* 2015). Genomicists have identified age-related change in messenger RNA transcription profiles (Cook *et al.* 2007; Meyer and Schumacher 2021), micro RNAs (Inukai *et al.*

Box 7.1: What are we measuring with epigenetic clocks?

Epigenetic clocks measuring proportions of CpGs that are methylated and unmethylated at a number of clock-like sites in specific animal tissues. The overall estimate is an aggregate of measured CpG site levels from all cells in a tissue. The type of tissue is often important, especially for epigenetic clocks with only a small number of sites because the cell composition of each tissue will affect these clocks, as shown in Fig. 7.2. Clocks with large numbers of sites can measure age consistently across tissues because cell-type variation in methylation levels has been selected out during the model construction, and because remaining cell-specific differences will be small enough in the overall dataset to not affect the age estimate significantly.

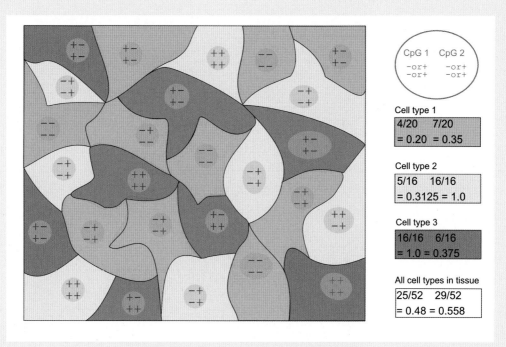

Fig. 7.2. A tissue with three cell types in it. Two CpG sites are being measured, each of which can be seen in each cell and is either unmethylated, hemimethylated (methylated on one strand only) or completely methylated. Cell type 2 is completely methylated at CpG site 2 in all cells, while cell type 3 is completely methylated at CpG site 1. Changes in tissue cell composition alter the overall tissue **beta (β) value** ranging from 0 (unmethylated) to 1 (methylated) for these CpG sites. The age-related changes that we measure with epigenetic clocks may be caused by consistent methylation changes across cell types, or may be the result of age-related changes in tissue cell composition.

2018), telomeres (Dantzer and Fletcher 2015), and DNA methylation (Wagner 2017). A broader range of biomolecules have been analysed with chemical methods outside the domain of genomic methods, including lipofuscin (Terman and Brunk 1998), pentosidine (Fallon *et al.* 2006), amino acid racemisation (Dobberstein *et al.* 2010), and lipid profiles (Herman *et al.* 2009). For cross-sectional age studies of vertebrate populations, analysis of cytosine DNA methylation analysis is the basis for the most successful of these approaches (Fig. 7.1).

'Epigenetic clocks' combine data on the levels of CpG methylation at multiple CpG sites in animal genomes to produce an estimate of age. Epigenetic clocks are calibrated using CpG methylation levels from individuals of known age. These calibration samples are used to select 'clock-like' CpG sites with methylation levels that correlate with the known ages in individuals in a set of calibration samples. Estimates of age for individuals of unknown age can then be based on measurement of methylation at the same CpG sites using the same model (Box 7.1).

Ecological questions addressed with epigenetic clocks

Epigenetic clocks can be used to address two broad categories of ecological questions. The first type are studies of **'chronological age'** where the age value produced by an epigenetic clock is treated as an estimate of time that has passed since an early event in the life of the animal such as birth, hatching, or conception. The second category of questions are those that treat the age value as one of '**biological age**' and use the difference between this and chronological age as a measure of physiological condition of the animal. Biological age encompasses multiple measures of biological function and epigenetic clocks provide one measurement that can be considered to be biological age. This approach has been applied most extensively in humans (e.g. Horvath and Raj 2018), with some recent applications in other mammals (Little *et al.* 2020; Sugrue *et al.* 2021; Pinho *et al.* 2022).

The chronological age of individual animals is valuable for estimating associated physiological and ecological information, such as whether it is reproductively mature, or its probability of dying (Healy *et al.* 2019). The relative ages of individuals also have value for determining their kinship. Relatedness as determined by allele sharing (r) between two anonymous individuals can be determined by analysis of multiple polymorphic markers. However, r values are shared by multiple kinship categories, and the relative ages of two individuals are one way in which possible kinships can be differentiated within one class of r values (Jarman *et al.* 2015; Speed and Balding 2015). Relative ages also have a specific application for the polarising kin relationships identified from r values. For example, two animals sampled from a population with an r value of 0.5 between them are either a parent-offspring pair or full siblings. If they share an allele at each locus, then they are a parent-offspring pair. Relative age values identify which individual is the parent and which is the offspring. This is useful in kinship analysis (Kopps *et al.* 2015), and it enhances the accuracy of **close-kin mark-recapture** population size estimation (Bravington *et al.* 2016; Chapter 11).

Chronological age estimates derived from epigenetic clocks can be used in population biology as a direct replacement for traditional age data. Contemporary population age distributions produced by epigenetic clocks have been used to provide information on population growth rates in the recent past (Polanowski *et al.* 2014; Riekkola *et al.* 2018). The past distribution results from the interplay of age-specific mortality and fecundity rates. These vary extensively with age in a species-specific manner (Jones *et al.* 2014). The future growth rate of a population results from the combination of age distribution with other life cycle parameters such as the age of first reproduction, birth rate, and age of reproductive senescence as well as age-specific mortality and fecundity (Healy *et al.* 2019). Estimates of current population growth rates are one of the most useful data that managers of animal populations can have, and

epigenetic clocks can now provide the data that these estimates rely on.

Biological age determined with an epigenetic clock can predict characteristics like mortality or cognitive decline more accurately than chronological age does (Marioni *et al.* 2015; Xu *et al.* 2021). Ageing is associated with the deterioration of multiple organ systems, including immune-based defences, and a full understanding of what drives age acceleration is required to model and predict individual and population resilience in the face of infectious disease and other stressors, including environmental change. The differences found between biological age as estimated by epigenetic clocks and chronological age of different tissues have been proposed as a generalised indicator of tissue or organismal health (Horvath and Raj 2018). For example, in humans, epigenetic age accelerates relative to chronological age in response to obesity, lifestyle factors, infection, reproduction and numerous genetic syndromes known to shorten lifespan (Horvath 2013). In other mammals, environmental factors have been found to slow the epigenetic clock. For example, dietary restriction slows the clock in mice and rhesus macaques, and mice genetically engineered for longer life expectancy show decelerated epigenetic age (Horvath, Zoller, *et al.* 2021). Castrated sheep spared the stress of reproduction also have a lower rate of epigenetic clock ageing (Sugrue *et al.* 2021). Hibernation slows the epigenetic clock in marmots, in another example of reduced stress decreasing biological ageing rate (Pinho *et al.* 2022). In contrast, high social status, which has been established as a stressor, accelerates the epigenetic clock in baboons (Anderson *et al.* 2021), while rapid growth may accelerate epigenetic age in roe deer (Lemaître *et al.* 2022).

THE APPLICATION: EPIGENETIC CLOCKS
Molecular biological background – epigenetic regulation of gene expression

Specific parts of the **methylome** change with age. Finding and measuring the sites with the most consistent changes in DNA methylation is the first step in developing an epigenetic clock for an animal species of interest (Horvath 2013). DNA methylation regulates vertebrate gene expression at both small and large genomic scales (de Mendoza *et al.* 2019; Klemm *et al.* 2019). For example, methylation of DNA at promoter regions can directly affect gene expression, as 5-methylcytosines (5mCs) fill the major groove of DNA and block direct interactions with multiple components of the transcription complex. At a larger scale, 5mC acts a signal

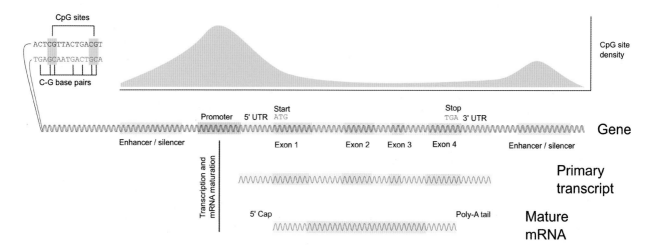

Fig. 7.3. CpG sites and CpG islands. In vertebrates, the most abundant and commonly studied form of methylated DNA is 5-methylcytosine. This occurs predominately at DNA sites where a cytosine is followed by a guanosine, termed 'CpG sites' where the 'p' refers to the phosphate backbone on the same strand, differentiating them from 'CG' base pairs between complementary DNA strands. CpG sites are strongly concentrated around vertebrate gene promoter regions, in areas called 'CpG islands'.

for **chromatin** condensation, which makes regulatory and coding regions of genes inaccessible to the transcription complex. In vertebrates, regions with high densities of cytosines, known as 'CpG islands', occur at the 5' and 3' regulatory regions of genes. This positioning of CpG islands relates to the function of DNA methylation as a transcriptional rate regulator (Fig. 7.3).

The process of developing an epigenetic clock

When developing an epigenetic clock for a new species of interest, several decisions need to be made based on available resources. These include:

- the tissues that can be sampled from the animal of interest
- the process for identifying clock-like CpGs
- the DNA methylation measurement technique that will be used in the clock analyses
- the approach to be applied for calibrating the epigenetic clock
- field sampling protocols.

Selection of tissues to sample

The animal tissue that will be used in the study of age in a wild population is an important consideration when developing an epigenetic clock. The methylome is cell-specific, which means that there is often variation in the relationship between age and CpG methylation levels among tissues within the same animal. Multi-tissue epigenetic clocks have been developed that deal with this variation by analysing a large number of CpG sites to reduce the variance between age and CpG methylation associated with each individual CpG site (Mammalian Methylation Consortium *et al.* 2021). However, the most accurate epigenetic clocks are calibrated with the same tissue type that will be sampled in the test population.

Live animals are the target for most ecological studies, so a tissue that can be sampled with minimal harm to the animal is generally chosen. For animals that can be captured and released alive, the range of tissues that have been used include skin (Riekkola *et al.* 2018), blood (Mayne *et al.* 2021), fin clips (Mayne *et al.* 2020), feather quill tips (de Paoli-Iseppi *et al.* 2018), and buccal cells (Weidner *et al.* 2014). Sampling of cetacean tissues from a distance with biopsy darts allows skin and adipose to be sampled and several cetacean epigenetic clocks for skin have been applied in this way (Polanowski *et al.* 2014; Beal *et al.* 2019). A similar approach may be useful for other large animals.

The use of trace DNA (see Chapter 10) for epigenetic ageing has not been demonstrated except in human forensic applications, where blood at crime scenes can provide an age estimate (Correia Dias *et al.* 2020). Tissues from dead animals may be useful, but this has not been established yet. Attempts to use the shed skin of whales for ageing produced markedly different age results to those of skin samples taken as biopsies from the same whale (Jarman unpublished obs.).

Identification of clock CpGs

Finding age associated CpG sites can be done through genome sequencing tailored to measure DNA methylation, or by genome pairwise alignments with the species of interest. DNA methylation is commonly measured through a process called bisulfite sequencing (Darst *et al.* 2010). During bisulfite conversion, one of the first steps in bisulphite sequencing, unmethylated cytosines are converted to thymines, whereas methylated cytosines are protected. Aligning the bisulphite sequencing data with original sequence data allows identification of unmethylated CpG sites. This is because, where a cytosine is expected but a thymine is found indicates that CpG site was unmethylated in the original sample. Similarly, if a cytosine is both expected and found, that CpG site was originally methylated, and thus protected from bisulphite conversion. Whole genome bisulfite sequencing (WGBS) enables measurement of all CpG sites in a genome and is an unbiased method for identifying the most age-associated CpG sites for an epigenetic clock. Unfortunately, WGBS is expensive, making it difficult to be carried out on sample sizes large enough for identification of clock-like CpGs. Most studies instead use a partial genome sequencing approach such as **reduced representation** bisulfite sequencing (RRBS). In RRBS, a fraction of the genome is sequenced, reducing cost and making it possible on large sample sizes. Prior to sequencing, DNA is digested with a restriction enzyme, such as MspI (cut site: C^CGG). This targets and sequences DNA that is enriched for CpG sites (Gu *et al.* 2011). Reduced representation bisulfite sequencing is advantageous for epigenetic clocks as it enriches for CpG rich regions. However, RRBS is still an expensive option, currently costing ~AU$500 per vertebrate genome sample. Unless this cost is substantially reduced, it is unlikely to be used in a wildlife management setting where hundreds of samples may be required for age analysis.

An alternative to identifying **clock CpGs** is to use sites identified in other species and reported in the literature, then perform genome pairwise alignments to identify their location in the species of interest. This has been successfully carried out in mammals and fish (Polanowski *et al.* 2014; Wright *et al.* 2018; Beal *et al.* 2019; Anastasiadi and Piferrer 2020; Little *et al.* 2020; Mayne *et al.* 2021). These studies have demonstrated transfer of known age associated CpG sites from distant related species such as rodents and cetaceans, or primates and elephants. However, there are limits to this, as age associated CpGs in mammals have been found to not correlate with age in birds (de Paoli-Iseppi *et al.* 2018). This suggests some evolutionary conservation of age associated CpG sites. To identify conserved age associated CpG sites between species, genome pairwise alignment tools such as LASTZ or Cactus can be used

(Armstrong *et al.* 2020). This then allows researchers to have the genomic coordinates of conserved CpG sites between species.

Methods for DNAm measurement

There is a variety of assays that exist for measuring DNA methylation. WGBS and RRBS are ideal for identifying biomarkers, however, because they are designed to produce methylation data that spans the entire genome, they capture CpG sites that may be inapplicable to the research question. Ideally, the DNA methylation assay should only target CpG sites of interest to the specific research question, which would reduce cost and allow for increased throughput. An approach similar to RRBS, DREAM analysis, has been used for both calibrating an epigenetic clock and measuring age in samples taken from the wild, but this was an expensive approach (de Paoli-Iseppi *et al.* 2018).

The number of CpG sites in and the target species of the epigenetic clock may influence which assay is used. For clocks with fewer than five CpG sites it may be useful to use a pyrosequencing-based method. Pyrosequencing is ideal when working with a limited number of sites and provides high resolution data. So far, it has been used in three epigenetic clocks (Polanowski *et al.* 2014; Wright *et al.* 2018; Beal *et al.* 2019). Unfortunately, the cost increases with additional CpG sites, and more recent clocks use more sites for increased accuracy. Multiplex PCR has been shown to work with up to 40 amplicons in a single PCR reaction and used in several species (Lu *et al.* 2017; Anastasiadi and Piferrer 2020; Mayne *et al.* 2020, 2021). In addition, several rounds of multiplex PCR can be run in parallel and pooled for high-throughput sequencing (HTS) after bisulfite conversion. Therefore, if one PCR reaction cannot hold every CpG site of interest it can be split to capture all that is required for the model.

When working with potentially hundreds of CpG sites such as the multi-tissue epigenetic clocks, it may be necessary to develop alternative high-throughput methods. The human and the universal mammalian epigenetic clocks use array-based sequencing technology (Horvath 2013; Mammalian Methylation Consortium *et al.* 2021). These arrays produce two signals: one for the methylated DNA and another for unmethylated. The signals are used to create a β-value ranging from 0 (unmethylated) to 1 (methylated; Wilhelm-Benartzi *et al.* 2013). Arrays are highly cost-effective for large sample sizes and large numbers of CpG sites, accurately interrogating >37 000 conserved CpG sites. Following the generation of 10 000 methylation arrays, epigenetic clocks have been constructed for 59 tissue types in

128 species (Mammalian Methylation Consortium *et al.* 2021), in addition to independent studies using these arrays in bats, elephants, and opossums (Horvath, Haghani, *et al.* 2021; Prado *et al.* 2021; Wilkinson *et al.* 2021). The same clock/CpG signatures have been demonstrated to be strikingly accurate in the vast majority of mammalian species (Mammalian Methylation Consortium *et al.* 2021). Importantly, the CpGs on the mammalian array map back to mammalian genomes, with most sites being very near genes. Thus, arrays offer insight into the genetic basis of ageing in the wild and are ideal for cross species comparisons.

Epigenetic clocks for high-throughput ageing, or for which only small amounts of DNA are available, generally follow a minimised approach (Mayne *et al.* 2020). This involves bisulfite treatment of purified DNA followed by high-throughput sequencing of PCR products. Several HTS systems have been used in this application, including pyrosequencing, Illumina amplicon sequencing, or Oxford Nanopore sequencing (Box 7.2). As minimised clocks inevitably examine only a small number of CpG sites, it is imperative that they examine the CpGs with methylation patterns that are the most tightly correlated with age. Thus, the starting point requires a whole genome approach or the use of a well-designed methylation array to identify these CpGs in the initial stages of assay development. Once suitable CpGs are identified, it is possible to design PCR primers that amplify the target CpGs on bisulphite-treated DNA. An attractive approach would be to adopt conserved CpG sites known to methylate with age in well-studied taxa such as humans or mice and develop an epigenetic clock based on orthologous sites in the species of interest, as was done for an early animal epigenetic clock (Polanowski *et al.* 2014). Indeed, the Mammalian Methyl array includes such conserved CpG sites, and they appear to be applicable across mammals and possibly other vertebrates.

Calibrating a clock

Locating CpG sites with 5mC levels that change with age requires a range of samples taken from known-age animals of the target species calibrate a model. Unfortunately, known age data series for wild animals are difficult to come by as they generally require long-term monitoring programs. However, it is possible to substitute samples with age derived from other methods, including bomb radiocarbon and growth ring increments (Campana 2001; Uno *et al.* 2013). Epigenetic clocks for non-human species have been calibrated with known-age sample sets of as small as 45 samples in whales (Polanowski *et al.* 2014) to as large as 302 in mice

(Stubbs *et al.* 2017). It is recommended a minimum sample size of 70, but simulations found that 134 samples were the minimum requirement to produce accurate and precise models (Mayne *et al.* 2021). Most researchers will have to work with samples that are available, but limited calibration data will limit accuracy of the final epigenetic clock.

The statistical power requirements for epigenetic clocks could be determined in theory, but the number of calibration samples required is unlikely to be collected within most researchers' careers, or even lifetimes. This is especially the case for long-lived species that, from birth to death, would normally outlive a generation of researchers. To circumvent the problem in the short term, researchers can calibrate epigenetic clocks for species closely related to the species of interest and transfer the age prediction models. For example, in primates, the human epigenetic clock can easily be transferred to chimpanzees (Pan), and gorillas (Gorilla; Horvath 2013). Furthermore, datasets of closely related species can be combined to increase statistical power. This has been demonstrated in freshwater fish where 37 samples of Mary River cod (*Maccullochella mariensis*) and 33 samples of Murray cod (*Maccullochella peelii*) were used to collectively calibrate an epigenetic clock (Mayne *et al.* 2021). If a clock were to be made for each species separately, both models would have both been considered under-powered. The maximum evolutionary distance an epigenetic clock can be transferred between species is yet to be determined. However, for species that do not have datasets sufficient for calibration, it may be worthwhile investigating closely related species and transferring the model.

Most studies that have thousands of candidate CpG sites for calibrating an epigenetic clock use an elastic net regression model (e.g. glmnet R package; Friedman *et al.* 2010). An elastic net regression combines a lasso and ridge model. A lasso model shrinks the number of predictors (CpG sites for an epigenetic clock) by assigning the coefficients to zero, whereas the ridge model works with the remaining predictors. Epigenetic clock studies set the elastic net regression model to work with both models (alpha-parameter in glmnet set to 0.5). The result is that the elastic net removes CpG sites that are unnecessary and identifies the minimum required for age prediction. Most studies using an elastic net regression approach, randomly assign 70% of the available known age samples to a training dataset (Horvath 2013; Stubbs *et al.* 2017; Thompson *et al.* 2017; Mayne *et al.* 2020). The training dataset is used to calibrate the model whereas the remaining 30% is used to validate the model.

The performance of the elastic net regression model is routinely measured using correlations, absolute error, relative error, and residuals with increasing age. Pearson correlations are used to compare the known/chronological ages with the predicted/epigenetic ages produced by the model. The higher the correlation, the better the performance of the model. The absolute error and relative error are useful to determine the overall performance of the clock and compare it to other methods. Absolute error can be measured in multiple units of time depending on the species' life history, such as days, weeks, and years. It can be compared to the lifespan of the species as an indicative measure of accuracy. Relative error is the ratio between the absolute error of the predicted age and the known age, expressed as a percentage. Although there is no consensus of what an acceptable measure of relative error is, most studies have a relative error of less than 10% (Horvath 2013; Stubbs *et al.* 2017; Thompson *et al.* 2017; Mayne *et al.* 2020).

One final measurement of the performance of the model is to compare the residuals versus increasing age. Here, the aim is to determine if the model is performing better at different age classes. This can be an issue when calibration datasets are skewed towards samples of a particular class. If there is no relationship between residuals and age, as determined by a Pearson correlation, it would indicate the model is not biased towards any age class.

Measuring DNAm in wild populations

Sampling DNA from wild animals for epigenetic clock age estimation has some specific requirements that differ from DNA sampling for other environmental genomics applications. For tissue-specific epigenetic clocks, the samples should be taken from one tissue type consistently as the clock may deliver different age estimates when applied to a

---

Box 7.2: Age estimation from animals in the field by nanopore sequencing

Oxford Nanopore sequencing technology can directly detect methylation without bisulfite treatment (Fig. 7.4). However, when using untreated genomic DNA as a starting material, sequencing depth over the whole methylome will be limited. As an alternative, nanopore sequencing can be valuable for the study of a minimised clock accessed via PCR. This approach using nanopore technology has an advantage over pyrosequencing or array methods as a specialised sequencing facility is not required and a larger number of amplicons can be efficiently studied. Sufficient genomic DNA can be extracted from a tiny amount of tissue, say, an ear biopsy, or a small volume blood (A). Conceivably, this could include tissue left behind by the animal, such as a faecal sample or even hair, as is done in criminal forensics. Following bisulfite treatment (B) of the DNA sample, PCR is performed using primers with clock loci (C). Amplicons from the same individual are indexed to identify individual animal samples (D), then sequenced (E). The Oxford Nanopore system allows native barcoding of up to 96 individuals, and once the pooled amplicons are barcoded, a single library preparation can be loaded together onto sequencing run.

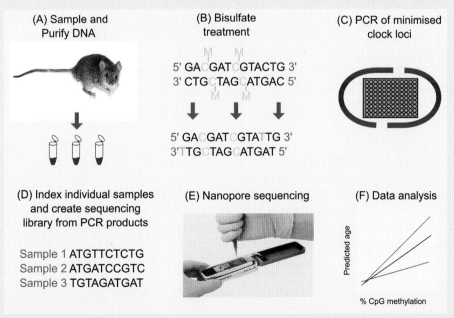

Fig. 7.4. Oxford Nanopore sequencing technology.

tissue on which it was not calibrated (see Box 7.1). The quantity and quality of DNA required for epigenetic clock analysis is often higher than that required for genotyping or similar genomic analyses. This is particularly true where bisulfite conversion is involved, as this fails if insufficient, or poor-quality DNA is used. DNA preservation upon field sampling is the same as for any procedure requiring high quality genomic DNA, so preservation in H_2O-sequestering solvents like ethanol, or snap freezing is sufficient. Portable sequencing technology has enabled age estimation without the need for dedicated genomics laboratories (Box 7.2).

SUMMARY AND FUTURE DIRECTIONS

Epigenetic clocks have several features of an ideal age biomarker. Their development and application are now moderately cheap by the standards of genomic technology. CpG methylation has an advantage in analysis simplicity when compared to other potential genomic age biomarkers in that its range is bounded between zero and complete methylation. This contrasts with other potential genomic age markers like messenger RNA and micro RNA that can vary over many orders of magnitude with no consistent upper bound, which complicates age prediction model construction (Rivero-Segura *et al.* 2020). Methylation levels can be measured with repeatable precision by a variety of methods, including field deployable options (Box 7.2). Signals from multiple sites can be aggregated into one clock and some clocks with many markers will work with multiple tissues (Horvath 2013).

Development of epigenetic clocks for vertebrates is feasible for most species where a known-age calibration sample set is available. Epigenetic clocks have been developed for a large range of mammal species (Polanowski *et al.* 2014; Thompson *et al.* 2017; Mammalian Methylation Consortium *et al.* 2021; Raj *et al.* 2021; Wilkinson *et al.* 2021), as well as some for birds (de Paoli-Iseppi *et al.* 2018), reptiles (Mayne *et al.* 2022), and fish (Anastasiadi and Piferrer 2020; Mayne *et al.* 2020). The process is becoming easier as DNA methylation analysis methods become cheaper, and clocks are developed for a broader range of vertebrate species. This makes the chance of a clock that could be adapted to a target species more likely (Mayne *et al.* 2021).

The taxonomic range over which standard 5mC-based clocks will be effective is not yet known. Some analysis has been done on promoter CpG density in non-vertebrates that shows similar 'CpG island' patterns in near relatives of vertebrates such as echinoderms (Mayne *et al.* 2019). The suite of enzymes that establish and maintain DNA methylation is somewhat conserved among vertebrates (Raddatz *et al.* 2021). Many components are conserved throughout the animal kingdom (with the exception of placozoans) and the sponge *Amphimedon queenslandica* has CpG islands (de Mendoza *et al.* 2019). The development of epigenetic clocks in non-vertebrate animals may require measurement of the epigenetic signals that control chromatin condensation in different ways to the methods described here for vertebrates (Parrott and Bertucci 2019). A recent example in the pine tree (*Pinus taeda*) shows that development of an epigenetic clock measuring a different DNA methylation context is possible (Gardner *et al.* 2022).

Epigenetic clocks provide age information from samples that can provide a range of complementary genomic data types. Environmental genomics can derive age, population provenance, sex, relatedness and physiological states from single samples. Integration of these data types into a larger picture of genomic ecology is only beginning to be explored. Likely future applications that integrate age from epigenetic clocks include combining it with relatedness, sex and linkage data to improve kinship estimation; and combining it with other DNA methylation, messenger RNA (mRNA) and microRNA markers to improve genomic measures of health, stress, fertility and other physiological conditions.

Epigenetic clocks are part of the increasing focus of ecological genomics on contemporary processes. Age information is complementary to analyses of trophic ecology (Chapter 4), kinship and population size (Chapter 11), physiological condition (Chapter 18), dispersal (Chapter 22), landscape genomics, and infection with pathogens (Chapter 25). Epigenetic clocks have added a valuable new tool to the environmental genomics toolkit for addressing questions on processes currently affecting animal populations.

DISCUSSION TOPICS

1. What are the main challenges to consider before starting experiments to build an epigenetic clock for a species of bird with no close relatives that have epigenetic clocks already?
2. What effects would the accuracy of an epigenetic clock have on estimates of a population's age structure?
3. What applications can you think of for age estimates of individual animals in a wild population?

4. What aspects of animal ecology could be studied with differences in biological and chronological age?

RESOURCES

An R package for elastic net regression analysis used to identify age-informative CpG sites from genome-wide scans: https://cran.r-project.org/web/packages/glmnet/index.html
Bioinformatics pipelines for development of minimal epigenetic clocks: https://github.com/WildANimalClocks/apollo.

ACKNOWLEDGEMENTS

The authors have worked with many scientists on epigenetic clock development and are grateful for their interest and contributions of samples for clock calibration. We thank Alyssa Budd and Olly Berry for constructive reviews of this chapter.

REFERENCES

Anastasiadi D, Piferrer F (2020) A clockwork fish: Age prediction using DNA methylation-based biomarkers in the European seabass. *Molecular Ecology Resources* **20**(2), 387–397. doi:10.1111/1755-0998.13111

Anderson JA, Johnston RA, Lea AJ, Campos FA, Voyles TN, *et al.* (2021) High social status males experience accelerated epigenetic aging in wild baboons. *eLife* **10**, e66128. doi:10.7554/eLife.66128

Armstrong J, Hickey G, Diekhans M, Fiddes IT, Novak AM, *et al.* (2020) Progressive Cactus is a multiple-genome aligner for the thousand-genome era. *Nature* **587**(7833), 246–251. doi:10.1038/s41586-020-2871-y

Arzoumanian Z, Holmberg J, Norman B (2005) An astronomical pattern-matching algorithm for computer-aided identification of whale sharks Rhincodon typus. *Journal of Applied Ecology* **42**(6), 999–1011. doi:10.1111/j.1365-2664.2005.01117.x

Beal AP, Kiszka JJ, Wells RS, Eirin-Lopez JM (2019) The Bottlenose Dolphin Epigenetic Aging Tool (BEAT): A molecular age estimation tool for small cetaceans. *Frontiers in Marine Science* **6**, 561. doi:10.3389/fmars.2019.00561

Begon M, Townsend CR (2020) *Ecology: From Individuals to Ecosystems*. John Wiley & Sons, Hoboken NJ, USA.

Bonter DN, Bridge ES (2011) Applications of radio frequency identification (RFID) in ornithological research: a review. *Journal of Field Ornithology* **82**(1), 1–10. doi:10.1111/j.1557-9263.2010.00302.x

Bravington MV, Skaug HJ, Anderson EC (2016) Close-Kin Mark-Recapture. *Statistical Science* **31**(2), 259–274. doi:10.1214/16-STS552

Campana SE (2001) Accuracy, precision and quality control in age determination, including a review of the use and abuse of age validation methods. *Journal of Fish Biology* **59**(2), 197–242. doi:10.1111/j.1095-8649.2001.tb00127.x

Cook PE, Hugo LE, Iturbe-Ormaetxe I, Williams CR, Chenoweth SF, *et al.* (2007) Predicting the age of mosquitoes using transcriptional profiles. *Nature Protocols* **2**(11), 2796–2806. doi:10.1038/nprot.2007.396

Correia Dias H, Cordeiro C, Corte Real F, Cunha E, Manco L (2020) Age estimation based on DNA methylation using blood samples from deceased individuals. *Journal of Forensic Sciences* **65**(2), 465–470. doi:10.1111/1556-4029.14185

Dantzer B, Fletcher QE (2015) Telomeres shorten more slowly in slow-aging wild animals than in fast-aging ones. *Experimental Gerontology* **71**, 38–47. doi:10.1016/j.exger.2015.08.012

Darst RP, Pardo CE, Ai L, Brown KD, Kladde MP (2010) Bisulfite sequencing of DNA. *Current Protocols in Molecular Biology* **91**(1), 7.9.1–7.9.17. doi:10.1002/0471142727.mb0709s91

Dobberstein RC, Tung S-M, Ritz-Timme S (2010) Aspartic acid racemisation in purified elastin from arteries as basis for age estimation. *International Journal of Legal Medicine* **124**(4), 269–275. doi:10.1007/s00414-009-0392-1

Fallon JA, Cochrane RL, Dorr B, Klandorf H (2006) Interspecies comparison of pentosidine accumulation and its correlation with age in birds. *The Auk* **123**(3), 870–876. doi:10.1093/auk/123.3.870

Friedman J, Hastie T, Tibshirani R (2010) Regularization paths for generalized linear models via coordinate descent. *Journal of Statistical Software* **33**(1), 1–22.

Gardner ST, Bertucci EM, Sutton R, Horcher A, Aubrey D, *et al.* (2022) Development of DNA methylation-based epigenetic age predictors in loblolly pine (*Pinus taeda*). *Molecular Ecology Resources* **23**, 131–144. doi:10.1101/2022.01.27.477887

Gu H, Smith ZD, Bock C, Boyle P, Gnirke A, *et al.* (2011) Preparation of reduced representation bisulfite sequencing libraries for genome-scale DNA methylation profiling. *Nature Protocols* **6**(4), 468–481. doi:10.1038/nprot.2010.190

Hansen MJ, Madenjian CP, Slade JW, Steeves TB, Almeida PR, *et al.* (2016) Population ecology of the sea lamprey (*Petromyzon marinus*) as an invasive species in the Laurentian Great Lakes and an imperiled species in Europe. *Reviews in Fish Biology and Fisheries* **26**(3), 509–535. doi:10.1007/s11160-016-9440-3

Havenhand JN (1995) Evolutionary ecology of larval types. In *Ecology of Marine Invertebrate Larvae*. pp. 79–122. CRC Press, Boca Raton, FL, USA.

Healy K, Ezard TH, Jones OR, Salguero-Gómez R, Buckley YM (2019) Animal life history is shaped by the pace of life and the distribution of age-specific mortality and reproduction. *Nature Ecology & Evolution* **3**(8), 1217–1224. doi:10.1038/s41559-019-0938-7

Herman DP, Ylitalo GM, Robbins J, Straley JM, Gabriele CM, *et al.* (2009) Age determination of humpback whales Megaptera novaeangliae through blubber fatty acid compositions of biopsy samples. *Marine Ecology Progress Series* **392**, 277–293. doi:10.3354/meps08249

Heydenrych MJ, Saunders BJ, Bunce M, Jarman SN (2021) Epigenetic measurement of key vertebrate population biology parameters. *Frontiers in Ecology and Evolution* **9**. doi:10.3389/fevo.2021.617376

Horvath S (2013) DNA methylation age of human tissues and cell types. *Genome Biology* **14**(10), 3156. doi:10.1186/gb-2013-14-10-r115

Horvath S, Haghani A, Zoller JA, Raj K, Sinha I, *et al.* (2021) Epigenetic clock and methylation studies in gray short-tailed opossums. *bioRxiv* [Preprint]. doi:10.1101/2021.10.13.464301

Horvath S, Zoller JA, Haghani A, Jasinska AJ, Raj K, *et al.* (2021) Epigenetic clock and methylation studies in the rhesus macaque. *GeroScience* 43(5), 2441–2453. doi:10.1007/s11357-021-00429-8

Horvath S, Raj K (2018) DNA methylation-based biomarkers and the epigenetic clock theory of ageing. *Nature Reviews Genetics* 19(6), 371–384. doi:10.1038/s41576-018-0004-3

Hu J, Barrett RDH (2017) Epigenetics in natural animal populations. *Journal of Evolutionary Biology* 30(9), 1612–1632. doi:10.1111/jeb.13130

Inukai S, Pincus Z, De Lencastre A, Slack FJ(2018) A microRNA feedback loop regulates global microRNA abundance during aging. *RNA* 24(2), 159–172. doi:10.1261/rna.062190.117

Iyer LM, Zhang D, Aravind L (2016) Adenine methylation in eukaryotes: Apprehending the complex evolutionary history and functional potential of an epigenetic modification. *BioEssays* 38(1), 27–40. doi:10.1002/bies.201500104

Jarman SN, Polanowski AM, Faux CE, Robbins J, De Paoli-Iseppi R, *et al.* (2015) Molecular biomarkers for chronological age in animal ecology. *Molecular Ecology* 24(19), 4826–4847. doi:10.1111/mec.13357

Jones OR, Scheuerlein A, Salguero-Gómez R, Camarda CG, Schaible R, *et al.* (2014) Diversity of ageing across the tree of life. *Nature* 505(7482), 169–173. doi:10.1038/nature12789

Keyfitz N, Caswell H (eds) (2005) Introduction: Population without age. In *Applied Mathematical Demography*. pp. 1–28. Springer New York (Statistics for Biology and Health), New York, NY doi:10.1007/0-387-27409-X_1

Klemm SL, Shipony Z, Greenleaf WJ (2019) Chromatin accessibility and the regulatory epigenome. *Nature Reviews Genetics* 20(4), 207–220. doi:10.1038/s41576-018-0089-8

Kopps AM, Kang J, Sherwin WB, Palsbøll PJ (2015) How well do molecular and pedigree relatedness correspond, in populations with diverse mating systems, and various types and quantities of molecular and demographic data? *G3 (Bethesda)* 5(9), 1815–1826. doi:10.1534/g3.115.019323

Lemaître J-F, Rey B, Gaillard JM, Régis C, Gilot-Fromont E, *et al.* (2022) DNA methylation as a tool to explore ageing in wild roe deer populations. *Molecular Ecology Resources* 22(3), 1002–1015. doi:10.1111/1755-0998.13533

Little TJ, O'Toole AN, Rambaut A, Chandra T, Marioni R, *et al.* (2020) Methylation-based age estimation in a wild mouse. *bioRxiv*, doi:10.1101/2020.07.16.203687

Lu J, Johnston A, Berichon P, Ru KL, Korbie D, *et al.* (2017) PrimerSuite: A high-throughput web-based primer design program for multiplex bisulfite PCR. *Scientific Reports* 7(1), 41328. doi:10.1038/srep41328

Mammalian Methylation Consortium *et al.* (2021) Universal DNA methylation age across mammalian tissues. *bioRxiv*, doi:10.1101/2021.01.18.426733

Marioni RE, Shah S, McRae AF, Ritchie SJ, Muniz-Terrera G, *et al.* (2015) The epigenetic clock is correlated with physical and cognitive fitness in the Lothian Birth Cohort 1936. *International Journal of Epidemiology* 44(4), 1388–1396. doi:10.1093/ije/dyu277

Mayne B, Berry O, Davies C, Farley J, Jarman S (2019) A genomic predictor of lifespan in vertebrates. *Scientific Reports* 9(1), 17866. doi:10.1038/s41598-019-54447-w

Mayne B, Korbie D, Kenchington L, Ezzy B, Berry O, *et al.* (2020) A DNA methylation age predictor for zebrafish. *Aging (Albany NY)* 12(24), 24817–24835. doi:10.18632/aging.202400

Mayne B, Espinoza T, Roberts D, Butler GL, Brooks S, *et al.* (2021) Nonlethal age estimation of three threatened fish species using DNA methylation: Australian lungfish, Murray cod and Mary River cod. *Molecular Ecology Resources* 21(7), 2324–2332. doi:10.1111/1755-0998.13440

Mayne B, Mustin W, Baboolal V, Casella F, Ballorain K, *et al.* (2022) Age prediction of green turtles with an epigenetic clock. *Molecular Ecology Resources* 22, 2275–2284. doi:10.1111/1755-0998.13621

Mayne B, Berry O, Jarman S (2021) Optimal sample size for calibrating DNA methylation age estimators. *Molecular Ecology Resources* 21(7), 2316–2323. doi:10.1111/1755-0998.13437

de Mendoza A, Hatleberg WL, Pang K, Leininger S, Bogdanovic O, *et al.* (2019) Convergent evolution of a vertebrate-like methylome in a marine sponge. *Nature Ecology & Evolution* 3(10), 1464–1473. doi:10.1038/s41559-019-0983-2

Meyer DH, Schumacher B (2021) BiT age: A transcriptome-based aging clock near the theoretical limit of accuracy. *Aging Cell* 20(3), e13320. doi:10.1111/acel.13320

Ogle DH, Isermann DA (2017) Estimating age at a specified length from the von Bertalanffy growth function. *North American Journal of Fisheries Management* 37(5), 1176–1180. doi:10.1080/02755947.2017.1342725

de Paoli-Iseppi R, Deagle BE, Polanowski AM, McMahon CR, Dickinson JL, *et al.* (2018) Age estimation in a long-lived seabird (Ardenna tenuirostris) using DNA methylation-based biomarkers. *Molecular Ecology Resources* 19(2), 411–425. doi:10.1111/1755-0998.12981

Parrott BB, Bertucci EM (2019) Epigenetic aging clocks in ecology and evolution. *Trends in Ecology & Evolution* 34(9), 767–770. doi:10.1016/j.tree.2019.06.008

Pinho GM, Martin JG, Farrell C, Haghani A, Zoller JA, *et al.* (2022) Hibernation slows epigenetic ageing in yellow-bellied marmots. *Nature Ecology & Evolution* 6(4), 418–426. doi:10.1038/s41559-022-01679-1

Polanowski AM, Robbins J, Chandler D, Jarman SN (2014) Epigenetic estimation of age in humpback whales. *Molecular Ecology Resources* 14(5), 976–987. doi:10.1111/1755-0998.12247

Prado NA, Brown JL, Zoller JA, Haghani A, Yao M, *et al.* (2021) Epigenetic clock and methylation studies in elephants. *Aging Cell* 20(7), e13414. doi:10.1111/acel.13414

Raddatz G, Arsenault RJ, Aylward B, Whelan R, Böhl F, *et al.* (2021) A chicken DNA methylation clock for the prediction of broiler health. *Communications Biology* 4(1), 1–8. doi:10.1038/s42003-020-01608-7

Raj K, Szladovits B, Haghani A, Zoller JA, Li CZ, *et al.* (2021) Epigenetic clock and methylation studies in cats. *GeroScience* 43, 2363–2378. doi:10.1007/s11357-021-00445-8

Ratel D, Ravanat JL, Berger F, Wion D (2006) N6-methyladenine: the other methylated base of DNA. *Bioessays* 28, 309–315.

Riekkola L, Zerbini AN, Andrews O, Andrews-Goff V, Baker CS, *et al.* (2018) Application of a multi-disciplinary approach to reveal population structure and Southern Ocean feeding grounds of humpback whales. *Ecological Indicators* **89**, 455–465. doi:10.1016/j.ecolind.2018.02.030

Rivero-Segura NA, Bello-Chavolla OY, Barrera-Vázquez OS, Gutierrez-Robledo LM, Gomez-Verjan JC (2020) Promising biomarkers of human aging: In search of a multi-omics panel to understand the aging process from a multidimensional perspective. *Ageing Research Reviews* **64**, 101164. doi:10.1016/j.arr.2020.101164

Speed D, Balding DJ (2015) Relatedness in the post-genomic era: Is it still useful? *Nature Reviews Genetics* **16**(1), 33–44. doi:10.1038/nrg3821

Stubbs TM, Bonder MJ, Stark AK, Krueger F, von Meyenn F, *et al.* (2017) Multi-tissue DNA methylation age predictor in mouse. *Genome Biology* **18**(1), 68. doi:10.1186/s13059-017-1203-5

Sugrue VJ, Zoller JA, Narayan P, Lu AT, Ortega-Recalde OJ, *et al.* (2021) Castration delays epigenetic aging and feminizes DNA methylation at androgen-regulated loci. *eLife* **10**, e64932. doi:10.7554/eLife.64932

Terman A, Brunk UT (1998) Lipofuscin: Mechanisms of formation and increase with age. *APMIS* **106**(1–6), 265–276. doi:10.1111/j.1699-0463.1998.tb01346.x

Thompson MJ, Horvath S, Pellegrini M (2017) An epigenetic aging clock for dogs and wolves. *Aging (Albany NY)* **9**(3), 1055–1068. doi:10.18632/aging.101211

Uno KT, Quade J, Fisher DC, Wittemyer G, Douglas-Hamilton I, *et al.* (2013) Bomb-curve radiocarbon measurement of recent biologic tissues and applications to wildlife forensics and stable isotope (paleo)ecology. *Proceedings of the National Academy of Sciences* **110**(29), 11736–11741. doi:10.1073/pnas.1302226110

Wagner W (2017) Epigenetic aging clocks in mice and men. *Genome Biology* **18**(1), 107. doi:10.1186/s13059-017-1245-8

Weidner CI, Lin Q, Koch CM, Eisele L, Beier F, *et al.* (2014) Aging of blood can be tracked by DNA methylation changes at just three CpG sites. *Genome Biology* **15**(2), 1–12. doi:10.1186/gb-2014-15-2-r24

Wilhelm-Benartzi CS, Koestler DC, Karagas MR, Flanagan JM, Christensen BC, *et al.* (2013) Review of processing and analysis methods for DNA methylation array data. *British Journal of Cancer* **109**(6), 1394–1402. doi:10.1038/bjc.2013.496

Wilkinson GS, Adams DM, Haghani A, Lu AT, Zoller J, *et al.* (2021) DNA methylation predicts age and provides insight into exceptional longevity of bats. *Nature Communications* **12**(1), 1615. doi:10.1038/s41467-021-21900-2

Wright PGR, Mathews F, Schofield H, Morris C, Burrage J, *et al.* (2018) Application of a novel molecular method to age free-living wild Bechstein's bats. *Molecular Ecology Resources* **18**(6), 1374–1380. doi:10.1111/1755-0998.12925

Xu M, Zhu J, Liu XD, Luo MY, Xu NJ (2021) Roles of physical exercise in neurodegeneration: Reversal of epigenetic clock. *Translational Neurodegeneration* **10**(1), 30. doi:10.1186/s40035-021-00254-1

8   Molecular sex identification for applications in conservation, industry and veterinary medicine

Clare E. Holleley, Sarah L. Whiteley, Floriaan Devloo-Delva, Andreas Bachler, Joshua Llinas and Arthur Georges

ABSTRACT

The ability to identify whether an organism is female or male is essential data feeding into a range of applications in biological research, animal-based industries and veterinary medicine. Many organisms show striking sexual dimorphism in secondary sexual characters and/or visible genitalia that make assigning a sex to an individual unambiguous. However, there are also many species where it is impossible to distinguish males from females on the basis of their outward appearance, and surprising complexity and lability exists in this seemingly binary trait (e.g. environmental sex reversal, natural sex change). Even in sexually dimorphic species, there are often life stages where sex cannot be confidently assigned (e.g. embryonic development, juvenile life stages and seasonal variation in reproductive plumage or colouration). Another challenge for **sex identification** exists when samples are collected without the researcher being able to inspect the organism, such as remote, non-invasive or environmental sampling. When phenotypes are challenging, researchers can instead use molecular data to establish the sex of individuals. Here we outline the application and importance of accurate molecular sex identification methods in a range of fields, including conservation, ecological research, food production, and veterinary medicine. We provide a framework to structure the sex-marker discovery process which will ensure that the strategy is appropriate for the biology of the organism and the budget of the researcher. Lastly, we detail how a core understanding of the evolution

of **sex chromosomes** and **sex determination** mechanisms is crucial to successful sex marker development.

HOW TO DEFINE THE SEXES?

Most vertebrates have a gonochoristic system of reproduction where two discrete phenotypic sexes exist – female or male (Bachtrog *et al.* 2014; Stöck *et al.* 2021). Differences in the size of and investment in **gametes** distinguishes and defines the two sexes. Male animals produce many smaller gametes (spermatozoa, sperm) whereas females produce fewer larger ones (ova, egg cells). A greater investment is directed to offspring by the female than by the male. Such investment can be material or behavioural, including striking an appropriate balance between risk to the parent and risk to the offspring. Sexual phenotypes might be strictly defined by the size and morphology of their gametes or the structure of the gonads that produce them, but internal character traits are generally not the most practical or observable trait to use for general research purposes. As most of us would know based on experience with our own species, female and male animals can be recognisable by the casual observer. Thus, more practically, sexual **phenotype** is often defined using the differences in primary and/or secondary sexual characteristics that vary between males and females. Some examples of definitive externally dimorphic traits are: body size, colouration, plumage or in extreme cases the often-spectacular outcomes of sexual selection (e.g. antlers in deer, outlandish plumage in peacocks and the dazzling structural colour displays seen in birds of paradise; Davies *et al.* 2012). This chapter will focus on sex identification using vertebrate examples, but the analytical techniques and decision-making frameworks are broadly applicable across kingdoms.

SEX IDENTIFICATION VERSUS SEX DETERMINATION

Phenotypic sex is usually concordant with some underlying genetic foundation that governs developmental fate – male or female. In some species, the underlying propensity to be one sex or the other can be overridden by environmental factors, which requires us to make also a distinction between genetic sex identification and phenotypic sex identification. In this chapter, we focus exclusively on describing robust methodologies for developing genetic sex identification markers and discuss the application and utility of these molecular tools. You may notice that in some publications the term 'sex determination' is used interchangeably with sex identification. However, we discourage this because it is imprecise and inaccurate to do so. Specifically, 'sex identification' should be the preferred term to refer to *methods* that a researcher uses to assign either the genotypic or phenotypic sex to an individual animal. The term 'sex determination' should be reserved exclusively for *biological processes* that initiate sexual differentiation in the embryo (e.g. gene-regulation, organogenesis). It is indeed possible for sex identification markers to inform the study of sex determination, in particular the characterisation of sex chromosome gene content. Likewise, studies of sex determination can provide valuable information that assists in the characterisation of sex identification markers. Thus, whilst they are interrelated, the terms should not be confused because they refer to fundamentally different areas of research with different goals, activities, and approaches.

WHY IDENTIFY GENETIC SEX AND WHAT ARE THE APPLICATIONS?

The sex of an individual is a critically important life history trait because it profoundly affects behaviour, phenotype, mode of reproduction, energetic investment and many other **fitness** components. The primary sex ratio of individuals in populations is a critical component in studies of sex allocation (the differential investment of the parents in female versus male offspring) and is the subject of a particular type of selection, that of Fisher's frequency-dependent selection (Fisher 1930; Edwards 2000). Fisher's frequency-dependent selection is a powerful form of natural selection that brings the primary sex ratio to equilibrium, typically a 1:1 sex ratio. The operational sex ratio, that is, the ratio of adult breeding males to adult breeding females in a population, which can depart dramatically from a 1:1 ratio because of differential mortality, has important demographic consequences, including a strong bearing on population viability. Thus, there are many reasons for wanting to unequivocally establish the sex of one or many individuals.

Population viability analysis

The use of molecular markers for sex identification has transformed the study of sexually monomorphic species in ecology, conservation, and wildlife management. In particular, operational sex ratios have a strong influence on **effective population size**. They can be used to determine if a population is experiencing problematic demographic shifts (Boyle *et al.* 2014; Lambert *et al.* 2021). These basic but essential biological data are required for population viability modelling, with sex ratio bias having both a direct and indirect influence on population viability (Heinsohn *et al.* 2019; Shaffer 1981). For example, management of harvested furbearer species (e.g. beavers or bobcats) has been problematic owing to errors in sex and age data from harvested animals, which biased the population viability models. To rectify these errors, Hiller *et al.* (2022) used a PCR-based test, developed by Pilgrim *et al.* (2005), to identify the sex of harvested bobcats, *Lynx rufus*, where they found a 20% error between visual sex (identified by furtakers) and genetic sex, mainly in juvenile individuals. In this case, the genetic sex identification increased precision of the population models and improved the local wildlife management strategies.

The demographic processes that influence local declines and extinction are the same processes that operate when species distributional boundaries shift (Andrewartha and Birch 1954), such as under climate change. Extreme sex ratio skews can occur at the boundaries of climatic tolerance. Sex ratio monitoring to detect demographic disruption at the trailing edge of a species distribution could be an indicator of pending distributional shifts under climate change (Boyle *et al.* 2014).

Animal behavioural ecology and sociobiology

Sex identification is critical for understanding the ecology and behaviour in species with little or no sexual dimorphism. An excellent example is the development of cross-species avian sex markers for non-ratites (Griffiths *et al.* 1998; Fridolfsson and Ellegren 1999) and ratites (Huynen *et al.* 2002). The non-ratite sex markers are based upon a W-specific size polymorphism in the sex-linked and otherwise highly conserved CHD (chromo-helicase-DNA-binding) genes. The ratite markers are based on a size polymorphism at an anonymous locus, derived from random amplification of polymorphic DNA (RAPD) analysis. Although not without some technical challenges (Dawson *et al.* 2001, 2015), these sex markers increased the power and accuracy of research in bird behaviour and also expanded the scope of questions that could be investigated (Hughes 1998). Before these markers were available, the sex of monomorphic species was often inferred by painstaking but ultimately subjective behavioural observation or invasive techniques such as laparoscopy (Richner 1989). Behavioural approaches rely on the assumption that there are suites of sexually dimorphic behavioural traits that are reliable indicators of sex. It is now appreciated the behavioural dynamics of avian populations are far more complex than previously assumed and that ecological, demographic, and behavioural methods to infer sex can be inaccurate, particularly in studies involving fewer than 200 birds (Dechaume-Moncharmont *et al.* 2011). The new-found accuracy provided by sex-linked avian molecular markers has facilitated applications including: mating system reconstruction, accurate long-term monitoring, revealing group structure in co-operative breeders, study of sex-biased dispersal dynamics and a host of other applications (Hughes 1998; Morinha *et al.* 2012).

Remote population monitoring

The capacity to identify the sex of animals from samples collected non-invasively without observing them, has generated a slew of new applications in wildlife management (Waits and Paetkau 2005). Molecular sex identification markers have been applied to a wide range of remote and/or non-invasive biological samples including hair, scats and environmental DNA from water or soil samples. For example, Zarzoso-Lacoste *et al.* (2018) used scat survey techniques for remote monitoring of endangered bat populations (*Rhinolophus hipposideros*) to assess variation in bat maternity colony demography. By combining a molecular **capture-mark-recapture** approach to estimate lesser horseshoe bat abundance (see Chapter 10 for this technique) and a mammalian sex-linked PCR test, they discovered that colonies are heavily female biased (74.2% female) and that the sex ratios vary between colonies and

through time within the same colonies. Using a sex-linked marker in combination with parentage assignment allowed this study to reliably delineate different categories of individuals (males, females, potential breeders, reproductive individuals) and contributed to a better understanding of bat reproduction. Remote sampling strategies can also combine sex identification with Y-chromosome haplotyping for unique biological inference. For example, Aarnes *et al.* (2015) developed a Y-chromosome multiplex **microsatellite** PCR assay with the goal of using it to resolve the regional provenance of illegally traded hunting trophies. This approach can also be useful for detecting ancient or historical trade routes. For example, Barrett *et al.* (2022) sex-typed ancient walrus remains to uncover a pattern of increased hunting pressure through time in the medieval European walrus ivory trade. Male walruses have larger tusks and are preferred for ivory harvesting. Female representation in ivory artefacts increased over time, suggesting that either males were depleted from the population or there was an increased harvest rate for both sexes. As with any study involving degraded or trace quantity DNA (Chapter 16), remote sex identification needs to plan an approach such that allelic drop-out, degraded DNA and a potentially high rate of false-negatives do not bias the interpretation of the assay (Waits and Paetkau 2005; Dawson *et al.* 2015).

Ex-situ conservation and captive breeding programs

Genetic sex identification has a variety of uses in the management and breeding of captive animal populations such as endangered species breeding programs, zoos and wildlife reserves (Pereira *et al.* 2021; Ryder *et al.* 2021). Juvenile sex identification can assist the planning of animal exchanges between zoos, allowing animals to be transported before they are sexually mature. Accurate sex identification is crucial to all pedigree planning and stud book record-keeping. Molecular sex identification can also be used to inform assisted reproductive technology, for example, when selecting embryos to implant or sorting X and Y bearing sperm. Sex identification markers can also be useful to confirm unusual events, such as spontaneous parthenogenesis, that may occur in captivity for a range of vertebrate species (Watts *et al.* 2006; Booth *et al.* 2014; Miller *et al.* 2019; Ryder *et al.* 2021).

Food production efficiency

Sexually dimorphic traits are key factors to improve food production efficiency and sustainability (see Box 8.1). Sex identification and manipulation technologies have

Box 8.1: Sex as a production trait in the seafood industry

Fisheries

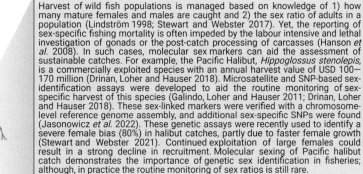

Harvest of wild fish populations is managed based on knowledge of 1) how many mature females and males are caught and 2) the sex ratio of adults in a population (Lindström 1998; Stewart and Webster 2017). Yet, the reporting of sex-specific fishing mortality is often impeded by the labour intensive and lethal investigation of gonads or the post-catch processing of carcasses (Hanson *et al.* 2008). In such cases, molecular sex markers can aid the assessment of sustainable catches. For example, the Pacific Halibut, *Hippoglossus stenolepis*, is a commercially exploited species with an annual harvest value of USD 100–170 million (Drinan, Loher and Hauser 2018). Microsatellite and SNP-based sex-identification assays were developed to aid the routine monitoring of sex-specific harvest of this species (Galindo, Loher and Hauser 2011; Drinan, Loher and Hauser 2018). These sex-linked markers were verified with a chromosome-level reference genome assembly, and additional sex-specific SNPs were found (Jasonowicz *et al.* 2022). These genetic assays were recently used to identify a severe female bias (80%) in halibut catches, partly due to faster female growth (Stewart and Webster 2021). Continued exploitation of large females could result in a strong decline in recruitment. Molecular sexing of Pacific halibut catch demonstrates the importance of genetic sex identification in fisheries; although, in practice the routine monitoring of sex ratios is still rare.

Photo by Dale Maschette

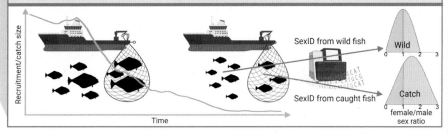

Aquaculture

In fish aquaculture, the reliable identification of sex has economic impact via the establishment of mono-sex stocks. The benefits of sex-skewed or monosex aquaculture include faster growth rates, larger body size, superior flesh quality, the presence of ovaries for egg production (e.g., sturgeon), or preventing uncontrolled reproduction (Budd *et al.* 2015; Wang *et al.* 2019). In Atlantic salmon aquaculture, females are more economically desirable than males due to their larger size and faster growth (Wang *et al.* 2019). In other cases, such as tilapia species, males grow faster (Ridha 2011). Aquaculture has been successful in developing monosex stocks through sex reversal (Piferrer *et al.* 1994; Wang *et al.* 2019). During development, sex can be manipulated by altering hormones (e.g., exogenous sex hormones), the environment (e.g., temperature), or chromosome ploidy (e.g., triploids). Manipulating adult broodstock sex ratios offers some control over the resulting offspring sex ratios (reviewed in Budd *et al.* 2015). However, females and males are often indistinguishable during their early life stages. Here, molecular sex markers are commonly employed to determine the sex and improve productivity. In modern aquaculture it is common for individuals to be SNP-genotyped for pedigree reconstruction and genetic selection of other important traits (such as disease resistance or fertility). The inclusion of sex-linked markers on the SNP panel for sex-ID could be easily done and at trivial extra expense, provided such markers are available.

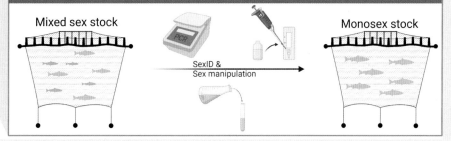

revolutionised food production from livestock since the 1980s (Hohenboken 1981; King 1984; Johnson and Clarke 1988). For example, cattle farming for dairy production favours the production of female animals capable of lactation (Weigel 2004), whereas in the beef livestock production, producing animals for eventual slaughter, there is a higher commercial value of male than female offspring for meat production (Hohenboken 1999). Thus, even within the same livestock species, sex as a production trait can have opposing financial drivers. The manipulation of off-spring sex ratios is routine now in the cattle industry via sex chromosome identification and the sorting of X- and Y-bearing sperm. Sexing of mammalian sperm is most efficiently done through flow cytometry, where the

X-bearing sperm have a 3–4% higher DNA content (Johnson and Clarke 1988; Garner 2006). Another method includes immunology sexing based on the H-Y antigen in the plasma membrane (Bradley 1989); however, this reduces the motility of sperm and the conception rate due to the long processing time (Xie *et al.* 2020).

Another example where there are clear cost, efficiency and ethical benefits to successful sex identification and manipulation is the poultry breeding and hatchery industry. Again, we observe a 50% efficiency cost of equal sex ratios in offspring. Egg production requires female poultry, while meat production generally favours male poultry. In both industries, the practice of culling day-old chicks of the undesired sex is standard (e.g. ~7 billion male chicks or ~40 million female ducklings per year globally). The sex of chicks is determined either by cloacal examination or, in some breeds, the development of sex-linked plumage traits. The culling of hatchlings in the poultry industry raises many ethical questions and public concerns (Krautwald-Junghanns *et al.* 2018). Despite there being compelling incentives for the creation of monosex poultry lines, this remains an unsolved technical challenge, unlike in fish aquaculture (see Box 8.1; e.g. Curzon *et al.* 2021). Sex-reversal of genotypically male chickens to produce reproductive egg-laying hens is rare to non-existent and is not viable at scale. Chickens possess cell-autonomous sex (Zhao *et al.* 2010), which presents particular challenges for achieving sex reversal that endures beyond embryonic manipulations. Genetic sexing of chicken embryos may improve animal welfare and productivity. Novel *in ovo* sexing methods have been developed based on hormone measurement, DNA analysis and spectroscopy, thus eliminating the need to incubate the male eggs (Porat *et al.* 2011; Weissmann *et al.* 2013; Galli *et al.* 2017). PCR-based tests, developed from sex-linked markers, have improved the efficiency of female-only egg-laying stocks (Porat *et al.* 2011; Chen *et al.* 2012; Clinton *et al.* 2016). However, these sexing techniques can be time consuming and require a laboratory setup. Therefore, an *in vivo* method has been suggested which adds the green fluorescent protein (GFP) gene to the mother's Z-chromosome. This genetic modification facilitates the detection of male eggs (ZZ) through expression of this GFP in male, but not in female, offspring (Doran *et al.* 2017). While this method is high throughput, it requires the production of genetically modified organisms which causes other public concerns.

Studying monomorphic life stages

Similar to the challenge of sexual monomorphism in behavioural ecology, sex identification remains difficult when studying the embryological development of most vertebrates. Indeed, during the bipotential phase of gonad differentiation, there are no observable structural differences between females and males. The study of embryogenesis underpins numerous research applications, from human disease and development to animal husbandry and assisted reproductive technologies. Thus, the ability to balance experimental design and implement appropriate controls in developmental biology is desirable for methodological, ethical and financial reasons. A similar issue is that organisms that are sexually dimorphic as adults are not always dimorphic as juveniles. Even though gonad differentiation occurs early in development, some species may exhibit external characteristics of the opposite sex until as late as sexual maturity (Neaves *et al.* 2006; Martínez-Torres *et al.* 2015; Whiteley *et al.* 2018). In these cases, molecular sex markers are the only way to determine whether an individual is female or male without lethal sampling and inspecting gonad morphology.

Veterinary medicine

There is often a medical need to identify the sex of domestically kept pets, to ensure their health (short or long term), make breeding recommendations and provide suitable behavioural enrichment conditions. The following veterinary treatments require sex identification to make clinical or breeding recommendations: 1) preventing and treating disorders of the reproductive system (Lumeij 1997; Harr 2002; Eatwell *et al.* 2014), 2) interpreting biochemical blood analytes, 3) preventing accidental mating between relatives, 4) preventing combat in cohabitated individuals, 5) selecting successful male-female mating pairs, 6) advising on sex-associated disease risk (Tamukai *et al.* 2011). The clinical need for sex identification methods is in addition to the natural curiosity that pet owners tend to have about the sex of their companion for naming purposes. For traditional companion animals (e.g. cats, dogs and other mammalian species) sex identification is a relatively simple matter of visual inspection. However, the recent increased uptake of exotic and unusual pet species means that sometimes the task is not so simple.

Avian pets are one of the most common species where sex identification is in high demand. Parrots are the most popular companion bird in Australia, many of which are not obviously sexually dimorphic. Typical methods employed for phenotypic sex identification in avian species include a visual assessment of sexual dimorphism, imaging such as coelomic rigid endoscopy, and radiographs, ultrasound, or computed tomography. Transcoelomic endoscopy requires a general anaesthetic and a surgical approach bringing increased risk to the patient and considerable cost. Endoscopy also requires specialised equipment and specially trained veterinarians. Ultrasound and CT are of limited use in young or small avian species. These procedures carry a risk to the animal (stress from handling, anaesthetic/radiation exposure), are expensive procedures and ultimately may not provide a definitive result. This is why commercial ventures now exist that provide avian molecular sex identification as a service either direct to the consumer or ordered through veterinary practices. Molecular sex identification carries very minimal risk to pet birds because the PCR amplification tests can be conducted using almost non-invasive sampling (e.g. a drop of blood or a blood feather). It is also the safest method to conduct on pre-reproductive age juveniles.

Equivalent commercial molecular sex identification capacity exists for a small minority of the reptiles, amphibians and fish that increasingly present to general veterinary practice. Commercial testing is currently available for colubrid snakes, cobras, kraits, pitvipers and true vipers. In the absence of molecular tests, hobbyists and breeders will often resort to performing physical (and sometimes surgical) identification themselves, incentivised by the higher price commanded for guaranteed 'breeding pairs'. Unfortunately, this means that sex identification injuries often present to the clinic such as spinal damage, cloacal prolapse and hemipenal trauma resulting in abscessation, prolapse or necrosis of the organ and eventual morbidity to the animal. Accessible molecular sex identification for these (and other) pet species would reduce the risk of injury and infection, reduce procedure costs to owners, increase the accuracy of sex identification and vacate time for veterinarians to allocate to more critical cases, thus contributing to general improved animal health and well-being.

Detecting and monitoring sex reversal

As outlined briefly above, there is usually a very close functional relationship between genetic sex and phenotypic sex, however the relationship is not always perfect. There are occasions when mismatches occur between genetic sex and phenotypic sex. This discordance can result from an environmental override of genetic sex determination, which occurs naturally in response to temperature in several squamates (Van Dyke et al. 2021; Whiteley et al. 2021), or alternatively, in response to anthropogenic contamination or pollutants (Lange et al. 2020; Nemesházi et al. 2020), or because of mutational processes (e.g. sex-determining region Y protein [SRY] mutants; Délot and Vilain 2018). There is an inherent assumption in any molecular test that

genetic and phenotypic sex are equivalent, but practitioners need to be very careful to test this assumption and ensure that undetected processes are not disrupting the accuracy of the test.

SEX DETERMINATION

Knowledge of the mode of sex determination is a critical aspect of developing sex identification markers. Female and male sexual development commences during embryogenesis. A developmental event occurs that pushes the embryo onto a trajectory that locks in the gene regulatory cascade that is required for it to develop either as a male or a female. This process is called sex determination. The initial factor that triggers sex determination can be genetic (genetic sex determination, GSD) or an external environmental factor such as temperature, pH, light exposure, or social hierarchies (environmental sex determination, ESD). Genetic sex determining factors or genes typically reside on the sex chromosomes; the alternative of polygenic sex determination, whereby differential combined expression of multiple independently segregating genes determine sex, is often considered transitory (Schartl et al. 2023). Examples of sex determining genes include the male-specific gene SRY in most mammals, dosage-based doublesex and Mab-3 related transcription factor 1 (DMRT1) in most birds, variants of anti-Müllerian hormone (AMH) in some fish, and many others. This chapter does not address the details of molecular sex determination. These regulatory processes are diverse, complex and labile across evolutionary time. See other reviews for current information on sex determination mechanisms (Capel 2017; Nagahama et al. 2021; Stöck et al. 2021).

THE FORMATION OF SEX CHROMOSOMES AND SEX-LINKED SEQUENCE

Sex chromosomes are thought to evolve from an ancestral autosomal pair of chromosomes when a gene on those chromosomes captures the process of sex determination, that is, comes to direct the regulatory processes leading to female or male sexual fate (Marshall Graves and Shetty 2001; Bachtrog et al. 2014). Capture of the master sex determining role is often achieved by a gene from the broader conserved vertebrate regulatory network that coordinates the process of sexual differentiation later in development. Many of these genes have potential to reverse sex under mutational influence. After the capture of a new master sex determining gene, a series of concurrent and consequential changes occur. Suppression of recombination in the chromosomal region with the novel sex determining gene occurs to cement the distinction between the male and female chromosomal complements (XX vs. XY or ZZ vs. ZW). This **non-recombining region** expands in stages along the sex chromosomes as new sexually antagonistic genes are recruited, those with alleles that are advantageous to the heterogametic sex and that incur a cost or are otherwise disadvantageous to the **homogametic** sex. Loss of recombination can result in accumulation of deleterious mutations that would otherwise be purged if there was recombination. Loss of gene function on the Y or W chromosome which, combined with the proliferation of repetitive sequence, leads to heterochromatinisation and often degeneration of the Y or W. Loss of function of alleles or loss of the locus altogether on the Y or W results in dosage imbalance in the heterogametic sex, which needs to be accommodated by mechanisms of dosage compensation. We need to understand these processes of sex chromosome evolution if we are to devise strategies to identify sex-linked markers.

The progressive degeneration of the Y or W chromosomes, the proliferation of repetitive sequence, and the accumulation of mutations that would otherwise be purged in the presence of recombination provide fodder for techniques to detect sex-linked markers (Charlesworth and Charlesworth 2020). Such markers are quite diverse. They include the recruitment of a male specific gene on the Y which has no clear homologue on the X and so is an abundant source of sex-linked sequence. Loss of a gene from the Y, leads to its presence in double copy number in the XX females and single copy in the XY males. In this case, there are not necessarily any sex-specific markers to be found, the difference lying instead in copy number signature. The sex-linked markers may establish on sequence that subsequently is involved in proliferation on the Y chromosome, such that there are multiple copies each embedded in a different context, and at different distances from the non-recombining region. Such markers have a common origin but can vary in sequence depending upon recombination, mutation and drift. Sex-linked and sex-specific markers can be in the form of SNPs, indels, microsatellites within exons or introns of coding genes or within promoter or enhancer regions, or in regions with no identifiable function. All can be a useful for sex identification marker development. These differences between species in the mode and degree of differentiation between the sexes can make genetic sex identification challenging and the most appropriate approach to detecting and characterising sex-specific sequence is typically species-specific.

GENOMIC APPROACHES TO CHARACTERISE SEX CHROMOSOMES AND IDENTIFY SEX-LINKED SEQUENCE

To develop molecular sex-identification markers, researchers first must characterise genetic differences between the sexes. There is a huge body of literature discussing ways to achieve this (Palmer *et al.* 2019). We have broadly categorised methodologies into nine analytical themes that share similarities in the basis of the approach (Table 8.1). The most effective strategies combine multiple analytical approaches to characterise sex chromosome sequence, but here we discuss each analytical theme separately to delineate their relative strengths and weaknesses. This will allow researchers to decide upon the best combination of analyses to suit species-specific sex chromosome evolutionary histories and genomic properties (Table 8.2). Successful hybrid approaches allow researchers to either validate the results independently (reducing the false discovery rate) or facilitate information from one technique to seed investigations using another (Cortez *et al.* 2014; Koyama *et al.* 2019; Cornejo-Paramo *et al.* 2020). Bioinformatic approaches to characterise sex chromosome sequence is a rapidly evolving research area with new tools and software available all the time. For example, a recent hybrid approach (SexFindR) has broad applicability, with the capacity to identify both large sections of highly differentiated sex chromosome sequence and very small differences up to single-base resolution (Grayson *et al.* 2022).

Cytogenetic differencing and mapping

Cytogenetic approaches were among the first techniques applied to identify sex chromosomes (Stevens 1905). Since Nettie Stevens's seminal discovery that inheritance of the Y chromosome initiated male development, modern staining techniques for nucleic acids, increased resolution of microscopy and the integration of molecular resources, such as recombinant genomic libraries have increased the power of cytogenetic approaches. Cytogenetic approaches were particularly popular prior to the availability of high-throughput and affordable next generation sequencing. Cytogenetic approaches remain a powerful method to associate anonymous sequence to specific chromosomes (including sex chromosomes). Cytogenetic techniques also remain the only way to directly visualise chromosomes and inspect chromosome morphology. However, the time, cost, and considerable technical expertise required to successfully deploy these methods means that they are not in as regular use currently. An additional barrier to the use of cytogenetic methods is the need for cell lines or live tissue cultures to capture and fix metaphase cells. For some organisms, owing to rarity or remoteness of collection sites, or because of fundamental challenges in establishing cell lines, it can be infeasible or impossible to bring viable tissue back to the lab and to establish cultures. For example, cell cultures from sharks are notoriously difficult to establish because of a high urea and NaCl content in the blood (Uno *et al.* 2020).

Direct sex chromosome sequencing

Physically isolating and direct sequencing of the heteromorphic sex chromosome generates high-confidence sex-chromosome derived sequences. However, this approach can be very technically challenging and dependent on how differentiated the sex chromosomes are. In mammals the highly degenerate small Y chromosome has been successfully isolated by flow sorting, which takes advantage of the disparate physical size of the Y compared to the X and autosomal chromosomes. For example, the first human Y chromosome of African descent was sequenced using long-read Oxford Nanopore sequencing of flow-sorted Y chromosome-enriched unamplified DNA template (Kuderna *et al.* 2019). The advent of long read sequencing has improved both the feasibility and accuracy of this approach, which prior to long read technologies required the use of large-insert recombinant libraries and painstaking manual curation, as was performed for the original Human Y chromosome assembly (Skaletsky *et al.* 2003). Challenges faced by chromosome flow sorting include the difficulty of separating small Y chromosomes from the fraction of cellular debris during flow sorting. The method also fails when the heterogametic sex chromosome is a similar size to one or more other autosomes. An alternative approach is to physically isolate single Y or W chromosomes via microdissection, apply whole genome amplification techniques and directly sequence this material (Ezaz *et al.* 2013; Zhu *et al.* 2022). Micro-dissecting the X or Z chromosome is also important for the identification of sequence differences useful in establishing genetic sex tests, but this can be particularly challenging because the X and Z are not subject to degeneration and heterochromatinisation and so can be difficult to distinguish from autosomes. This is particularly the case where the sex chromosome pair is one among many microchromosomes, a characteristic feature of avian and reptile karyotypes.

Comparative genomic approaches and recombinant genomic library screening

Comparative genomic approaches use existing gene content information for one species and apply it to another species to discover novel sex chromosome sequence. This approach boasted early success in defining the sequence variation, gene content, copy number and structure of mammalian Y chromosomes (Raudsepp *et al.* 2004; Murphy *et al.* 2006; Perelman *et al.* 2011; Cortez *et al.* 2014; Bidon *et al.* 2015). For example, Murtagh *et al.* (2012) doubled the number of marsupial Y chromosome genes identified at the time, by developing a suite of Y-specific PCR loci for the five genes known to exist on both the tammar wallaby and human Y chromosome. They then used conserved, invariant regions as an anchor point to screen a male bacterial artificial chromosome (BAC) library, then identify and sequence new Y-specific BACs. This approach is sometimes referred to as 'genome walking'. Genome walking can also be applied in the absence of recombinant large insert libraries, using short sex-linked markers extended by mapping to draft genome assembly contigs (Liu *et al.* 2018).

The accuracy of comparative approaches improves if you combine other sources of information and genomic resources. For example, Murtagh also used flow-sorted Y-enriched DNA as a BAC probe and applied the biological knowledge that mammalian Y chromosomes tend to be enriched for genes with testis-specific expression to narrow the number of candidate BACs for full sequencing efforts. While comparative approaches can be very successful in taxa with relatively stable sex chromosomes, the rapid turnover of sex chromosomes observed in other taxa (like many fish, amphibian, and squamate clades) means it can be a risky approach. Additionally, the dynamic process of novel gene acquisition and gene loss via degeneration in non-recombining regions means that the assumption of cross-species homology is by no means guaranteed, even in closely related species.

Pedigree-reliant approaches

Linkage group mapping uses a statistical framework to identify regions of the genome that show very low rates of recombination, which often corresponds to the non-recombining region of the Y or W chromosome (Palmer *et al.* 2019). The challenge with linkage mapping approaches is that very large sample sizes with an accurately known pedigree are required. It is typical for experiments to require hundreds to thousands of progeny from multiple independent families to accurately estimate genome-wide recombination rates. It is these requirements that mean linkage mapping tends to be restricted to plants, insects and other easily bred, and reproductively prolific species (Goldberg *et al.* 2010; Charlesworth 2018).

Segregation analyses take advantage of the different patterns of inheritance that occur in X and Y (or Z and W) alleles. Specifically, Y-linked alleles are exclusively paternally inherited (father to son) and X-linked alleles are passed from mother to son and/or father to daughter. Using the known relationships between the input parents and offspring, the program SEX-DETector assigns a likelihood to each SNP in the dataset of being in one of three states: autosomal, X-linked with a Y-linked ortholog (X/Y pair) and those without (X-hemizygous) (Muyle et al. 2016). Once assigned a mode of inheritance, SNPs can be mapped to a reference genome to assign sequence to the sex chromosomes.

Reduced representation methods

A popular approach to discover sex markers uses restriction enzymes (such as *EcoRI*, *MspI*, *PstI*, and *SphI*) to reduce the representation and complexity of whole genomes (e.g. Gamble 2016; Drinan et al. 2018; Devloo-Delva et al. 2022). In the past, randomly amplified polymorphic DNA (RAPD) or amplified fragment length polymorphisms (AFLP) were screened for an association to sex, but these methods had a low success rate and are labour-intensive (Quinn et al. 2009; Lee et al. 2011). Currently, approaches such as RAD-seq (restriction site-associated DNA sequencing), ddRAD-Seq (double digest RAD-seq), genotyping-by-sequencing (GBS), or DArT-seq are widely used because they are high throughput and cost-effective (Jaccoud et al. 2001; Baird et al. 2008; Elshire et al. 2011; Kilian et al. 2012; Peterson et al. 2012). See Campbell et al. (2018) for an overview of available techniques. Large sample sizes and high read depths allow for robust detection of sex-linked markers. However, these different techniques target only a small percentage of the whole genome (typically 5–10%). Thus, failure to identify sex-linked sequences does not necessarily suggest that sex chromosomes are absent. This bias is especially relevant for species with homomorphic sex chromosomes that are not substantially differentiated. Despite this limitation, reduced representation methods can still be successful with complex sex chromosome systems, such as those observed in monotremes (Keating et al. 2022).

Many analytical frameworks exist to identify sex-linked sequences from reduced-representation data by exploring distinct patterns of coverage and **heterozygosity** (e.g. Fowler and Buonaccorsi 2016; Jeffries et al. 2018; Hu et al. 2019; Lange et al. 2020). Here, the appropriate method to identify sex-linked sequences or SNPs depends on the sex-determination system (Palmer et al. 2019). In species with an XX/XY system, unique Y-linked sequences will be present only in males whereas the opposite pattern is expected in

ZZ /ZW systems (Trenkel et al. 2020; Feron et al. 2021; Devloo-Delva et al. 2022). Of course, SNP differences between the XX and XY (or ZZ and ZW) individuals can arise from autosomal and X or Z polymorphisms, so particular care needs to be taken to ensure sufficient individuals are screened to constrain the likelihood of false-positives. Statistical analyses need to admit the possibility of linkage owing either to the large number of markers screened or the presence of haploblocks. It is advisable to establish panels of validated sex markers to control for the possibility of low frequency recombination in any one marker misleading sex identification. For example, seven markers were developed for the Australian eastern three-lined skink *Bassiana duperreyi* to manage the possibility that any one of them might be subject to low level recombination (Dissanayake et al. 2020). These markers proved concordant in subsequent studies where they were applied (Dissanayake et al. 2021a, b). Another example, where multiple marker types increase the confidence of sex assignment, is the Pacific halibut where both Z-linked and W-specific sex-linked sequences were identified (Drinan et al. 2018). When read depth information per marker is available, the read depth for X-linked markers should be double in females (Devloo-Delva et al. 2022). Generally, read-depth methods require large sample sizes (n = 20–100 individuals) to acquire statistical significance, but where sample sizes are modest, Bayesian inference methods with additional prior information can improve the marker classification (Gautier 2014).

Genome subtraction

Genome subtraction can be conducted using either an *in vitro* approach using the annealing properties of double stranded DNA or computationally *in silico* using shotgun whole sequencing read data. The laboratory-based *in vitro* approach suppression subtractive analysis (Diatchenko et al. 1996) is usually referred to as representational difference analysis (RDA). Applied to naked genomic DNA, the method relies on PCR to preferentially amplify non-homologous DNA regions between digested fragments from XX and XY samples. 'Tester' DNA contains a sequence of interest, that is, unique Y sequence, that is non-homologous to the 'driver' DNA of the XX individual. When the two are mixed, the driver sequence is added in excess to tester to anneal to homologous DNA fragments from the tester sample. This blocks PCR amplification and there is no increase in homologous fragments. Fragments that are different between the two samples will not anneal to a complementary counterpart and will be amplified by PCR. As more cycles of RDA are performed, the pool of unique sequence fragment copies will grow exponentially whereas fragments found in both samples, the XX and XY samples, will be proportionally eliminated. Various refinements to this technique have been developed (Luo *et al.* 1999), but it remains technically challenging when applied to genomic DNA and is capable of driving the most meticulous researcher to leave science.

An alternative is to undertake genome subtraction *in silico* drawing upon recent techniques for accurately and comprehensively sequencing genomes (Dissanayake *et al.* 2020). By this approach, two sets of genome sequences or 'reads', one for an XX individual and one for an XY individual, are generated using one of the next-generation sequencing platforms (e.g. Illumina short-reads). These reads are then decomposed into k-mers of odd-integer length (to eliminate palindromic sequence). The **k-mer** sets are a highly redundant but unique representation of each genome. A subset of k-mers present in the XY set but not in the XX set are chosen to enrich for Y-specific sequence. The Y-enriched set of k-mers is then reassembled into contigs using a stringent inchworm assembler (Dissanayake *et al.* 2020) to provide a basis for identifying primers for a PCR sex test which can then be validated.

A challenge with this approach is that it will identify both Y-specific sequence and interindividual polymorphisms that occur between the XX individual and the XY individual. Such autosomal polymorphisms can result in a large number of false-positives, that is, contigs that are distinct between the two focal individuals, but that fail when applied to the panel of 20 males and 20 females. To avoid this high false-positive rate, one can subtract multiple XX individuals from the focal XY individual. Alternatively, the false-positive rate can be reduced by selecting samples from highly inbred populations (e.g. invasive populations with very few founders) or captive bred lines.

Sequencing read depth comparisons

When sex chromosomes are sufficiently diverged, the copy number of regions on the X and Y (or Z and W) chromosomes can differ. In non-recombining regions, females are expected to have double the read depth for X-chromosome regions and males are expected to have half the read depth of females, females having only one X, or vice versa for a ZW/ZZ system (Vicoso *et al.* 2013; Vicoso and Bachtrog 2015; Müller *et al.* 2020; Sigeman *et al.* 2022). This method is widely used because it can be applied with a few individuals (with associated risks of high false-positive rate) and can be performed on samples that are pooled by sex (Nursyifa *et al.* 2021). Additionally, examination of SNP density in the sex-specific

regions can provide information on the age of sex-chromosomes and synteny between species (Sigeman *et al.* 2022). However, the analysis is generally performed on **whole genome sequencing (WGS)** data with high average read depth (>20×; Vicoso and Bachtrog 2015; Palmer *et al.* 2019). Obtaining such data is still expensive and requires high DNA quality and quantity from accurately sexed animals, which can be problematic for rare species or where sampling occurs in remote locations. Moreover, for comparing read depth between sexes, a good-quality reference genome (for a closely related species) is needed to accurately map sequencing reads. Mapping errors, owing to X-Y (or Z-W) orthology or repeated regions on sex chromosomes, can bias the observed coverage patterns (Palmer *et al.* 2019; Nursyifa *et al.* 2021). Any markers developed using this technique need to be validated against a panel of known sex individuals from across the range for which the markers are to be applied.

Genome-transcriptome assisted methods

The advent of affordable shotgun genome and transcriptome sequencing has facilitated an array of approaches that use combinations of these two data types to characterise sex chromosomes (Cortez *et al.* 2014). Such a combination of genomic sequence data and transcriptomic data is essential because many genes will become sex specific in expression well after sex determination and as the consequential **sex differentiation** process plays out. A common approach is to use the property of sex-specific and/or tissue-specific expression of Y or W genes to map sequence to the sex chromosomes. For example, Ayers *et al.* (2013), used the genome assembly of a male chicken (ZZ) to map sex-specific *de novo* assembled transcripts to the draft Z chromosome reference. This allowed them to define and differentiate W gene sequences from their Z gametologue sequences. These Z/W variable sites are the necessary information to generate sex identification tests. Other approaches are similar to subtraction analyses. Here, RNA-seq reads from the heterogametic sex are mapped to a homogametic refence genome, and unmapped reads are investigated as potential sex-limited regions (Cortez *et al.* 2014). Expression-based approaches tend to be most successful in species with sufficiently differentiated sex chromosomes that sex-specificity among RNA-seq reads is expected and/or there has been novel acquisition of genes to the Y or W chromosome (Palmer *et al.* 2019).

de novo whole genome sequencing and haplotype phasing

The revolution in high-throughput next generation sequencing is still progressing rapidly, and likely to transform our

Table 8.1. Analytical approaches and molecular methodologies to identify sex chromosome sequence which you can use as a template to develop sex identification markers. This table groups approaches thematically and provides examples for each but is not an exhaustive list.

Approaches and methodologies	Basis of the approach	Pros/Cons	Cost	Technical difficulty	Example references and software
1. Cytogenetic differencing and mapping					
Comparative Genomic Hybridisation	The application of labelled male of female DNA to chromosome spreads of the opposite sex, to highlight regions of the genome that differ between males and females.	Very labour intensive, requires specialised skills and laboratory equipment, low throughput	Moderate	High	(Traut et al. 2001; Wang et al. 2015)
Random repeat/microsatellite motif mapping	Identifies Y or W sex chromosomes if they are highly enriched repetitive elements and retroviral insertions.	Random selection of motifs is hit or miss, unless you complement it with a sequencing-based method to characterise sex-specific repeats.	Moderate	High	(Ezaz et al. 2013; Matsubara et al. 2016)
C- Banding	Identifies heterochromatin on chromosomes.	Sex chromosomes not necessarily identifiable using this technique.	Moderate	High	(Ezaz, Quinn, et al. 2009)
2. Direct sex chromosome sequencing					
Sex chromosome microdissection	The heterogametic sex chromosome is physically isolated either with a very fine probe or laser-microdissection. The single chromosome is whole genome amplified and sequenced.	Very challenging technically. Very low-input material results in low complexity libraries and potential biases arise during amplification of a single molecule.	High	High	(Ezaz et al. 2013; Matsubara et al. 2016; Kuderna et al. 2019; Zhu et al. 2022)
Sex chromosome flow sorting	Relies on the size of the sex chromosomes to physically separate them from the rest of the genome.	Difficult to isolate the W or Y in species with either small sex chromosomes or poorly differentiated sex chromosomes.	High	High	(Sankovic et al. 2006)
3. Comparative genomic approaches and recombinant genomic library screening					
Cross-species probes/PCR amplification	Requires characterised sex chromosomes in at least one target species. Assumes homology of sex chromosomes across distantly related taxa.	Less successful in rapidly evolving or divergent sex chromosome systems. Risky because it is not targeted to detect sex differences.	Low	Moderate	(Bidon et al. 2015)
BAC mapping and sequencing	Uses bacterial artificial constructs to map regions to sex chromosomes.	Labour intensive, requires screening of large BAC libraries to identify sex chromosome specific sequences, low throughput	High	High	(Sankovic et al. 2006; Ezaz, Moritz, et al. 2009; Quinn et al. 2010; Ayers et al. 2013)
4. Pedigree-reliant approaches					
Linkage group mapping	Identifies areas of low recombination in the genome that might be the non-recombining region.	Requires known pedigree and very large sample size. May not work well in species with young sex chromosome at the early stages of recombination inhibition.	High	High	(Tao et al. 2020; Ayllon et al. 2020)
Segregation analysis	Infers sex-linked genes using patterns of allelic segregation.	Requires data from parents and offspring, sensitive to pipeline parameters.	Moderate	Moderate	SEX-DETector (Muyle et al. 2016)
5. Reduced representation methods					
RAPDs (randomly amplified polymorphic DNA)	Genome complexity reduction using short synthetic primers. Then identification of sex-specific amplified fragments.	No longer a recommended approach due to low reproducibility. Generates anonymous loci.	Low	Low	(Viñas et al. 2012; Sun et al. 2014)

Approaches and methodologies	Basis of the approach	Pros/Cons	Cost	Technical difficulty	Example references and software
AFLPs (amplified fragment length polymorphisms)	Genome complexity reduction via selective PCR amplification of restriction fragments from a total digest of genomic DNA. Then identification of sex-specific amplified fragments.	Less informative than sequencing-based approaches. Generates anonymous loci.	Low	Low	(Quinn et al. 2009; Lee et al. 2011)
RAD-seq	Genome complexity reduction via RE single digest coupled with sonication and then the identification of alleles that are sex-specific.	Fast turnaround. Can screen large numbers of individuals. But only surveying a small portion of the genome (typically 5–10%). Problematic for small sex chromosomes, especially repetitive ones.	Low per sample; but many samples required	Low	(Peterson et al. 2012; Fowler and Buonaccorsi 2016; Brelsford et al. 2017; Gamble et al. 2017)
DArT-seq / ddRAD-seq	Genome complexity reduction via RE double digest and then the identification of alleles that are sex-specific.	Fast turnaround. Can screen large numbers of individuals. But only surveying a small portion of the genome (typically 5–10%). Problematic for small sex chromosomes, especially repetitive ones.	Low per sample; but many samples required	Low	(Kilian et al. 2012; Lambert et al. 2016; Hill et al. 2018)
Sex-linked pattern analysis from fastq files or SNP genotype calls	Investigates contrasting heterozygosity and coverage patterns between sexes.	Existing SNP datasets can be combined and re-analysed for comparative studies. Yet, partial genome coverage and homomorphic sex chromosomes can yield false-negative results.	Low if utilising existing data	Low	(Gamble 2016; Feron et al. 2021; Devloo-Delva et al. 2022)
F_{ST}-based approaches	Identifies allelic differences between sexes (e.g. via F_{ST} and outlier detection) to identify an association with sexual phenotype.	Able to identify sex-linked markers where sex-determining genes located on multiple chromosomes. However, F_{ST}-based methods can yield false-positive/negative results due to technical error (e.g. genotyping error) or bias in sample schemes (e.g. population structure).	Low per sample; but many samples required	Low	(Benestan et al. 2017; Drinan et al. 2018; Dixon et al. 2019; Trenkel et al. 2020)
Bayesian classification	Model-based approach that accounts for differences in allele frequencies due to distinct demographic histories and genotyping errors.	Provides higher confidence in the identified markers, even at relatively low sample sizes (n>20). By accounting for genotyping error the model can combine data from different genotyping platforms.	Low per sample; but many samples required	Low	(Gautier 2014)
6. Genome subtraction					
Sequencing-based in silico subtraction and re-assembly	Computational approach to identify sex specific k-mers that are then re-assembled to form larger sex-specific contigs.	Reference genome free. Only requires low coverage sequencing (<10x). Can be conducted with a low number of individuals.	Moderate	Low	(Cornejo-Paramo et al. 2020; Dissanayake et al. 2020)
Subtraction to identify sex-specific repetitive motifs	After a genome subtraction, the sex-specific Kmer frequency distribution is plotted and inspected to identify very high frequency sequence motifs.	A bioinformatic approach to assist the selection of motifs for cytogenetic repeat mapping.	Moderate	Low	Arthur Georges - unpublished

Approaches and methodologies	Basis of the approach	Pros/Cons	Cost	Technical difficulty	Example references and software
in vitro genome subtraction and sequencing	A lab-based approach that uses the annealing properties of DNA from different sexes followed by rounds of PCR amplification to amplify sex-specific sequence.	PCR-bias towards sex-linked repetitive elements can swamp the signal and leave very few reads containing gene-rich single-copy regions.	Low	High	(Diatchenko *et al.* 1996; Luo *et al.* 1999)
7. Sequencing read depth comparisons					
Read depth ratios	Looks for hemizygous regions by comparing read-depths of reciprocally mapped reads.	Sequencing at relatively high read depth (>20×) is needed. Requires a good-quality reference genome and is sensitive to read-mapping algorithm parameters.	High	Moderate	(Chen *et al.* 2014; Wu *et al.* 2021; Nursyifa *et al.* 2021
Chromosome quotient	A variation of the read coverage ratio method that identifies the equidistant point between the peaks of the read distributions from female and male low coverage sequencing.	Can use lower coverage sequencing (>5×) at Y-chromosome regions. Reduces the noise from mapping algorithms, but still requires a good-quality reference genome.	Moderate	Moderate	Reviewed in (Palmer *et al.* 2019) Original reference (Hall *et al.* 2013)
8. Genome-transcriptome assisted methods					
Opposite sex RNA-seq mapping	Mapping transcriptome reads to a reference genome of the same sex to identify either unmapped regions or hemizygous regions.	Requires reference genome of known sex. Only assesses coding regions of the sex chromosomes. Samples need to be from gonad tissues.	Moderate	Moderate	(Ayers *et al.* 2013)
Pool-seq	Many individuals are grouped by sex and sequenced as two DNA or RNA samples. Male and female pools are then mapped to a reference to identify either unmapped regions or hemizygous regions.	Requires reference genome. Susceptible to biases from sex reversed individuals. Best used for species without environmentally sensitive sex determination.	Low - Moderate	Moderate	(Adolfi *et al.* 2021; Kuhl *et al.* 2021)
9. *de novo* whole genome sequencing and haplotype phasing					
Haplotype reconstruction	*De novo* assembly of a whole genome of the heterogametic sex, with long read sequencing at sufficient coverage to assemble and phase both sex chromosome haplotypes.	Very costly and computationally expensive. Over-kill if only short sex markers are required for the application.	Very high	High	(Xue *et al.* 2021)

approaches to identifying sex-specific sequence. In particular, the advent of long-read sequencing technology (e.g. PacBio HiFi, Oxford Nanopore Technology, BGI srLTR) and chromatin conformation capture sequencing technology (e.g. Hi-C, DoveTail) has overcome many challenges of *de novo* assembling sex chromosomes. Short-read assembly algorithms are not able to disambiguate regions of high sex chromosome homology, extensive tracts of repetitive elements and mega-base long high sequence-identity palindromes (Rozen *et al.* 2003; Skaletsky *et al.* 2003; Katsura *et al.* 2012). It is now possible to generate high quality assemblies using PacBio HiFi sequencing as the backbone, Oxford Nanopore ultralong reads to gap fill difficult regions and scaffold the HiFi reads, and Hi-C sequencing to provide additional scaffolding including across difficult to assemble repetitive regions such as the centromeres. These techniques can be applied to single DNA strands and so deliver telomere to telomere fully **phased** haplotypes (Xue *et al.* 2021). Near complete X and Y or Z and W sequence can be obtained, with obvious benefits for those interested in the sequence differences between sex chromosomes.

A FRAMEWORK TO CHARACTERISE MOLECULAR SEX-IDENTIFICATION MARKERS

On the face of it, developing a molecular marker to identify the genotypic sex of individuals sounds like a simple task: discover sex-specific polymorphisms and screen individuals. However, it is important to recognise that there is a great diversity of sex determination modes in the animal kingdom, and this will greatly influence which analytical approaches are feasible. It is important for researchers inexperienced in the field of sex determination and sex chromosome evolution not to underestimate the complexity or the time it can take to develop robust sex markers. Here we outline a discovery framework that articulates the full process of sex marker discovery. This framework will guide decision making at all stages from articulating the necessary biological information, deciding on the sequence discovery strategy, to developing, validating, and deploying a test. The framework is a five-stage process summarised in Fig. 8.1 and described in detail below.

PLAN a strategy to discover novel sex-identification markers

It is essential when planning a strategy to develop sex-identification markers, to first assemble and use all the available *biological information* and *genomic resources* you have at your disposal (Table 8.2). Once this is collected, an informed decision can be made about which of the multitude of approaches you should employ to discover sex chromosomes and/or sex-linked sequence. However, a difficulty that regularly emerges, is that the information required to plan your approach is incomplete and the researcher will be forced to make decisions in the absence of reliable information.

First, you must consider the biology of the study organism. A factor that will greatly influence how readily a sex test can be developed, and which analytical approach is suitable, is whether the sex determination mode of the

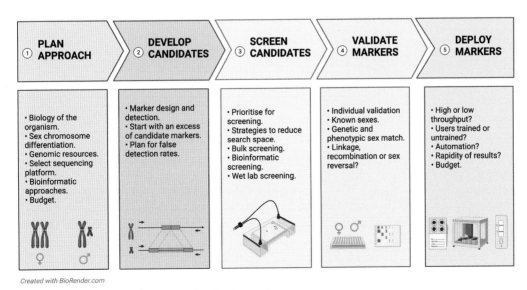

Created with BioRender.com

Fig. 8.1. Framework for the discovery of molecular sex-identification markers.

Table 8.2. The ideal but often incomplete information needed to plan a strategy to characterise sex chromosomes and sex-linked sequence.

	Planning implications	Options if information unknown or resource unavailable?
Biological and evolutionary knowledge		
Sex chromosomes present?	Informs appropriate sequencing techniques to identify sex chromosome complement and content.	1. Incubation experiments to detect the presence/absence of thermosensitive sex determination. 2. Studies of sex ratio variability in the wild. 3. Cytogenetic or karyotypic investigations.
Female or male heterogamety?	Can target discovery to the heterogametic sex.	1. Conducting analysis of sex linkage for both scenarios. This will increase the cost because it requires more individuals and computational investment.
Young/old sex chromosomes?	Young sex chromosomes require high depth sequencing approaches as they are typically not well differentiated from each other. They may not be identifiable using cytogenetic approaches (homomorphic). Old sex chromosomes with highly divergent content are easier to detect cytogenetically or with lower coverage sequencing.	1. Cytogenetic or karyotypic investigations. 2. Drawing inference from related species or lineages that have this data.
The actual and relative size of sex chromosomes?	Can facilitate physical isolation methodology if the heteromorphic sex chromosome is larger than cellular debris and a unique size compared to the rest of the karyotype.	1. Perform necessary karyotypic analysis. 2. Draw inference from related species or lineages that have this data.
Existence of microchromosomes?	Increases the difficulty of cytogenetic approaches. Will require specialist expertise.	1. Cytogenetic or karyotypic investigations. 2. Draw inference from related species or lineages that have this data.
Environmentally sensitive sex determination and the possibility of sex reversal?	Need to combine genotyping and phenotyping to ensure that both the homogametic and heterogametic sex are compared. Be very rigorous in the selection of individuals analysed.	1. Incubation experiments to detect the presence/absence of thermosensitive sex determination. 2. Studies of sex ratio variability in the wild. 3. Study the offspring sex ratios of individuals chose for sequencing and avoid individuals that do not produce 50:50. 4. Use statistical methods that are robust to a low level of sex reversal (e.g. reduced representation methods).
Rapid sex chromosome turnover?	Do not assume homology of sex determination modes and/or sex chromosomes to sister taxa.	1. Drawing inference from based on lineages that have this data.
Molecular and genomic resources		
Assembled genome/s (M/F/Unknown)	Increases the choice of methods and will increase	1. Choose reference-free methods, such as reduced representation (6.5) or subtraction approaches (6.6).
BAC library	Enables screening and/or cytogenetic FISH approaches	1. It is now possible to synthesise large custom oligonuclotide probes if one is needed for library screening. Alternatively, you could use methods that do not rely on this resource.
Cell lines	Enables cytogenetic approaches.	1. Cytogenetic approaches are possible without established cell lines e.g. short-term blood cultures.
Karyotype	Can distinguish species with highly degenerate heteromorphic sex chromosomes from ones with weakly differentiated homomorphic sex chromosomes. Can assist in establishing female/male **heterogamety**.	1. Rely on bioinformatic approaches where you can test for female/male heterogamety.

species is known (genetic sex determination [GSD]/ temperature dependent sex determination [TSD]/gene-environment interaction). It is critically important to establish that the species does indeed have sex chromosomes, prior to any work attempting to develop genotypic sex-identification markers. If the mode of sex determination is unknown, there is a variety of experimental approaches to ascertain this (Whiteley *et al.* 2021). If breeding experiments are not feasible, comparative phylogenetic methods exist to infer the likelihood of the species displaying a thermosensitive aspect to their sex determination, that could disrupt marker development. In many species, particularly amphibians, fishes and non-avian reptiles, sex can be influenced by a variety of factors and sex reversal may occur under environmental influence. See Ayllon *et al.* (2020) for a recent example of how a commonly used sex marker displays discordance with phenotypic sex in a salmonid.

After the presence of sex chromosomes is established, there are several characteristics of these sex chromosomes that you need to consider before selecting an appropriate analytical approach (Table 8.2). For example, can the sex chromosomes be distinguished using standard (G-banding) or advanced cytogenetic techniques (CGH, comparative genomic hybridisation), are you expecting the sex chromosomes to be very similar in sequence content or very different, and/or is there an environmental override that can cause sex reversal in your species?

After weighing the biological and molecular considerations, it is also important take practical considerations into account, such as: the constraints of time and money, sample volumes (high throughput or low throughput), does the test need to be deployed by non-experts. Additionally, you should also decide what the ultimate goal of the project is. For example, if your project aims to develop a simple test to identify the species' chromosomal sex, it is not necessary to sequence and assemble the whole sex chromosome. In contrast, if the project aims to characterise the gene content of the sex chromosomes and discover sex determining genes then a much higher investment of resources is required.

DEVELOP a suite of candidate markers

Developing candidate sex markers requires a characterised set of sequences associated with sex. This can be achieved by employing one or more of the sex chromosome sequence discovery approaches discussed extensively in Table 8.1. The next task is to use these sequences as a template to develop a suite of candidate sex-identification markers.

A common and cost-effective approach is to design PCR primers in regions that flank putative sex specific variation (e.g. a sex-specific insertion/deletion). By priming the reaction with sequence common to both sexes, the amplification of X or Z sequence functions as an internal PCR control band, that ensures that failed PCRs are not interpreted as a positive result for the homogametic sex. A similar style of assay can also be achieved by co-amplifying an autosomal control with Y or W specific primers in a multiplex PCR. After amplification, the result of the assay can be easily established using a range of common DNA fragment size analysis lab techniques (e.g. agarose/polyacrylamide gel electrophoresis). If you are limited to designing presence/absence style markers that only amplify in one sex (Y or W chromosome markers), the risk of PCR failure being misinterpreted as identification of the homogametic sex must be mitigated by performing additional positive control PCRs that amplify autosomal regions and/or amplifying several presence/absence loci. Another PCR-based marker development strategy involves using real-time quantitative PCR to detect differences in gene-dosage on the sex chromosomes (Rovatsos *et al.* 2014; Wiggins *et al.* 2020). However, quantitative PCR can be challenging due to the need for high accuracy to detect the difference in single versus double copy number. Technical replicates are necessary, which increase the time and cost investment. It is also best practice to use more than a single sex-linked locus to assign the sex of individuals based on this approach.

Designing assays to survey for sex-specific repeats is difficult if the flanking sequence is unknown. However, even if only the sex-specific repeat-motif is identified, this information can be used to develop chromosome-specific cytogenetic markers such as Y or W probes for use with fluorescent *in situ* hybridisation (FISH; Matsubara *et al.* 2016).

For methods that identify sex-linked SNPs, implementing a sequencing capture-array that targets and enriches for many loci simultaneously is usually the most time and cost-effective strategy that has superseded methods for typing individual SNP loci. Additionally, a SNP panel or microarray can be designed to identify sex, species, and origin of tissue samples, which is a cost-effective method for the monitoring of wildlife and international trade of species or derived products (Arenas *et al.* 2017). Alternatively, if there is a sufficiently high budget and a reference genome, it is possible to whole genome re-sequence all individuals of unknown sex at low coverage and use pipelines such as sex assignment through coverage (SATC; Nursyifa *et al.* 2021).

SCREEN many sex markers on a few individuals to assess the success of your discovery approach

After developing a suite of sex identification markers, the next stage is to screen them to ensure sex-linkage. All the methods described to characterise sex chromosome sequence (Table 8.1) are imperfect, which will result in a false discovery rate for sex identification markers that can vary considerably. Therefore, you should always initially screen many more candidate markers than you require. The biology of the organism and differentiation of the sex chromosomes will also affect the false discovery rate for marker design. For example, the same *in silico* subtraction approach was recently applied to two Australian lizards with a large difference in marker discovery success. A skink with dimorphic XY sex chromosomes had a success rate of 8% (7 markers from 92 loci screened); whereas a dragon lizard with homomorphic micro sex chromosomes failed to discover any sex-linked loci, thus had an undefined success rate of <1% (0 markers from 90 loci screened; Zhang *et al.* 2022) and instead revealed a high incidence of large polymorphic indels within wild populations. Sex is determined in the fugu fish by a single base pair difference on the sex chromosomes (Kamiya *et al.* 2012). This could easily be missed by representational approaches, buried in typically millions of autosomal SNP polymorphic variants assembled as contigs using genome subtraction, and mistaken for an infrequent read error using even the latest genome sequencing technologies. The biology of the organism matters. These studies demonstrate how the evolutionary history of sex chromosomes affects the power to detect sex differences, even when the same methods are applied. Marker screening can be a big job with a low success rate, so it is important to develop a strategy that will rapidly reduce the search-space; for example, this can be achieved through combinatorial sample pooling strategies (Dissanayake *et al.* 2020). It is also important to consider the goals of your study and prioritise your candidates for full screening. For example, you may prioritise based on the size of the putative sex chromosome contig, the presence of open reading frames or gene ortholog BLAST hits if you are searching for sex chromosome genes. During the screening process it is essential to conduct appropriate positive, negative and no-template controls for every screen. Omitting these essential quality control measures risks false detections, biased results, wasted time, effort and money.

VALIDATE sex-linkage of the few putative markers to many individuals

After you have narrowed the search space and arrived at a small number of high-confidence sex-marker loci, it is time to invest in detailed individual-based validation of the test. Initially this involves employing the test across a panel of *known* genotypic males and females (minimum 20 individuals per sex) to show that the test is consistently sex specific. From these data, researchers can establish at least a preliminary estimate of the false-positive and false-negative rates for the test and use this as criteria to prioritise the use of the most accurate markers. In addition to reporting on the accuracy of the test, it is also important to quantify reproducibility (i.e. include technical replicates) and sensitivity (i.e. minimum required DNA quality and quantity). Once the test is routinely used, it is important to continually assess the accuracy of the test and to always use male, female and no-template PCR controls. These best practises will ensure that if mutation, recombination or transposition events occur that disrupt sex-linkage, they will be detected and will not generate spurious biological inference (Georges *et al.* 2021).

DEPLOY the sex test in a research or industry setting

In many cases the molecular methodology used to screen and validate the putative sex markers will be appropriate, manageable and cost-effective enough for routine use. For example, PCR-based methods including presence/absence (Dissanayake *et al.* 2020) and size polymorphism detection (Huynen *et al.* 2002; Quinn *et al.* 2009, 2010; Keating *et al.* 2022), genomic dosage detection via quantitative real-time PCR (Rovatsos *et al.* 2014; Wiggins *et al.* 2020), or SNP-capture based arrays (Hill *et al.* 2022). However, there are also situations where how you deploy a test requires additional consideration. For example, if there is a need for a large volume of samples to be processed or if the results are needed rapidly for time-sensitive decision making or diagnostics, or perhaps both.

There are many ways to optimise and translate a successful low-throughput PCR-based test, into a more time and cost-effective methodology. Each stage of the test needs to be investigated to make efficiency gains. For example, sample collection and other downstream processes can be streamlined and standardised using FTA cards. PCR set up can be miniaturised and/or automated using robotic liquid handlers. Thus, the significant gains in time and cost efficiency that depend on how you deploy the test are worth considering. Sometimes, it is the immediacy of the sex identification result, to enable rapid decision making that is highest priority, above high-throughput sample processing. The style of test where you can go from a fresh sample to a result in a matter of minutes in any location, is usually referred to as a 'point of collection' (POC) test. However, depending on the setting and application these can also be referred to by similar names, such as 'point of care' tests in medical of veterinary science or 'point of capture' tests for ecological research. Most people would be familiar with the style of test, due to the global deployment of at home rapid antigen tests (RATs) during the COVID-19 pandemic. In addition to the immediacy of the result, the potential benefit of this style of test is that it does not require specialised laboratory equipment and can be deployed by untrained personnel or citizens. However, budget can be a major constraint due to the high cost of consumables and reagents. To enable extraction, amplification and detection of nucleic acids in a point of collection sex test requires thoughtful design and manufacture of the final test (Box 8.2).

Box 8.2: Design, implementation and examples of point of collection sex identification tests

Point of collection (POC) tests require significant additional optimisation (Centeno-Cuadros *et al.* 2017). For example, the DNA extraction method will depend upon the sample type, which can vary in their composition and the presence of inhibitors. Liquid samples are usually the easiest (e.g. blood, saliva) to transfer to a POC workflow and are readily implemented using either room temperature extractions (e.g. Alk-PEG; Chomczynski and Rymaszewski 2006) or high temperature incubations (e.g. HotSHOT; Truett *et al.* 2000).

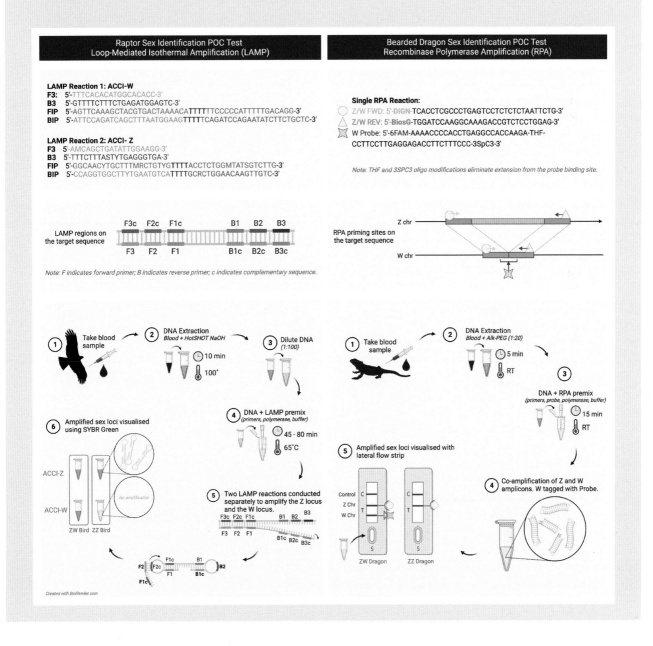

Another major difference between standard PCR and POC tests is the method of DNA amplification, which requires newly designed primers and thermal cycling regimes. There are two main **isothermal amplification** approaches: Loop-mediated isothermal amplification (LAMP) and recombinase polymerase amplification (RPA). LAMP utilises 4–6 primers to target a sex-specific locus and the primers amplify at a constant temperature continuously until the reaction is exhausted (between 55–65°C). Continuous amplification can facilitate the use of less sensitive downstream detection methods. RPA utilises two primers and a probe to target a sex-specific locus. Similar to LAMP, the enzyme and primer mix bind and continuously amplify, but do so at a much lower constant temperature (~ 37°C). The probe is designed to be 'blocked' until it binds to the target site, and upon binding is cut at the THF site by an enzyme (Endonuclease IV), enabling extension and generation of tagged, W-specific double-stranded DNA product. Significantly, RPA isothermal amplification occurs at approximately body temperature, and this has the benefit of eliminating the need for high temperature incubation equipment.

The final step of a POC test is to visualise the result by detecting the amplified DNA. A variety of detection methods exist depending on the specific application and amplification technology used. In the case of a binary presence/absence expected outcome a number of methods are available, including simply observing turbidity in the reaction tube or adding standard DNA fluorescent dyes (e.g. SYBR Safe) and then shining a hand-held UV torch on the sample. If the diagnostic test produces multiple targets, then more complex methods are required. Tagging of RPA products is achieved through designing the primers to generate double-stranded DNA product, which is specific to the target region, leading to naked-eye detection via commercially available lateral flow devices.

For applications that require both high-throughput and rapid decision making, *in vivo* test deployment is desirable. Industrial and commercial applications can have sufficient throughput of individuals to justify the extensive additional investment in research and development. For example, *in ovo* sex testing in the poultry industry is not yet deployed but is in active development, with a range of solutions in consideration, including hormone measurement, DNA analysis and spectroscopy, and even gene-editing CRISPR technology (Galli *et al.* 2017; Khwatenge and Nahashon 2021).

SEX REVERSAL: WHEN GENETIC AND PHENOTYPIC SEX DON'T MATCH

In many species, environmental conditions can override the influence of sex chromosomes to cause sex reversal during embryogenesis, while in others, sex reversal can happen during adulthood (Radder *et al.* 2008; Holleley *et al.* 2015; Todd *et al.* 2016). Sex reversal can also be induced via environmental contamination (for examples see Tubbs and McDonough 2018; Chen *et al.* 2019; Nemesházi *et al.* 2020; Kar *et al.* 2021; Mikó *et al.* 2021). By definition, sex reversal is the discordance between the sex chromosome complement and phenotypic sex of an individual, so identification of sex reversal requires the reliable definition of both the genotypic and phenotypic sex of an animal. The first step is to develop a reliable molecular-based sex test for the species, following the principles discussed in sections above. The second step requires phenotypic sex identification. Phenotypic sex identification

will be most accurate if the gonads are inspected, but for non-lethal methods phenotypic sex should be confirmed by several traits and/or reproductive status (e.g. pregnancy, gravidity, egg laying, maternity/paternity assignment).

Once sex reversal is established to occur in a species through reliable documentation of genotype-phenotype mismatch, the phenomenon can be used as a powerful indicator of environmental or anthropogenic change. In the central bearded dragon (*Pogona vitticeps*), sex reversal occurs in the wild (Holleley *et al.* 2015), but at varying rates across the species range (Castelli *et al.* 2020), showing the evolvability of sex determination systems in response to local climatic conditions. Similarly, wild populations of the eastern three-lined skink (*Bassiana duperreyi*) display sex reversal, but the rates of reversal are influenced by elevation in montane areas (Dissanayake *et al.* 2021a, b). For both species, modelling has shown the potential for the loss of the heteromorphic sex chromosome (W chromosome for *P. vitticeps* and Y chromosome for *B. duperreyi*) under certain climatic conditions. Sex chromosome loss would have profound implications for the affected populations of both species (Schwanz *et al.* 2020; Dissanayake *et al.* 2021b).

Rapid evolutionary changes can occur in captive colonies maintained for research or aquaculture. Many studies using independently maintained captive zebrafish colonies yielded inconsistent results for sex linkage to one of three different chromosomes; sex ratios were far from 1:1. Studies of wild zebrafish show an unequivocal ZW system (Wilson *et al.* 2014). Female-to-male sex reversal of fish with the ZW genotype during domestication appears to have led to the eventual loss of the Z chromosome (Wang *et al.* 2022).

The domesticated zebrafish strains are composed of only WW genotypes, some of which become females and other become fertile males. This is a case of polygenic sex determination, presumably transitory, and a wonderful opportunity to study the first steps in evolution of new sex determining genes (Schartl *et al.* 2023).

Lastly, some fish switch sexes as they grow, through a process of natural sex change. For example, Barramundi begin life as males and switch to females after reaching a threshold size (Davis 1982). Others will switch sex on receipt of social cues, such as when the dominant male in a school dies (Gemmell *et al.* 2019). In these and many other cases, genetic sex and phenotypic sex are decoupled, and the application of molecular sex markers is more complicated.

MOLECULAR MARKERS FOR PHENOTYPIC SEX

Up until now, this chapter has focused exclusively on developing molecular markers that are informative about *genetic* sex. However, there are species that do not have sex chromosomes at all. In such species, sex is typically determined during embryonic development by some environmental factor, which is broadly known as environmental sex determination (ESD). The most well-known is temperature (TSD), which is widespread in reptiles. Many fish species are sensitive to such cues in adulthood, which can trigger sex change during an individual's lifetime (e.g. in the wrasse, Todd *et al.* 2016). In these instances, sex chromosome markers are either absent or insufficient in isolation to answer applied research questions.

Species with ESD systems are the most difficult to develop a sex test for. As these species do not have sex chromosomes, there is no difference in the genome between males and females for which a sex test can be developed. Instead 'gene-expression-based' approaches will be required. It is important to note that these approaches are all based on assessing the expression of genes, or gene products (rather than sequence differences), involved in sex-specific functions, so ultimately will determine the phenotypic sex of the animal. Ideally, a gene-expression-based sex test will use a non-lethal sampling method, which currently presents considerable technical challenges.

The first epigenetic based sex test developed used a multiplex bisulfite sequencing approach to predict sex with ~90% accuracy using a panel of seven genes in the European sea bass (Anastasiadi *et al.* 2018). However, this approach requires sampling of gonadal tissue (fatal to the animal) as methylation levels are tissue specific. As epigenetic techniques continue to advance there is hope that in the future methylation differences between sexes will be detectable using samples that can be obtained non-fatally (Piferrer *et al.* 2019). Again, there are major advances in methylome sequencing on the horizon. Oxford Nanopore sequencers can distinguish methylated and non-methylated bases in its ultralong reads, and PacBio HiFi sequencing uses the dynamics of the florescence-based sequencing to achieve a similar goal. Generating such methylomes for tissues for which expression profiles differ between species will provide a basis for development of phenotypic sex markers that, once discovered, can be characterised and optimised for more targeted and cost-effective phenotypic sex tests.

Researchers studying sex in endangered sea turtles with TSD whose sex is notoriously difficult to identify at the embryonic, hatchling and subadult stages, have attempted to develop non-fatal or non-invasive techniques. These have generally been based on hormone levels, obtained either from blood or amniotic fluid in the egg, and have varying degrees of accuracy (Gross *et al.* 1995; Xia *et al.* 2011; Allen *et al.* 2015). A novel approach used immunohistochemical staining of CIRBP, a known thermosensitive gene, on gonad tissue biopsies. This technique was used to identify sex with 93–100% accuracy for loggerhead and leatherback turtles (Tezak *et al.* 2017). More recently, Western Blots for AMH isolated from the blood of turtle neonates had between 90–100% accuracy (Tezak *et al.* 2020). All of these approaches come with considerable caveats. Hormone levels, regardless of how they are detected, are influenced by age and reproductive state, affecting the accuracy of sex assignment. Antibody based approaches (like immunostaining and Western Blots) are often problematic for non-model species, as they may not cross-react if the evolutionary separation is too great.

FUTURE DIRECTIONS AND OUTSTANDING QUESTIONS

The most likely future application of large-scale sex testing initiatives is in aquaculture and agriculture. We anticipate that the driving financial and ethical incentives will see a rollout of *in vivo* sex identification approaches. As genomic technologies advance and as knowledge of the genetic and epigenetic mechanisms of sex determination expands (Deveson *et al.* 2017; Whiteley *et al.* 2022; Zhang *et al.* 2022), sexual phenotype manipulation and management has the potential to become a commonplace food production technique. However for this to occur, regulatory restrictions, policy and the governance of genetically modified organisms will also need to evolve (see recent review Xie *et al.* 2020). Once the safety and efficacy of these techniques has been established by the deployment in industry, opportunities arise for technology transfer to more high-stakes applications, such as the conservation of endangered species. It is very unlikely that sex manipulation will be incorporated as a standard assisted reproductive technology until long-term data are available on the safety of this intervention.

An advance that is on the immediate horizon and is likely to change the shape of sex determination research is the generation of chromosome-length fully phased reference genomes for the heterogametic sex, using long-read sequencing data. This technical and bioinformatic advance will accelerate sex chromosome research which has up until recently been stymied by almost exclusively homogametic reference genomes and plagued by insurmountable assembly challenges with short read sequencing and highly repetitive DNA templates. Fully characterising both sex chromosomes will rectify a genomic blind spot that the community has long experienced. Given the importance of sex chromosomes for healthy development, organogenesis and reproductive success later in life, we anticipate that the release of a new standard of completely characterised whole genomes, will facilitate medical research into sex-specific pathologies and spur evolutionary biologists to discover further complexities of sex determination and genomic novelty hidden in these unexplored regions. Further expanding on this area, the ability to simultaneously characterise genomic and epigenomic variation using single-molecule sequencing technology (e.g. PacBio HiFi and Oxford Nanopore Promethion) promises to transform our capacity to determine both genotypic and phenotypic sex.

CONCLUSION

Ultimately what we hope is for sex-identification markers to be a simple but powerful tool to advance ecological, evolutionary, and veterinary research. Sex markers have the potential to make huge practical contributions the implementation of conservation recommendations, the efficient production of more ethically farmed food, and the health and wellbeing of animals being treated by veterinarians. Now that you are armed with the evolutionary knowledge, the molecular strategies and the analytical tools to develop robust sex-identification markers, their application is only limited by your imagination. Remember that sex is a complicated and surprising trait to study; it is not immutable and evolutionary processes are actively at play. Do not be

beguiled by the seeming simplicity of a trait with two phenotypes, instead use this chapter as a roadmap to navigate the complexity.

DISCUSSION TOPICS

1. What do you see as the biggest challenge when developing a molecular sex identification test for your organism of choice and why?
   a. Use Table 8.2 to structure your argument.
   b. Use Table 8.1 to choose potential strategies.
2. What are the ethical and safety concerns regarding manipulation of sexual outcomes in populations? Guiding questions:
   a. What is the potential for adverse unintended consequences with this intervention?
   b. Does the risk-return equation change based on the intended application (e.g. conservation versus the food chain; captive versus wild populations)?
   c. Are there disadvantages to having monosex lines?
3. How does the lability of sex determination and intermediate sexual phenotypes feed into our social and biological concept of sex?

   Consider: species that undergo natural sex changes (sequential hermaphrodite life histories; Gemmell *et al.* 2019), temporary pseudo hermaphroditism during reptile embryonic development (Whiteley *et al.* 2018), intersex morphology (Real *et al.* 2020) and environmental sex reversal (Whiteley *et al.* 2021).

RESOURCES

Tree of Sex: A database of eukaryotic sex determination systems, <http://treeofsex.org/>.

ACKNOWLEDGEMENTS

Thank you to Sarah Mathews for contributions to *Pogona vitticeps* RPA test description.

REFERENCES

Aarnes SG, Hagen SB, Andreassen R, Schregel J, Knappskog PM, *et al.* (2015) Y-chromosomal testing of brown bears (*Ursus arctos*): Validation of a multiplex PCR-approach for nine STRs suitable for fecal and hair samples. *Forensic Science International. Genetics* **19**, 197–204. doi:10.1016/j.fsigen.2015.07.018

Adolfi MC, Du K, Kneitz S, Cabau C, Zahm M, *et al.* (2021) A duplicated copy of id2b is an unusual sex – determining candidate gene on the Y chromosome of arapaima (*Arapaima gigas*). *Scientific Reports* **11**, 21544. doi:10.1038/s41598-021-01066-z

Allen CD, Robbins MN, Eguchi T, Owens DW, Meylan AB, *et al.* (2015) First assessment of the sex ratio for an east pacific green sea turtle foraging aggregation: Validation and application of a testosterone ELISA. *PLoS ONE* **10**(10), 1–25. doi:10.1371/journal.pone.0138861

Anastasiadi D, Vandeputte M, Sánchez-Baizán N, Allal F, Piferrer F (2018) Dynamic epimarks in sex-related genes predict gonad phenotype in the European sea bass, a fish with mixed genetic and environmental sex determination. *Epigenetics* **13**(9), 988–1011. doi:10.1080/15592294.2018.1529504

Andrewartha H, Birch L (1954) *The Distribution and Abundance of Animals*. University of Chicago Press, Chicago.

Arenas M, Pereira F, Oliveira M, Pinto N, Lopes AM, *et al.* (2017) Forensic genetics and genomics: Much more than just a human affair. *PLoS Genetics* **13**(9), e1006960. doi:10.1371/journal.pgen.1006960

Ayers KL, Davidson NM, Demiyah D, Roeszler KN, Grützner F, *et al.* (2013) RNA sequencing reveals sexually dimorphic gene expression before gonadal differentiation in chicken and allows comprehensive annotation of the W-chromosome. *Genome Biology* **14**(3), 1–16. doi:10.1186/gb-2013-14-3-r26

Ayllon F, Solberg MF, Besnier F, Fjelldal PG, Hansen TJ, *et al.* (2020) Autosomal sdY pseudogenes explain discordances between phenotypic sex and DNA marker for sex identification in Atlantic salmon. *Frontiers in Genetics* **11**(October), 1–10. doi:10.3389/fgene.2020.544207

Bachtrog D, Mank JE, Peichel CL, Kirkpatrick M, Otto SP, *et al.* (2014) Sex determination: Why so many ways of doing it? *PLOS Biology* **12**(7), e1001899. doi:10.1371/journal.pbio.1001899

Baird NA, Etter PD, Atwood TS, Currey MC, Shiver AL, *et al.* (2008) Rapid SNP discovery and genetic mapping using sequenced RAD markers. *PloS one* **3**(10), e3376.

Barrett JH, Khamaiko N, Ferrari G, Cuevas A, Kneale C, *et al.* (2022) Walruses on the Dnieper: New evidence for the intercontinental trade of Greenlandic ivory in the Middle Ages. *Proceedings of the Royal Society B: Biological Sciences* **289**(1972), 20212773. doi:10.1098/rspb.2021.2773

Benestan L, Moore JS, Sutherland BJ, Le Luyer J, Maaroufi H, *et al.* (2017) Sex matters in massive parallel sequencing: Evidence for biases in genetic parameter estimation and investigation of sex determination systems. *Molecular Ecology* **26**(24), 6767–6783. doi:10.1111/mec.14217

Bidon T, Schreck N, Hailer F, Nilsson MA, Janke A, (2015) Genome-wide search identifies 1.9 Mb from the polar bear Y chromosome for evolutionary analyses. *Genome Biology and Evolution* **7**(7), 2010–2022. doi:10.1093/gbe/evv103

Booth W, Schuett GW, Ridgway A, Buxton DW, Castoe TA, *et al.* (2014) New insights on facultative parthenogenesis in pythons. *Biological Journal of the Linnean Society* **112**(3), 461–468. doi:10.1111/bij.12286

Boyle M, Schwanz LE, Hone J, Georges A, (2014) How do climate-linked sex ratios and dispersal limit range boundaries? *BMC Ecology* **14**(1), 19. doi:10.1186/1472-6785-14-19

Bradley MP (1989) Immunological sexing of mammalian semen: current status and future options. *Journal of Dairy Science* **72**(12), 3372–3380.

Brelsford A, Lavanchy G, Sermier R, Rausch A, Perrin N (2017) Identifying homomorphic sex chromosomes from wild-caught adults with limited genomic resources. *Molecular Ecology Resources* **17**(4), 752–759. doi:10.1111/1755-0998.12624

Budd A, Banh QQ, Domingos JA, Jerry DR (2015) Sex control in fish: Approaches, challenges and opportunities for aquaculture. *Journal of Marine Science and Engineering* **3**(2), 329–355. doi:10.3390/jmse3020329

Campbell EO, Brunet BM, Dupuis JR, Sperling FA (2018) Would an RRS by any other name sound as RAD? *Methods in Ecology and Evolution* **9**(9), 1920–1927. doi:10.1111/2041-210X.13038

Capel B (2017) Vertebrate sex determination: Evolutionary plasticity of a fundamental switch. *Nature Reviews Genetics* **18**(11), 675–689. doi:10.1038/nrg.2017.60

Castelli MA, Georges A, Cherryh C, Rosauer DF, Sarre SD, *et al.* (2020) Evolving thermal thresholds explain the distribution of temperature sex reversal in an Australian dragon lizard. *Diversity and Distributions* **27**, 427–438. doi:10.1111/ddi.13203

Centeno-Cuadros A, Abbasi I, Nathan R (2017) Sex determination in the wild: A field application of loop-mediated isothermal amplification successfully determines sex across three raptor species. *Molecular Ecology Resources* **17**(2), 153–160.

Charlesworth B, Charlesworth D (2020) Evolution: A new idea about the degeneration of Y and W chromosomes. *Current Biology* **30**(15), R871–R873. doi:10.1016/j.cub.2020.06.008

Charlesworth D (2018) The guppy sex chromosome system and the sexually antagonistic polymorphism hypothesis for Y chromosome recombination suppression. *Genes* **9**(5). doi:10.3390/genes9050264

Chen L, Lam JC, Hu C, Tsui MM, Lam PK, *et al.* (2019) Perfluorobutanesulfonate exposure skews sex ratio in fish and transgenerationally impairs reproduction. *Environmental Science and Technology* **53**(14), 8389–8397. doi:10.1021/acs.est.9b01711

Chen N, Bellott DW, Page DC, Clark AG (2012) Identification of avian W-linked contigs by short-read sequencing. *BMC Genomics* **13**(1), 2–9. doi:10.1186/1471-2164-13-183

Chen S, Zhang G, Shao C, Huang Q, Liu G, *et al.* (2014) Whole-genome sequence of a flatfish provides insights into ZW sex chromosome evolution and adaptation to a benthic lifestyle. *Nature Genetics* **46**(3), 253–260. doi:10.1038/ng.2890

Chomczynski P, Rymaszewski M (2006) Alkaline polyethylene glycol-based method for direct PCR from bacteria, eukaryotic tissue samples, and whole blood. *BioTechniques* **40**(4), 454–458. doi:10.2144/000112149

Clinton M, Nandi S, Zhao D, Olson S, Peterson P, *et al.* (2016) Real-time sexing of chicken embryos and compatibility with in ovo protocols. *Sexual Development* **10**(4), 210–216.

Cornejo-Paramo P, Dissanayake DS, Lira-Noriega A, Martínez-Pacheco ML, Acosta A, *et al.* (2020) Viviparous reptile regarded to have temperature-dependent sex determination has old XY chromosomes. *Genome Biology and Evolution* **12**(6), 924–930. doi:10.1093/gbe/evaa104/5841216

Cortez D, Marin R, Toledo-Flores D, Froidevaux L, Liechti A, *et al.* (2014) Origins and functional evolution of Y chromosomes across mammals. *Nature* **508**(7497), 488–493. doi:10.1038/nature13151

Curzon AY, Shirak A, Zak T, Dor L, Benet-Perlberg A, *et al.* (2021) All-male production by marker-assisted selection for sex determining loci of admixed *Oreochromis niloticus* and *Oreochromis aureus* stocks. *Animal Genetics* **52**(3), 361–364. doi:10.1111/age.13057

Davies N, Krebs J, West S (2012) *An Introduction to Behavioural Ecology.* 4th edn. Wiley-Blackwell, Hoboken, NJ, USA.

Davis TLO (1982) Maturity and sexuality in Barramundi, *Lates calcarifer* (Bloch), in the Northern Territory and south-eastern Gulf of Carpentaria. *Marine and Freshwater Research* **33**(3), 529–545. doi:10.1071/MF9820529

Dawson DA, Darby S, Hunter FM, Krupa AP, Jones IL, *et al.* (2001) A critique of avian CHD-based molecular sexing protocols illustrated by a Z-chromosome polymorphism detected in auklets. *Molecular Ecology Notes* **1**(3), 201–204. doi:10.1046/j.1471-8278.2001.00060.x

Dawson DA, Brekke P, Dos Remedios N, Horsburgh GJ (2015) A marker suitable for sex-typing birds from degraded samples. *Conservation Genetics Resources* **7**(2), 337–343. doi:10.1007/s12686-015-0429-3

Dechaume-Moncharmont F-X, Monceau K, Cezilly F (2011) Sexing birds using discriminant function analysis: A critical appraisal. *The Auk* **128**(1), 78–86. doi:10.1525/auk.2011.10129

Délot EC, Vilain E (2018) Disorders of sex development. *Yen & Jaffe's Reproductive Endocrinology: Physiology, Pathophysiology, and Clinical Management.* 8th edn. Elsevier, Amsterdam.

Deveson IW, Holleley CE, Blackburn J, Marshall Graves JA, Mattick JS, *et al.* (2017) Differential intron retention in *Jumonji* chromatin modifier genes is implicated in reptile temperature-dependent sex determination. *Science Advances* **3**(6), e1700731. doi:10.1126/sciadv.1700731

Devloo-Delva F, Gosselin T, Butcher PA, Grewe PM, Huverneers C, *et al.* (2022) An R-based tool for identifying sex-linked markers from Restriction Site-Associated DNA sequencing with applications to elasmobranch conservation. *Research Square* [Pre-print]. doi:10.21203/rs.3.rs-1797792/v1

Diatchenko L, Lau YF, Campbell AP, Chenchik A, Moqadam F, *et al.* (1996) Suppression subtractive hybridization: A method for generating differentially regulated or tissue-specific cDNA probes and libraries. *Proceedings of the National Academy of Sciences* **93**(12), 6025–6030. doi:10.1073/pnas.93.12.6025

Dissanayake DSB, Holleley CE, Hill LK, O'Meally D, Deakin JE, *et al.* (2020) Identification of Y chromosome markers in the eastern three-lined skink (*Bassiana duperreyi*) using in silico whole genome subtraction. *BMC Genomics* **21**(1), 1–12. doi:10.1186/s12864-020-07071-2

Dissanayake DS, Holleley C, Georges A (2021a) Effects of natural nest temperatures on sex reversal and sex ratios in an Australian alpine skink. *Scientific Reports* **11**(1), 1–12. doi:10.1038/s41598-021-99702-1

Dissanayake DS, Holleley CE, Deakin JE, Georges A (2021b) High elevation increases the risk of Y chromosome loss in Alpine skink populations with sex reversal. *Heredity* **126**, 805–816. doi:10.1038/s41437-021-00406-z

Dixon G, Kitano J, Kirkpatrick M (2019) The origin of a new sex chromosome by introgression between two stickleback fishes. *Molecular Biology and Evolution* **36**(1), 28–38.

Doran TJ, Morris KR, Wise TG, O'Neil TE, Cooper CA, *et al.* (2017) Sex selection in layer chickens. *Animal Production Science* **58**(3), 476–480.

Drinan DP, Loher T, Hauser L (2018) Identification of genomic regions associated with sex in Pacific halibut. *Journal of Heredity* **109**(3), 326–332. doi:10.1093/jhered/esx102

Van Dyke JU, Thompson MB, Burridge CP, Castelli MA, Clulow S, *et al.* (2021) Australian lizards are outstanding models for reproductive biology research. *Australian Journal of Zoology* **68**(4), 168–199. doi:10.1071/ZO21017

Eatwell K, Hedley J, Barron R (2014) Reptile haematology and biochemistry. *In Practice* **36**(1), 34–42. doi:10.1136/inp.f7488

Edwards AWF (2000) Carl Düsing (1884) on the regulation of the sex-ratio. *Theoretical Population Biology* **58**(3), 255–257. doi:10.1006/tpbi.2000.1482

Elshire RJ, Glaubitz JC, Sun Q, Poland JA, Kawamoto K, *et al.* (2011) A robust, simple genotyping-by-sequencing (GBS) approach for high diversity species. *PloS one* **6**(5), e19379.

Ezaz T, Quinn A, Sarre SD, O'Meally D, Georges A, *et al.* (2009) Molecular marker suggests rapid changes of sex-determining mechanisms in Australian dragon lizards. *Chromosome Research* **17**(1), 91–98. doi:10.1007/s10577-008-9019-5

Ezaz T, Moritz B, Waters P, Marshall Graves JA, Georges A, *et al.* (2009) The ZW sex microchromosomes of an Australian dragon lizard share no homology with those of other reptiles or birds. *Chromosome Research* **17**(8), 965–973. doi:10.1007/s10577-009-9102-6

Ezaz T, Azad B, O'Meally D, Young MJ, Matsubara K, *et al.* (2013) Sequence and gene content of a large fragment of a lizard sex chromosome and evaluation of candidate sex differentiating gene R-spondin 1. *BMC Genomics* **14**, 899. doi:10.1186/1471-2164-14-899

Feron R, Pan Q, Wen M, Imarazene B, Jouanno E, *et al.* (2021) RADSex: a computational workflow to study sex determination using restriction site-associated DNA sequencing data. *Molecular Ecology Resources* **21**(5), 1715–1731. doi:10.1101/2020.04.22.054866

Fisher R (1930) *The Genetical Theory of Natural Selection.* (Ed J Bennett). Oxford University Press, Oxford.

Fowler BLS, Buonaccorsi VP (2016) Genomic characterization of sex-identification markers in *Sebastes carnatus* and *Sebastes chrysomelas* rockfishes. *Molecular Ecology* **25**(10), 2165–2175. doi:10.1111/mec.13594

Fridolfsson A-K, Ellegren H (1999) A simple and universal method for molecular sexing of non-ratite birds. *Journal of Avian Biology* **30**(1), 116–121. doi:10.2307/3677252

Galindo HM, Loher T, Hauser L (2011) Genetic sex identification and the potential evolution of sex determination in Pacific halibut (*Hippoglossus stenolepis*). *Marine Biotechnology* **13**(5), 1027–1037.

Galli R, Preusse G, Uckermann O, Bartels T, Krautwald-Junghanns ME, *et al.* (2017) In ovo sexing of chicken eggs by fluorescence spectroscopy. *Analytical and Bioanalytical Chemistry* **409**(5), 1185–1194.

Gamble T (2016) Using RAD-seq to recognize sex-specific markers and sex chromosome systems. *Molecular Ecology* **25**(10), 2114–2116. doi:10.1111/mec.13648

Gamble T, Castoe TA, Nielsen SV, Banks JL, Card DC, *et al.* (2017) The discovery of XY sex chromosomes in a Boa and Python. *Current Biology* **27**(14), 2148–2153.e4. doi:10.1016/j.cub.2017.06.010

Garner DL (2006) Flow cytometric sexing of mammalian sperm. *Theriogenology* **65**(5), 943–957.

Gautier M (2014) Using genotyping data to assign markers to their chromosome type and to infer the sex of individuals: A Bayesian model-based classifier. *Molecular Ecology Resources* **14**(6), 1141–1159. doi:10.1111/1755-0998.12264

Gemmell NJ, Todd EV, Goikoetxea A, Ortega-Recalde O, Hore TA, (2019) Natural sex change in fish. *Current Topics in Developmental Biology* **134**, 71–117. doi:10.1016/bs.ctdb.2018.12.014

Georges A, Holleley CE, Graves JAM (2021) Concerning an article by Ehl *et al.*: False premise leads to false conclusions. *Sexual Development* **15**(4), 286–288. doi:10.1159/000518374

Goldberg MT, Spigler RB, Ashman T-L (2010) Comparative genetic mapping points to different sex chromosomes in sibling species of wild strawberry (Fragaria). *Genetics* **186**(4), 1425–1433. doi:10.1534/genetics.110.122911

Grayson P, Wright A, Garroway CJ, Docker MF, *et al.* (2022) SexFindR: A computational workflow to identify young and old sex chromosomes. *bioRxiv* [Preprint]. doi:10.1101/2022.02.21.481346

Griffiths R, Double MC, Orr K, Dawson RJ (1998) A DNA test to sex most birds. *Molecular Ecology* **7**(8), 1071–1075. doi:10.1046/j.1365-294x.1998.00389.x

Gross TS, Crain DA, Bjorndal KA, Bolten AB, Carthy RR (1995) Identification of sex in hatchling loggerhead turtles (*Caretta caretta*) by analysis of steroid concentrations in chorioallantoic/amniotic fluid. *General and Comparative Endocrinology*, 204–210. doi:10.1006/gcen.1995.1103

Hall AB, Qi Y, Timoshevskiy V, Sharakhova MV, Sharakhov IV, *et al.* (2013) Six novel Y chromosome genes in Anopheles mosquitoes discovered by independently sequencing males and females. *BMC Genomics* **14**(1), 2–13. doi:10.1186/1471-2164-14-273

Hanson KC, Gravel MA, Graham A, Shoji A, Cooke SJ (2008) Sexual variation in fisheries research and management: when does sex matter? *Reviews in Fisheries Science* **16**(4), 421–436.

Harr KE (2002) Clinical chemistry of companion avian species: A review. *Veterinary Clinical Pathology* **31**(3), 140–151. doi:10.1111/j.1939-165X.2002.tb00295.x

Heinsohn R, Olah G, Webb M, Peakall R, Stojanovic D (2019) Sex ratio bias and shared paternity reduce individual fitness and population viability in a critically endangered parrot. *Journal of Animal Ecology* **88**(4), 502–510. doi:10.1111/1365-2656.12922

Hill P, While GM, Burridge CP, Ezaz T, Munch KL, *et al.* (2022) Sex reversal explains some, but not all, climate mediated differences in sex ratio within a viviparous reptile. *Proceedings of the Royal Society B: Biological Sciences* **289**(1976), 20220689. doi:10.1098/rspb.2022.0689

Hill PL, Burridge CP, Ezaz T, Wapstra E (2018) Conservation of sex-linked markers among conspecific populations of a viviparous skink, *Niveoscincus ocellatus*, exhibiting genetic and temperature-dependent sex determination. *Genome Biology and Evolution* **10**(4), 1079–1087. doi:10.1093/gbe/evy042

Hiller TL, Nistler C, Reding D, White PA, Bled F (2022) Sex identification and age estimation of bobcats and implications for management. *Wildlife Society Bulletin* **46**(3), e1328. doi:10.1002/wsb.1328

Hohenboken WD (1981) Possibilities for genetic manipulation of sex ratio in livestock. *Journal of Animal Science* **52**(2), 265–277.

Hohenboken WD (1999) Applications of sexed semen in cattle production. *Theriogenology* **52**(8), 1421–1433. doi:10.1016/S0093-691X(99)00227-7

Holleley CE, O'Meally D, Sarre SD, Marshall Graves JA, Ezaz T, *et al.* (2015) Sex reversal triggers the rapid transition from genetic to temperature-dependent sex. *Nature* **523**(7558), 79–82. doi:10.1038/nature14574

Hu Q, Chang C, Wang Q, Tian H, Qiao Z, *et al.* (2019) Genome-wide RAD sequencing to identify a sex-specific marker in Chinese giant salamander *Andrias davidianus*. *BMC Genomics* **20**(1), 1–8. doi:10.1186/s12864-019-5771-5

Hughes C (1998) Integrating molecular techniques with field methods in studies of social behavior: A revolution results. *Ecology* **79**(2), 383–399. doi:10.1890/0012-9658(1998)079[0383:IMTWFM]2.0.CO;2

Huynen L, Millar CD, Lambert DM (2002) A DNA test to sex ratite birds. *Molecular Ecology* **11**(4), 851–856. doi:10.1046/j.1365-294X.2002.01483.x

Jaccoud D, Peng K, Feinstein D, Kilian A (2001) Diversity arrays: A solid state technology for sequence information independent genotyping. *Nucleic Acids Research* **29**, e25–e25. doi:10.1093/nar/29.4.e25

Jasonowicz AJ, Simeon A, Zahm M, Cabau C, Klopp C, *et al.* (2022) Generation of a chromosome-level genome assembly for Pacific halibut (*Hippoglossus stenolepis*) and characterization of its sex-determining genomic region. *Molecular Ecology Resources* **22**(7), 2685–2700. doi:10.1111/1755-0998.13641

Jeffries DL, Lavanchy G, Sermier R, Sredl MJ, Miura I, *et al.* (2018) A rapid rate of sex-chromosome turnover and non-random transitions in true frogs. *Nature Communications* **9**(1), 4088. doi:10.1038/s41467-018-06517-2

Johnson LA, Clarke RN (1988) Flow sorting of X and Y chromosome-bearing mammalian sperm: Activation and pronuclear development of sorted bull, boar, and ram sperm microinjected into hamster oocytes. *Gamete Research* **21**(4), 335–343.

Kamiya T, Kai W, Tasumi S, Oka A, Matsunaga T, *et al.* (2012) A trans-species missense SNP in Amhr2 is associated with sex determination in the tiger pufferfish, *Takifugu rubripes* (Fugu). *PLOS Genetics* **8**(7), 1–10. doi:10.1371/journal.pgen.1002798

Kar S, Sangem P, Anusha N, Senthilkumaran B (2021) Endocrine disruptors in teleosts: Evaluating environmental risks and biomarkers. *Aquaculture and Fisheries* **6**(1), 1–26. doi:10.1016/j.aaf.2020.07.013

Katsura Y, Iwase M, Satta Y (2012) Evolution of genomic structures on Mammalian sex chromosomes. *Current Genomics* **13**(2), 115–123. doi:10.2174/138920212799860625

Keating SE, Fenelon JC, Pyne M, Pinto BJ, Guzmán-Méndez IA, *et al.* (2022) Research Article Genetic sex test for the short-beaked echidna (*Tachyglossus aculeatus*). *Conservation Genetics Resources* **14**, 271–278. doi:10.1007/s12686-022-01258-3

Khwatenge CN, Nahashon SN (2021) Recent advances in the application of CRISPR/Cas9 gene editing system in poultry species. *Frontiers in Genetics* **12**(February). doi:10.3389/fgene.2021.627714

Kilian A, Wenzl P, Huttner E, Carling J, Xia L, *et al.* (2012) Diversity arrays technology: A generic genome profiling technology on open platforms. In *Data Production and Analysis in Population Genomics. Methods in Molecular Biology, Vol. 888.* (Eds F Pompanon, A Bonin) pp. 67–89. Humana Press, Totowa, NJ. doi:10.1007/978-1-61779-870-2_5

King WA (1984) Sexing embryos by cytological methods. *Theriogenology* **21**(1), 7–17.

Koyama T, Nakamoto M, Morishima K, Yamashita R, Yamashita T, *et al.* (2019) A SNP in a steroidogenic enzyme is associated with phenotypic sex in seriola fishes. *Current Biology* **29**(11), 1901–1909.e8. doi:10.1016/j.cub.2019.04.069

Krautwald-Junghanns ME, Cramer K, Fischer B, Förster A, Galli R, *et al.* (2018) Current approaches to avoid the culling of day-old male chicks in the layer industry, with special reference to spectroscopic methods. *Poultry Science* **97**(3), 749–757.

Kuderna LFK, Lizano E, Julià E, Gomez-Garrido J, Serres-Armero A, *et al.* (2019) Selective single molecule sequencing and assembly of a human Y chromosome of African origin. *Nature Communications* **10**(1), 4. doi:10.1038/s41467-018-07885-5

Kuhl H, Guiguen Y, Höhne C, Kreuz E, Du K, *et al.* (2021) A 180 Myr-old female-specific genome region in sturgeon reveals the oldest known vertebrate sex determining system with undifferentiated sex chromosomes. *Philosophical Transactions of the Royal Society B: Biological Sciences* **376**(1832). doi:10.1098/rstb.2020.0089

Lambert MR, Ezaz T, Skelly DK (2021) Sex-biased mortality and sex reversal shape wild frog sex ratios. *Frontiers in Ecology and Evolution* **9**(October), 1–14. doi:10.3389/fevo.2021.756476

Lambert MR, Skelly DK, Ezaz T (2016) Sex-linked markers in the North American green frog (*Rana clamitans*) developed using DArTseq provide early insight into sex chromosome evolution. *BMC Genomics* **17**. doi:10.1186/s12864-016-3209-x

Lange A, Paris JR, Gharbi K, Cézard T, Miyagawa S, *et al.* (2020) A newly developed genetic sex marker and its application to understanding chemically induced feminisation in roach (*Rutilus rutilus*). *Molecular Ecology Resources* **20**(4), 1007–1022. doi:10.1111/1755-0998.13166

Lee BY, Coutanceau JP, Ozouf-Costaz C, D'Cotta H, Baroiller JF *et al.* (2011) Genetic and physical mapping for sex-link AFLP markers in Nile tilapia (*Oreochromis niloticus*). *Marine Biotechnology* **13**(3), 557–562. doi:10.1007/s10126-010-9326-7.Genetic

Lindström J (1998) Harvesting and sex differences in demography. *Wildlife Biology* **4**(4), 213–221.

Liu H, Pang M, Yu X, Zhou Y, Tong J, *et al.* (2018) Sex-specific markers developed by next-generation sequencing confirmed an XX/XY sex determination system in bighead carp (*Hypophthalmichthys nobilis*) and silver carp (*Hypophthalmichthys molitrix*). *DNA Research* **25**(3), 257–264. doi:10.1093/dnares/dsx054

Lumeij J (1997) Avian clinical biochemistry. In *Clinical Biochemistry of Domestic Animals.* 5th edn. (Eds J Kaneko, J Harvey, M Bruss) pp. 857–883. Academic Press, Cambridge, MA, USA.

Luo JH, Puc JA, Wright Jr TC, Parsons R, Slosberg ED, *et al.* (1999) Differential subtraction chain, a method for identifying differences in genomic DNA and mRNA. *Nucleic Acids Research* **27**(19), e24. doi:10.1093/nar/27.19.e24

Marshall Graves JA, Shetty S (2001) Sex from W to Z: Evolution of vertebrate sex chromosomes and sex determining genes. *The Journal of Experimental Zoology* **290**(5), 449–462. doi:10.1002/jez.1088

Martínez-Torres M, Rubio-Morales B, Piña-Amado JJ, Luis J (2015) Hemipenes in females of the mexican viviparous lizard *Barisia imbricata* (Squamata: Anguidae): An example of heterochrony in sexual development. *Evolution and Development* **17**(5), 270–277. doi:10.1111/ede.12134

Matsubara K, O'Meally D, Azad B, Georges A, Sarre SD, *et al.* (2016) Amplification of microsatellite repeat motifs is associated with the evolutionary differentiation and heterochromatinization of sex chromosomes in Sauropsida. *Chromosoma* **125**(1), 111–123. doi:10.1007/s00412-015-0531-z

Mikó Z, Nemesházi E, Ujhegyi N, Verebélyi V, Ujszegi J, *et al.* (2021) Sex reversal and ontogeny under climate change and chemical pollution: Are there interactions between the effects of elevated temperature and a xenoestrogen on early development in agile frogs? *Environmental Pollution* **285**. doi:10.1016/j.envpol.2021.117464

Miller KL, Castañeda Rico S, Muletz-Wolz CR, Campana MG, McInerney N, *et al.* (2019) Parthenogenesis in a captive Asian water dragon (*Physignathus cocincinus*) identified with novel microsatellites. *PLoS One* **14**(6), e0217489. doi:10.1371/journal.pone.0217489

Morinha F, Cabral JA, Bastos E (2012) Molecular sexing of birds: A comparative review of polymerase chain reaction (PCR)-based methods. *Theriogenology* **78**(4), 703–714. doi:10.1016/j.theriogenology.2012.04.015

Müller NA, Kersten B, Leite Montalvão AP, Mähler N, Bernhardsson C, *et al.* (2020) A single gene underlies the dynamic evolution of poplar sex determination. *Nature Plants* **6**(6), 630–637.

Murphy WJ, Wilkerson AJ, Raudsepp T, Agarwala R, Schäffer AA, *et al.* (2006) Novel gene acquisition on carnivore Y chromosomes. *PLoS Genetics* **2**(3), e43. doi:10.1371/journal.pgen.0020043

Murtagh VJ, O'meally D, Sankovic N, Delbridge ML, Kuroki Y, *et al.* (2012) Evolutionary history of novel genes on the tammar wallaby Y chromosome: Implications for sex chromosome evolution. *Genome Research* **22**(3), 498–507. doi:10.1101/gr.120790.111

Muyle A, Käfer J, Zemp N, Mousset S, Picard F, *et al.* (2016) Sex-detector: A probabilistic approach to study sex chromosomes in non-model organisms. *Genome Biology and Evolution* **8**(8), 2530–2543. doi:10.1093/gbe/evw172

Nagahama Y, Chakraborty T, Paul-Prasanth B, Ohta K, Nakamura M, (2021) Sex determination, gonadal sex differentiation and plasticity in vertebrate species. *Physiological Reviews* **101**(3), 1237–1308. doi:10.1152/physrev.00044.2019

Neaves L, Wapstra E, Birch D, Girling JE, Joss JM (2006) Embryonic gonadal and sexual organ development in a small viviparous skink, *Niveoscincus ocellatus*. *Journal of Experimental Zoology Part A: Comparative Experimental Biology* **305**(1), 74–82. doi:10.1002/jez.a.249

Nemesházi E, Gál Z, Ujhegyi N, Verebélyi V, Mikó Z, *et al.* (2020) Novel genetic sex markers reveal high frequency of sex reversal in wild populations of the agile frog (*Rana dalmatina*) associated with anthropogenic land use. *Molecular Ecology* **29**, 3607–3621. doi:10.1111/mec.15596

Nursyifa C, Brüniche-Olsen A, Garcia-Erill G, Heller R, Albrechtsen A (2021) Joint identification of sex and sex-linked scaffolds in non-model organisms using low depth sequencing data. *Molecular Ecology Resources* **22**, 458–467. doi:10.1111/1755-0998.13491

Palmer DH, Rogers TF, Dean R, Wright AE (2019) How to identify sex chromosomes and their turnover. *Molecular Ecology* **28**(21), 4709–4724. doi:10.1111/mec.15245

Pereira DC, Mirabal B, de França AM, de Antonio ES, Fraga RE, *et al.* (2021) Molecular sexing in the formation of pairs of blue-and-yellow macaw (Ara ararauna) in reintroduction programs. *Research, Society and Development* **10**(10), 570101019330. doi:10.33448/rsd-v10i10.19330

Perelman P, Johnson WE, Roos C, Seuánez HN, Horvath JE, *et al.* (2011) A molecular phylogeny of living primates. *PLoS Genetics* **7**(3), e1001342. doi:10.1371/journal.pgen.1001342

Peterson BK, Weber JN, Kay EH, Fisher HS, Hoekstra HE (2012) Double digest RADseq: An inexpensive method for de novo SNP discovery and genotyping in model and non-model species. *PLoS ONE* **7**(5). doi:10.1371/journal.pone.0037135

Piferrer F, Zanuy S, Carrillo M, Solar II, Devlin RH, *et al.* (1994) Brief treatment with an aromatase inhibitor during sex differentiation causes chromosomally female salmon to develop as normal, functional males. *Journal of Experimental Zoology* **270**(3), 255–262.

Piferrer F, Anastasiadi D, Valdivieso A, Sánchez-Baizán N, Moraleda-Prados J, *et al.* (2019) The model of the conserved epigenetic regulation of sex. *Frontiers in Genetics* **10**(SEP). doi:10.3389/fgene.2019.00857

Pilgrim KL, McKelvey KS, Riddle AE, Schwartz MK (2005) Felid sex identification based on noninvasive genetic samples. *Molecular Ecology Notes* **5**(1), 60–61. doi:10.1111/j.1471-8286.2004.00831.x

Porat N, Bogdanov K, Danielli A, Arie A, Samina I, *et al.* (2011) Direct detection of chicken genomic DNA for gender determination by thymine-DNA glycosylase. *British Poultry Science* **52**(1), 58–65.

Quinn AE, Radder RS, Sarre SD, Georges A, Ezaz T, *et al.* (2009) Isolation and development of a molecular sex marker for *Bassiana duperreyi*, a lizard with XX/XY sex chromosomes and temperature-induced sex reversal. *Molecular Genetics and Genomics* **281**(6), 665–672. doi:10.1007/s00438-009-0437-7

Quinn AE, Ezaz T, Sarre SD, Graves JA, Georges A, *et al.* (2010) Extension, single-locus conversion and physical mapping of sex chromosome sequences identify the Z microchromosome and pseudo-autosomal region in a dragon lizard, *Pogona vitticeps*. *Heredity* **104**(4), 410. doi:10.1038/hdy.2009.133

Radder RS, Quinn AE, Georges A, Sarre SD, Shine R, *et al.* (2008) Genetic evidence for co-occurrence of chromosomal and thermal sex-determining systems in a lizard. *Biology Letters* **4**(2), 176–178. doi:10.1098/rsbl.2007.0583

Raudsepp T, Santani A, Wallner B, Kata SR, Ren C, *et al.* (2004) A detailed physical map of the horse Y chromosome. *Proceedings of the National Academy of Sciences* **101**(25), 9321–9326. doi:10.1073/pnas.0403011101

Real F, Haas SA, Franchini P, Xiong P, Simakov O, *et al.* (2020) The mole genome reveals regulatory rearrangements associated with adaptive intersexuality. *Science* **370**(6513), 208–214. doi:10.1126/science.aaz2582

Richner H (1989) Avian laparoscopy as a field technique for sexing birds and an assessment of its effects on wild birds. *Journal of Field Ornithology* **60**(2), 137–142. http://www.jstor.org/stable/4513412

Ridha MT (2011) Evaluation of monosex culture of GIFT and non-improved strains of Nile tilapia *Oreochromis niloticus* in recirculating tanks. *International Aquatic Research* **3**(3), 189–195.

Rovatsos M, Altmanová M, Pokorná MJ, Kratochvíl L (2014) Novel X-linked genes revealed by quantitative polymerase chain reaction in the green anole, *Anolis carolinensis*. *G3-Genes Genomes Genetics* **4**(11), 2107–2113. doi:10.1534/g3.114.014084

Rozen S, Skaletsky H, Marszalek JD, Minx PJ, Cordum HS, *et al.* (2003) Abundant gene conversion between arms of palindromes in human and ape Y chromosomes. *Nature* **423**(6942), 873–876. doi:10.1038/nature01723

Ryder OA, Thomas S, Judson JM, Romanov MN, Dandekar S, *et al.* (2021) Facultative parthenogenesis in California condors. *The Journal of Heredity* **112**(7), 569–574. doi:10.1093/jhered/esab052

Sankovic N, Delbridge ML, Grützner F, Ferguson-Smith MA, O'Brien PC, *et al.* (2006) Construction of a highly enriched marsupial Y chromosome-specific BAC sub-library using isolated Y chromosomes. *Chromosome Research* **14**(6), 657–664. doi:10.1007/s10577-006-1076-z

Schartl M, Georges A, Graves JAM (2023) Polygenic sex determination in vertebrates – is there any such thing? *Trend in Genetics* **39**, 242–250.

Schwanz LE, Georges A, Holleley CE, Sarre SD (2020) Climate change, sex reversal and lability of sex-determining systems. *Journal of Evolutionary Biology* **33**(3), 270–281. doi:10.1111/jeb.13587

Shaffer ML (1981) Minimum population sizes for species conservation. *BioScience* **31**(2), 131–134. doi:10.2307/1308256

Sigeman H, Sinclair B, Hansson B (2022) FindZX: an automated pipeline for detecting and visualising sex chromosomes using whole-genome sequencing data. *BMC Genomics* **23**(1), 1–14.

Skaletsky H, Kuroda-Kawaguchi T, Minx PJ, Cordum HS, Hillier L, *et al.* (2003) The male-specific region of the human Y chromosome is a mosaic of discrete sequence classes. *Nature* **423**(6942), 825–837. doi:10.1038/nature01722

Stevens N (1905) *Studies in Spermatogenesis*. Carnegie Institution of Washington, Washington DC, USA.

Stewart IJ, Webster R (2021) Overview of data sources for the Pacific halibut stock assessment, harvest policy, and related analyses. Available at: https://protect-au.mimecast.com/s/vL3YC1WZg1fkG6pqIK0l_n?domain=iphc.int

Stöck, M., Kratochvíl L, Kuhl H, Rovatsos M, Evans BJ, *et al.* (2021) A brief review of vertebrate sex evolution with a pledge for integrative research-towards 'sexomics'. *Philosophical Transactions of the Royal Society B: Biological Sciences* **376**, 20200426. doi:10.1098/rstb.2020.0426

Sun Y-L, Jiang DN, Zeng S, Hu CJ, Ye K, *et al.* (2014) Screening and characterization of sex-linked DNA markers and marker-assisted selection in the Nile tilapia (*Oreochromis niloticus*). *Aquaculture* **433**, 19–27. doi:10.1016/j.aquaculture.2014.05.035

Tamukai K, Takami Y, Akabane Y, Kanazawa Y, Une Y (2011) Plasma biochemical reference values in clinically healthy captive bearded dragons (*Pogona vitticeps*) and the effects of sex and season. *Veterinary Clinical Pathology* **40**(3), 368–373. doi:10.1111/j.1939-165X.2011.00329.x

Tao W, Xu L, Zhao L, Zhu Z, Wu X, *et al.* (2020) High-quality chromosome-level genomes of two tilapia species reveal their evolution of repeat sequences and sex chromosomes. *Molecular Ecology Resources* **21**, 543–560. doi:10.1111/1755-0998.13273

Tezak BM, Sifuentes-Romero I, Milton S, Wyneken J (2020) Identifying sex of neonate turtles with temperature-dependent sex determination via small blood samples. *Scientific Reports* **10**(5012), 1–8. doi:10.1038/s41598-020-61984-2

Tezak BM, Guthrie K, Wyneken J (2017) An immunohistochemical approach to identify the sex of young marine turtles. *Anatomical Record* **300**(8), 1512–1518. doi:10.1002/ar.23589

Todd EV, Liu H, Muncaster S, Gemmell NJ (2016) Bending genders: The biology of natural sex change in fish. *Sexual Development* **10**(5–6), 223–241. doi:10.1159/000449297

Traut W, Eickhof U, Schorch JC (2001) Identification and analysis of sex chromosomes by comparative genomic hybridization (CGH). *Methods in Cell Science* **23**(1–3), 155–161. doi:10.1007/978-94-010-0330-8_16

Trenkel VM, Boudry P, Verrez-Bagnis V, Lorance P (2020) Methods for identifying and interpreting sex-linked SNP markers and carrying out sex assignment: Application to thornback ray (*Raja clavata*). *Molecular Ecology Resources* **20**(6), 1610–1619. doi:10.1111/1755-0998.13225

Truett G, Heeger P, Mynatt RL, Truett AA, Walker JA, *et al.* (2000) Preparation of PCR-quality mouse genomic DNA with hot sodium hydroxide and Tris (HotSHOT). *Biotechniques* **29**(1), 29–30.

Tubbs CW, McDonough CE (2018) Reproductive impacts of endocrine-disrupting chemicals on wildlife species: Implications for conservation of endangered species. *Annual Review of Animal Biosciences* **6**(November), 287–304. doi:10.1146/annurev-animal-030117-014547

Uno Y, Nozu R, Kiyatake I, Higashiguchi N, Sodeyama S, *et al.* (2020) Cell culture-based karyotyping of orectolobiform sharks for chromosome-scale genome analysis. *Communications Biology* **3**(1), 652. doi:10.1038/s42003-020-01373-7

Vicoso B, Emerson JJ, Zektser Y, Mahajan S, Bachtrog D (2013) Comparative sex chromosome genomics in snakes: Differentiation, evolutionary strata, and lack of global dosage compensation. *PLoS Biology* **11**(8), e1001643.

Vicoso B, Bachtrog D (2015) Numerous transitions of sex chromosomes in Diptera. *PLoS Biology* **13**(4), e1002078. doi:10.1371/journal.pbio.1002078

Viñas A, Taboada X, Vale L, Robledo D, Hermida M, *et al.* (2012) Mapping of DNA sex-specific markers and genes related to sex differentiation in turbot (*Scophthalmus maximus*). *Marine Biotechnology* **14**(5), 655–663. doi:10.1007/s10126-012-9451-6

Waits LP, Paetkau D (2005) Noninvasive genetic sampling tools for wildlife biologists: A review of applications and recommendations for accurate data collection. *The Journal of Wildlife Management* **69**(4), 1419–1433. http://www.jstor.org/stable/3803503

Wang C, Tang X, Xin Y, Yue F, Yan X, *et al.* (2015) Identification of sex chromosomes by means of comparative genomic hybridization in a lizard, *Eremias multiocellata*. *Zoological Science* **32**(2), 151–156. doi:10.2108/zs130246

Wang H-P, *et al.* (2018) *Sex Control in Aquaculture*. John Wiley & Sons, Ltd, Hoboken, NJ, USA. doi:10.1002/9781119127291

Wang L, Sun F, Wan ZY, Yang Z, Tay YX, *et al.* (2022) Transposon-induced epigenetic silencing in the X chromosome as a novel form of *dmrt1* expression regulation during sex determination in the fighting fish. *BMC Biology* **20**(1), 5. doi:10.1186/s12915-021-01205-y

Watts PC, Buley KR, Sanderson S, Boardman W, Ciofi C, *et al.* (2006) Parthenogenesis in Komodo dragons. *Nature* **444**(7122), 1021–1022. doi:10.1038/4441021a

Weigel KA (2004) Exploring the role of sexed semen in dairy production systems. *Journal of Dairy Science* **87**, E120–E130. doi:10.3168/jds.S0022-0302(04)70067-3

Weissmann A, Reitemeier S, Hahn A, Gottschalk J, Einspanier A (2013) Sexing domestic chicken before hatch: A new method for in ovo gender identification. *Theriogenology* **80**(3), 199–205. doi:10.1016/j.theriogenology.2013.04.014

Whiteley SL, Weisbecker V, Georges A, Gauthier AR, Whitehead DL, *et al.* (2018) Developmental asynchrony and antagonism of sex determination pathways in a lizard with temperature-induced sex reversal. *Scientific Reports* **8**(1), 1–9. doi:10.1038/s41598-018-33170-y

Whiteley SL, Castelli MA, Dissanayake DS, Holleley CE, Georges A (2021) Temperature-induced sex reversal in reptiles: Prevalence, discovery, and evolutionary implications. *Sexual Development* **15**, 148–156. doi:10.1159/000515687

Whiteley SL, Wagner S, Holleley CE, Deveson IW, Marshall Graves JA, *et al.* (2022) Truncated *jarid2* and *kdm6b* transcripts are associated with temperature-induced sex reversal during development in a dragon lizard. *Science Advances* **8**, eabk0275. doi:10.1126/sciadv.abk0275

Wiggins JM, Santoyo-Brito E, Scales JB, Fox SF (2020) Gene dose indicates presence of sex chromosomes in collared lizards (*Crotaphytus collaris*), a species with temperature-influenced sex determination. *Herpetologica* **76**(1), 27–30. doi:10.1655/herpetologica-d-19-00036

Wilson CA, High SK, McCluskey BM, Amores A, Yan YL, *et al.* (2014) Wild sex in zebrafish: Loss of the natural sex determinant in domesticated strains. *Genetics* **198**(3), 1291–1308. doi:10.1534/genetics.114.169284

Wu X, Zhao L, Fan Z, Lu B, Chen J, *et al.* (2021) Screening and characterization of sex-linked DNA markers and marker-assisted selection in blue tilapia (*Oreochromis aureus*). *Aquaculture* **530**(July 2020), 735934. doi:10.1016/j.aquaculture.2020.735934

Xia ZR, Li PP, Gu HX, Fong JJ, Zhao EM (2011) Evaluating noninvasive methods of sex identification in Green sea turtle (*Chelonia mydas*) hatchlings. *Chelonian Conservation and Biology* **10**(1), 117–123. doi:10.2744/CCB-0852.1

Xie Y, Xu Z, Wu Z, Hong L (2020) Sex manipulation technologies progress in livestock: A review. *Frontiers in Veterinary Science* **7**(August), 1–9. doi:10.3389/fvets.2020.00481

Xue L, Gao Y, Wu M, Tian T, Fan H, *et al.* (2021) Telomere-to-telomere assembly of a fish Y chromosome reveals the origin of a young sex chromosome pair. *Genome Biology* **22**(1), 203. doi:10.1186/s13059-021-02430-y

Zarzoso-Lacoste D, Jan PL, Lehnen L, Girard T, Besnard AL, *et al.* (2018) Combining noninvasive genetics and a new mammalian sex-linked marker provides new tools to investigate population size, structure and individual behaviour: An application to bats. *Molecular Ecology Resources* **18**(2), 217–228. doi:10.1111/1755-0998.12727

Zhang X, Wagner S, Holleley CE, Deakin JE, Matsubara K, *et al.* (2022) Sex-specific splicing of Z- and W-borne *nr5a1* alleles suggests sex determination is controlled by chromosome conformation. *Proceedings of the National Academy of Sciences of the United States of America* **119**(4). doi:10.1073/pnas.2116475119

Zhao D, McBride D, Nandi S, McQueen HA, McGrew MJ, *et al.* (2010) Somatic sex identity is cell autonomous in the chicken. *Nature* **464**, 237–242. doi:10.1038/nature08852

Zhu Z, Matsubara K, Shams F, Dobry J, Wapstra E, *et al.* (2022) Diversity of reptile sex chromosome evolution revealed by cytogenetic and linked-read sequencing. *Zoological Research* **43**, 719–733. doi:10.1101/2021.10.13.462063

9   Perspective – Whole genome assemblies, devils and disease

Carolyn J. Hogg, Emma Peel, Yuanyuan Cheng and Katherine Belov,
School of Life and Environmental Sciences, The University of Sydney,
Sydney, Australia

A theme that has been emerging over the past decade in conservation is the creation and use of reference genomes to inform conservation actions. These whole genome assemblies (WGAs) consist of DNA sequences for vast fractions of an organism's genome stitched together at some level of completeness. The value of these WGAs is significantly increased when they are annotated to allow for functional interpretation of the DNA sequences. While they are information-rich, creating WGAs can be time-consuming and expensive, and as most chapters in this book attest, such detailed information is often not essential for genomics to provide impactful information in support of environmental management. So, what use are WGAs to environmental management? In this perspective, we address this question with an illustration of more than 10 years of research and management of devil facial tumour disease (DFTD) and the Tasmanian devil (*Sarcophilus harrisii*). This pioneering work has made extensive use of the rich information content of one of the first marsupial genome assemblies and has provided unique understanding of disease and how it can best be managed.

The Tasmanian devil is the world's largest marsupial carnivore. It fulfils a key role in Tasmanian ecosystems as the apex carnivore, but its survival is threatened by an infectious clonal cancer known as devil facial tumour disease (Fig. 9.1). Devil populations have declined by up to 80% across the Australian island state of Tasmania since the disease was first documented in 1996 (Lazenby *et al.*

2018; see also Chapter 14). Significant effort has gone into understanding DFTD, the epidemiology-relevant ecology of the devil, the development and management of an insurance metapopulation, and the undertaking of a trial translocation program. Of particular importance has been research into understanding the interplay between the devils' immune system and DFTD because this has potential to inform management as well as treatment and vaccination opportunities (reviewed in Hogg *et al.* 2019).

A reference genome for the Tasmanian devil was first published in 2012 (Murchison *et al.* 2012). This was pioneering work, but by today's genome standards it had a relatively low level of completeness ('contiguity'), meaning that it is now considered a low-quality genome assembly (Brandies *et al.* 2019). However, this reference genome combined with further sequencing permitted the characterisation of complex gene families within the genome, in particular the immune genes and their obvious relevance to DFTD. Immune genes are some of the most complex and variable genes within species' genomes, owing to an organisms' need to recognise and respond to a diverse and rapidly evolving range of pathogens (Janeway 2005). They are often poorly characterised in non-model species due to their complex and repetitive nature, which require careful manual annotation (identification of features).

When DFTD was first characterised, it was only the second time an infectious cancer had been detected in any species, the other being an infectious cancer in dogs (canine transmissible venereal tumour, CTVT; Murchison 2008). Unfortunately, since then a second transmissible cancer has been observed in Tasmanian devils. These two distinct contagious cancers are now collectively known as DFTD; devil facial tumour 1 (DFT1) was first observed in 1996 in the far north-east of Tasmania at Mt William/wukalina (Loh *et al.* 2006); and DFT2 (Pye, Pemberton *et al.* 2016) was discovered in the south-east corner of Tasmania in 2012. DFT1 has since swept south and westwards across Tasmania and is responsible for an 80% decline in the devil population. Our understanding of DFT2 is still relatively limited and what we present in this perspective relates to DFT1. DFT1 transmits between individuals during fighting and mating and remarkably devils do not initiate an immune response to the DFT1 infection (Woods *et al.* 2020). DFT1 is mostly fatal with infected individuals usually dying within 6 months of presentation of tumours although tumour regression has been observed in a small number of individuals (Pye, Hamede *et al.* 2016; Wright *et al.* 2017).

So, how does DFT1 evade the immune system in Tasmanian devils? Prior to assembling the devil reference genome, research based on immune gene markers and microsatellite DNA provided an important understanding of the complexity of marsupial immune systems (Belov *et al.* 2007), and how DFT1 could potentially evade the immune response (Woods *et al.* 2007). The Major Histocompatibility Complex genes (MHC) are a key immune gene family in all jawed vertebrates. The MHC code for cell-surface receptors that recognise and present antigens on pathogen-affected and cancerous cells to the immune system. Characterisation of MHC genes (Siddle *et al.* 2007; Cheng, Stuart *et al.* 2012), and development of markers for MHC diversity in devils (Cheng and Belov 2012), led to the revelation that the Tasmanian devil population harboured unusually low levels of MHC diversity (Siddle *et al.* 2007; Cheng, Sanderson *et al.* 2012; Cheng, Stuart *et al.* 2012). Not only that, but a high proportion of MHC alleles were shared between devils and DFT1 (Siddle *et al.* 2007). Because MHC is used to distinguish self from non-self, the devil's immune system is unable to recognise DFT1 as foreign and so does not mount an appropriate immune response against the tumour (Woods *et al.* 2007). This was a breakthrough insight.

Sequencing the reference genome of the devil in 2012 (Murchison *et al.* 2012) fuelled rapid research into devil host immunity and DFTD (Fig. 9.1). Further work, including multiple transcriptome datasets (Murchison *et al.* 2012; Morris *et al.* 2015; Hewavisenti *et al.* 2016), enabled detailed characterisation of the immune gene functional repertoire beyond MHC diversity (e.g. Cheng and Belov 2014; Cui *et al.* 2015; Morris *et al.* 2015; Peel *et al.* 2016), and showed that DFT1 also down-regulates MHC expression on tumour cells, making them effectively invisible to the devil immune system (Siddle *et al.* 2013). MHC genes are not the only immune genes, and the WGA and associated sequencing showed that devils have remarkably low functional diversity across multiple immune gene families (Cui *et al.* 2015; Morris *et al.* 2015).

So, how does our knowledge of DFT1 epidemiology and devil genetic diversity aid in their conservation? There are two primary ways: 1) through the development of vaccines, and 2) informing management actions that maximise natural immunity by mixing genetically differentiated populations.

Vaccines are a valuable management tool for wildlife disease as they have the potential to prevent infection in both incumbent wild populations and translocated individuals. As DFTD hides from the immune system, vaccination against DFTD aims to induce MHC expression in DFTD cells in culture which are then used with an adjuvant to induce an immune response (Kreiss *et al.* 2015; Patchett *et al.* 2015; Patchett *et al.* 2017). Early DFTD vaccines were based on killed DFTD cells to stimulate an immune response. An anti-DFTD immune response was not observed in all devils, and immunisations only provided short-term protection against DFTD infection (Kreiss *et al.* 2015). The next generation of immunisation and immunotherapy was based on DFTD cells treated with interferon gamma to induce MHC expression, thereby enabling recognition and activation of the host immune response (Tovar *et al.* 2017; Pye *et al.* 2018). Initial testing was promising (Tovar *et al.* 2017) and ensuing use in a larger cohort of devils revealed anti-DFTD antibodies in >95% of individuals, although devil MHC type influenced response to immunisation (Pye *et al.* 2018). More recent work has shown that anti-DFTD antibodies can persist for up to 2 years after immunisation, although the vaccine is still not fully protective against DFTD infection (Pye *et al.* 2020). Further work is underway exploring non-MHC antigens as potential immunisation targets (Owen and Siddle 2019; Tovar *et al.* 2018), although field deployment has not been trialled at time of writing. Over a decade of research has been conducted to understand the potential of vaccines against DFTD, many of which has used the devil reference genome (Owen and Siddle 2019; Phillips *et al.* 2019).

For the past 20 years, **genetic rescue** (via conservation translocations) has been used to improve the fitness of species suffering from **inbreeding depression**, including the

Florida panther (*Puma concolor coryi*, Johnson *et al.* 2010), and the mountain pygmy possum (*Burramys parvus*, Weeks *et al.* 2017). These often-cited genetic rescue events used neutral microsatellite loci to measure improvements in genetic diversity relative to fitness (relative reproductive output). However, for species where the major threatening process is disease, such as seen in devils, an understanding of population-level differences in functional diversity is important for maximising natural immunity. There have been two investigations where whole genome re-sequencing (WGR) has been used to compare between individuals that have showed signs of obvious tumour regression and those that have not (Wright *et al.* 2017; Margres *et al.* 2018). Lower-coverage WGR (10–15X) of 12 individuals identified two genomic regions that may be associated with resistance to DFTD including the PAX3 and TLL1 genes (Wright *et al.* 2017). Margres *et al.* (2018) re-sequenced 10 individuals to a higher coverage (30X) and was able to identify 11 highly differentiated genomic regions that may underlie tumour regression in the Tasmanian devil. Building on these WGR studies, a recent study used a target capture method developed from the annotated reference genome to investigate over 830 devils from 31 wild populations, and 553 devils from the insurance metapopulation. Using a combination of reduced representation sequencing (RRS) and target capture methods, they were able

to assess both genome-wide diversity and localised diversity at over 500 functional genes, including loci that have been putatively associated with DFTD resistance, across the entire species' range (Farquharson *et al.* 2022). This study found previously unreported fine-scale genetic structuring reflective of the biogeographic patterns in Tasmania, previously undescribed immune gene variation and characterised the geographic differences in the putatively DFTD-associated loci (Farquharson *et al.* 2022). All these studies demonstrate the value of an annotated reference genome, along with WGR, RRS and target capture data, in exploring the genetic basis of phenotypic traits that inform conservation decisions, like translocations.

The Tasmanian devil exemplifies a case where there have been benefits of access to an annotated reference genome, or WGA, because of the clear linkages between the selective pressure (DFTD) and how an understanding of this pressure has provided clear paths for management. In this case, genome resources have been essential to characterising the very complex molecular basis for the pressure, revealed the most promising avenues for vaccine design, and provided a toolset for selection of individuals for translocation and maximising natural immunity.

Wildlife disease is increasingly contributing to global decline and extinction of vulnerable species and

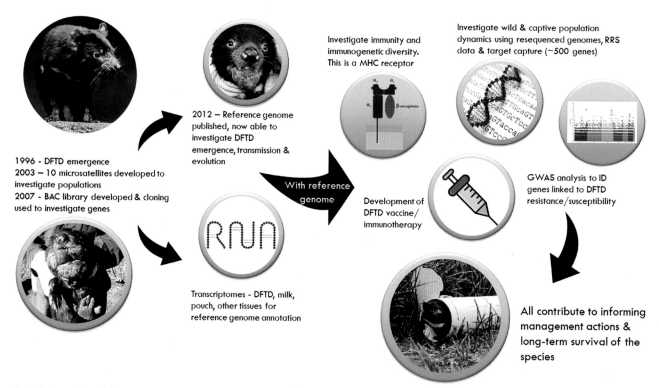

Fig. 9.1. Examples of the conservation outcomes facilitated by having a reference genome and additional complementary sequencing methods in the Tasmanian devil (modified from Brandies *et al.* 2019).

populations (Storfer *et al.* 2021), and as COVID-19 illustrates, posing threats to human health. These may be some of the most compelling cases for the utility of WGAs to manage such threats and are increasingly accessible financially and practically. However, the benefits of WGAs in environmental management are not restricted to complex diseases and other pressures with a molecular basis. Other examples include epigenetic ageing and lifespan analysis, Chapters 6 and 7; inbreeding risk assessment and **runs of homozygosity (ROH)**, Chapter 13; characterising reproduction-related genes harboured on sex chromosomes (Chapter 8).

Although, not all species require a 'platinum' reference genome (Lewin *et al.* 2018), as evidenced by other chapters in this book, those species with known selective drivers, such as disease, need either a complete chromosome-level genome to understand the organisation and evolution of complex gene families, or additional sequencing to fill the gaps created by a lower-quality genome. In these instances, investing in a higher quality reference genome will pay dividends in the longer term by permitting faster annotation and interpretation of any genetic differences and a species' ability to respond to threatening processes. WGAs may become essential to biodiversity conservation in the future as our understanding between disease, wildlife and climate change increases, and our ability to take transformational action continues to decline as habitat is lost.

A lesson learned from devils is that successful management of wildlife species cannot be built on WGAs alone. We married together the fields of molecular biology, informatics, and ecology in such a way that our current specialised, narrow fields were expanded, and we have been able to utilise the devil WGA to its full potential in conservation management for this species (see review in Brandies *et al.* 2019). Moving forward, the use of WGA for other species of conservation concern requires cross-pollination between fields of expertise, training, and new technological solutions to allow non-geneticists access to the information that genomes contain and contribute to our understanding of biodiversity and ecosystems and how to conserve them for the future (Hogg *et al.* 2022).

REFERENCES

Belov K, Sanderson CE, Deakin JE, Wong ES, Assange D, *et al.* (2007) Characterization of the opossum immune genome provides insights into the evolution of the mammalian immune system. *Genome Research* **17**(7), 982–991.

Brandies P, Peel E, Hogg CJ, Belov, K (2019) The value of reference genomes in the conservation of threatened species. *Genes* **10**(11). doi:10.3390/genes10110846

Cheng Y, Belov K (2012) Isolation and characterisation of 11 MHC-linked microsatellite loci in the Tasmanian devil (*Sarcophilus harrisii*). *Conservation Genetics Resources* **4**(2), 463–465. doi:10.1007/s12686-011-9575-4

Cheng Y, Belov K (2014) Characterisation of non-classical MHC class I genes in the Tasmanian devil (*Sarcophilus harrisii*). *Immunogenetics* **66**(12), 727–735. doi:10.1007/s00251-014-0804-3

Cheng Y, Sanderson CE, Jones M, Belov K (2012) Low MHC class II diversity in the Tasmanian devil. *Immunogenetics* **64**, 525–533.

Cheng Y, Stuart A, Morris K, Taylor R, Siddle HV, *et al.* (2012) Antigen-presenting genes and genomic copy number variations in the Tasmanian devil MHC. *BMC Genomics* **13**, 87.

Cui J, Cheng Y, Belov K (2015) Diversity in the Toll-like receptor genes of the Tasmanian devil (Sarcophilus harrisii). *Immunogenetics* **67**(3), 195–201. doi:10.1007/s00251-014-0823-0

Farquharson KA, McLennan EA, Cheng Y, Alexander L, Fox S, *et al.* (2022) Restoring faith in conservation action: Maintaining wild genetic diversity through the Tasmanian devil insurance program. *Iscience* **25**(7), 104474.

Hewavisenti RV, Morris KM, O'Meally D, Cheng Y, Papenfuss AT, *et al.* (2016) The identification of immune genes in the milk transcriptome of the Tasmanian devil (*Sarcophilus harrisii*). *PeerJ* **4**, 1569.

Hogg CJ, Fox S, Pemberton D, Belov K (2019) *Saving the Tasmanian Devil: Recovery Through Science-based Management.* CSIRO Publishing.

Hogg CJ, Ottewell K, Latch P, Rossetto M, Biggs J, *et al.* (2022) Threatened species initiative: Empowering conservation action using genomic resources. *Proceedings of the National Academy of Sciences* **119**(4), e2115643118. doi:10.1073/pnas.2115643118

Janeway CA (2005) *Immunobiology: The Immune System in Health and Disease* 6th edn. Garland Science, New York.

Johnson WE, Onorato DP, Roelke ME, Land ED, Cunningham M, *et al.* (2010) Genetic restoration of the Florida panther. *Science* **329**(5999), 1641–1645.

Kreiss A, Brown GK, Tovar C, Lyons AB, Woods GM (2015) Evidence for induction of humoral and cytotoxic immune responses against devil facial tumour disease cels in Tasmanian devils (*Sarcophilus harrisii*) immunized with killed cell preparations. *Vaccine* **33**, 3016–3025.

Lazenby BT, Tobler MW, Brown WE, Hawkins CE, Hocking GJ, *et al.* (2018) Density trends and demographic signals uncover the long-term impact of transmissible cancer in Tasmanian devils. *Journal of Applied Ecology* **55**, 1365–2664. doi:10.1111/1365-2664.13088

Lewin HA, Robinson GE, Kress WJ, Baker WJ, Coddington J, *et al.* (2018) Earth BioGenome Project: Sequencing life for the future of life. *Proceedings of the National Academy of Sciences* **115**(17), 4325–4333.

Loh R, Hayes D, Mahjoor A, O'Hara A, Pyecroft S, *et al.* (2006) The immunohistochemical characterization of Devil facial tumor disease (DFTD) in the Tasmanian devil (*Sarcophilus harrisii*). *Veterinary Pathology* **43**, 896–903.

Margres MJ, Ruiz-Aravena M, Hamede R, Jones ME, Lawrance MF, *et al.* (2018) The genomic basis of tumor regression in Tasmanian devils (*Sarcophilus harrisii*). *Genome Biology and Evolution* **10**(11), 3012–3025.

Morris B, Cheng Y, Warren W, Papenfuss AT, Belov K (2015) Identification and analysis of divergent immune gene families within the Tasmanian devil genome. *BMC Genomics* **16**(1), 1–12.

Murchison EP (2008) Clonally transmissible cancers in dogs and Tasmanian devils. *Oncogene* **27**(2), S19–S30.

Murchison EP, Schulz-Trieglaff OB, Ning Z, Alexandrow LB, Bauer MJ, *et al.* (2012) Genome sequencing and analysis of the Tasmanian devil and its transmissible cancer. *Cell* **148**, 780–791.

Owen RS, Siddle HV (2019) Devil facial tumours: Towards a vaccine. *Immunological Investigations* **48**(7), 719–736. doi:10.1080/08820139.2019.1624770

Patchett AL, Latham R, Brettingham-Moore KH, Tovar C, Lyons AB, *et al.* (2015) Toll-like receptor signaling is functional in immune cells of the endangered Tasmanian devil. *Developmental and Comparative Immunology* **53**, 123–133.

Patchett AL, Tovar C, Corcoran LM, Lyons AB, Woods GM (2017) The toll-like receptor ligands Hiltonol (polyICLC) and imiquimod effectively activate antigen-specific immune responses in Tasmanian devils (*Sarcophilus harrisii*). *Developmental and Comparative Immunology* **76**, 352–360.

Peel E, Cheng Y, Djordjevic JT, Fox S, Sorrell TC, *et al.* (2016) Cathelicidins in the Tasmanian devil (*Sarcophilus harrisii*). *Scientific Reports* **6**, e35019.

Phillips S, Quigley BL, Timms P (2019) Seventy years of *Chlamydia* vaccine research – limitations of the past and directions for the future. *Frontiers in Microbiology* **10**(70). doi:10.3389/fmicb.2019.00070

Pye R, Darby J, Flies A, Fox S, Carver S, *et al.* (2020) Post release immune responses of Tasmanian devils vaccinated with an experimental devil facial tumour disease vaccine. *Wildlife Research* **48**, 701–712. doi:10.1071/WR20210

Pye R, Hamede R, Siddle HV, Caldwell A, Knowles GW, *et al.* (2016) Demonstration of immune responses against devil facial tumour disease in wild Tasmanian devils. *Biology Letters* **12**(10), 20160553.

Pye R, Pemberton D, Tovar C, Tubio JMC, Dun KA, *et al.* (2016) A second transmissible cancer in Tasmanian devils. *PNAS* **113**(2), 374–379.

Pye R, Patchett AL, McLennan E, Thomson R, Carver S, *et al.* (2018) Immunization strategies producing a humoral IgG immune response against devil facial tumour disease in the majority of Tasmanian devils destined for wild release. *Frontiers in Immunology* **9**, 259.

Siddle HV, Kreiss A, Eldridge MDB, Noonan E, Clarke CJ, *et al.* (2007) Transmission of a fatal clonal tumor by biting occurs due to depleted MHC diversity in a threatened carnivorous marsupial. *PNAS* **104**(41), 16221–16226.

Siddle HV, Kreiss A, Tovar C, Yuen CK, Chen Y, *et al.* (2013) Reversible epigenetic down-regulation of MHC molecules by devil facial tumour disease illustrates immune escape by a contagious cancer. *PNAS* **110**(13), 5103–5108.

Storfer A, Kozakiewicz CP, Beer MA, Savage AE (2021) Applications of population genomics for understanding and mitigating wildlife disease. In *Population Genomics: Wildlife.* (Eds PA Hohenlohe, OP Rajora) pp. 357–383. Springer International Publishing, Cham.

Tovar C, Pye E, Kreiss A, Cheng Y, Brown GK, *et al.* (2017) Regression of devil facial tumour disease following immunotherapy in immunised Tasmanian devils. *Scientific Reports* **7**, e43827.

Tovar C, Patchett AL, Kim V, Wilson R, Darby J, *et al.* (2018) Heat shock proteins expressed in the marsupial Tasmanian devil are potential antigenic candidates in a vaccine against devil facial tumour disease. *PLoS One* **13**(4), e0196469. doi:10.1371/journal.pone.0196469

Weeks AR, Heinze D, Perrin L, Stoklosa J, Hoffmann AA, *et al.* (2017) Genetic rescue increases fitness and aids rapid recovery of an endangered marsupial population. *Nat Commun* **8**(1), 1071. doi:10.1038/s41467-017-01182-3

Woods GM, Kreiss A, Belov K, Siddle HV, Obendorf DL, *et al.* (2007) The immune response of the Tasmanian devil (*Sarcophilus harrisii*) and devil facial tumour disease. *EcoHealth* **4**(3), 338–345.

Woods GM, Lyons AB, Bettiol SS (2020) A devil of a transmissible cancer. *Tropical Medicine and Infectious Disease* **5**(2), 50.

Wright B, Willet CE, Hamede R, Jones M, Belov K, *et al.* (2017) Variants in the host genome may inhibit tumour growth in devil facial tumours: evidence from genome-wide association. *Scientific Reports* **7**(1), 1–6.

10 Genetic-based inventories of wildlife abundance

Garth Mowat, Joseph D. Clark, Alexander Kopatz, Clayton Lamb and Anita J. Norman

ABSTRACT

Abundance and density are key demographic parameters of wildlife populations used by field biologists to evaluate whether conservation goals have been reached. Genomic and genetic analyses can be used to assign individual identity to samples collected from animals without capturing or sighting them. Repeated detections of the same individual are confirmed using match probabilities, creating a dataset similar to traditional live-capture and recapture surveys, which have been the backbone of abundance estimation for many species. Because genetic-based inventories of individuals do not require the physical capture of individuals they often allow large sample sizes over extensive areas and are less hazardous for both animals and researchers. DNA can be obtained from numerous sources, including hair, feathers, faeces, urine and saliva. New DNA biomarkers broaden the range of information obtainable from samples to include age, stress level, and diet, which opens the door to addressing many complex challenges in wildlife management. In the future, genetic-based inventories may be the preferred tool for a single inventory or, they may underpin long-term population sampling and contribute to more integrated approaches for population analysis that address complex ecological questions or conservation decisions.

INTRODUCTION TO WILDLIFE INVENTORY USING GENETIC IDENTIFICATION METHODS

Abundance and density are key demographic parameters of wildlife populations used by field biologists to evaluate whether conservation goals have been reached (Sinclair *et al.* 2006). Total counts are rare for wildlife populations because detection rates – the proportion of animals in the population that are detected – are rarely 100%. Although there are many ways to estimate population size such as count surveys, distance sampling, or capture-recapture, these methods are all related because they all estimate the detection rate. Given an estimate of detection, the number of animals present in the population is a function of the number of individuals detected divided by the detection rate (Box 10.1). Detections can consist of sightings, animal calls, live-capture and tagging, hunter returns, and many other methods, as long as captured and recaptured animals, or groups of animals, can be identified and the animals detected are representative of the population as a whole. Most of these methods are expensive and hence are most often used across smaller scales.

The development of polymerase chain reaction (PCR) techniques in the 1980s allowed the analysis of minute

Box 10.1: Spatial capture-recapture analysis

Traditional capture-mark-recapture (CMR) models use repeat detections of individual animals to estimate population abundance (*N*). By knowing which animals were captured and how frequently they were recaptured, CMR models can estimate the detection probability (p; Fig. 10.1 part I). Population abundance (*N*) can then be estimated by dividing the number of individual animals detected (*M*) by *p*. Density (*D*) is derived by dividing *N* by the area sampled. Unfortunately, the area sampled can be difficult to determine in many field situations (Fig. 10.1 part II). Most traditional CMR users add a buffer strip around the sampling grid to estimate this area, but there is no explicit way to estimate the width of this buffer, which can lead to uncertainty in *D* (see Mowat *et al.* 2005 for an example of this problem). Moreover, animals living along the periphery of the sampling grid may have fewer detectors in their home range and lower detection probability than animals in the centre of the grid, which can violate model assumptions and lead to estimation bias (Boulanger and McLellan 2001).

Spatially explicit capture-recapture (**SCR**) models were developed to overcome these challenges. SCR models leverage the spatial information inherent in the repeat detections, but unused in CMR, to estimate population density explicitly. By assuming detection rates are highest when a detection device is located at an animal's activity centre, and decreases as that distance increases, a half normal (or other) detection function is used to estimate *p*, based on the distance from the animal's activity centre (Fig. 10.1 parts III and IV). The detection function is fit based on the estimate of each animal's activity centre, which is calculated from repeat captures of individual animals at different fitted traps. The area under the curve specified by the detection function is *p*. Animals (detected and not detected) are assumed to be uniformly or homogeneously distributed on the

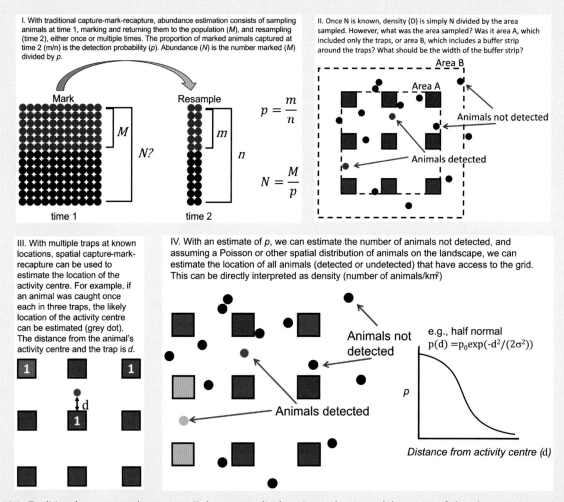

I. With traditional capture-mark-recapture, abundance estimation consists of sampling animals at time 1, marking and returning them to the population (*M*), and resampling (time 2), either once or multiple times. The proportion of marked animals captured at time 2 (m/n) is the detection probability (*p*). Abundance (*N*) is the number marked (*M*) divided by *p*.

$$p = \frac{m}{n}$$

$$N = \frac{M}{p}$$

II. Once N is known, density (D) is simply N divided by the area sampled. However, what was the area sampled? Was it area A, which included only the traps, or area B, which includes a buffer strip around the traps? What should be the width of the buffer strip?

III. With multiple traps at known locations, spatial capture-mark-recapture can be used to estimate the location of the activity centre. For example, if an animal was caught once each in three traps, the likely location of the activity centre can be estimated (grey dot). The distance from the animal's activity centre and the trap is *d*.

IV. With an estimate of *p*, we can estimate the number of animals not detected, and assuming a Poisson or other spatial distribution of animals on the landscape, we can estimate the location of all animals (detected or undetected) that have access to the grid. This can be directly interpreted as density (number of animals/km²)

e.g., half normal
$$p(d) = p_0 \exp(-d^2/(2\sigma^2))$$

Fig. 10.1. Traditional capture-mark-recapture (I) does not explicitly estimate density and the extent of abundance estimates is often unknown (II). Spatially explicit capture-recapture uses data on trap locations to estimate animal activity centres (III) which can then be used to estimate a detection function that directly produces unbiased estimates of density (IV).

landscape and statistically represented as a Poisson point process. The models also allow animals to be clumped or unevenly distributed based on habitat features that can be modelled as spatial covariates. With an estimate of p, and the location of activity centres of animals that were detected, the number and location of activity centres for undetected animals can then be estimated. Following that, the number of animals for a given area can be tallied and density can be explicitly estimated without the need for buffer strips or other ad hoc correction methods. Density can then be mapped based on the spatial variation in animal detections and spatial covariates. Models for gregarious animals have also been developed (McFarlane *et al.* 2020).

amounts of DNA. This opened the door for field biologists to collect small amounts of DNA from samples such as hair or scat and use them to assign animal identity and gender without actually handling the animal (Box 10.2; Selkoe and Toonen 2006; Morin *et al.* 2009). Recaptures are identified based on a DNA match to a previously genotyped individual rather than with a leg band, ear tag, or other mark. From an animal welfare standpoint, sampling methods involving the collection of genetic material from sources such as hair or feathers are often less invasive than other methods (Lamb *et al.* 2019). Other sample sources such as saliva, eggshells, and faeces are even less intrusive because they are naturally shed by animals and collected without disturbance to the animal that left them. After a period of intense evaluation of results to control lab errors (Paetkau 2003; Bellemain *et al.* 2005; Kendall *et al.* 2009), genetically identifying individuals from minimally invasive samples has become routine in established laboratories and has been used on many species around the globe to inventory animal populations. Genetic methods have also allowed inventories of species that cannot be live-captured or readily counted, such as whales (Palsbøll *et al.* 1997). The collection of tiny tissue samples can be repeated across broad spatial scales that are impractical for live-capture; these large spatial extents are often most relevant to conservation questions (Mowat *et al.* 2019).

The use of genetic analysis to identify individuals has largely replaced the live-capture of many large animal species for inventory purposes. Genetic sampling typically follows a capture-mark-recapture (CMR) design (Box 10.1); these statistical methods are well-established, robust, powerful, and in a constant state of advancement (Efford 2004; Royle *et al.* 2013). The ability to identify individuals and calculate their detection rates, instead of calculating detection rates of unidentified individuals, provides greater statistical power to estimate abundance, and allows the estimation of vital rates such as survival, recruitment, emigration, or immigration if sampling is repeated annually. Estimation of vital rates allows practitioners to estimate how the population is changing over time and investigate why. Longitudinal studies based on genetic sampling can be very economical because sample collection methods are often simple and efficient (Box 10.4; Clark 2019; Bischof *et al.* 2020). Further, the longitudinal capture-recapture dataset can serve as a basis for more unified analyses using such tools as Integrated Population Models (Bischof *et al.* 2020). Ongoing methods development revolves around three axes: 1) sampling design (Box 10.3) and statistical analysis of the detection data (Box 10.1); 2) improving genetic analysis methods (Box 10.2); and 3) the development of novel ways to collect genetic samples.

Box 10.2: Microsatellites versus SNPs for genetic-based inventories

The two most common diagnostic genetic markers in wildlife inventory methods are microsatellites, and **single nucleotide polymorphisms (SNPs)**. Microsatellites are strings of repeated nucleotide motifs, such as ACACAC, that vary in numbers of repeats, and hence, length, at specific parts of a genome. This length variation can be measured and is used to distinguish individual genomes (Fig. 10.2). Each unique length for one marker is called an allele and there can be many different alleles (polyallelic) at the same location in the genome (locus) within a population. Thus, the information content in one microsatellite marker can be high. Microsatellites have been used since the 1990s and are relatively easy and cost-efficient to apply (see for example Bruford and Wayne 1993). However, there are some fundamental challenges with microsatellites including high genotyping error rates, particularly when using non-invasive biological samples such as faeces or hair, lack of repeatability between experiments and laboratories, and their rarity across the genome (Taberlet and Luikart 1999).

SNPs are a single base **substitution** at one location in the genome. Most often a SNP will contain one of two nucleotides and are hence termed biallelic. Compared with microsatellites, the information content of a single SNP is much lower. However, SNPs are plentiful across the genome and thus enough SNPs can usually be found to obtain the required statistical power. SNPs have only been used in wildlife studies since about 2005 (Morin *et al.* 2004). With the onset of next generation sequencing, the use of SNPs has become much more feasible, and they are now commonly developed for new species. However, the initial development of SNPs is still more costly and requires more effort than for microsatellites. Once developed, SNPs are much simpler and more cost-effective to use, abundant across the genome, have lower error rates particularly with non-invasive samples, and are reproducible across studies and laboratories. The fact that SNP data does not require calibration allows for quick method harmonisation, direct data comparison and the sharing of genetic databases for meta-analyses (Brumfield *et al.* 2003; De Barba *et al.* 2010; Kraus *et al.* 2015).

A single microsatellite or SNP-marker alone does not contain sufficient information for individual identification. Several microsatellite or SNP-markers are required to provide enough statistical power to distinguish individuals and to calculate population parameters such as genetic diversity of the sampled individuals or population. For both microsatellites and SNPs, their informativeness shifts gradually according to the geographical space of the study area and time, which is known as **ascertainment bias** (Morin *et al.* 2009). For instance, a marker may display variation in one population but is invariant (monomorphic) in an adjacent population. Therefore, it is important to evaluate each set of markers for its informativeness on the focal population prior to their application. This will also help determine the number of markers required to answer the specific questions. Genetic markers are species-specific, but cross-species amplification can happen, especially for related species. Careful selection and evaluation of the marker system will help avoid possible challenges in interpretation, ascertainment bias, or cross-species amplification (Selkoe and Toonen 2006).

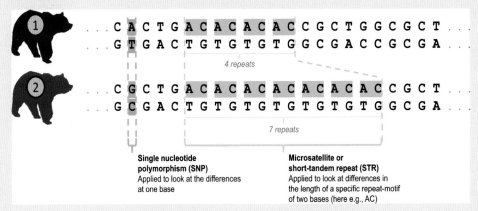

Fig. 10.2. A snapshot of the genotype profile of two different individuals highlighting how SNP and microsatellite markers can distinguish between individuals. Note that a number of SNP or microsatellite markers are typically analysed to increase the statistical power to discriminate between individuals.

THE APPLICATION – HOW GENETIC-BASED INVENTORIES WORK

Study and sample design

Spatial capture-recapture (SCR) methods are relatively new but have resolved many of the outstanding issues that traditional capture-recapture (CMR) could not (Box 10.1). SCR offers a universal way of accommodating the spatial variation in capture success across a study area because this method explicitly includes where an animal was captured in the analysis (Box 10.1; Efford 2004). In addition to accounting for differences in detection probability among animals based on their location within the trapping grid, spatial variation in density can be accommodated if density is correlated with landscape attributes such as forest cover, distance to roads, or mortality risk (Fig. 10.4).

Spatial covariates improve model fit and accuracy and, because equal detection rates among animals are not assumed, they enable the model to estimate density in areas that were not sampled. This allows for gaps in the sampling array, which allows for many more sample design options than CMR (Fig. 10.1). This is particularly important for studies at large spatial extents; clustering detectors across the landscape means that fewer detectors can be used which saves on travel costs. For example, data from Settlage and colleagues (Settlage *et al.* 2008) indicated that 11 496 hair traps would be needed for a CMR estimate of American black bear density in a 66 678 km² region in the southern Appalachian Highlands in the south-eastern USA. Using SCR and cluster sampling, only 888 traps were needed to provide a robust population estimate with similar precision (Humm and Clark 2021). Genetic methods combined with cluster sampling and SCR analysis can allow inventories for areas and species that have previously not been achievable. Moreover, these large spatial extents allow for 'economies of scale' whereby large studies, even those that cross management jurisdictions, can provide better estimates than smaller studies (Howe *et al.* 2013; Clark 2019; Efford and Boulanger 2019). Larger sampling extents enable estimation of shared model parameters such as detection rate (p_0) or range size (σ) when biologically appropriate. Finally, SCR provides a simple framework for extrapolating density which is very useful for conservation decisions that are often made for much larger areas than could previously be inventoried.

Whether CMR or SCR models are used, study design is the first consideration in proposing an inventory. If abundance and not density is of greatest interest, CMR methods may be appropriate. A critical assumption with CMR is that all animals in the study area have an equal probability of detection, regardless of their location in the area. This assumption can often be accommodated in CMR studies if sampling intensity is high (e.g. several traps are available to each individual in the population), but this often means that study areas are small by necessity. Density can be estimated using CMR if the study area has well-defined ecological boundaries such as land surrounded by ocean or forest surrounded by agriculture; the area sampled will be known and density estimation straightforward.

If the boundaries of the study area are not ecologically defined, animal movements are large relative to the sampling grid, or the study area is large, then SCR has many advantages. Study design is important for all studies but trap spacing is especially important for SCR studies. If traps are too far apart relative to animal movements, then the likelihood of capturing an individual at more than one trap will be low and it will be impossible to estimate the animal's activity centre and the scale parameter (σ). The SCR model assumes the range centre is the capture location for those animals that are detected only once and bias may occur if there are too many individuals with single locations. Similarly, if the trap clusters are smaller than a single animal home range, σ will be underestimated, and density estimates will be biased high.

Given rough estimates of population density, detection probability, and range size, computer simulations can be used to evaluate the precision and bias associated with a given study design (Box 10.3). Precision and accuracy of the survey are related to both the number of unique animals detected and the number of recaptures of those individuals. Recaptures of the same individual in different places (spatial recaptures) are key to accurate modelling of the spatial component. By simulating capture history data, the number and location of detectors, and the number of sampling occasions can be compared to determine the arrangement that produces the most unbiased and precise estimates (Clark 2019; Efford and Boulanger 2019). Simulated study designs can be compared before sampling ever begins, so alternate designs can be considered, or the study abandoned before wasting valuable resources (McFarlane *et al.* 2020).

Box 10.3: Simulations to evaluate spatially explicit capture-recapture study designs: an example for grizzly bears in the Greater Yellowstone Ecosystem

Trap spacing, the number of sampling occasions, spatial extent, and other factors can be critical for obtaining reliable estimates using spatially explicit models. It can be very helpful to conduct simulations to evaluate feasibility and efficiency of various sampling designs. Data required for the simulation analysis are a study area boundary, a ballpark estimate of density, a rough estimate of the probability of detection at each animal's activity centre (p_0), and a ballpark estimate of the scaling parameter which is related to range size and movements (σ). These estimates can be taken from previous work in the study area or similar environments, or based on best guesses. In either case, a range of simulated scenarios will help to compare design options. As an illustration, the objective of the following analysis was to determine whether spatially explicit capture-recapture analysis based on cluster sampling with hair traps would be efficient for estimating population density and abundance for the grizzly bear population in the Greater Yellowstone Ecosystem (GYE), USA.

The study area is large (~50 000 km^2) so we wanted to evaluate clustering of traps to reduce field sampling costs. Whittington and Sawaya (2015) reported density estimates for females and males in Banff National Park, Canada of 0.000086/ha and 0.000068/ha (8.6 and 6.8/1000 km^2), respectively, which is a similar environment to Yellowstone. These estimates were similar to earlier conservative estimates from Yellowstone so we used 0.00008 for females and 0.00007 for males in our simulations. These can, of course, be adjusted as needed.

Table 10.1.   Performance of spatially explicit estimation models under various sampling scenarios.

The true density is 0.00008 female/ha and 0.00007 male/ha (scenarios 1–3), σ = 5000 m for females, 8000, for males, p_0 = 0.075 for females and 0.023 for males, trap spacing = 7000 m, cluster spacing = 40 000 m, and nine traps per cluster.

Scenario #	Sex	Cluster spacing	Occ.	# Clusters	# Traps	# Hair samples	Rel. bias	Rel. SE	CI coverage
1	F	40 000	6	39	268	141.2	0.007	0.157	0.93
1	M	40 000	6	39	268	110.6	0.039	0.548	0.91667
2	F	30 000	6	67	501	248.4	−0.002	0.117	0.96
2	M	30 000	6	67	501	203.2	0.017	0.415	0.9596
3	F	40 000	8	40	284	176.8	0.008	0.124	0.99
3	M	40 000	6	40	284	151.4	−0.020	0.419	0.97

We had no estimate of p_0 for the GYE population, but Whittington and Sawaya (2015) reported an average p_0 for females and males of about 0.0758 and 0.0229 (after back transformation), respectively. We used 0.075 and 0.023 for our simulations. There were also no estimates of the scaling parameter σ, but that can be estimated by dividing the 95% home range radius by 2.5. Home-range diameter was previously estimated as 24 and 43 km (M. Haroldson, US Geological Survey, unpublished data) resulting in estimates of σ of 4.78 and 8.38 km, so we used σ = 5000 m and 8000 m in our simulations for females and males, respectively (Table 10.1). We used R packages secr and secrdesign for the simulations (Efford 2020a, 2020b; R code available from the authors).

A range of trap spacings can be used and we began with 3-trap × 3-trap clusters with traps spaced 7 km apart and cluster centres spaced 40 km apart, and 6 sampling occasions (Fig. 10.3; Clark 2019). To evaluate our simulations, we calculated relative bias (the relative difference between the estimated density and the true density), relative standard error (SE; a measure of precision), and confidence interval (CI) coverage (how often the estimated CI contained the true density).

Density estimates for females were more precise and less biased than for males (Table 10.1). The most efficient scenario for females featured a trapping grid consisting of 40 clusters and a total of 284 traps, with clusters spaced 40 km apart, and 8 sample occasions. The relative SE for females was reasonable at about 12% but was high for males at 42%. We conclude that population estimates for females are probably estimable based on these trap spacings but males will likely require more traps or a different spacing configuration to obtain unbiased estimates.

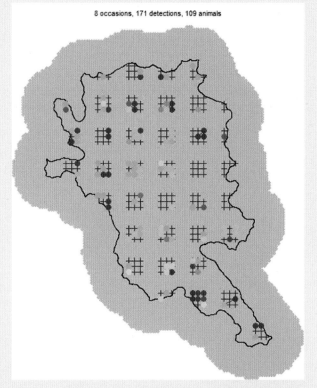

8 occasions, 171 detections, 109 animals

Fig. 10.3. Simulated capture locations for female grizzly bears in the Greater Yellowstone Ecosystem (0.00008/ha) based on a 3 × 3 trapping grid, traps spaced 7000 m apart, clusters spaced 40 000 m apart on the centre, p_0 = 0.075 and = 5000 m. Red crosses are hair traps and dots of the same colour within each cluster are captures of the same bear.

There are several caveats with this analysis that should be mentioned. First, we used the most simplistic model structure possible. We assumed no difference in p_0 or σ by sampling occasion, we assumed no individual capture heterogeneity or behavioural effects, and we did not use land cover covariates to model heterogeneous densities. In the real world, those effects will likely be present in the data and accounting for them may increase the standard errors (decrease precision) but reduce bias. Telemetry data can also be incorporated into these models to estimate σ which should increase precision.

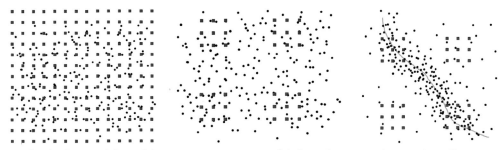

Fig. 10.4. Sequence showing how spatially explicit capture-recapture can result in fewer detectors and assumptions of homogeneous densities can be relaxed. Red squares represent detectors, black dots represent simulated animal range centres. Left: No expectation that all animals have access to a trap, that is, the sampling grid can have holes. Centre: Density can be estimated in areas, not samples allowing for more cost-efficient trapping designs, assuming homogeneity. Right: Using habitat covariates such as a river.

SCR methods also allow for stratified sampling. For example, if population densities are low in areas along the periphery of core populations or perhaps high when associated with a particular landscape feature (e.g. near a river), then practitioners might consider sampling more intensively in areas where densities are expected to be highest. Even clumsy stratification can improve precision. We suggest users also consider relative risk of error when they stratify. If a portion of the study area is at lower conservation risk then the user may want to stratify and assign sample effort to each strata relative to risk. Areas with very low conservation risk, for example a park or unharvested area, could even be excluded from sampling. The design must ensure that trap clusters capture all variation in density and its correlates across the study area if extrapolation is to be accurate (Efford and Boulanger 2019). Areas that are deemed unsuitable for the species being studied (e.g. lakes, urban areas) can be excluded during sampling or during analysis.

It is straightforward to combine data from multiple studies, or years, across broad areas with SCR methods (Mowat *et al.* 2019). With multiple years of data, open models, which allow for the addition and loss of individuals among years, can often be deployed and there is a growing array of models and tools for doing so (Efford and Schofield 2020). Open models can estimate vital rates, which provide important insights into the factors that determine changes in population abundance or density (Bischof and Swenson 2012). Like non-spatial models, users of SCR can incorporate behavioural effects, temporal effects, and individual capture heterogeneity that cause variation in capture probabilities, to create models that better fit the data (Royle *et al.* 2013; Efford 2020b). Several software packages are available for fitting SCR models in a maximum likelihood framework (Sutherland *et al.* 2019; Efford 2020b), and Bayesian methods have been developed as well (Royle *et al.* 2013).

Collecting genetic samples

Every part of an animal contains genetic material. The optimal sample type for investigators to collect will depend on the behaviour and ecology of the species, past work assessing the efficacy of different sampling methodologies for that species, and user imagination for developing and testing new sample collection methods. Sampling can occur by a variety of means such as collecting tissue from live or dead individuals, or by collecting genetic material found in the environment such as hair, faeces, urine, or feathers from living animals. Samples can be acquired opportunistically, or systematically via the use of tissue removal devices, or some combination of the two.

Once the type of sample to collect has been decided, there are several logistical considerations to increase sampling efficiency and data quality. Biological material exposed to the environment can be degraded to the extent that DNA molecules in the sample are destroyed. Thus, evaluating the length of time that samples might be exposed to inclement weather and how to protect the sample once collected are important considerations (Murphy *et al.* 2007). For example, Stetz *et al.* (2014) experimentally exposed black and grizzly bear hair samples to varying degrees of time, sunlight, and moisture to measure their influence on genotyping success. They found genotyping success was lower for samples that were exposed to high levels of sunlight and moisture. Liquid or moist faeces samples may pose a particular challenge for inventories conducted in regions with humid environmental conditions. Several studies recorded higher rates of genotyping success using dry samples, or samples from dry environments, and thus recommended conducting sampling during dry or colder seasons (Maudet *et al.* 2004; Murphy *et al.* 2007). Effects and results, however, may vary among seasons, species, and regions. The genotyping success of faeces for instance appears to be influenced by multiple interacting factors. Collected samples should be promptly stored out of direct sun or high heat. Biological samples should be collected as fresh as possible to avoid DNA degradation caused by environmental conditions and storage time (Stetz *et al.* 2014; Bourgeois *et al.* 2019). The best sample storage technique varies with sample type and best advice will often be available from the genetic lab that practitioners are using.

Handling samples should be done with care to avoid destroying the DNA and to prevent contamination between samples. To help identify degraded DNA and contamination events, a workflow should be adopted that includes quality assurance checks so possible irregularities can be identified. This can be achieved by simple, continuous documentation of crucial information about not only the sample itself (thorough and legible labelling is key!), but also of the people involved and the entire process leading to sample collection. Once a sample has been collected, optimally stored for DNA conservation, and additional data recorded, such as sample quality information, it needs to be either archived or sent directly to the laboratory to process. Use of databases with barcodes for each sample can reduce errors due to mishandling, mislabelling, or misreading of samples. Modern phones and tablets can read barcodes and a number of applications, such as Tap Forms©, can be used to collect data and scan barcodes, reducing keystroke errors. We suggest preparing labels prior to sampling that include barcodes with sample numbers and other pertinent information and using electronic devices to simplify field data recording and minimise field-based errors. Contact the authors for examples of digital field forms.

Genetic methods to assign identity

Genetic methods are a proven tool used to identify individuals, particularly with non-invasive sampling or when working with biological material of which the identity of the individual is ambiguous or unknown. Managers of wild populations can incorporate genetic methods by partnering with geneticists and a laboratory that provides genetic services. Genetic analysis for inventory is not traditional research and is often closer to a fee-for-service relationship than an academic partnership. It is important to choose a lab that is set up to deal with the sample types and volumes required for the inventory and ensure that the lab has the capacity to effectively communicate the required results to a non-geneticist. Some universities have a lab that can process external inventory samples for a fee. They may ask if the results can also be used as a part of their research efforts, which may add value to the study. Additionally, it might be worth checking your local zoo as some may have genetic labs that can analyse samples. There are also private labs that can provide similar services. Choosing a lab can be a challenge for field biologists who are not familiar with genetic data or products. Contacting or collaborating with other biologists with previous experience in that field can be beneficial.

Based on the goal and questions to be answered, the type of genetic marker must be chosen. Typically, it will either be microsatellites or SNPs (see Box 10.2) but can include whole or a reduced representation of a genome. For wildlife inventory, genomic data would essentially increase the number of genetic markers being used, thereby increasing the statistical power of individual identification methods. Such data could provide additional information beyond individual identification that may be helpful. However, whole genomic analysis is still costly and requires greater expertise to analyse and is usually not necessary for wildlife inventories. One example of this application involves the white-phased black bear, known as spirit or Kermode bears, which can be found on the northern coast of British Columbia, Canada. The gene responsible for this colour morph has been identified and, through whole or partial genome sequencing, the colour morph can be identified in non-invasive samples (Ritland *et al.* 2001).

The first step after selecting a marker type is to determine if there are already markers that have been developed for the species in question. A check of a public repository such as the National Center for Biotechnology Information

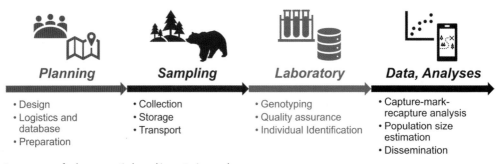

Fig. 10.5. Four stage process for how genetic-based inventories work.

(www.ncbi.nlm.nih.gov) is a good start but contacting experienced practitioners can also help answer this question. If genetic markers have been previously developed, it is important to know where and which populations samples were obtained from to avoid ascertainment bias (see Glossary). If there are no markers available, or if there is risk of ascertainment bias, you will need to develop a new set of markers specifically for the questions and population being assessed. When selecting genetic markers, it is often helpful to include specialised markers, for example those found on the sex chromosomes that can help identify sex and reflect the maternal and paternal lineage (see Chapter 8). Developing markers must be done by specialised genetic laboratories and field biologists will usually need to provide a set of samples from their study area to use for marker development and testing.

The next step is to collect a representative collection of biological samples from the target population and to genotype these samples. For each run, sample, and genetic marker, it is important to perform a quality check to identify any erroneous genotypes. This may include allelic drop-out where one allele failed to amplify (in a diploid species), ghost alleles where an allele is detected where none exists, or misprints where the wrong allele is detected. The error rate can be calculated based on the number of erroneous genotypes identified and is an important metric to include in any published report or article. This step must be done by experienced personnel. For non-invasively collected sample material, such as hair and faeces, genotyping should be independently repeated because these types of samples often have variable genotyping success. All runs from the same sample are used to determine the consensus genotype of a sample. Genotyping success will vary and not all samples will necessarily deliver a complete genetic profile. We suggest practitioners examine the relationship between DNA available per sample and minimum sample quality levels to reduce failed genotyping events (e.g. Berry *et al.* 2012). For example, to reduce genotyping failures we use three guard hairs or 15 underfur as the minimum sample quality for our study in Box 10.4 because average genotyping success improved from about 40% for one guard hair to about 70% for three (Lamb *et al.* 2016). Samples also

---

Box 10.4: Citizen science and long-term population monitoring: the South Rockies Grizzly Bear Project

Obtaining genetic samples from wildlife often requires no specialised skills, allowing the involvement of the public in the sample collection process. This is particularly helpful for long-term studies because the public often live in the study area, know the area well, and traverse it regularly for other reasons, making it efficient for them to repeatedly collect samples. Some studies integrate stakeholders by creating a data stream based on their actions such as hunting (Bischof *et al.* 2020). This is a common framework because animal harvest is regulated in most parts of the world and governments can mandate some forms of data collection, such as sample collection from harvested animals.

The conservation of grizzly bears has been contentious in south-eastern British Columbia, Canada for many decades. Some local residents felt there were too many bears because conflicts with people were common, but the available data suggested bear mortality rates were already high. Efforts to inventory the population using genetic sampling began in 1996 (Boulanger and McLellan 2001) and occurred piecemeal for the following decade. This work did little to resolve the local conflict (Mowat *et al.* 2013). In 2006, a government-led monitoring program was begun based on traditional hair sampling methods using trained field biologists and mechanical access including helicopters. As time passed and funding became more difficult to secure, it was obvious that local people could sample the area much more efficiently than government field crews. Bears can be sampled at trees where they naturally rub, and these sites are easier to sample than baited sites and are found on low use roads and trails. We solicited volunteers from the local area to check these trees and collect samples when hair was present. We used local media and the internet (www.grizzlyresearch.ca) to contact people and created live interactions by having yearly public meetings where we reported results and answered questions. The project now has over 50 volunteers, most of whom return each year and sample bears while they are hiking, biking, hunting, and driving. Volunteers have collected about 60% of the approximately 2000 samples collected annually in the more accessible portions of our 8000 km^2 study area for the past decade. Employees are also key to this project because they cover volunteer absences, find and set up new rub trees, and check trees in areas not frequented by volunteers. These efforts are key to reducing biases associated with the more opportunistic sampling conducted by volunteers. Volunteers record their data on sample envelopes and drop these off in designated boxes throughout the area. They also record when they check sites in a shared virtual document and a coordinator ensures that each site is checked monthly. Sample collection has been so successful that genetic analysis, rather than field data collection, is now the single largest annual project cost (Mowat *et al.* 2020). This large and repeated sample has resolved many local questions about grizzly bear management (Mowat *et al.* 2013; Lamb *et al.* 2019) and conservation (Lamb *et al.* 2017) and local involvement has generated greater confidence in the findings.

deteriorate when exposed to sun and moisture and we suggest users plot genotyping success against the time each sample was exposed to the environment (Stetz *et al.* 2014; Lamb *et al.* 2016). This relationship can be used to help select how often to check each detection site or to screen samples that may have lower genotyping success due to exposure to the environment. Also, for faeces, even with consistent volumes per sample collected, the combination of different factors such as exposure time, humidity, or diet may influence genotyping success (Nsubuga *et al.* 2004; Murphy *et al.* 2007). With genotypes assigned, the final step is to identify the number of unique individuals within the samples using software that calculates the **probability of identity** for each sample, and tests for matches within the entire sample database. For most field biologists it is important that the lab chosen to do the genetic analysis has a comprehensive process to control for genetic errors and presents final identification results in clearly understandable written summaries and interpretable databases. There are various algorithms that can be used to help identify genotyping errors and more are being developed on a regular basis.

To minimise costs and manage expectations associated with genotyping, there are a few things to consider:

- Consider whether genotyping is the best way forward. For instance, a one-time assessment of a population across a limited scale may not warrant the time and costs associated with genotyping. Also, if genetic samples are too difficult to obtain for your species of interest, perhaps another method is warranted.
- The whole project should be considered prior to commencing a genetic inventory with each step reviewed in detail including how the results will be disseminated (Fig. 10.5).
- The choice of marker is important. For example, if inventories will be conducted on a regular basis, it might be worthwhile to invest in the development of a set of SNPs, as genetic analysis will cost less in the long run if thousands of samples are analysed. The development of specific SNPs can also limit the possibility of spurious or even negative genetic results, especially when using non-invasive sample material.
- While sampling, take care to avoid sun or rain exposure for long periods and ensure the samples are labelled correctly.
- Try to identify different labs to do the analysis and ask about their experience. Get price quotes on a sample basis as well as set-up costs. Ensure that the lab you

decide on is reputable and knowledgeable to avoid costly mistakes such as lab-based contamination or misidentification genotyping errors. It is worth considering having an agreement in writing. In this agreement, be sure to include a statement that specifies who is responsible for the additional costs if the lab makes a mistake and some or all the work needs to be repeated.
- Lastly, discuss publication and dissemination of the key findings. Information on the methodology and transparent communication of the results is key for wide acceptance of the results.

FUTURE DIRECTIONS AND OUTSTANDING QUESTIONS

An exciting facet of genetic-based inventories is that how samples are collected is limited only by the imagination of the practitioners. New ways to collect DNA are regularly developed, some based on the skill of laboratory biologists, such as eDNA (Chapter 1), whereas other novel approaches have been based on close observation of the species in its environment and repeated testing to select among various options (MacKay *et al.* 2008; Magoun *et al.* 2011). The testing and development of new DNA field sampling methods will increase the use of DNA-based inventories in the future, particularly in organisms that have not yet been sampled. Often, no special expertise is needed to collect DNA samples so much of the field work can be accomplished by citizen scientists (Beausoleil *et al.* 2016).

The cost of sample analysis is a limitation to the application of DNA-based inventories and the method will be used more regularly as genetic analysis costs are reduced. The application of SNPs in place of microsatellites may help in this regard but further advances in genotyping that reduce costs will also help expand the application of DNA-based inventories.

There are several projects aimed at producing complete reference genomes for every species on earth (e.g. Earth BioGenome Project, Vertebrate Genomes Project). As more species have a representative reference genome, possibilities for research applications expand greatly. Within species, research can focus on genetic diversity, including assessing levels of inbreeding or outbreeding, gene-specific inheritance patterns, identifying family units and reproductive rates of individuals (Mikle *et al.* 2016), landscape patterns such as barriers to gene flow (Proctor *et al.* 2012), and more. All of this can enhance wildlife inventory projects or be used to advance research on the species of interest or a combination of both. Furthermore, research using genomic methods between species becomes possible, particularly when studying genome evolution. Comparing genomes across species of varying relatedness, enables the identification of specific genes that have evolved to aid a species in adapting to its environment. For example, in a comparison of sister species such as the polar bear (*Ursus maritimus*) and brown bear (*Ursus arctos*), one could identify how the polar bear evolved in its specialised polar environment, or one could compare genomes between polar bear and arctic fox to identify genes that have evolved simultaneously for their specialised environment. This is beyond the goals of wildlife inventory studies. However, these questions are important in light of climate change and the need to detect changes in a species ability to adapt to what was formerly a suitable environment. Inventories are prodigious sources of data for these types of studies because many individuals are sampled over large areas. For any genome that is sequenced, planning for long-term storage of the data would allow researchers to track evolutionary changes in the genome over time.

The DNA-based inventory framework marries well with other new tools such as the use of epigenetic biomarkers to assign individual age (Chapter 7). Measures of individual age allow the use of many powerful demographic tools which can greatly expand the scope of investigation. Similarly, measures of individual diet using stable isotopes or metabarcoding (Chapter 4) enables the analysis of diet across large spatial scales (Mowat and Heard 2006; Adams *et al.* 2017). These metrics could be integrated with individual measures of fitness, such as reproduction, to investigate relationships between diet and fitness. Now that these methods can be applied to samples that do not require the handling of the animal, it is possible to address these questions at large scales. This will be of great benefit to management agencies who regularly must make and assess decisions across entire countries or groups of countries.

Spatial methods to map and extrapolate density can also be used to forecast and back cast demographic parameters in time (Bischof *et al.* 2020). The incorporation of genetic data into integrated population models that use all available data about the study or management system can provide a new platform for data analysis, decision making and planning future data needs (Fieberg *et al.* 2010). These models are almost universal decision-making tools and have the potential to revolutionise resource management. Computational advances such as supercomputers or cloud-based parallel computing resources are helping to speed up run times of these models, which can be a limitation to their use (Turek *et al.* 2021).

Beyond estimating demographic parameters, capture-recapture data can also be used to estimate movement and connectivity in larger landscapes. Repeat captures of the same animal, through space, in the case of SCR, are key to model precision, and movement trajectories and directional preferences are embedded in these data. A growing body of literature is using SCR data to estimate population connectivity and the factors that influence it (Fuller *et al.* 2016; Morin *et al.* 2017). Also, the combination of capture-recapture and genetic data enables numerous possibilities for using genetic data to further characterise the population, such as close-kin mark-recapture (Marcy-Quay *et al.* 2020; Waples and Feutry 2021, chapter 11), which allows for comprehensive assessments of species distribution, dispersal, census and effective population size (Skrbinšek *et al.* 2012; Kamath *et al.* 2015), survival, and reproductive output (Bischof *et al.* 2020). We expect the broad array of ecological questions now answerable with capture-recapture methods and genetic methods will further increase the application of these approaches. Such approaches will become a necessity as investigators become increasingly interested in demographic processes occurring at broad spatial scales.

DISCUSSION TOPICS

1. How might you ensure your inventory data can be extrapolated most accurately to areas you did not sample?
2. What population insights might a researcher gain from using SNPs to assign identity instead of microsatellites?
3. Do DNA-based methods of inventory improve animal welfare?
4. How can the use of genomic data help prevent a species or a population from going extinct?

RESOURCES

A search tool for publicly available genetic markers: NCBI Management Services Inc. www.ncbi.nlm.nih.gov
Earth BioGenome Project: https://www.earthbiogenome.org/
Vertebrate Genomes Project: https://vertebrategenomesproject.org/
South Rockies Grizzly Bear Project: https://grizzlyresearch.ca/

ACKNOWLEDGEMENTS

We would like to acknowledge the many colleagues who have helped us develop and apply these methods over the past 25 years. We are especially grateful to Murray Efford who has provided advice to countless people, including ourselves, on the use of spatial capture-recapture. His effort has greatly expanded the conservation toolbox and the aspirations of many dedicated biologists. Lastly, we would like to thank Frank van Manen, Sam Banks, Mark Haroldson and Oliver Berry for their thoughtful reviews of the manuscript.

REFERENCES

Adams MS, Service CN, Bateman A, Bourbonnais M, Artelle KA, et al. (2017) Intrapopulation diversity in isotopic niche over landscapes: Spatial patterns inform conservation of bear–salmon systems. *Ecosphere* **8**, 1843.

De Barba M, Waits LP, Garton EO, Genovesi P, Randi E, et al. (2010) The power of genetic monitoring for studying demography, ecology and genetics of a reintroduced brown bear population. *Molecular Ecology* **19**, 3938–3951.

Beausoleil RA, Clark J, Maletzke B (2016) A long-term evaluation of biopsy darts and DNA to estimate cougar density: An agency-citizen science collaboration. *Wildlife Society Bulletin* **40**, 583–592.

Bellemain E, Swenson JE, Tallmon D, Brunberg S, Taberlet P, (2005) Estimating population size of elusive animals with DNA from hunter-collected feces: Four methods for brown bears. *Conservation Biology* **19**, 150–161.

Berry O, Algar D, Angus J, Hamilton N, Hilmer S, et al. (2012) Genetic tagging reveals a significant impact of poison baiting on an invasive species. *The Journal of Wildlife Management* **76**, 729–739.

Bischof R, Milleret C, Dupont P, Chipperfield J, Tourani M, et al. (2020) Estimating and forecasting spatial population dynamics of apex predators using transnational genetic monitoring. *Proceedings of the National Academy of Sciences of the United States of America* **117**, 30531–30538.

Bischof R, Swenson JE (2012) Linking noninvasive genetic sampling and traditional monitoring to aid management of a trans-border carnivore population. *Ecological Applications* **22**, 361–373.

Boulanger JG, McLellan BN (2001) Closure violation bias in DNA based mark-recapture population estimates of grizzly bears. *Canada Journal of Zoology* **79**, 642–651.

Bourgeois S, Kaden J, Senn H, Bunnefeld N, Jeffery KJ, et al. (2019) Improving cost-efficiency of faecal genotyping: New tools for elephant species. *PLOS ONE* **14**, 210811.

Bruford MW, Wayne RK (1993) Microsatellites and their application to population genetic studies. *Current Opinion in Genetics and Development* **3**, 939–943.

Brumfield R, Beerli P, Nickerson DA, Edwards SV (2003) The utility of single nucleotide polymorphisms in inferences of population history. *Trends in Ecology and Evolution* **18**, 249–256.

Clark JD (2019) Comparing clustered sampling designs for spatially explicit estimation of population density. *Population Ecology* **61**, 93–101.

Efford M (2004) Density estimation in live-trapping studies. *Oikos* **106**, 598–610.

Efford M (2020a) Package 'secrdesign'.

Efford M (2020b) Package 'secr' – spatially explicit capture–recapture in R.

Efford MG, Boulanger J (2019) Fast evaluation of study designs for spatially explicit capture–recapture. *Methods in Ecology and Evolution* **10**, 1529–1535.

Efford MG, Schofield MR (2020) A spatial open-population capture-recapture model. *Biometrics* **76**(2), 392–402. doi:10.1111/biom.13150

Fieberg JR, Shertzer KW, Conn PB, Noyce KV, Garshelis DL (2010) Integrated population modeling of black bears in minnesota: Implications for monitoring and management. *PLOS ONE* **5**, 12114.

Fuller AK, Sutherland CS, Royle JA, Hare MP (2016) Estimating population density and connectivity of American mink using spatial capture–recapture. *Ecological Applications* **26**, 1125–1135.

Howe E, Obbard M, Kyle C (2013) Combining data from 43 standardized surveys to estimate densities of female American black bears by spatially explicit capture–recapture. *Population Ecology* **55**, 595–607.

Humm J, Clark JD (2021) Estimates of abundance and harvest rates of female black bears across a large spatial extent. *Journal of Wildlife Management* **85**, 1321–1331.

Kamath PL, Haroldson MA, Luikart G, Paetkau D, Whitman C, et al. (2015) Multiple estimates of effective population size for monitoring long-lived vertebrate: An application to Yellowstone grizzly bears. *Molecular Ecology* **24**, 5507–5521. doi:10.1111/mec.13398

Kendall K, Stetz JB, Boulanger J, Macleod AC, Paetkau D, et al. (2009) Demography and genetic structure of a recovering grizzly bear population. *Journal of Wildlife Management* **73**, 3–16.

Kraus RH, Vonholdt B, Cocchiararo B, Harms V, Bayerl H, et al. (2015) A single-nucleotide polymorphism-based approach for rapid and cost-effective genetic wolf monitoring in Europe based on noninvasively collected samples. *Molecular Ecology Resources* **15**, 295–305.

Lamb C, Mowat G, McLellan BN, Nielsen SE, Boutin S (2017) Forbidden fruit: human settlement and abundant fruit create an ecological trap for an apex omnivore. *Journal of Animal Ecology* **86**(1), 55–65. doi:10.1111/1365-2656.12589/full

Lamb CT, Ford AT, Proctor MF, Royle JA, Mowat G, et al. (2019) Genetic tagging in the Anthropocene: scaling ecology from alleles to ecosystems. *Ecological Applications* **29**, 1876.

Lamb CT, Walsh D, Mowat G (2016) Factors influencing detection of grizzly bears at genetic sampling sites. *Ursus* **27**, 31–44.

MacKay P, Zielinski WJ, Long RA, Ray JC, (2008) Noninvasive research and carnivore conservation. In *Noninvasive Survey Methods for Carnivores.* (Eds R Long et al.) pp. 1–7. Island Press.

Magoun A, Long CD, Schwartz MK, Pilgrim KL, Lowell RE, et al. (2011) Integrating motion-detection cameras and hair snags for wolverine identification. *Journal of Wildlife Management* **75**, 731–739.

Marcy-Quay B, Sethi SA, Therkildsen NO, Kraft CE (2020) Expanding the feasibility of fish and wildlife assessments with close-kin mark-recapture. *Ecosphere* **11**, 3259.

Maudet C, Luikart G, Dubray D, Von Hardenberg A, Taberlet P (2004) Low genotyping error rates in wild ungulate faeces sampled in winter. *Molecular Ecology Notes* **4**, 772–775.

McFarlane S, Manseau M, Steenweg R, Hervieux D, Hegel T, *et al.* (2020) An assessment of sampling designs using SCR analyses to estimate abundance of boreal caribou. *Ecology and Evolution* **10**, 11631–11642.

Mikle N, Graves TA, Kovach R, Kendall KC, Macleod AC (2016) Demographic mechanisms underpinning genetic assimilation of remnant groups of a large carnivore. *Proceedings of the Royal Society B: Biological Sciences* **283**, 20161467.

Morin DJ, Fuller AK, Royle JA, Sutherland C (2017) Model-based estimators of density and connectivity to inform conservation of spatially structured populations. *Ecosphere* **8**, 1623.

Morin PA, Luikart G, Wayne RK, SNP Workshop Group (2004) SNPs in ecology, evolution and conservation. *Trends in Ecology and Evolution* **19**, 208–216.

Morin PA, Martien KK, Taylor BL (2009) Assessing statistical power of SNPs for population structure and conservation studies. *Molecular Ecology Resources* **9**, 66–73.

Mowat G, Heard DC, Seip DR, Poole KG, Stenhouse G, *et al.* (2005) Grizzly *Ursus arctos* and black bear *U. americanus* densities in the interior mountains of North America. *Wildlife Biology* **11**(1), 31–48. doi:10.2981/0909-6396(2005)11[31:GUAABB]2.0.CO;2

Mowat G, Efford M, Mclellan BN, Nielsen S (2013) *South Rockies & Flathead Grizzly Bear Monitoring Final Report 2006–2011*. British Columbia Ministry of Forests, Lands, Natural Resource Operations and Rural Development, Nelson, BC, Canada.

Mowat G, Clevenger AP, Kortello AD, Hausleitner D, Barrueto M, *et al.* (2019) The sustainability of wolverine trapping mortality in Southern Canada. *Journal of Wildlife Management* **84**, 213–226.

Mowat G, Heard DC (2006) Major components of grizzly bear diet across North America. *Canada Journal of Zoology* **84**, 473–489.

Mowat G, Smit L, Lamb C, Faught N (2020) *South Rockies grizzly bear inventory: progress report 2006–2019*. British Columbia Ministry of Forests, Lands, Natural Resource Operations and Rural Development, Nelson, BC, Canada.

Murphy M, Kendall KC, Robinson A, Waits LP (2007) The impact of time and field conditions on brown bear (*Ursus arctos*) faecal DNA amplification. *Conservation Genetics* **8**, 1219–1224.

Nsubuga A, Robbins MM, Roeder AD, Morin PA, Boesch C, *et al.* (2004) Factors affecting the amount of genomic DNA extracted from ape faeces and the identification of an improved sample storage method. *Molecular Ecology* **13**, 2089–94.

Paetkau D (2003) An empirical exploration of data quality in DNA-based population inventories. *Molecular Ecology* **12**, 1375–1387.

Palsbøll P, Allen J, Berube M, Clapham PJ, Feddersen TP, *et al.* (1997) Genetic tagging of humpback whales. *Nature* **388**, 767–769.

Proctor MF, Paetkau D, McLellan BN, Stenhouse GB, Kendall KC, *et al.* (2012) Population fragmentation and inter-ecosystem movements of grizzly bears in western Canada and the northern United States *Wildlife Monographs* **180**, 1–46.

Ritland K, Newton C, Marshall H (2001) Inheritance and population structure of the white-phased 'Kermode' black bear. *Current Biology* **11**, 1468–1472.

Royle J, Chandler RB, Sollmann R, Gardner B (2013) *Spatial Capture-Recapture*. Academic Press, Cambridge, MA, USA.

Selkoe KA, Toonen RJ (2006) Microsatellites for ecologists: a practical guide to using and evaluating microsatellite markers. *Ecology* **9**, 615–629.

Settlage KE, Van Manen FT, Clark JD, King TL (2008) Challenges of DNA-based mark-recapture studies of American black bears. *Journal of Wildlife Management* **72**, 1035–1042.

Sinclair A, Fryxell J, Caughley G (2006) *Wildlife Ecology, Conservation and Management*. 2nd edn. Wiley-Blackwell, Hoboken, NJ, USA.

Skrbinšek T, Jelenčič M, Waits L, Kos I, Jerina K, *et al.* (2012) Monitoring the effective population size of a brown bear (*Ursus arctos*) population using new single- sample approach. *Molecular Ecology* **21**, 862–875. doi:10.1111/j.1365-294X.2011.05423.x

Stetz JB, Seitz T, Sawaya M (2014) Effects of exposure on genotyping success rates of brown and American black bears hair samples. *Journal of Fish and Wildlife Management* **5**, 1944–687.

Sutherland C, Royle J, Linden D (2019) oSCR: A spatial capture–recapture R package for inference about spatial ecological processes. *Ecography* **42**, 1459–1469.

Taberlet P, Luikart G (1999) Non-invasive genetic sampling and individual identification. *Biological Journal of the Linnean Society* **68**, 41–55.

Turek D, Milleret C, Ergon T, Brøseth H, Dupont P, *et al.* (2021) Efficient estimation of large-scale spatial capture–recapture models. *Ecosphere* **12**, 3385.

Waples RS, Feutry P (2021) Close-kin methods to estimate census size and effective population size. *Fish and Fisheries* **23**(2), 273–293.

Whittington J, Sawaya M (2015) A comparison of grizzly bear demographic parameters estimated from non-spatial and spatial open population capture-recapture models. *PloS one* **10**, 134446.

11 The practical magic of close-kin mark-recapture

Mark V. Bravington and Emma L. Carroll

ABSTRACT

The measurement of population abundance and other demographic parameters such as survival rate is fundamental to wildlife monitoring and the effective management of fisheries, hunting, and pest species. However, the task is often difficult, for example when a species is cryptic, widely dispersed, or difficult to biopsy alive. The field of close-kin mark-recapture (CKMR) has developed over the past decade to estimate abundance and demographics where other methods cannot. The tissue samples that it requires can if necessary be taken just from animals already dead (unlike with conventional mark-recapture of the same animal). CKMR has been made possible by the advent of high-throughput sequencing, which has facilitated genetic identification of kin pairs, and concurrent advances in demographic statistical models. The key idea is very simple: each sampled animal 'marks' its two parents at birth, and those 'marks' can be 'recaptured' later by comparing that sample to each other sample in turn. The rates of recapture depend on the size of the adult population, and on the demographic changes that the population undergoes over time. In this chapter, we provide a conceptual overview of CKMR models and how they can be used to estimate demographic parameters such as abundance, survival rate, and connectivity. We then give practical guidance on the five key steps involved in developing a CKMR project: design (qualitative and quantitative), kin-finding, sampling, modelling, and genotyping. Finally, we highlight current applications and future directions of this powerful technique.

INTRODUCTION TO CLOSE-KIN MARK-RECAPTURE (CKMR)

CKMR leverages the power of modern genomics to find pairs of close relatives (kin) within sets of genetic samples. The number of kin-pairs found, and the details about them (sizes, sexes, etc.), contain information on population abundance, survival rates, and other demographic parameters. The concept of CKMR is that any individual animal has 'marked' its two parents at birth, and those 'marks' can be 'recaptured' later by genetic identification of kin in pairwise analysis of all samples taken from the population. In each of those pairwise comparisons, a mark can be recaptured in one of two ways: either directly, when two animals turn out to be a parent-offspring pair (POP); or indirectly, when a full-sibling pair (FSP) or more usually half-sibling pair (HSP) is revealed. Finding a HSP means that both animals marked the same adult, even though the mark itself is not actually seen. Thanks to modern genomics, large numbers of samples can be genotyped affordably and accurately enough to classify the kinship of each pairwise comparison, at least to the level of POP, FSP, HSP, or 'Unrelated' pair (UP) which includes all more-distant kinships. To estimate demographic parameters, the results of all pairwise comparisons are embedded in an extended mark-recapture (MR) framework, adapted to the biology and sampling arrangements of the species and study system in question.

The approach has several useful, indeed almost magical, properties:

Time travel:
marking happened back when the samples were born, which, depending on their ages, may date to before the study's conception. Thus, CKMR projects do not need to wait years for samples to 'mix' or demographics to take effect; the samples' own lifespans are a window back in time. This can give us decades-long understanding of demographic parameters (e.g. population growth rate), without the need for a decades-long study, depending on the lifespan of the study species.

Crystal balls:
learning about adults without ever seeing them, by finding their offspring as half-siblings. This is important for some species that cannot readily be sampled as adults, including large sharks.

Reincarnation:
recapturing an animal after it is dead, via its surviving offspring.

A key point is that samples can, if necessary, come *only* from dead animals; unlike conventional MR, there is no need for any live-release, which can be an expensive or impossible undertaking for many species (see Chapter 10). CKMR is therefore well suited to settings like fisheries and hunting, where large sample sizes can be obtained incidentally at little cost.

Of course, it is also fine to collect biopsy samples from live animals. CKMR is very useful for endangered species as well as exploited ones, both in its own right and in conjunction with conventional MR. While there are slight statistical nuances between live- and dead-sampling, in practice either could normally give good results; ethical and practical circumstances will usually dictate which to use.

WHAT DOES CKMR TELL YOU?

The basic concepts are intuitive, although some complex statistical machinery is often required to turn data into

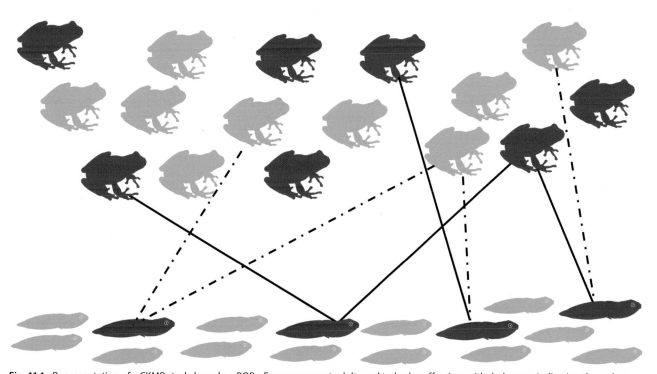

Fig. 11.1. Representation of a CKMR study based on POPs. Frogs represent adults and tadpoles offspring, with dark green indicating those that were sampled. Lines show parentage of each sampled tadpole: solid lines where that parent was also sampled (i.e. a detected POP), and dashed lines for other, unsampled, parents. There are 28 possible comparisons between the 7 sampled frogs and the 4 sampled tadpoles, from which 4 POPs were found. Assuming equal sampling probabilities between male and female adult frogs, and that there are (unknown) N adults in total, each such comparison has chance $2/N$ of yielding a POP, so we would expect $56/N$ POPs in total. Since we actually found 4 POPs, the data suggest an estimate of $\hat{N} = 14$; the true value in this case is 16. Real CKMR models usually have to be much more complicated!

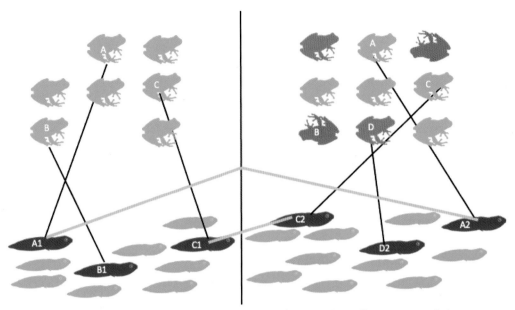

Fig. 11.2. Representation of a CKMR that uses HSPs, for simplicity only showing females, where offspring are sampled across two successive cohorts (left and right panels). Frogs represent adults and tadpoles offspring, with dark green indicating those that were sampled; no adult frogs were sampled. Dark lines show each sampled tadpole's (unsampled) mother, and orange lines show the HSPs detected amongst the sampled tadpoles, each representing an 'indirect recapture' of the first tadpole's mother. The tadpoles A1, B1, C1 sampled in the first cohort have three mothers A, B, and C. By the time the second cohort is born, mother B and one other female have died (in grey), and three other female frogs have reached adulthood (in blue). The samples from the second cohort of tadpoles are B2, C2, and D2. Survival of adults A and C is deduced from the existence of their HSP offspring (A1-A2 and C1-C2).

Fig. 11.3. Representation of a CKMR study where fecundity varies by age or size. Frogs represent adults and tadpoles offspring, with dark green indicating those that were sampled. The solid lines show POPs detected within the sample, whereas the dotted lines represent the unsampled offspring each individual female has produced; larger females have more offspring (and more POPs detected per capita) compared with smaller ones.

reliable estimates. To begin with, the more adults in the population, the more potential parents each sampled animal could have, and the lower the probability that any single pairwise comparison will turn out to be a mother-offspring pair (MOP) or a father-offspring pair (FOP). Therefore, the observed proportion of comparisons that turn out to be MOPs, say, is approximately the reciprocal of adult female abundance (Fig. 11.1).

A similar idea works for (half-)brothers and sisters (Fig. 11.2): the chance that two tadpoles share the same mother is approximately the reciprocal of the number of female adults, and similarly for fathers. Unfortunately, this doesn't work for same-cohort siblings, whose frequency is affected by random litter-to-litter variation in parentage as well as by adult abundance, but it does work well for cross-cohort siblings (usually HSPs). A useful feature of cross-cohort sibling identification is that the mother of the first-born HSP might die before the second HSP is born. This causes a declining frequency of HSPs with increasing birth gap, which can be used to estimate adult survival rates without even having to sample the adults.

There is other information in CKMR. In Fig. 11.3, bigger frogs tend to have more offspring, which means they are 'marked' more often. In such a situation, bigger sampled adults will feature more often in POPs than smaller sampled adults per capita, so the relative fecundity of the two size classes can be compared directly. Not all organisms have a link between fecundity and size (or age, etc.), but for those that do, it can be difficult to get empirical data on the strength of the relationship, especially for male adults. Knowing the relative reproductive contributions of different ages is important for management, e.g. with fish or sharks where the usual goal is to maintain the total reproductive capacity.

The other main benefit from close-kin data is insight into demographically important spatial structure (Waples and Gaggiotti 2006). Fig. 11.4 shows a simple example where CKMR can reveal structure and even allow estimation of 'exchange rates' (Patterson *et al.* 2022). CKMR can also rule out hypotheses, e.g. when kin-pairs are commonly found crossing a putative stock boundary. This ability contrasts with conventional population-genetic analyses based on allele or haplotype frequencies in two ways. First, demographically trivial levels of genetic connectivity can be sufficient to nearly eliminate signals of genetic differentiation between two populations (Waples 1998). Second, CKMR informs directly on connectivity over one to two generations, the timescale usually of relevance to management, compared with tens to hundreds of generations for typical population genetic metrics (Palsbøll *et al.* 2010; Waples *et al.* 2018).

An important general point about the interpretation of CKMR data is that abundance and survival parameters normally relate only to the adult part of the population. Each offspring always marks one adult mother and one adult father, but this is a 'one-way fact'; the average number of surviving offspring per adult is usually unknown.

Almost all CKMR applications will be more complicated than the frog example in Figs 11.1–11.4, often covering multiple cohorts of offspring and sampling across several years. Abundance can often change over that period. Different samples will have different covariates (year of sampling, age, location, etc.), the values of which affect demographic probabilities of kinship via the phenomena just discussed. Overall, the kin-pair data contain information about several demographic parameters linked together in such a way that they can only be estimated jointly via statistical modelling.

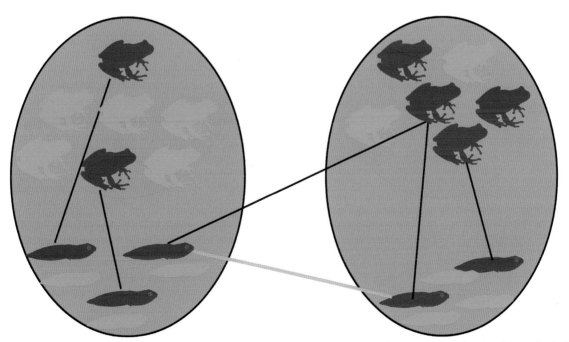

Fig. 11.4. Representation of a CKMR with spatial structure and only maternal descent considered. Frogs represent female adults and tadpoles offspring, with dark green indicating those that were sampled; black and orange lines represent detected MOPs and HSPs, respectively. There are more within-pond than between-pond POPs, although one HSP/MOP between ponds indicates some demographic interchange.

CKMR IN PRACTICE

CKMR may seem almost magical, because so much insight comes from such simple principles; but, as with all magic, the spell must be performed just right to succeed. There are five components to any CKMR project, and if any one of them fails, the whole project will fail with it (Fig. 11.5). Although the components are linked, they need quite different types of expertise: advanced coding and statistical analysis for modelling; lab skills and an understanding of the pitfalls of genetic analysis for genotyping; logistics of sampling; and, crucially, enough biological understanding to underpin the high-level strategy of the project. There is probably no single person on the planet who could deal well with all of these; usually, at least three or four people would be needed. Successful CKMR requires a team effort!

The process should start at the top with Design: planning the sampling to give the best chance of ultimately delivering usefully precise and robust estimates, while still being economical. But since the Design process actually needs to have a Model ready, we start by describing the core of CKMR: the framework for building models.

CKMR FRAMEWORK

CKMR is not just 'a' model – it is a framework that can be used to build different models for a wide range of biological and sampling schemes. The price of that flexibility is that a case-specific CKMR model needs to be built for each

dataset; there is no 'CKMR package' and none is imminent. Actually, this is not a bad thing, because having to build the model forces each team to think through what's appropriate to the study species. Once the CKMR principles are understood in relation to a specific project, devising the appropriate equations and writing the corresponding code is usually not that complicated. In fish stock assessments, for example, we have found that the code for dealing with CKMR data is often the simplest part. Of course, many species do have qualitatively similar properties, so code from previous applications can often be re-used or slightly adapted; CKMR models do become much easier to build with experience.

There are two components to any CKMR model, both of which should be adjusted to the situation at hand kinship probabilities, and population-dynamics (demographic) equations. The latter can be much the same as for any demographic modelling of the species, noting that adult sexes should be disaggregated; only the adult part of the population needs to be represented; and the time period covered must cover the span of likely birth dates of potential offspring samples. When fecundity stays fairly constant through adulthood, a simple exponential increase/decrease model for 'number of adults' might do. In contrast, for typical fish whose fecundity increases throughout adulthood as they grow, an explicit age-structured model is needed (Mills 2012).

Kinship probabilities are the key feature of CKMR models, and their calculation must consider covariates such as age, sex, and time of capture. The demographic probability that two individuals will turn out to have a particular kinship will depend on their particular covariates, as well as on the overall demographic parameters. Therefore, the key is to come up with biologically appropriate formulae for the situation at hand (see Bravington, Skaug *et al.* 2016 and Box 11.1). The right way to estimate parameters is to code a log-likelihood that combines the population-dynamics model and the kinship probability formulae for each comparison. That code constitutes 'the CKMR model', and it can be fitted to all the pairwise-comparison outcomes by numerical optimisation: that is, maximum likelihood estimation (MLE) or a Bayesian variant. The general properties of MLE ensure that parameter estimates are unbiased, and with an easily computed variance. Diagnostics of model-fit can be checked by comparing observed and expected numbers of kin-pairs (e.g. Trenkel *et al.* 2022).

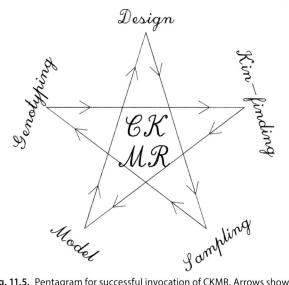

Fig. 11.5. Pentagram for successful invocation of CKMR. Arrows show the direction of successive stages.

Box 11.1: Kinship probabilities

What does a kinship probability formula actually look like, say for a comparison between a potential father Adam and potential offspring Jane? The core of CKMR is the principle of Expected Relative Reproductive Output (ERRO), in this case of Adam relative to all males:

$$\text{Prob} \begin{bmatrix} \text{Jane's father will turn out to be Adam,} \\ \text{given what we know about Adam} \end{bmatrix}$$

$$= \frac{\text{Adam's ERO of "Jane-like" offspring}}{\text{Total ERO of "Jane-like" offspring from all male adults}}$$

Here 'Jane-like' means having the same key covariates as Jane, including birth year; and Adam's Expected Reproductive Output (ERO) (i.e. without the 'Relative') will depend on what we know about Adam, such as his age and year of sampling. If all (male, in this case) adults are equally fecund on average, and if sampling is lethal, then the formula would just become:

Prob [Jane's Father will be Adam]

$$= \begin{cases} \dfrac{1}{N_{\male,\,Jane's\,birth}} & \text{if Adam was alive and mature at Jane's birth …} \\ & \text{… and he had not yet been sampled by then} \\ 0 & \text{if not} \end{cases}$$

where $N_{\male,\,Jane's\,birth}$ is the number of male adults alive then. The 'if' condition can be checked based on Adam's age when he was sampled. Essentially, unless Adam was too young or dead at Jane's conception, then he had as good a chance of being her father as any other living male adult, because of the equal-fecundity assumption. The unknown parameter(s) here are the time series of male abundances, normally controlled by a smaller number of fundamental parameters via the population-dynamics model. Non-lethal sampling is similar, except that a survival probability enters for the case when Adam was sampled before Jane's conception. Often, the assumption of equal fecundity does not hold (e.g. Fig. 11.3), and the formula becomes more complicated (see Bravington, Skaug et al. 2016).

The ERRO idea sometimes leads to simple formulae, as above, but there can be subtle complications both in biology and sampling. One example is limited movement combined with uneven sampling; there it may no longer just be *when* Jane was born that matters, but also *where* she was born, and the probability that Adam was at the right place at the right time. Another challenge is to measure covariates accurately, age especially. The ERRO formulae can be adapted so that parameter estimates remain unbiased, but large inaccuracies in covariates can lead to large parameter variances, even when plenty of kin-pairs are found (Trenkel et al. 2022).

ERRO can be extended to other types of kin, most usefully cross-cohort HSPs. Maternal and paternal half-sibs should be considered separately because adult dynamics might differ by sex. The complication is that we do not know who the first-born's parents were, so we have to consider in turn each possible female/male adult at that time, write down its ERRO for the second-born (including a survival probability over the interval), and take an average. See Bravington et al. (2016) for the principle, Hillary et al. (2018) for an example with 'mammal-like' dynamics, and Davies et al. (2020) for a 'fish-like' example.

QUALITATIVE DESIGN

With a little ingenuity, the principles in the last section can be used to write down a valid CKMR model for just about any species and sampling situation. Nevertheless, just having a valid model is not enough; for some demographies and sampling situations, it can still be impossible to estimate all parameters of the model. The parameters may statistically confound each other, even when sample sizes are large and plenty of kin-pairs are found. Basically, not all species are intrinsically amenable to CKMR, even if sampling resources (e.g. budgets) are not limiting. In addition, there may be practicalities that prevent collecting samples from some life stages/places, or that prevent measuring certain covariates. For example, sometimes only young animals, or only dead ones, or only males, etc., can be sampled; sometimes it is not possible to measure age accurately or affordably; sometimes samples can only be collected from small parts of a species' range; and so on. Such limitations might not cause any problem for CKMR for certain species, yet would make it impossible for others;

everything depends on the underlying demography. When contemplating CKMR for a new species, the first requirement is a qualitative evaluation of its demography in relation to feasible sampling. Only if that looks promising, is it worth going on to consider quantitative issues around sample size and composition, as per the next section.

There are two cross-cutting issues that apply regardless of demographics. First, some measure of age is almost always required. Inadequate age data can be a deal-breaker; it is most important to have reasonable age estimates for the potential offspring (as HSPs/FSPs, and the O in POPs), and preferably for potential parents (adults) as well. Depending on species, live/dead sampling arrangements, life stage, budget, accuracy requirements, etc., age estimates might be obtainable just from body size, from a 'hard part' such as otoliths or, most excitingly, via epigenetic estimates from the CKMR tissue samples themselves (see 'Future directions' and Chapter 7). Second, in some cases, spatial aspects may need attention; this could range from basic stratification of samples for robustness, through modification of the kinship probability equations, to a no-go flag in extreme cases (see Box 11.2).

Box 11.2: Spatial CKMR

Spatial structure generates potential for complication in CKMR, whenever the probability of two sampled individuals being POP or HSP depends strongly on where they are at the times of sampling. Spatial complications are a big issue in conventional MR (e.g. Chapter 10) but often less so for CKMR, because there can be a long gap between marking and recapture that gives time for *both* animals in the pair to disperse. Most CKMR applications to date have been marine, where mixing is generally better than on land. Regardless of the system, though, incomplete mixing combined with uneven sampling can still create bias. The best general advice is to sample at life stages, times of year, and places where the animals are likely to be 'well-mixed'; that is, where any persistent breeding subgroups are likely to have equal per capita chance of being sampled.

If well-mixed sampling is not possible, there are two main options (see next page).

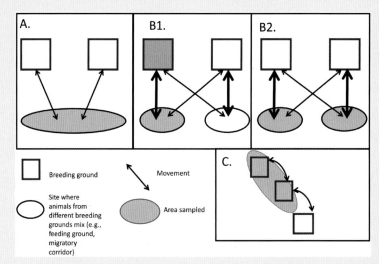

Fig. 11.6. In case A, individuals from two different breeding sites mix evenly at a third site (e.g. feeding, migratory corridor); sampling that mixing site should give an unbiased estimate of total abundance. In case B, there is incomplete mixing, with preferential migration from each breeding site to its closest mixing site. Sampling scheme B1 (e.g. juveniles sampled in the mixing oval and adults in the breeding square) would produce a biased estimate of total abundance, though possibly a good estimate of left-hand abundance. Since only the left-hand side is sampled in B1, there is no possibility to detect spatial complications, let alone to try to model them away. Sampling scheme B2 is more promising, especially if adults and juveniles are both sampled in the mixing sites. At least any patterns could be detected *a posteriori*, based on higher rates of within-oval vs. across-oval kinship. If per capita sampling probabilities are equal in the ovals, then an overall non-spatial model should be unbiased, but that might be a rather strong assumption. Case C is a stepping-stone or isolation-by-distance model, with only partial sampling. If there is not enough information in the case C sample to fit an explicitly spatial CKMR model, then a 'naive' estimate of total abundance may be biased, and the estimated survival rate will encompass both true survival and emigration, just as in conventional MR. On the other hand, sampling the first two stones may lead to quite a reasonable estimate of *their* abundance, with or without an explicitly spatial model.

1. Stick to a simple, non-spatial CKMR model and use simulations to check that the estimates will be robust enough to some plausible level of spatial complexity. Conn *et al.* (2020) follow this approach, to support the use of a simple non-spatial model for bearded seals, noting that any severe spatial problems could at least be detected after the fact from kin-clustering.

2. Build a spatially explicit CKMR model. This is largely uncharted territory. It is not necessarily that difficult to write down spatial versions of kinship probability formulae, but the population dynamics may be more difficult to make spatial. In any case, even if sensible equations can be devised, it does not automatically follow that all the parameters can be estimated reliably; statistical confounding may or may not be a problem, and case-by-case consideration will be needed.

There are far too many spatial scenarios to give a list, but we outline some possibilities in Fig. 11.6. In each case, the pattern or extent to which kin-pairs (HSPs and POPs) are clustered within-site versus across-sites will be affected in different ways by whether offspring tend to return to breed where they were born (heritable; philopatry), and by whether individual adults tend to repeatedly breed in the same place (not necessarily heritable; recruitment). Thus, such behaviours can be distinguished using CKMR data, in principle; whether a useful abundance estimate can be concocted is a separate question that varies from case to case.

All in all, spatial CKMR can be complicated, but the good news is that there are many applications where it is irrelevant. If there is a suspicion that spatial effects might turn out to be important, then the worst design mistake is to concentrate sampling into such limited regions that no effect could even be detected. We expect that much of the future development of CKMR will be in spatially explicit models.

There is no comprehensive 'taxonomy of demographies' for CKMR, but we outline a few archetypes below. While we find it helpful to give descriptive labels, the boundaries are not strict, and these archetypes certainly do not correspond exactly to conventional taxonomy: for example, sharks can be 'fish-like' or 'mammal-like'; some birds are 'fish-like'; and some species cross the boundaries entirely.

Fish-like
e.g. bluefin tuna, that tend to reproduce many times through random mating, with individual fecundity changing substantially through adulthood thanks to somatic growth. That variation in fecundity makes the interpretation of 'abundance' rather subtle, being linked not just to the total number of adults but also their age composition: one large adult might be worth three small ones, reproductively speaking. Details are out of scope here, but it turns out that POPs on their own naturally yield an abundance estimate on the fecundity-weighted scale usually of most interest to management (e.g. spawning stock biomass). Unfortunately, HSPs on their own do not give a directly interpretable abundance estimate, so juvenile-only sampling for fish would not work.

POPs and HSPs together provide enough information to disentangle the age-structure, yielding *both* numerical and fecundity-weighted abundance, as well as an estimate of the natural mortality rate (Davies *et al.* 2020). That is everything and more than a conventional stock assessment aims to deliver, without needing any other information apart from catches. To reap all those benefits, sampling needs to include known-age juveniles from multiple cohorts, as well as adults of both sexes and all sizes, preferably with approximate age measurements. The 'juveniles' do not actually have to be immature, although in general younger is better for three reasons: abundance estimates, which are back-dated to the most-recent births, will be more up-to-date; there is no risk of confusion between possible grandparent-grandchild pairs (GGPs, see 'Finding kin-pairs' section); and because length is often a good no-cost predictor of age for young animals. However, animals so young that they may still be associated with littermates are best avoided.

Mammal-like
e.g. baleen whale, grey nurse shark. These are similar to 'fish-like', except with little or no variation in fecundity, either within adult lifetime or between individuals of the same sex. That provision greatly simplifies modelling, and more importantly relaxes some demands on sampling. The safest way is still as for fish, with the HSPs and POPs allowing a cross-check. If necessary, though, census abundance could be estimated just from immature animals via HSPs.

Harem-like
e.g. elephant seals (polygynous), wattled jacanas (polyandrous). Here, one sex is 'mammal-like', but only a few of the other sex may be reproductively successful at any one time, and they may not last long in that role.

'Female-oriented' CKMR for elephant seals should be perfectly possible using MOPs, and possibly with maternal cross-cohort HSPs/FSPs (but see Birds below). However, for adult males, sampling probability may well be correlated with breeding success, which would be a source of hard-to-fix bias from FOPs; and paternal HSPs/FSPs would only provide information on breeding males.

Bird-like

e.g. penguins. From a CKMR perspective, longer-lived birds that do not pair-bond are just 'generic mammals'. Pair-bonding species should also be amenable to POP-based CKMR, but HSP/FSP approaches may prove problematic. Unlike in random-mating species, FSPs from different cohorts will be common, and in turn will generate a large number of full-**thiatic** pairs (FTPs: aunts and uncles paired with nieces and nephews) which are genetically indistinguishable from HSPs (at least using the genetic marker systems available today for most CKMR species, though see 'Future directions'). 'Divorce rates' as well as survival rates also enter the kinship probabilities. Overall, CKMR should be possible at some level, but is likely to present some challenges; these are uncharted waters.

Squid-like

e.g. squid or Pacific salmonids that are **semelparous** (breed-and-die). CKMR is impossible unless special sampling conditions can be met. The obvious and cheap approach of lethally sampling immature animals would prevent them from ever turning into parents, so POPs are ruled out. Siblings are only found within (not across) cohorts, which is precisely where HSPs/FSPs are useless for CKMR. However, if non-lethal sampling of immature animals is possible, then those individuals will subsequently have the chance to turn into adults and could be used in CKMR to estimate the number of immatures. And if (dead) adults can be collected post-breeding, as with some Pacific salmonids, then they can be used for CKMR estimates of the number of breeding adults (Rawding *et al.* 2014). In both cases, the abundance estimate pertains to a cohort which has already died off.

Oddballs

where for some reason genetics does not permit reliable identification of close-kin, and/or it is not clear how many adults each offspring 'marks'. Possible examples include some whiptail lizards (parthenogenesis), armadillos of the genus *Dasypus* (monozygosis), several marmoset monkeys (chimerism). Problems might also occur with polyploidy, or with minimal genetic diversity from bottlenecks. The approach we describe will not work off-the-shelf for such species, though extensions might conceivably be devised for some.

QUANTITATIVE DESIGN

Even if CKMR is in principle suitable for a particular species, doing it for real will generally entail a lot of time and appreciable expense, notwithstanding the excellent return on investment if management uncertainties are reduced as a result. One of the worst research mistakes is to spend lots of money, but not enough to deliver anything useful, at least when that outcome could reasonably have been foreseen. Quantitative design in CKMR is about preventing such problems, by making sure that a project has the following:

1. adequate number of samples, that are ...
2. adequately stratified over different parts of the population in space and time (e.g. by age/size, sex, birth cohort, sampling years, locations), and have ...
3. adequate covariate measurements about each sample (e.g. length, age, sex).

The point is to figure out what 'adequate' means for the situation at hand, without drastically overspending. All sampling and subsequent genotyping incurs some cost; some classes of samples may be more expensive than others for some species (e.g. juveniles versus adults); and some types of covariate measurement may be relatively expensive (e.g. age readings from otoliths). The three items above can often be traded off against each other; for example, having highly informative covariate measurements rather than cheap inaccurate ones will sometimes reduce the total number of samples required. There is usually no simple way to answer the invariable question of 'how many samples will I need?', because that depends on several things: biology, the unknown parameters (abundance, in particular), and the interaction with points 2 and 3 above. But there is a more complicated way, coming through a systematic mathematical process, to design a CKMR project with realistic prospects of success, addressing all three of the above points.

There are two levels of sophistication. The simpler level is: will some proposed sampling scheme (i.e. stratified numbers of samples) yield enough kin-pairs? Good precision

(CV < 15%, say) requires finding at least 50–100 useful kin-pairs (POPs and/or cross-cohort HSPs; see Bravington, Skaug *et al.* 2016). This process needs to start with a CKMR model (i.e. code) appropriate to the biology of the study system, and with guesstimates for the unknown demographic parameters. From those, kinship probabilities can be calculated for each type of pairwise comparison (i.e. each combination of covariates for two individuals). Next, the proposed stratified sample sizes imply how many pairwise comparisons of each type there will be. Finally, by multiplying the probabilities by the number of comparisons and adding them all up, the expected number of kin-pairs can be guesstimated. One can then manually experiment with different sampling schemes, until promising numbers of kin-pairs are attained. Once the model has been set up, this is a quick process; no repetitive simulation is required.

However, it is not just the number of kin-pairs that affects precision, but also their pattern: spread of cohorts sampled, quality of covariate measurements, etc. Here a more sophisticated approach to design is needed, starting from the same place as the previous paragraph, but now using simulation to check numerically what precision the parameter estimates of interest are likely to have. Happily, the mathematics of CKMR make this easier than for other types of data, usually bypassing the need for actual simulation (Bravington, Skaug *et al.* 2016). The details, which are beyond our scope here, can be fiddly, but we expect that software to help with 'CKMR design mechanics' will become available in the next couple of years. Building an appropriate underlying CKMR model, though, will remain a project-specific responsibility.

Formal quantitative design is certainly advisable for large-scale CKMR, say in fisheries or hunting settings. This is because there is often enough prior information for guesstimating the unknown demographic parameters, the expense will be significant in absolute terms, and failures will have repercussions. However, it may not be necessary in some conservation-only settings where population size is expected to be 'small', but little is known about demography. In those scenarios, sometimes the feasible sample size is known in advance (perhaps already collected), and the question is really 'could CKMR be worth a try?'. Even in such a demographic information vacuum, it is still a good idea to try the 'how many kin-pairs likely?' calculation for a few trial abundances, just to see whether anything worthwhile might result.

Iterating the design

Once the samples have been collected and genotyped, and a CKMR model has been fitted, new parameter estimates will be available. It is quite possible that reality will turn out to be rather different from the assumptions behind the original design, which can then be revisited for another iteration. Here, CKMR has an attractive property: 'vague good news, or precise bad news'. If the number of kin-pairs turns out much lower than expected, the true abundance must clearly be higher, even though the precision of its estimate will be poor. This is usually good news, albeit imprecise, and will often motivate extending the study. The original samples continue to add power, as potential offspring, or potential half-siblings of new samples, so that extending CKMR is much easier than starting *de novo*. On the other hand, if the number of kin-pairs is very high, then the abundance estimate will be lower than expected, with a tight confidence band: bad news, but precise bad news.

In many scenarios, the cost of genotyping a sample is considerably higher than the cost of collection and storage. A wise strategy is then to collect many more samples in the first place than the original design suggests, and archive the surplus. The first round of genotyping need only correspond to the design, but the results may motivate immediate genotyping of the archive. If the samples weren't collected in the first place, there is no way to collect them retrospectively; even the magic of CKMR has its limits.

General quantitative considerations

Project specifics aside, there are some interesting general links between abundance, sample size, and precision in CKMR. For an adult abundance of N animals, each CKMR comparison has a probability on the order of $\frac{1}{N}$ of yielding a kin-pair, because there are approximately N possible parents. With m samples and thus $\sim m^2$ pairwise comparisons, the number of kin-pairs expected is on-the-order-of $\frac{m^2}{N}$.

Consequently, the number of samples required to discover 50–100 kin-pairs is proportional to $\sqrt{N}$. That 'proportional to' hides a factor which could easily vary between 3 and 30 in different situations – which is why designs must be case-specific – but the point here is only the form of the equation, and in particular the square root.

Large populations are often assumed to be hard for CKMR, because the absolute sample size will need to be large. However, because of that square-root, the required sample size is actually a smaller fraction of abundance in larger populations. CKMR should thus be surprisingly affordable for large-scale fisheries with populations of many millions because the fraction of the catch revenue that needs to be spent on sampling can be very low. In contrast, for tiny high conservation-value populations, the number of samples required may not be large in absolute terms but may still approach or exceed the actual number of adults. Smaller populations can also lead to technical problems with variance calculations and robustness for CKMR, because comparisons cease to be statistically independent. While 'large', 'small', and 'tiny' are not precise, as some indication 500 000 is comfortably large; 500 is rather small; and 50 is tiny.

These equations have another important implication. The number of expected kin-pairs grows with the square of the sample size; so, for example, the first half of the samples will only contain about a quarter of the eventual kin-pairs. As samples accumulate, new pairs are found more and more rapidly. This quadratic effect substantially lowers the cost of extending a CKMR study once it has reached an initial answer. However, it also makes small-scale testing basically impossible. If design calculations suggest that 10 000 samples would be needed to expect 100 POPs, then from 1000 samples only one lonely and useless POP might typically result.

GENOTYPING

In the past decade, the field of genomics has undergone a revolution that has made possible the large-scale, low-cost, high-reliability genotyping required to find close-kin pairs for CKMR. Prior to the advent of cost-effective sequencing approaches for rapid SNP genotyping (e.g. ddRAD Peterson *et al.* 2012), wildlife population genetic studies generally used microsatellite markers (see

Chapter 10) to investigate genetic connectivity. If a sufficient number of microsatellite markers were available, this 'panel' could be also used to identify individuals and perhaps parents, particularly if one parent was already known. For example, if mother-offspring were sampled together, the non-maternal alleles in the offspring could be used to identify likely fathers (see Carroll and Garland 2022 for a recent review). However, CKMR typically requires not only the identification of first-order kin in the absence of such contextual information, but usually also the identification of second-order kin such as HSPs. This entails a step up in the size of the genotyping panel: from 10+ microsatellite loci or 60+ SNPs for identification of individuals; to 25+ microsatellites or a few hundred SNPs for POPs; and for HSPs, where microsatellites are probably infeasible, to 2000/3000+ SNPs. There are several technologies for developing and applying SNP genotyping panels capable of confidently detecting HSPs, both in-house (e.g. Andrews *et al.* 2016; or Campbell *et al.* 2015) and outsourced (e.g. Diversity Array Technology Pty Ltd., as used by CSIRO in the 'Applications' section). Costs and expertise requirements can differ substantially; detailed discussion is beyond our scope.

The first large-scale CKMR application, CSIRO's POP-only study of southern bluefin tuna from 2006 to 2012 (Bravington, Grewe *et al.* 2016; see Box 11.3), has moved from microsatellites to SNPs over time. As has been noted elsewhere (e.g. Morin *et al.* 2004), SNPs have distinct advantages over microsatellites, including being cheaper, easier, and more scalable than microsatellites, and are now the markers of choice for conservation and ecology.

Box 11.3: Southern bluefin tuna: from pariah to paradigm

Southern bluefin tuna (SBT) is the best-developed application of the general-purpose CKMR framework. The project began in 2005 when it was clear that this charismatic, valuable, and formerly abundant species had been drastically overfished, and that conventional fisheries data were not making sense. The saving grace was a well-established biological sampling program from the fisheries for adults in Indonesia and juveniles in Australia. This, combined with CSIRO's genetics program and the pairwise-kinship idea proposed in Skaug (2001), inspired what became CKMR. After an initial design using best guesses of abundance from previous stock assessments, CSIRO collected 7000 juvenile and adult samples between 2006 and 2010. These were genotyped at a panel of 25 microsatellite loci, chosen to have enough power for finding POPs. The covariates measured were juvenile age, and adult sex, length, and age. Model development proceeded in parallel, and we liaised regularly with an international panel of genetic and fisheries experts, so that the process and outcomes were transparent. In 2010, initial kin-finding on a subset of 4000 revealed fewer POPs than anticipated. This meant two things: the original plan for 7000 samples would not yield a precise abundance estimate; and the original guesses at abundance used in design were too low. This is the 'vague good news' of the 'Quantitative design' section, and it stimulated the release of more funds. By 2012, there were over 13 000 samples genotyped, and a POP-only CKMR analysis was ready. SBT has 'fish-like' demography (see 'Qualitative design' section) and, since only POPs were available, some of the less-contentious fishery data (e.g. adult length) were still needed to develop a model more comparable to a full stock assessment. Nevertheless, the *de novo* construction of a transparent, reliable, absolute abundance estimate, without requiring catch data, was a landmark result in fisheries (Bravington, Grewe *et al.* 2016). After intense scientific scrutiny, the approach was endorsed by the Commission for the Conservation of Southern Bluefin Tuna (CCSBT), and led to substantial revision of hypotheses about the state of the stock (CCSBT 2013).

The original appeal of CKMR for SBT had been to get a one-off reliable abundance estimate. Once accomplished, annual updates were an obvious and straightforward extension. In 2015, we switched from microsatellites to SNPs, primarily to allow use of HSPs. By 2017, we had a complete stand-alone POP+HSP analysis which, unlike the earlier POP-only model, could if necessary be run without any other fishery-derived data (Davies *et al.* 2019). Updating the CKMR now requires 3000 samples per year, costing on the order of 0.01% of annual fishery value, and provides a robust way to monitor the adult stock. At the other end of the life cycle, the abundance of incoming juveniles is now monitored by live-release genetic mark-recapture (Preece *et al.* 2018; see Chapter 10). These two fishery-independent genomic data sources now underpin CCSBT's simulation-tested 'Management Procedure' for ongoing data collection, analysis, and setting of catch limits. The population has recovered from around 5% of unexploited levels in 2006 to 20% in 2022 (CCSBT 2021). Thanks in large part to genomics and CKMR, SBT has gone from being a cautionary tale to an aspirational example in 15 years: from pariah to paradigm!

The first step is to select the loci with CKMR in mind. The number required depends mainly on how powerful each locus is for kin-finding (section 'Finding kin-pairs'), for which a useful proxy is the **minor allele frequency** (MAF); the closer to 0.5, the better. However, it may not be easy to find enough SNPs with high MAFs, and it is fine instead to use more loci with lower MAFs, as long as the overall power of the panel is adequate. For example, two SNPs each with MAF ≈ 0.15 are about as good as one with MAF ≈ 0.50. Using an inadequate panel would be a disaster, because the 'kin bumps' in Fig. 11.7 would overlap to the point where reliable kin-finding becomes impossible. If a preliminary set of samples (100–200) can be genotyped to estimate allele frequencies, then the adequacy of a proposed panel can be checked with the software mentioned in the 'Finding kin-pairs' section.

The pilot study should also be used for locus-specific quality control (QC) checks (see Morin *et al.* 2010; O'Leary *et al.* 2018), such as heterozygosity excess/deficiency and consistency with **Hardy-Weinberg equilibrium** genotype proportions. Null alleles, which are heritable and therefore important in the context of kin-finding, might require special attention. They are best detected through failure of 'null-naive' HWP tests; it is not a good idea to rely on call-rate, since that reflects only double-nulls (homozygotes), and a locus can still have a substantial null frequency, say 10%, without any double-nulls being present in a pilot of 200 samples. The usual advice is to exclude loci that have nulls. However, at least with several species of tuna, there have simply not been enough null-free ddRAD loci with usefully high MAF to make that affordable. It turns out that having a modest null-allele frequency at a locus does not greatly impair its power for kin-finding, provided that 'null-aware'

software is used throughout. At CSIRO, we have designed our locus-selection, genotyping, and kin-finding algorithms accordingly. Null-awareness may turn out to be important in CKMR generally, because of the technique's suitability for high-abundance species with high historical effective population size and consequent high density of mutation sites.

Once a panel is chosen, the genotyping procedure must be more accurate for CKMR than for population genetics, or even individual-based MR (Chapter 10). This means avoiding genotyping methods with high error rates (e.g. low coverage restriction-site associated DNA sequencing (RADseq)), and above all having good-quality DNA to begin with. Biopsy samples that yield high quantities of high-quality DNA, with minimal risk of contamination and low incidence of allelic dropout, are ideal. Although genotyping panels have been developed specifically for use on lower quality or quantity DNA sources (e.g. Hayward *et al.* 2022), this often requires a 'multiple tube approach' (Taberlet *et al.* 1997) whereby samples are repeatedly genotyped, and such panels may not be informative enough to confidently identify second order kin. Whatever the approach, repeat-genotyping a proportion of the samples is always desirable, for estimating or bounding the genotyping error rate (Morin *et al.* 2010). Additionally, it is important to undertake QC on individual samples; e.g. checking for deficiency or excess of heterozygosity, indicative of dropout or contamination respectively (O'Leary *et al.* 2018). Such samples are best discarded for close-kin work, even if they would be tolerable for other purposes such as individual MR. In our experience, CKMR-grade kin-finding is hard enough with reliable genotypes, and a nightmare without them.

Besides loci for kin-finding, other genetic data can also be important for CKMR. When samples include individuals from more than one genetically distinct population, markers for population assignment are a powerful if not essential addition to the panel. It is also useful to know the sex of each potential parent, so, unless sex can be determined cheaply and reliably by non-genetic means, sex-chromosome markers are another good addition (see Chapter 8). Mitochondrial DNA (mtDNA), which is inherited only from the mother, is important for checking whether HSPs are maternally or paternally linked, a distinction which is important in the CKMR model: different mtDNA haplotypes must imply paternal descent, whereas a shared haplotype suggests maternal descent. Strictly, mtDNA only needs to be genotyped for those individuals which turn up in HSPs, rather than for the entire sample, which may offer an appreciable cost saving. Finally, as mentioned in Chapter 7 and 'Future directions', epigenetic age has transformational potential for the many CKMR applications where it is otherwise difficult to get reliable age estimates.

FINDING KIN-PAIRS

Unambiguous detection of all POPs, all FSPs, and most second-order kin, should be possible using just pairwise comparisons, given good-quality DNA and enough reliably genotyped loci. However, this requires great care in statistical algorithms (Thompson 2000; Bravington, Skaug *et al.* 2016), as well as genetic analyses. The task is basically to hunt for a small and unknown number of 'needles' (pairs with the target kinship, say POP) in a vast 'haystack' (all pairwise comparisons). The first essential is to keep the false-positive rate extremely low: typically, below 1 in 100 000 000 for 'hay', that is, unrelated pairs masquerading as the target; and below 1 in 100 for 'other sharp objects', i.e. non-target kin pairs. There should be little or no ambiguity with POPs but, for second-order kin, exclusion of false-positives entails setting conservative thresholds that exclude some genuine 'needles'. Hence it is also necessary to estimate a false-negative rate.

Note that, for CKMR, we deliberately focus only on pairwise yes/no comparisons, rather than the more ambitious task of pedigree reconstruction (e.g. sequoia: Huisman 2017), for several reasons. Most importantly, by keeping each comparison distinct, we can achieve equal false-negative probabilities for every pairwise comparison, which greatly simplifies subsequent modelling. Also, *sequoia* and related software (e.g. CERVUS, Kalinowski *et al.* 2007) require inputs in the form of prior estimates

on the very demographic parameters we are trying to estimate, such as abundance. These priors are used to compute posterior assignment probabilities: fine for pedigrees, but something of a paradox if the outputs are then used to estimate abundance! Other benefits to the pairwise approach advocated here include that it is comparatively simple to code, and computationally efficient. The pairwise approach is implemented in two R packages: kinference (available on request from MVB) and CKMRsim (Anderson 2020).

The prerequisite for CKMR-grade kin-finding is an informative genotyping panel with loci that have met strict QC criteria (see previous section). If more than one genetically distinct population is present in the samples, then there will be HWP failures among many loci. In that case, the sample first needs to be subsetted to population using individual assignments (ambiguous samples can be discarded), with allele-frequency-estimation and kin-finding done separately within each subset.

For the target of POPs, either a Mendelian-exclusion or likelihood-ratio approach is satisfactory (Thompson 2000; Bravington, Skaug *et al.* 2016), adjusted for genotyping errors or null alleles if necessary (e.g. Davies *et al.* 2020). It is possible that some FSPs may be detected too. They can usually be distinguished from POPs by further statistical tests, but it is often easier just to look at birth dates, since (at least with mammal-like and fish-like animals) FSPs normally have to be within-cohort, whereas POPs must be separated by at least the age of maturity.

For the target of second-order kin (i.e. HSPs, GGPs, and FTPs), a different pairwise likelihood-ratio statistic should be used. Fig. 11.7 shows a typical histogram across all pairwise comparisons. The observed bumps should closely match their predicted locations, which are calculated from allele frequencies. If not, more QC is required, otherwise kin-finding will be unreliable (see Fig. 11.7).

One slight complication is that HSPs are indistinguishable genetically from GGPs and FTPs, at least with currently affordable genotyping methods. In practice, HSPs are usually the real target because they are the most informative demographically, and the other two kinships are just a nuisance. Any risk of 'contamination' can be minimised by restricting comparisons to pairs that *a priori* are very unlikely to be GGP based on birth-date separation. If covariate data are too poor for that, the CK model can be adjusted to simply deal with an aggregate target of second-order kin by adding up the demographic probabilities of HSP, GGP, and FTP (e.g. Bradford *et al.* 2018).

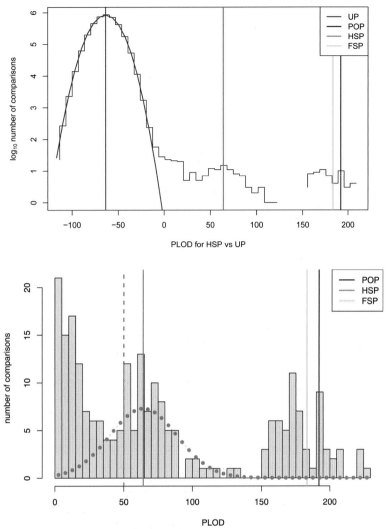

Fig. 11.7. Typical histogram of statistic used for finding second-order kin, across all pairwise comparisons. The PLOD ('Pseudo-Log-ODds') statistic for a pair is the log of the ratio of two quantities: the probability of the pair's observed genotypes if their kinship is actually HSP, to the analogous probability if their kinship is actually UP. It is calculated as if the loci were unlinked (Thompson 2000, and references below). Top figure shows all pairwise comparisons, with the *y*-axis on a log-scale to make interesting features visible (the vast majority of comparisons are of nearly unrelated animals). Lower figure is unlogged but zoomed to the right-hand side where close-kin are found. *A priori* expected values for various kin-types are shown by solid vertical lines, and the bumps are clearly where they should be. Note, although the HSP bump is obvious, it is not completely separated from the foothills of the UP mountain to its left, where the third- and higher-order kin-pairs dwell. To avoid false-positives, we therefore choose a threshold that will clearly exclude 'spillover' from more distantly related kin (grey dashed line in lower figure) and retain only definite HSPs to its right. This will create false-negatives by excluding some genuine HSPs, but the proportion can be estimated and incorporated into the kinship probability formula so as to avoid overall bias (see Bravington, Skaug *et al.* 2016 section 5; Davies *et al.* 2020 appendix C for more details). It has generally been around 10–15% in the CSIRO applications (e.g. Box 11.3). We have found that the thresholding approach leads to simplicity in subsequent modelling, also allowing diagnostics based on observed and expected numbers of definite kin.

APPLICATIONS

The idea that parent-offspring pairs could be used to inform on adult population size has been in the literature for over 20 years (Garrigue *et al.* 2004; Nielsen *et al.* 2001). Skaug (2001) was the first to propose a formal statistical model for pairwise comparisons, but the approach was limited by then-inadequate loci and the absence of a full demographic framework. Development of fully fledged CKMR

began in 2006 with CSIRO's southern bluefin tuna project; see Box 11.3. Rawding *et al.* (2014) was another successful application in the 2000s, based on recovery of dead post-spawning chinook salmon. Both projects used microsatellite markers. Meanwhile, although not strictly CKMR and for a somewhat easier kinship problem, SNPs were being pioneered in much larger-scale hatchery studies of salmon parentage (Anderson and Garza 2006). As noted in

Table 11.1.   Summary of completed CKMR studies.

Source: samples from dead (D) and/or alive (L) animals; Genotyping method (Geno): DArTCap™ (Cap), DArTSeq™ (Seq), SNP array or microsatellites (Usat). Model: Fully age structured (Full); Single-cohort adjusted Lincoln-Peterson (Single); exponential change with survival estimated (N, z, p); exponential change assuming quasi-equilibrium stable age composition, plus survival estimated (Stable age); exponential change, no survival estimate (N, z). Abundance is order-of-magnitude, so $\log_{10}(N_{adult}) = 3$ means closer to 1000 than to 100 or to 10 000.

Species	Source	Geno	POP	HSP	Model	$\log_{10}(N_{adult})$	$N_{samples}$	Ageing	Citation
Southern bluefin tuna (*Thunnus maccoyii*)	D	Usat	X		Full	6	13 000	Length (juveniles); Otolith+length (adult)	Bravington, Grewe *et al.* 2016
Southern bluefin tuna	D	Cap	X	X			>25 000		Davies *et al.* 2020
Chinook salmon (*Oncorhynchus tshawytscha*)	D	Usat	X		Single	3	2000	Inspection	Rawding *et al.* 2014
School shark (*Galeorhinus galeus*)	D	Cap		X	Full	5	3000	Vertebra	Thomson *et al.* 2020
White shark (*Carcharodon carcharias*)	L+D	Cap		X	*N, z, p*	2	200	Length	Hilary *et al.* 2018
Grey nurse shark (*Carcharias taurus*)	L+D	Seq	X	X	Stable age	3	378	Length	Bradford *et al.* 2018
Speartooth shark (*Glyphis glyphis*)	L	Seq		X	*N, z, p*	3	226	Length	Patterson *et al.* 2022
Northern River shark (*Glyphis garricki*)	L	Cap		X	*N, z, p*	3	300	Length	Bravington *et al.* 2019
Brook trout (*Salvelinus fontinalis*)	L	Usat	X		Single	3	300	Length	Ruzzante *et al.* 2019
Thornback ray (*Raja clavata*)	D	SNP array	X		*N, z*	4	>7000	Length	Trenkel *et al.* 2022

the Genotyping section, the advent of high-throughput sequencing enabled SNP genotyping to become a reliable and affordable tool for second-order kinship in wild populations. This has opened the door for many more applications.

Table 11.1 shows species with completed CKMR studies as of mid-2022, to the best of our knowledge. The studies are not usually quick exercises and setting up the infrastructure to handle thousands of samples can be time-consuming. The main applications have been in medium-size commercial fisheries, high conservation value elasmobranchs, and salmonids. However, we also know of several more studies that have at least got as far as finding numerous kin-pairs, and are awaiting modelling: southern right whales, flying-foxes, arctic seals, Atlantic bluefin tuna, and halibut. Various other design and sample-collection programs are underway, and there are also several papers on methodological developments (for example Conn *et al.* 2020).

The use of kinship just for connectivity, as opposed to being one parameter of a full demographic CKMR model (e.g. Patterson *et al.* 2022), is more widespread, although largely out of scope here. An interesting recent example, making full use of SNPs, is Jasper *et al.* (2019)'s study of mosquito dispersal rates, based on comparative pairwise distances between kinships of different orders. As we

discuss next, the future is bright for CKMR, with statistical and technological developments set to fuel further innovation in the field.

FUTURE DIRECTIONS

Although CKMR is still quite new, its genetic techniques and mathematical theories are amply developed to permit direct application in many situations. The main challenge is in assembling teams with the right range of skills and experience. That said, there are several opportunities where technical and statistical innovations could help to broaden applicability, and to learn even more from close-kin datasets.

The first is epigenetic age (Chapter 7). Some sort of age information is always essential in CKMR. Age can sometimes be inferred well from body parts, such as teeth or otoliths, and for some fish, accurate length measurements may even be enough. However, such data or measurements cannot always be obtained and associated with genetic samples. For example, market products may be the only practical source of samples from bycaught or hunted species (e.g. shark fins). Furthermore, length can either be ethically problematic to measure because of handling stress, and/or impossible to measure accurately in the field, and/or largely useless for inferring age anyway (e.g. whales). Hence, if age can be estimated just from the very biopsies needed for kin-finding, then CKMR becomes feasible for many more species (Polanowski *et al.* 2014; Mayne *et al.* 2021). We expect that the biggest challenges will be around calibration for 'non-zoo' species.

As well as molecular age biomarkers, the genomic tools that underpin kin-finding CKMR have rapidly developed over the past decade. What might the next decade bring? Several potentially useful techniques are more becoming affordable: long-read sequencing, for example, and high-quality reference genomes. These could certainly improve discrimination within first- and second-order close-kin, which are usually the most informative demographically. But they might also give access to third- and perhaps even fourth-order kin; what further parts of the demographic puzzle might those unlock?

There is one area that we think is unlikely to succumb to technological advances: the need for good samples. High-quality (uncontaminated and undegraded) DNA is crucial for intrinsically difficult tasks like finding second-order kin, and techniques such as epigenetic ageing need it in substantial quantities. Biopsies remain the most reliable source, though there may be other options for particular species. But some types of 'remote' sample popular in non-invasive studies, for example eDNA and scat, seem fundamentally unsuited to CKMR, even if sometimes adequate for the less demanding task of individual re-identification (e.g. Chapter 10). Aside from DNA quality, the big problem with remote samples is the lack of individual-specific covariates, most obviously age and size, which are essential to CKMR in all but a few niche situations.

The demographic and statistical side of CKMR also offers exciting future prospects. Terrestrial applications will often need to account explicitly for spatial population structure, such as isolation-by-distance or metapopulations. Additionally, there is the intriguing prospect of integrating individual MR and CKMR into one framework, thereby 'closing the demographic loop' across the whole life cycle.

DISCUSSION TOPICS

1. If you think that there might be some persistent spatial structure in your population, what would you want to ensure when designing your study? How would you go about checking for it, after you have all the data?

2. Suppose some of the frogs are blue and some are red, but all tadpoles are green. Does it matter to CKMR if red frogs are easier to catch than blue ones? What if colour was heritable in the tadpoles?

ACKNOWLEDGEMENTS

Editors Simon Jarman and Olly Berry for their extended patience. Silhouettes of frog and tadpole were created by Natasha Sinegina, used under Creative Commons Attribution 4.0, sourced from http://phylopic.org. Thanks to Shane Baylis for Fig. 11.7. ELC was supported by a Rutherford Discovery Fellowship from the Royal Society of New Zealand Te Apārangi.

REFERENCES

Anderson EC (2020) CKMRsim: Inference of pairwise relationships using likelihood ratios. R package version 0.1. Available from: <https://rdrr.io/github/eriqande/CKMRsim/>.

Anderson EC, Garza JC (2006) The power of single-nucleotide polymorphisms for large-scale parentage inference. *Genetics* **172**(4), 2567–2582. doi:10.1534/genetics.105.048074

Andrews KR, Good JM, Miller MR, Luikart G, Hohenlohe PA (2016) Harnessing the power of RADseq for ecological and evolutionary genomics. *Nature Reviews Genetics* **17**, 81–92. doi:10.1038/nrg.2015.28

Bradford RW, Thomson RC, Bravington VM, Foote D, Gunasekera R, *et al.* (2018) A close-kin mark-recapture estimate of the population size and trend of east coast grey nurse. Report to the National Environmental Science Program. *Report to the National Environmental Science Program.*

Bravington VM, Grewe PM, Davies CR (2016) Absolute abundance of southern bluefin tuna estimated by close-kin mark-recapture. *Nature Communications* **7**, 2041–1723. doi:10.1038/ncomms13162

Bravington VM, Skaug HJ, Anderson EC (2016) Close-Kin Mark-Recapture. *Statistical Science* **31**(2), 259–274. doi:10.1214/16-STS552

Bravington M, Feutry P, Pillans RD, Hillary R, Johnson G, *et al.* (2019) Close-Kin Mark-Recapture population size estimate of *Glyphis garricki* in the Northern Territory. Report to the National Environmental Science Program, Marine Biodiversity Hub. CSIRO Oceans & Atmosphere, Hobart.

Campbell NR, Harmon SA, Narum SR (2015) Genotyping-in-Thousands by sequencing (GT-seq): A cost effective SNP genotyping method based on custom amplicon sequencing. *Molecular Ecology Resources* **15**(4), 855–867. doi:10.1111/1755-0998.12357

Carroll EL, Garland EC (2022) Viewing the lives of whales through a molecular lens. In *Ethology and Behavioral Ecology of Mysticetes.* (Eds CW Clark, EC Garland) pp. 125–146. Springer, New York, USA.

CCSBT (2013) *Presentation of the report of the 2013 meeting of the extended scientific committee from the ESC chair.* Retrieved from https://www.ccsbt.org/en/past-meeting-documents/356

CCSBT (2021) *Report of the Twenty Sixth Meeting of the Scientific Committee.* Retrieved from https://www.ccsbt.org/en/content/reports-past-meetings

Conn PB, Bravington VM, Baylis S, Ver Hoef JM (2020) Robustness of close-kin mark–recapture estimators to dispersal limitation and spatially varying sampling probabilities.

Ecology and Evolution **10**(12), 5558–5569. doi:10.1002/ece3.6296

Davies C, Bravington M, Eveson P, Lansdell M, Aulich J, *et al.* (2020) *Next-generation Close-kin Mark Recapture: Using SNPs to identify half-sibling pairs in Southern Bluefin Tuna and estimate abundance, mortality and selectivity.* Retrieved from https://www.frdc.com.au/sites/default/files/products/2016-044-DLD.pdf:

Garrigue C, Dodemont R, Steel DJ, Baker CS (2004) Organismal and 'gametic' capture-recapture using microsatellite genotyping confirm low abundance and reproductive autonomy of humpback whales on the wintering ground of New Caledonia. *Marine Ecology Progress Series* **274**, 251–262.

Hayward KM, Clemente-Carvalho RBG, Jensen EL, de Groot PVC, Branigan M, *et al.* (2022) Genotyping-in-thousands by sequencing (GT-seq) of noninvasive faecal and degraded samples: A new panel to enable ongoing monitoring of Canadian polar bear populations. *Molecular Ecology Resources* **22**(5), 1906–1918. doi:10.1111/1755-0998.13583

Hilary RM, Bravington VM, Patterson TA, Grewe P, Bradford R, *et al.* (2018) Genetic relatedness reveals total population size of white sharks in eastern Australia and New Zealand. *Scientific Reports* **8**, 2045–2322. doi:10.1038/s41598-018-20593-w

Huisman J (2017) Pedigree reconstruction from SNP data: parentage assignment, sibship clustering and beyond. *Molecular Ecology Resources* **17**(5), 1009–1024. doi:10.1111/1755-0998.12665

Jasper M, Schmidt TL, Ahmad NW, Sinkins SP, Hoffmann AA (2019) A genomic approach to inferring kinship reveals limited intergenerational dispersal in the yellow fever mosquito. *Molecular Ecology Resources* **19**(5), 1254–1264 doi:10.1111/1755-0998.13043

Kalinowski ST, Taper ML, Marshall TC (2007) Revising how the computer program CERVUS accommodates genotyping error increases success in paternity assignment. *Molecular Ecology* **16**(5), 1099–1106. doi:10.1111/j.1365-294X.2007.03089.x

Mayne B, Espinoza T, Roberts D, Butler GL, Brooks S, *et al.* (2021) Nonlethal age estimation of three threatened fish species using DNA methylation: Australian lungfish, Murray cod and Mary River cod. *Molecular Ecology Resources* **21**(7), 2324–2332.

Mills LS (2012) *Conservation of Wildlife Populations: Demography, Genetics, and Management.* John Wiley & Sons, Hoboken, NJ, USA.

Morin P, Luikart G, Wayne RK (2004) SNPs in ecology, evolution and conservation. *Trends in Ecology & Evolution* **19**, 208–216. doi:10.1016/j.tree.2004.01.009

Morin P, Martien K, Archer F, Cipriano F, Steel DJ, *et al.* (2010) Applied conservation genetics and the need for quality control and reporting of genetic data used in fisheries and wildlife management. *Journal of Heredity* **101**, 1–10.

Nielsen R, Mattila D, Clapham PJ, Palsbøll PJ (2001) Statistical approaches to paternity analyses in natural populations and applications to the North Atlantic humpback whale. *Genetics* **157**, 1673–1682.

O'Leary SJ, Puritz JB, Willis SC, Hollenbeck CM, Portnoy DS (2018) These aren't the loci you're looking for: Principles of effective SNP filtering for molecular ecologists. *Molecular Ecology* **27**, 3193–3206. doi:10.1111/mec.14792

Palsbøll PJ, Peery MZ, Bérubé M (2010) Detecting populations in the 'ambiguous' zone: kinship-based estimation of population

structure and genetic divergence. *Molecular Ecology Resources* **10**, 797–805.

Patterson T, Hillary R, Feutry P, Gunasakera R, Marthick J, *et al.* (2022) Rapid estimation of cryptic adult abundance and breeding dynamics in a critically endangered elasmobranch from close-kin mark recapture. *bioRxiv.* doi:10.1101/2022.02.24.481858

Peterson B, Weber J, Kay E, Fisher H, Hoekstra H (2012) Double digest RADseq: An inexpensive method for De Novo SNP discovery and genotyping in model and non-model species. *PLoS ONE* **7**, e37135.

Polanowski AM, Robbins J, Chandler D, Jarman SN (2014) Epigenetic estimation of age in humpback whales. *Molecular Ecology Resources* **14**, 976–987. doi:10.1111/1755-0998.12247

Preece AL, Eveson JP, Bradford R, Lansdell M, Grewe PM, *et al.* (2018) Report of the SBT gene-tagging program 2021. Report CCSBT-ESC/2108/8 to the Commission for the conservation of southern bluefin tuna. Retrieved from <https://www.ccsbt.org/ja/system/files/ESC25_06_CCSBT_GeneTagggingProgramReport2020.pdf>.

Rawding DJ, Sharpe CS, Blankenship SM (2014) Genetic-based estimates of adult chinook salmon spawner abundance from carcass surveys and Juvenile out-migrant traps. *Transactions of the American Fisheries Society* **143**(1), 55–67. doi:10.1080/00028487.2013.829122

Ruzzante DE, McCracken GR, Førland B, MacMillan J, Notte D, *et al.* (2019) Validation of close-kin mark–recapture (CKMR) methods for estimating population abundance. *Methods in Ecology and Evolution* **10**(9), 1445–1453.

Skaug HJ (2001) Allele-sharing methods for estimation of population size. *Biometrics* **57**(3), 750–756. doi:10.1111/j.0006-341x.2001.00750.x

Taberlet P, Camarra J-J, Griffin S, Uhres E, Hanotte O, *et al.* (1997) Noninvasive genetic tracking of the endangered Pyrenean brown bear population. *Molecular Ecology* **6**(9), 869–876. doi:10.1111/j.1365-294X.1997.tb00141.x

Thompson EA (2000) Statistical inference from genetic data on pedigrees. *NSF-CBMS Regional Conference Series in Probability and Statistics* **6**, 1–169.

Thomson R, Bravington M, Feutry P, Gunasekera R, Grewe P (2020) Close kin mark recapture for School Shark in the SESSF. FRDC report for project 2014/024. Fisheries Research and Development Corporation, ACT, Australia.

Trenkel VM, Charrier G, Lorance P, Bravington VM (2022) Close-kin mark-recapture abundance estimation: Practical insights and lessons learned. *ICES Journal of Marine Science* **79**(2), 413–422. doi:10.1093/icesjms/fsac002

Waples RS (1998) Separating the wheat from the chaff: Patterns of genetic differentiation in high gene flow species. *Journal of Heredity* **89**(5), 438–450.

Waples RS, Gaggiotti O (2006) What is a population? An empirical evaluation of some genetic methods for identifying the number of gene pools and their degree of connectivity. *Molecular Ecology* **15**, 1419–1439 doi:10.1111/j.1365-294X.2006.02890.x

Waples RS, Hoelzel RA, Gaggiotti OE, Tiedemann R, Palsbøll PJ, *et al.* (2018) Guidelines for genetic data analysis. *Journal of Cetacean Research and Management* **18**, 33–80.

12 Perspective – Genomics and bear management

Michael Proctor, Trans-border Grizzly Bear Project, British Columbia, Canada

For many years, researchers and managers suspected that human development was fragmenting grizzly bear (*Ursus arctos*) populations in the Canada-USA trans-boundary region, potentially undermining what appeared to be recovery after a century of range contraction driven by persecution. So, which was it: were bear populations recovering, being fragmented into smaller subunits, or both? We needed to know the answer to this conundrum to inform a management program that would achieve real recovery.

It turns out that the answer was a complex mix of both paradigms, but in ways that varied spatially. Importantly, these insights were made possible by adopting novel genetic analyses to understand what was essentially an ecological issue. The integration of genetic analysis in our project, and in others worldwide, was part of a global wave in the way we research, understand, and manage bears around the world.

Researching grizzly bears is not a trivial task, especially radio collaring – the dominant method throughout the last half of the 20th century. It is dangerous for researchers and bears and early use of VHF transmitters required hand-held receivers to track bears that was time-consuming, yielding minimal (but insightful) return. Newer GPS collars yielded massive amounts of data, but you tended to learn a lot about a few bears. Counting bears is practically impossible with radio collars, and studies of how habitat fragmentation affects bears, while theoretically possible, took many years. To assess large landscape-scale patterns and issues we needed to be able to learn about bears over broad spatial scales – 100 000s of km² – and gather insights beyond movement and habitat use – we needed insights into their sex lives.

To uncover this story, we used microsatellite genotypes (DNA fingerprints) that by enabling individual bears to be identified in the wild with minimal disturbance, allowed us to measure sex-specific effects of fragmentation almost in real time, and certainly within the 1 to 20 years or the lifespan of the bears we were studying.

We collected genetic samples in multiple field surveys using what was at that time, a new method of remotely sampling bear hairs (the roots contained the DNA) using barb wire and sent lure in a mark-recapture study design (Fig. 12.1; Woods *et al.* 1999). These samples contained rich information beyond individual identification, and we were finally able to learn something about a lot of bears over large spatial scales. Using individual-based analyses including assignment tests (Pritchard *et al.* 2000; Paetkau *et al.* 2004; Piry *et al.* 2004), family pedigrees, and recapture patterns, we mapped an extensive network of sub-populations across ~300 000 km² that were in various states of landscape fragmentation. To look at this system in 'real time,' using only genetics we followed individual bear movements (or lack thereof) between adjacent areas. We sampled a sufficient proportion of bears in multiple adjacent areas, determined each individual's population of origin, and revealed a mosaic of small and larger

Fig. 12.1. A grizzly bear entering a DNA sampling site of a small barb wire corral with a scent lure. Inset is a hair sample with visible roots that contain the bear's DNA that provide individual identification, parentage information, population of origin and more.

'sub-populations,' mainly defined by the limits of female movements. Several sub-populations were completely isolated with <50 animals, many had no female- and reduced male-interchange, and only a few contained >600 animals (Proctor *et al.* 2005, 2012).

Female bears in the region have natal dispersal that takes several years over much shorter distances than males, and their eventual home ranges typically overlap their mother's range (McLellan and Hovey 2001; Proctor *et al.* 2004). This meant that the focus of management needed to be promoting the movement and survival of females. Over decades, bears were being killed in human-settled valleys resulting in fragmented populations. While the more mobile males could sometimes compensate for male mortality, females were replaced less often. Now we needed to establish corridors where females survived within those valleys to provide demographic connectivity for population rescue. At that time, studies of wildlife genetics primarily focused on genetic processes. Yet, our conservation concerns were demographic rather than genetic. Human-caused mortality on these small populations was driving declines and fragmentation faster than losses of genetic diversity. Also, in most cases males were still moving between populations, albeit at reduced rates, mediating gene flow and maintaining genetic diversity.

These revelations were followed by a decade of GPS radio telemetry to delve more deeply into bear habitat preferences, movement patterns, and to identify and secure movement corridors across human environments (Proctor *et al.* 2015).

Fast forward 15 years: after more than a decade of connectivity management designed to reconnect the most isolated small population in our study area, we used those same analytic tools of population assignments, pedigrees, and sampling histories, now coupled with GPS telemetry, to evaluate our connectivity management program. Were bears now moving into this previously isolated population? And if so, were they breeding? Amazingly, we found that it worked – we reconnected a grizzly bear population that had been completely isolated for over 60 years (Proctor *et al.* 2005, 2015, 2018, 2023a).

Reconnecting isolated populations was only part of the puzzle. We also needed to solve within-population demographic issues to ensure recovery. To accomplish this, our use of genetics to understand grizzly ecology took another interesting twist. While we used extensive family pedigrees to measure increases in connectivity that were accompanied by breeding (functional connectivity), we also measured spatially explicit variability in female reproductive success and sex-specific density (Proctor *et al.* 2017, 2023b). Combining this with the distribution of potentially explanatory covariates, our analyses revealed that human-caused mortality in the backcountry away from human settlements is mediated by extensive networks of forestry roads left behind after timber harvest. Roads that pass through the best food patches are particularly detrimental to bears. Those mortality patterns in turn limited female reproductive success and ultimately density. We are now working to manage those road networks to reduce female bear mortality, simultaneously recovering the population and growing a cohort of potential inter-population migrants. It was our extensive genetic sampling, pedigree analysis, and telemetry data that allowed us to uncover these patterns in our backcountry, and relate it to grizzly bear fitness patterns, the ultimate mechanism in ecology. These insights moved land-use managers to act.

We have come to realise that combining the power of genetic analyses with GPS telemetry allows us to almost see bear ecology and conservation in 'colour'. Our long-term genetic dataset, coupled with telemetry data over both the human-settled valleys and the wilder backcountry, allowed us to understand population characteristics and processes that previously had been invisible to us. This in turn has revealed solutions to conservation issues bears face.

REFERENCES

McLellan N, Hovey F (2001) Natal dispersal of grizzly bears. *Canadian Journal of Zoology* **79**, 838–844.

Paetkau D, Slade R, Burden M, Estoup A (2004) Genetic assignment methods for the direct, real-time estimation of migration rate: A simulation based exploration of accuracy and power. *Molecular Ecology* **13**, 55–65.

Piry S, Alapetite A, Cornuet JM, Paetkau D, Baudouin L, *et al.* (2004) GeneClass2: A software for genetic assignment and first-generation migrant detection. *Journal of Heredity* **95**, 536–539.

Pritchard K, Stephens M, Donnelly P (2000) Inference of population structure using multilocus genotype data. *Genetics* **155**, 945–959.

Proctor M, McLellan BN, Strobeck C, Barclay RM (2004) Gender-specific dispersal distances of grizzly bears estimated by genetic analysis. *Canadian Journal of Zoology* **82**, 1108–1118.

Proctor M, McLellan BN, Strobeck C, Barclay RM (2005) Genetic analysis reveals demographic fragmentation of grizzly bears yielding vulnerably small populations. *Proceedings of the Royal Society, London* **272**, 2409–2416.

Proctor M, Paetkau D, McLellan BN, Stenhouse GB, Kendall KC, *et al.* (2012) Population fragmentation and inter-ecosystem movements of grizzly bears in western Canada and the northern United States. *Wildlife Monographs* **180**, 1–46.

Proctor M, Kasworm WF, Annis KM, MacHutchon AG, Teisberg JE, *et al.* (2015) Grizzly bear connectivity mapping in the Canada-US trans-border region. *Journal of Wildlife Management* **79**, 554.

Proctor M, Lamb C, MacHutchon A (2017) *The Grizzly Dance between Berries and Bullets: Relationships among Bottom-up Food Resources and Top-Down Mortality Risk on Grizzly Bear Populations in Southeast British Columbia.* Trans-border Grizzly Bear Project, Kaslo, BC, Canada.

Proctor MF, Kasworm WF, Annis KM, MacHutchon AG, Teisberg JE, *et al.* (2018) Conservation of threatened Canada-USA trans-border grizzly bears linked to comprehensive conflict reduction. *Human Wildlife Interactions* **12**, 248–272.

Proctor MF, MacHutchon AG, Boulanger J, Paetkua D (2023a) Evaluating grizzly bear conservation management: Quantifying recovery in the Canadian South Selkirk population unit in southeast British Columbia. Trans-border Grizzly Bear Project. Kaslo, BC.

Proctor MF, Lamb CT, Boulanger J, MacHutchon AG, Kasworm WF, *et al.* (2023b) Berries and bullets: Influence of food and mortality risk on grizzly bear in British Columbia. Trans-border Grizzly Bear Project. Kaslo, BC.

Woods J, Paetkau D, Lewis D, McLellan BN, Proctor M, *et al.* (1999) Genetic tagging of free-ranging black and brown bears. *Wildlife Society Bulletin* **27**, 616–627.

13 How can we use genomics to predict and improve population viability?

Fred W. Allendorf, Nils Ryman and Marty Kardos

ABSTRACT

Genetics can have important effects on the viability of populations. In the short-term, inbreeding depression can reduce population viability. In the long-term, the amount of genetic variation will affect the ability of a population to adapt to environmental change. Genomics can provide measures and procedures that allow estimating crucial parameters useful for predicting the viability of populations. The proportion of an individual's genome that is **identical by descent** (F) can now be estimated directly by identifying continuous segments of the genome that are homozygous because of inbreeding (runs of homozygosity). This procedure is superior to the traditional use of pedigrees to estimate F. Genomics also provides procedures to estimate both the current and historical effective population size. Increased **homozygosity** of recessive or partially recessive deleterious alleles is the primary cause of inbreeding depression. Genomics makes it possible to estimate the frequency of deleterious alleles that allows predicting the strength of inbreeding depression. This makes it possible to identify populations that are threatened by inbreeding depression before it can be detected with demographic measures. This would permit employing genetic rescue proactively when it is more likely to be successful. Individuals with fewer deleterious alleles can be chosen to found new populations to increase the probability of success. Genomics can also be used to predict the potential of a population to adapt to environmental change by estimating genome-wide variation, identifying alleles that are likely to be advantageous given anticipated environmental change (e.g. climate change), and identifying the genetic architecture of traits that strongly affect fitness in a changing environment.

INTRODUCTION

Charles Darwin (1896, p. 99) was the first to suggest that genetics could affect the viability of populations. He expressed concern that fallow deer (*Dama dama*) in British nature parks could be subject to loss of vigor because of their small population size and isolation. Michael Soulé (Soulé 1987) edited a book 35 years ago that synthesised the demographic and genetic understanding of predicting the viability of populations. In 2002, Beissinger and McCullough edited a book entitled *Population Viability Analysis* that reviewed our understanding of population viability (Beissinger and McCullough 2002). We wrote a chapter for that book in which we considered the role of genetics in understanding and predicting population viability (Allendorf and Ryman 2002). In this chapter, we consider how genomics has enhanced this understanding and our ability to predict population viability.

There are two conceptually different applications of 'genomics' to understand the genetics of populations (Luikart *et al.* 2018): 1) broad sense genomics is population genetics as usual with many markers (Charlesworth 2010) and 2) narrow sense genomics is sampling a mapped genome at sufficient density to detect evolutionary forces affecting different regions of the genome. That is, instead of using a representative sample of loci to address the average effect of processes acting across the whole genome, narrow sense genomics describes variation in those processes among regions of a mapped genome. Johri *et al.* (2022) provide an extremely useful overview of the statistical inference of population genomic data.

In this paper, we show how genomics in the narrow sense presents opportunities to understand the genetics and viability of populations that were not possible before. We have two primary objectives: 1) describe how the use of genomics can increase our understanding of population viability and 2) describe how that understanding can be applied to increase population viability through management actions.

THE GENETICS OF POPULATION VIABILITY

Genetics can have important effects on the viability of populations. In the short term, inbreeding depression can affect life history traits that affect population viability. In the long term, the amount of genetic variation in a population will affect the potential of a population to adapt to environmental change.

The primary genetic concern about viability refers to small population size and **genetic drift** resulting in inbreeding and loss of genetic variation. Genetic drift is stronger in small populations than in larger ones, and inbreeding and loss of genetic variation therefore proceed at a faster rate in smaller populations. This rate is not determined by the census population size (the number of adult individuals; N_C). Rather it is determined by the genetically effective population size (N_e), which is typically much smaller than N_C. In an isolated population, inbreeding (F) is expected to increase at a rate of $\Delta F = 1/(2N_e)$ per generation, and loss of heterozygosity follows the same pattern. Assessing effective size of the target population is a key objective of many management plans. Effective size constitutes the basis for the '50/500' rule of Franklin (1980) that has become widely established in conservation biology. This rule suggests that for an isolated population, $N_e > 50$ is needed to avoid the harmful effects of inbreeding depression in the short-term, and $N_e > 500$ is needed to maintain sufficient genetic variation to allow adaptation to environmental changes in the long-term (Jamieson and Allendorf 2012). The values 50 and 500 are not true thresholds; that is, there is nothing very different about an N_e of 49 or 50. Rather they represent useful general guideposts for managing populations.

Effective population size

Effective population size (N_e) is the size of the 'ideal population' that would experience the same amount of genetic drift as the observed population (Charlesworth 2009). The ideal population is an isolated (i.e. no immigration) and randomly mating population of constant size with non-overlapping generations without mutation and selection where all adults have the same *expected* lifetime production of progeny (Allendorf *et al.* 2022, p. 133). Census and effective sizes are the same in an ideal population ($N_e = N_C$), and the rate of inbreeding in an ideal population of, for example, size 20 ($N_e = N_C = 20$), is therefore $\Delta F = 1/40 = 0.025$ per generation. That is, 2.5% of the heterozygosity is expected to be lost per generation. It follows from the definition of N_e that any population with an inbreeding rate of $\Delta F = 0.025$ has an effective size of $N_e = 20$ regardless of demographic characteristics such as census size or sex ratio. The N_e/N_C ratio varies widely among species and populations. It is typically in the range 0.05–0.30 in natural populations (Palstra and Fraser 2012; Frankham *et al.* 2019; Hoban *et al.* 2020), but Waples *et al.* (2013) discuss situations where it can be higher and even exceed one ($N_e/N_C > 1$).

The concept of effective size is seemingly straightforward; nevertheless, it frequently turns into a quite complex issue when applied to real world situations (Waples *et al.* 2013; Ryman *et al.* 2019; Allendorf *et al.* 2022, chapter 7). First, there are different effective sizes relating to the different effects of genetic drift. The two primary concepts are the inbreeding effective size (N_{eI}), which refers to the rate of inbreeding, and the variance effective size (N_{eV}), which refers to the amount of allele frequency change. Gilbert and Whitlock (2015) review and evaluate a variety of different approaches for estimating N_e from genotypic data.

Further, the ideal population has discrete generations, whereas generations overlap in most natural populations. When generations overlap the temporal change of quantities such as allele frequencies is not only determined by genetic drift, but also by life history characteristics, such as age at maturity, annual survival rates, and reproduction rates. When estimating N_e from genotypic data this dependence must be accounted for and requires evaluation of the portion the genetic change that is due to genetic drift and to life history, respectively (Jorde and Ryman 1995). The effect of life history is most pronounced when measuring genetic change over a small number of generations, and it becomes gradually reduced as the time interval increases. Therefore, the effect of life history factors can often be ignored when estimating N_e from samples separated by many generations (Jorde and Ryman 2007; Jorde 2012).

In some species, it is easier to quantify changes over a single reproductive cycle (e.g. 1 year) than over a generation and estimate the effective number of breeders (N_b) in a breeding cycle (Luikart *et al.* 2021). When appropriate demographic data are available, the effective size per generation (N_e) can be inferred from N_b (Waples *et al.* 2014).

Additionally, the ideal population is completely isolated, whereas most natural populations are part of a metapopulation and exchange migrants with the rest of the global population. In an isolated population of constant size, the two measures of effective size are identical ($N_{eI} = N_{eV}$). In contrast, they are not the same in a local population with migration, and the difference can be dramatic.

For example, the so-called temporal method estimates variance effective size (N_{eV}) from temporal changes of allele frequencies. This estimate can be safely used as a proxy for N_{eI} (that relates to the rate of inbreeding rather than allele frequency change), when applied to an isolated population. In contrast, the N_{eI} of a local population is systematically underestimated when employing the temporal method approach to a local population that exchanges migrants with a metapopulation (Ryman *et al.* 2019). The effect of this bias is to overestimate the rate of inbreeding. It is therefore crucial that the correct N_e estimator be employed and interpreted appropriately for populations experiencing migration, though this is often ignored (Ryman *et al.* 2019).

Inbreeding depression

Franklin (1980) suggested, as a general rule of thumb, that the N_e of a population should be greater than 50 in the short term. This recommendation was based on the experience of animal breeders who observed that selection for performance and fertility could not overcome inbreeding depression when the inbreeding coefficient (F) increased by 2–3% or more per generation. Under the assumption that inbreeding depression might be more pronounced in wild than in domestic animals, a 1% increase in F per generation was taken as a conservative estimate of the maximum tolerable rate of the increase in F per generation. Using the equation $\Delta F = 1/(2N_e)$ per generation, a 1% change in F per generation corresponds to an N_e of 50. Therefore, an N_e of at least 50 was deemed desirable to reduce the likelihood of extinction in the short term because of harmful effects of inbreeding depression on demography.

One problem with using N_e = 50 as a guideline is that organisms with a short generation time may accumulate inbreeding rather quickly. For example, a population with a generation time of 1 year, such as annual plants and many insects, is expected to lose over 25% of its original heterozygosity in 30 years. Another approach is to decide on a minimum amount of heterozygosity that should be retained over some predefined time period. Allendorf and Ryman (2002) suggest that at least 95% of initial heterozygosity should be retained over 100 years.

Adaptation

The long-term '500' rule is based on the theoretical N_e required to balance the loss of **additive genetic variation** per generation due to genetic drift with the incorporation of new genetic variation due to mutation (Franklin 1980). The underlying arguments refer to the variation of quantitative characters and to the amount of variation considered necessary for a population's response to environmental change. They are based on mathematical and statistical considerations and on estimates of mutation rates and the relative importance of environmental factors for the total variation of a quantitative trait (see Allendorf and Ryman 2002). The appropriateness of the 50/500 rule has been debated (e.g. Jamieson and Allendorf 2012; Frankham *et al.* 2014; Franklin *et al.* 2014), but Franklin's original suggestion of 50/500 has strong support in the field of conservation genetics (Hoban *et al.* 2020; Laikre *et al.* 2020), and it remains a useful guideline for conservation practitioners. Unfortunately, genetic considerations generally have not been included in international policies related to species conservation (Hoban *et al.* 2020). However, several recent papers have recommended that the 50/500 rule be incorporated into the assessment procedures of the International Union for Conservation of Nature (IUCN) Red List of Threatened Species (e.g. Garner *et al.* 2020; Hoban *et al.* 2020, 2022).

APPLICATIONS OF GENOMICS
Application 1: Genomic measures to predict population viability

Genomics, in both the broad and narrow sense, can provide useful measures and procedures that allow estimating crucial parameters useful for predicting the viability of populations. In so doing, genomic analyses can support the most effective conservation decision making.

Inbreeding and effective population size

Inbreeding is the mating between related individuals which results in an increase of homozygosity in the progeny because they inherit alleles that are identical by descent

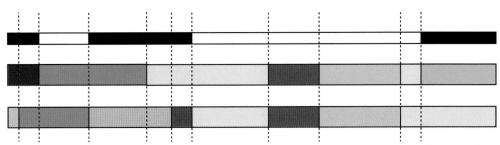

Fig. 13.1. Two homologous chromosomes in an individual sampled from a population that was founded by a small number of individuals a few generations before sampling (Allendorf *et al.* 2022, p. 217). The colours of these 'strands' represent different chromosomes that were present in the founders. The two white sections of the bar above the two chromosomes indicate regions originating from the same ancestral chromosomes. There are five regions (i.e. chromosomal tracts) of these chromosomes where this individual is identical by descent (IBD) that represent ~57% of the total length of these chromosomes. These so-called runs of homozygosity (ROH) can be summed to estimate the proportion of this chromosome that is IBD ($F_{ROH} = 0.57$).

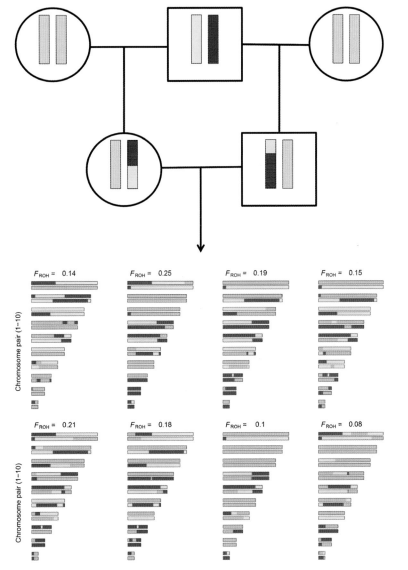

Fig. 13.2. Runs of homozygosity in eight offspring produced by a mating between two half-sibs (see pedigree on top) that share the same father (Allendorf *et al.* 2022, p. 379). The theoretically expected proportion of the genome IBD in these individuals based on their pedigree inbreeding coefficient is $F_P = 0.125$. The values above each offspring shows the actual proportion of their genome which they are IBD based upon runs of homozygosity. F_{ROH} differs by chance alone among these offspring depending upon the locations of **crossover events** during meiosis.

(IBD). The inbreeding coefficient of individual (F) is the proportion of an individual's genome that is IBD because of inbreeding. The proportion of the genome IBD has traditionally been estimated by the inbreeding coefficient (F_p) calculated from a pedigree (Pemberton 2008). However, F_p has two major shortcomings. First, it does not account for inbreeding caused by more distant ancestors not included in the pedigree. In addition, F_p is an imprecise predictor of the actual proportion of the genome IBD in a given individual because the proportion of the genome IBD will vary substantially among individuals with the same pedigree by chance alone depending upon the locations of crossover events during meiosis (see Fig. 13.2). Genomic analysis now allows us to estimate F for individuals in populations in which pedigrees are not available (Fig 13.1).

Genomics also provides improved estimates of effective population size (N_e). Estimates of N_e are useful for planning management actions and predicting genetic risks of populations (Schwartz *et al.* 2007; Waples 2016). Most traditional estimates of N_e were based on the 'temporal method' which compares allele frequencies in samples collected one or more generations apart (Waples 1989; Ryman *et al.* 2019). Estimation procedures are now available that only require a single temporal sample which is much more practical than requiring multiple temporal samples.

The most popular of these single sample methods uses the amount of **linkage disequilibrium (LD)** between **unlinked markers** to estimate N_e. The smaller the population, the more LD that will be generated. Therefore, the effective size of a population can be estimated by the amount of LD present between unlinked loci (Waples and Do 2008). The number of pairwise LD measurements increases with the square of the number of loci, so genomic datasets greatly increase the number of pairwise LD available to estimate N_e and thereby increase the accuracy. However, this method assumes that the loci are inherited independently (i.e. unlinked), and this assumption will be violated in datasets with many loci because some pairs of loci will be linked just by chance (Waples *et al.* 2016). Linked pairs of loci are expected to have greater LD than unlinked loci; this will downwardly bias estimates of N_e that assume independence. This problem can be solved with statistical corrections or by only using pairs of loci on different chromosomes if a genetic map is available.

There is a variety of new and more powerful methods that use narrow-sense genomic data to estimate N_e. These methods allow estimation of N_e not only in the present, but also in the past by considering the length of regions of the genome that are IBD. Consider Fig. 13.1 showing regions of the genome that are IBD in a single individual. Recombination will break-up haplotypes over generations into smaller segments. Individuals might have the same total proportion of the genome IBD because of inbreeding, but these segments will be smaller if the common ancestors of parents occurred further in the past.

Understanding changes in population size can be important for how a species is managed. A small population would not be of immediate demographic concern if its population size has been relatively constant over time. However, a small population would be of immediate conservation concern if its population size had declined dramatically in recent times. Identifying the environmental causes of such a decline in population size would be crucial. In addition, populations that were historically larger are expected to have a greater **mutation load** than populations that have historically been small (see Box 13.1).

Runs of homozygosity (ROH) and pattern of genome wide IBD between individuals can be used to estimate N_e, as well as changes in N_e over time (Kardos *et al.* 2017; Nadachowska-Brzyska *et al.* 2021). Browning *et al.* (2018) provide a method using the pattern of pairwise genome-wide IBD to estimate current effective size of the population and the changes in effective size over the past few hundred generations. Santiago *et al.* (2020) provide a method using the decay of LD over time to estimate N_e over the past 100 generations from the observed pattern of LD of pairs of loci over a wide range of recombination rates in a single sample of individuals. However, as described below, it remains unclear how well these methods perform for populations with very small contemporary population sizes.

Mutation load

Increased homozygosity of recessive or partially recessive deleterious alleles is the primary cause of inbreeding depression (Charlesworth and Willis 2009). Genomic approaches now facilitate estimating the frequency of such deleterious alleles in a population which allows predicting the expected relative strength of inbreeding depression in different populations. There are two primary approaches of measuring the mutation load of individuals: 1) estimating the frequency of **substitutions** at sites that are under evolutionary constraint and 2) estimating the frequency of **loss of function** (LOF) and **missense alleles** in coding regions of the genome.

Box 13.1 presents the estimation of the relative mutation load in four populations of killer whales on the west coast of North America. The small and isolated Southern Resident killer whale (SRKW) population had the lowest frequency of LOF substitutions (Fig. 13.3A) as expected. Consider a large population which goes through a bottleneck. Many of the LOF alleles in the large population will be at low frequency and will be lost during the bottleneck by drift (Allendorf 1986), and additional LOF alleles will be removed by selection (purging). Thus, LOF alleles are expected to be less frequent in a small post-bottlenecked population.

Nevertheless, the reduction in the frequency of LOF alleles in the SRKW population has not removed the harmful effects of inbreeding. LOF alleles are less frequent in the SRKW, but many of these alleles are homozygous because of inbreeding in this small population. The effects of inbreeding on fitness are likely determined largely by the abundance of homozygous genotypes for deleterious alleles

that are generally at least partially recessive. The frequency of homozygous deleterious mutations was highest in the SRKW population (Fig. 13.3B).

Kardos *et al.* (2023) concluded that deleterious alleles at fixation or high frequencies likely contribute to the lower average fitness in the SRKW compared to the other populations. This is consistent with the observed inbreeding depression for survival in the SRKW, and the increase in population size for North Pacific populations other than the SRKW following federal protection. Specifically, the yearly survival probability was lower among more highly inbred individuals as determined with genomic data. Incorporating the observed inbreeding depression into demographic projections indicated that this inbreeding depression was sufficient to limit population growth. Importantly, the use of genome sequencing that provided high coverage of the genome was crucial to detect inbreeding depression. A previous study that used 94 SNP loci did not detect inbreeding depression in this population (Ford *et al.* 2018).

Box 13.1: Estimates of mutation load and fitness effects of inbreeding in killer whales

Northeastern Pacific killer whale (*Orcinus orca*) populations initially recovered following protection from culls, harassment, and captures in the early 1970s (Kardos *et al.* 2023). However, unlike the other populations that have continued to grow, the southern resident killer whales (SRKW) have had roughly flat population growth over the last 50 years, have declined since the mid-1990s, and are now listed as endangered in both the United States and Canada. The SRKW population is one of several non-interbreeding groups of fish-eating killer whales in the northeastern Pacific Ocean.

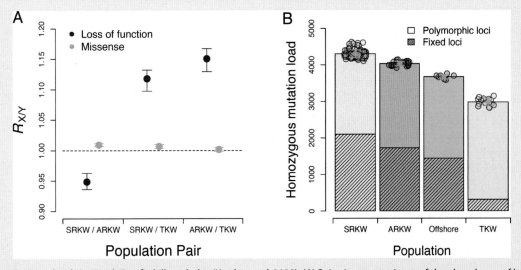

Fig. 13.3. Mutation loads in North Pacific killer whales (Kardos *et al.* 2023). (A) Pairwise comparisons of the abundance of loss-of-function and missense alleles ($R_{X/Y}$) between the three populations with the largest sample sizes. $R_{X/Y} > 1$ means that deleterious alleles are more abundant in population X than in population Y; $R_{X/Y} < 1$ means that deleterious alleles are less abundant in population X than in population Y. (B) The total **homozygous mutation load** for each individual (colored points), and the population means partitioned between homozygous genotypes for fixed deleterious alleles (hatched bars), and loci polymorphic for a putatively deleterious allele (solid bars).

The SRKW are thought to face a number of threats, including contaminants, anthropogenic noise and disturbance, and reduced prey abundance. Despite nearly 50 years of conservation efforts focused on environmental factors, a population census of 73 whales in 2022 and chronically low survival and fecundity rates have highlighted the need to improve understanding of the factors impacting the population growth of North Pacific killer whales in general, and the SRKW in particular. Kardos *et al.* (2023) hypothesised that inbreeding depression might be a major factor contributing to the failure of the SRKW population to recover following legal protection.

Kardos *et al.* (2023) used genomic analyses to evaluate the relative genetic loads and fitness effects of inbreeding on the four eastern North Pacific killer whale populations: SRKW, ARKW (Alaska resident), offshore, and TKW (transient) populations. They identified >28 000 putatively deleterious missense and LOF alleles.

Missense mutations, which are likely to be less detrimental than LOF mutations, had similar frequencies in these three populations (Fig. 13.3A). Putatively deleterious alleles had lower average frequencies than alleles that are most likely neutral within each population, suggesting that part of the genetic load has been removed in each population via natural selection. Thus, the SRKW population appears to have purged some deleterious recessive alleles, but this does not appear to have offset the inbreeding that created a greater frequency of homozygous deleterious genotypes in this population.

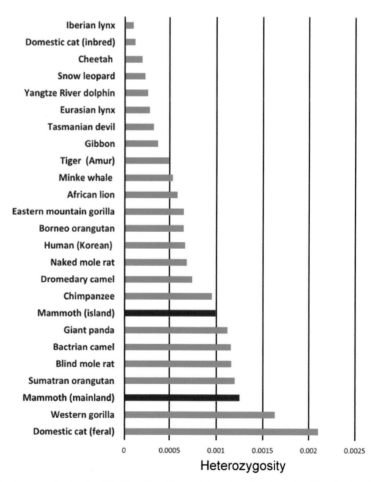

Fig. 13.4. Genome-wide SNP heterozygosity (nucleotide diversity, π) in a variety of mammal species (Allendorf *et al.* 2022, p. 59).

Adaptive potential

The rate of change in response to natural selection is proportional to the amount of genetic variation present (Fisher 1930). Therefore, the amount of heterozygosity or allelic diversity at molecular markers that are likely to be neutral with respect to natural selection provide an indication of the amount of genetic variation at loci that potentially could be involved in response to natural selection (Shaw 2019).

The most commonly used measure to quantify variation within populations is heterozygosity (*H*). At a single locus, heterozygosity is the proportion of individuals that are heterozygous. Two different measures of heterozygosity are used. H_o is the observed proportion of heterozygotes, and H_e is the expected proportion of heterozygotes if the population is mating at random assuming Hardy-Weinberg proportions. H_e provides a better measure than H_o to compare the relative amount of variation in different populations as long as the populations are mating at random (Nei 1977). Average heterozygosity is typically calculated across many loci in a population to estimate genetic variation.

Genome-wide analysis of single nucleotide polymorphisms (SNPs) provides an opportunity to compare heterozygosity among species, as long as SNP genotypes are generated in a comparable way; that is, genome wide, or targeting the same regions (e.g. random, intergenic, exons, or introns). Expected heterozygosity can also be calculated for DNA sequence data as the expected proportion of nucleotide differences among chromosome pairs. This is called nucleotide diversity (π). SNP heterozygosity for a wide range of mammals is shown in Fig. 13.4.

The lowest heterozygosity was in the Iberian lynx (*Lynx pardinus*), which went through a bottleneck of fewer than 100 individuals in the second half of the 20th century (Abascal *et al.* 2016). Two ancient samples from woolly mammoths (*Mammuthus primigenius*) revealed approximately 20% higher heterozygosity in a sample from the mainland of Asia than in a sample from Wrangel Island, presumably reflecting smaller population size and isolation of the island population. Fry *et al.* (2020) found that the genome of the Wrangel Island mammoth had many putatively damaging substitutions affecting development, reproduction, and olfaction that might have contributed to the extinction of this population. Another interesting comparison is feral and inbred domestic cats (*Felis catus*); the former has exceptionally high heterozygosity, while the latter has almost no variation.

The total number of alleles at a locus has also been used as a measure of genetic variation. Most SNPs are biallelic, but multiple SNPs which occur within the same region can be genotyped jointly from high-throughput short-read DNA sequences to derive multiallelic microhaplotype markers (Kidd *et al.* 2014; Allendorf *et al.* 2022, fig. 10.9). Microhaplotypes are also more powerful than individual SNPs to detect relationships among individuals in natural populations (Baetscher *et al.* 2018). The number of alleles is a valuable complementary measure of genetic variation because it is more sensitive to the loss of genetic variation in small

populations than heterozygosity, and it is an important measure of the long-term evolutionary potential of populations (Allendorf 1986).

Application 2: Detection of adaptive genetic variation
Genomics facilitates detection of **adaptive genetic variation** that is crucial for understanding and predicting the ability of species to respond to human-induced environmental challenges (e.g. climate change, pollution, and disease). In this paper, we do not discuss this important topic because Razgour *et al.* (Chapter 14) in this volume consider the genomics of adaptation, including applications to conservation, in detail.

There is currently an ongoing debate on the relative importance of adaptive genomic variation versus genome-wide variation in conservation (see recent overview in Kardos *et al.* 2021). Artificial selection to increase the frequency of an adaptive allele at a single locus can result in the loss of genetic variation over the rest of the genome. Conserving genome-wide genetic variation is crucial to prevent inbreeding depression and loss of adaptive potential from driving populations towards extinction. Focusing conservation efforts on functional genetic variation will always be difficult, can be misleading, and can be potentially harmful when done at the cost of genetic variation across the whole genome (Kardos *et al.* 2021).

The genetic architecture of a trait (i.e. the number and distribution of the effect sizes of alleles affecting the trait) can strongly affect the response of a population to selection. Historically, it has been assumed that most traits are affected by many loci with a small effect (i.e. that they are polygenic). However, genomic studies have shown many life history traits appear to be largely influenced by a few loci with major effects (Waples *et al.* 2022). Kardos and Luikart (2021) have shown that the genetic architecture of a trait can have a major effect on the demography and viability of a population. They found that evolutionary potential and population viability are often higher when the selected trait is affected by many loci with small effect than when large-effect loci are involved. In the case of large-effect beneficial alleles, population viability depended strongly on the initial allele frequencies.

Incorporating information on the genetic architecture of selected traits can improve predictions of adaptive response of populations to natural selection imposed by environmental changes and management actions. Probable adaptive responses to selection can then be incorporated into analyses of population viability. However, there are substantial challenges to incorporating adaptive genomic information into population viability analysis. The complexities inherent in the stochasticity of environmental change and demography, combined with, for example, genotype-by-environment interactions, and phenotypic plasticity mean that simultaneously predicting evolutionary and demographic responses of wild populations to environmental change will always be challenging.

Application 3: Management actions

Many species that historically were nearly continuously distributed across broad geographic areas are now restricted to increasingly smaller and more isolated patches of habitat. In some cases, human-mediated gene flow has been used to restore functional connectivity to small, isolated populations to infuse new genetic variation, reduce inbreeding depression, and restore evolutionary potential – a management strategy known as genetic rescue. In this section, we consider practical ways in which genomics can inform the use of genetic rescue in management.

Early detection of populations facing effects of inbreeding depression

We saw in Box 13.1 how genomics can be used to measure the mutation load of deleterious alleles in populations. The

identification of populations with high homozygous mutation load could be used to detect populations suffering from inbreeding depression before they can be detected demographically through measurement of reproductive success or mortality. This would allow employing genetic rescue proactively when it is more likely to be successful.

Predicting outbreeding depression

The use of genetic rescue requires considering the possibility of **outbreeding depression** which is much less predictable than inbreeding depression (Frankham *et al.* 2011). All populations have some deleterious recessive alleles that will reduce fitness when they become homozygous because of inbreeding. However, the effects of matings between genetically distinct populations depend upon a combination of factors. Fitness can increase because of the sheltering of deleterious recessive alleles. On the other hand, fitness can decrease because of genetic incompatibilities (e.g. **structural chromosomal differences**) or loss of local adaptations.

Traditionally, predicting the likelihood of intrinsic outbreeding depression has been based on the amount of genetic divergence between the hybridising populations as measured primarily by differences in allele frequencies. However, differences in chromosome numbers and structure also play an important role in the outbreeding

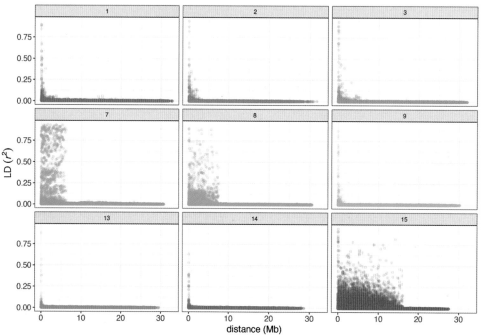

Fig. 13.5. LD (r^2) versus the physical distance (one million base pairs) between pairs of SNP loci in Pacific herring (Petrou *et al.* 2021; Allendorf *et al.* 2022, p. 221). LD (r^2) is the square of the correlation coefficient between alleles at the two loci. Nine of the 26 pairs of chromosomes in this species are shown. High LD over long physical distances is present on chromosomes 7, 8, and 15 because of chromosomal inversions that reduce recombination between chromosomes with inverted and standard sequences.

depression. These types of major structural variants can underlie outbreeding depression by reducing fertility by the production of **aneuploids** because of pairing problems during meiosis (Allendorf *et al.* 2022, pp. 47–48). Unfortunately, very little karyotypic information is available about chromosome numbers and structure for most species. Fortunately, the rapidly increasing number of species with chromosome-level genome assemblies will partially fill this void.

High-throughput genomics methods have discovered that chromosomal structural variation is much more widespread than previously thought (Wellenreuther and Bernatchez 2018; Wold *et al.* 2021). Genomics potentially allows improved prediction of outbreeding depression through the detection of chromosomal structural differences between populations. For example, Petrou *et al.* (2021) genotyped 6718 SNP loci in over 1000 Pacific herring (*Clupea pallasii*) from spawning aggregations along the Pacific Coast of North America. Plots of LD versus physical distance indicated the presence of major inversions on four of the 26 pairs of chromosomes (Fig. 13.5).

Selection of individuals to be translocated

The founding of new populations has become a valuable tool in conservation efforts. Such populations are necessarily small and vulnerable to the effects of genetic drift and inbreeding depression. Genomics provides the potential to select individuals to be used as founders that have a smaller mutation load in order to increase the likelihood of success.

Assisted gene flow involves moving pre-adapted individuals from their native origins to locations with favorable climates within the current species range (Aitken and Whitlock 2013). Assisted gene flow has the greatest potential to facilitate or accelerate **evolutionary rescue** in a changing climate in moderate to large populations that are locally adapted to recent historic climates and have not been separated for long enough for outbreeding depression to be a substantive risk. Razgour *et al.* (Chapter 14) discuss the use of genomic information to select individuals to use in assisted gene flow and colonisation.

FUTURE DIRECTIONS AND OUTSTANDING QUESTIONS

One of the most exciting, and challenging, aspects of conservation genomics is that we still do not know just how much we can learn from genomic data. For example, it is likely that emerging sequencing technologies (e.g. Porubsky

et al. 2021) will eventually enable the assembly of **fully phased** individual genomes *de novo* for any species, potentially making the concept of a **reference genome** obsolete. Use of a single reference genome cannot capture all of the diversity within a species.

The **pangenome** approach allows the study of all of the genetic variation within a species (Bayer *et al.* 2020; Miga and Wang 2021). The pangenome concept will transform how genomic analyses are done, and facilitate new analyses that will be useful to our understanding of population viability (Brockhurst *et al.* 2019). Additionally, new approaches to data analysis are continually improving our ability to understand crucial parameters such as demographic history and genetic loads. The rapid advancement of approaches to analysis and sequencing technology highlights the need to identify the limitations of what we can learn from genomics, and how we could go wrong interpreting results. Here we highlight two areas where substantially more information is needed to advance the contribution of genomics to population viability in a positive direction.

Can we reliably estimate genetic load from sequence data?

One of the most exciting possibilities, now being realised from genomics (Box 13.1), is to try to predict fitness solely from genomic data, without using demographic data. Individuals that are homozygous for a larger number of deleterious, partially recessive alleles should have lower average fitness than individuals who are heterozygous at such loci. As highlighted above, several recent studies have estimated genetic loads in populations of concern using genomic approaches (Grossen *et al.* 2020; Dussex *et al.* 2021; Khan *et al.* 2021; Kardos *et al.* 2023). In principle, such analyses should enable us to infer whether a particular population has a higher or lower intrinsic fitness (and thus lower viability) compared to other conspecific populations.

We still have little understanding of how molecular genomic measures of load translate into actual contemporary fitness effects. These analyses usually begin by identifying putatively deleterious alleles as derived variants that either have a predicted negative impact on protein function, or at loci that are conserved over a long evolutionary time (e.g. across a broad phylogeny). Putatively deleterious **derived alleles** tend to be less frequent than putatively neutral alleles (Grossen *et al.* 2020; Dussex *et al.* 2021; Khan *et al.* 2021), suggesting that putatively deleterious alleles were indeed deleterious historically, on average. However, these alleles can sometimes be beneficial and under positive selection, and some historically deleterious alleles can be neutral or even beneficial under current ecological conditions.

A great need for the field is therefore to test whether genomic predictions of fitness hold up empirically. For example, do genomic predictors of homozygous mutation load explain a larger fraction of variation in fitness among individuals than genomic measures of inbreeding alone? This will likely require study in ecological model systems where samples sizes are large enough to obtain high enough statistical power to distinguish the explanatory power of two highly correlated parameters (homozygous mutation load and F). We urge caution when evaluating population viability solely on the basis of genomic predictions of fitness until the performance of these methods are thoroughly evaluated. Demographic analysis of the effects of inbreeding and lost genetic variation remain crucial to understand population viability.

Can we reliably estimate the demographic history of small populations?

A major priority for advancing genomic aspects of population viability analysis is to carefully evaluate what we can learn from genomic data about the demographic history of small populations. The effect of population declines on intrinsic aspects of fitness (e.g. inbreeding depression) depend in part on historical demography. For example, bottlenecked populations that have historically smaller population sizes are likely to have lower **inbreeding loads** than historically larger populations (Garcia-Dorado 2012; Hedrick and Garcia-Dorado 2016; Kardos *et al.* 2021).

We should, in principle, be able to learn something of the likely fitness effect of a recent bottleneck from information on deeper historical population size. Analyses of historical demography are particularly useful for analysing small populations where the detailed demographic data needed to directly measure inbreeding depression are unavailable. A major issue is that it is unclear how reliably current genomic methods to infer historical population size perform for the majority of endangered populations that are currently very small.

Approaches to estimate historical N_e are divided into those looking at recent versus deep historical population dynamics (Nadachowska-Brzyska *et al.* 2021). Recent changes in N_e can be inferred from patterns of LD at different genetic distances across chromosomes (Santiago *et al.* 2020). LD between loci separated by larger genetic distances is informative of more recent N_e, and LD between closely linked loci is informative of N_e in deeper history. Similarly, the length distribution of segments shared IBD between

individuals is informative of historical N_e (Browning and Browning 2015). Longer IBD segments have more recent **coalescent** times and are therefore informative of more recent N_e, while shorter IBD segments are informative of deeper historical N_e because they have longer coalescent times.

A major challenge for both of these approaches is that they assume that populations are closed, and violating this assumption will introduce bias. For example, strong LD spanning entire chromosomes would naturally be interpreted as a signature of small recent population size, but recent admixture can generate this same pattern, thereby introducing potentially strongly downwardly biased estimates of historical population size. An important issue for IBD-based methods is that long IBD segments characterising small populations are often actually composed of multiple shorter IBD segments, each with coalescent time that can be substantially longer than inferred under the assumption of constant coalescent time across the whole segment. The extent to which this problem generates bias in estimates of N_e is unknown.

There are also potentially important challenges to inferring deep historical N_e (i.e. thousands of generations ago) that are particular to populations that are currently very small. The most common approaches, such as the pairwise sequentially Markovian coalescent (pairwise sequentially Markovian coalescent [PSMC]; Li and Durbin 2011), use the distribution of estimated coalescent times across an individual diploid genome to infer N_e from thousands to millions of generations ago. While it is known that population structure can introduce substantial bias in PMSC (Mazet *et al.* 2016), the effect of severe inbreeding and low diversity on the reliability of coalescent-based inference of deep historical populations size remains unclear.

It might be difficult to infer deep historical N_e using the genomes of highly inbred populations, which are typical of populations of conservation concern. Specifically, most of the coalescent events are expected to occur in very recent generations in small, highly inbred populations with low genetic diversity (Thompson 2013). This means that a substantial proportion of the genomic signal picked up by PSMC-type analyses might arise from sequencing errors in very small populations. A priority is to understand the extent of this problem, and to identify possible solutions.

How can genomic information be integrated into population projections?

Perhaps the most important future question relating to genomics and population viability is how can genomic information be incorporated into predicting the viability of individual populations? Answering this question is dependent on our ability to predict fitness effects directly from sequence data, as discussed above. It will be interesting to see how this challenging question is answered in the coming years.

DISCUSSION TOPICS

1. Our consideration of N_e has assumed that the population of concern is isolated from other populations. However, most populations in nature experience some gene flow from other populations. How do you think a little gene flow, say one individual or so per generation, would affect the 50 and the 500 recommendations?

2. The vaquita porpoise (*Phocoena sinus*) is one of the rarest mammals in the world; fewer than 19 individuals remained in the wild in 2018 (Morin *et al.* 2021). These authors found extremely low genetic variation in the vaquita (π = 0.000105), approximately the same amount as in the Iberian lynx in Fig. 13.4. These authors estimated that the vaquita has had an N_e of less than 5000 for over 200 000 years using PSMC analysis. They concluded that the vaquita is not threatened by genetic factors because: 'The vaquita genome has had ample opportunity to purge highly deleterious alleles and potentially maintain diversity necessary for population health.' Do you agree with these two conclusions of the authors? Justify your answer.

3. Australian news media have reported that conservation managers are wasting resources and money trying to save 'lost-cause' species such as the kākāpō (*Strigops habroptilus*) of New Zealand. The kākāpō is a large, flightless, and nocturnal parrot that is the only species in the genus *Strigops*. The extant population consisted of just 201 individuals in 2021(Dussex *et al.* 2021). The targeted goal of recovery for this species is just a few hundred individuals, far below the N_e of 500 guideline if we assume an N_e/N_C ratio in the range of 0.05–0.30, as presented above. Do you believe that species such as the kākāpō are worth trying to save?

4. Genomic techniques make it possible to genotype hundreds of thousands of loci. As a result, genetic parameters, such as effective size (N_e), can be estimated with extremely tight confidence limits. For example, it is possible to obtain an estimate of N_e (with a 95% confidence interval) on the order of '114 (113–115)'. In what kind of situations is this precision likely to be useful? How can such precision be misleading?

RESOURCES

1. *Vortex* 10.5.5 software and manuals can be downloaded from the link below. *Vortex* is an individual-based simulation model of the demography and genetics of populations that incorporates deterministic forces, as well as demographic, environmental and genetic stochastic events on populations. *Vortex* has been used for over 30 years to model the population dynamics of many threatened species.
http://www.cbsg.org/download-vortex

2. This 8 minute video from PBS Eons describes the genetic deterioration and extinction of the Wrangel Island woolly mammoth (Fig. 13.4) because of its small population size and isolation.
https://www.pbs.org/video/the-island-of-the-last-surviving-mammoths-fnpmr0/

ACKNOWLEDGEMENTS

We thank Olly Berry for inviting us to contribute this paper and his helpful comments; Scott Edwards for suggesting pangenome references; Chris Funk for help with the figures; Paul Hohenlohe for help with distinguishing broad and narrow genomics; Jason Kennington for his helpful suggestions; Linda Laikre with help on policy applications of the 50/500 rule; Eleni Petrou for providing Figure 13.5; and Robin Waples for help with using many loci to estimate N_e. FWA and NR thank each other for their nearly 50 years of friendship and collaboration.

REFERENCES

Abascal F, Corvelo A, Cruz F, Villanueva-Cañas JL, Vlasova A, et al. (2016) Extreme genomic erosion after recurrent demographic bottlenecks in the highly endangered Iberian lynx. *Genome Biology* **17**(1), 251. doi:10.1186/s13059-016-1090-1

Aitken SN, Whitlock MC (2013) Assisted gene flow to facilitate local adaptation to climate change. *Annual Review of Ecology, Evolution, and Systematics* **44**, 367–388. doi:10.1146/annurev-ecolsys-110512-135747

Allendorf FW (1986) Genetic drift and the loss of alleles versus heterozygosity. *Zoo Biology* **5**(2), 181–190. doi:10.1002/zoo.1430050212

Allendorf FW, Ryman N (2002) The role of genetics in population viability analysis. In *Population Viability Analysis*. (Eds SR Beissinger, DR McCullough) pp. 50–85. University of Chicago Press, Chicago, IL, USA.

Allendorf FW, Funk WC, Aitken SN, Byrne M, Luikart G (2022) *Conservation and the Genomics of Populations*. 3rd edn. Oxford University Press, Oxford, UK.

Baetscher DS, Clemento AJ, Ng TC, Anderson EC, Garza JC (2018) Microhaplotypes provide increased power from short-read DNA sequences for relationship inference. *Molecular Ecology Resources* **18**(2), 296–305. doi:10.1111/1755-0998.12737

Bayer PE, Golicz AA, Scheben A, Batley J, Edwards D (2020) Plant pan-genomes are the new reference. *Nature Plants* **6**(8), 914–920. doi:10.1038/s41477-020-0733-0

Beissinger S, McCullough D (2002) *Population Viability Analysis.* University of Chicago Press, Chicago, Illinois.

Brockhurst MA, Harrison E, Hall JP, Richards T, McNally A, *et al.* (2019) The ecology and evolution of pangenomes. *Current Biology* **29**(20), R1094–R1103. doi:10.1016/j.cub.2019.08.012

Browning SR, Browning BL, Daviglus ML, Durazo-Arvizu RA, Schneiderman N, *et al.* (2018) Ancestry-specific recent effective population size in the Americas. *PLoS Genetics* **14**(5), e1007385.

Browning SR, Browning BL (2015) Accurate non-parametric estimation of recent effective population size from segments of identity by descent. *American Journal of Human Genetics* **97**(3), 404–418.

Charlesworth B (2009) Effective population size and patterns of molecular evolution and variation. *Nature Reviews Genetics* **10**, 195–205. doi:10.1038/nrg2526

Charlesworth B (2010) Molecular population genomics: a short history. *Genetics Research* **92**(5–6), 397–411. doi:10.1017/S0016672310000522

Charlesworth D, Willis JH (2009) The genetics of inbreeding depression. *Nature Reviews Genetics* **10**(11), 783–796. doi:10.1038/nrg2664

Darwin C (1896) *The Variation of Animals and Plants under Domestication.* Vol. II. D. Appleton and Co., New York, USA.

Dussex N, van der Valk T, Wheat CW, Díez-del-Molino D, von Seth J, *et al.* (2021) Population genomics reveals the impact of long-term small population size in the critically endangered kākāpō. *Cell Genomics* **1**(1), 100002.

Fisher R (1930) *The Genetical Theory of Natural Selection.* Clarendon Press, Oxford, UK.

Ford MJ, Parsons KM, Ward EJ, Hempelmann JA, Emmons CK, *et al.* (2018) Inbreeding in an endangered killer whale population. *Animal Conservation* **21**(5), 423–432. doi:10.1111/acv.12413

Frankham R, Ballou JD, Eldridge MD, Lacy RC, Ralls K, *et al.* (2011) Predicting the probability of outbreeding depression. *Conservation Biology* **25**(3), 465–475. doi:10.1111/j.1523-1739.2011.01662.x

Frankham R, Ballou JD, Ralls K, Eldridge M, Dudash MR, *et al.* (2019) *A Practical Guide for Genetic Management of Fragmented Animal and Plant Populations.* Oxford University Press, Oxford, UK.

Frankham R, Bradshaw CJA, Brook BW (2014) Genetics in conservation management: Revised recommendations for the 50/500 rules, Red List criteria and population viability analyses. *Biological Conservation* **170**, 56–63.

Franklin IR (1980) Evolutionary changes in small populations. In *Conservation Biology – An Evolutionary-Ecological Perspective.* (Eds ME Soulé, BA Wilcox) pp. 135–149. Sinauer Associates, Sunderland, Massachusetts.

Franklin IR, Allendorf FW, Jamieson IG (2014) The 50/500 rule is still valid – Reply to Frankham *et al. Biological Conservation* **176**, 284–285.

Fry E, Kim SK, Chigurapti S (2020) Functional architecture of deleterious genetic variants in the genome of a Wrangel Island mammoth. *Genome Biology and Evolution* **12**(3), 48–58. doi:10.1093/gbe/evz279

Garcia-Dorado A (2012) Understanding and predicting the fitness decline of shrunk populations: Inbreeding, purging, mutation, and standard selection. *Genetics* **190**(4), 1461–1476. doi:10.1534/genetics.111.135541

Garner BA, Hoban S, Luikart G (2020) IUCN Red List and the value of integrating genetics. *Conservation Genetics* **21**(5), 795–801.

Gilbert KJ, Whitlock MC (2015) Evaluating methods for estimating local effective population size with and without migration. *Evolution* **69**(8), 2154–2166. doi:10.1111/evo.12713

Grossen C, Guillaume F, Keller LF, Croll D (2020) Purging of highly deleterious mutations through severe bottlenecks in alpine ibex. *Nature Communications* **11**(1), 1–12.

Hedrick PW, Garcia-Dorado A (2016) Understanding inbreeding depression, purging, and genetic rescue. *Trends in Ecology & Evolution* **31**(12), 940–952. doi:10.1016/j.tree.2016.09.005

Hoban S, Bruford M, Jackson JD, Lopes-Fernandes M, Heuertz M, *et al.* (2020) Genetic diversity targets and indicators in the CBD post-2020 Global Biodiversity Framework must be improved. *Biological Conservation* **248**, 108654. doi:10.1016/j.biocon.2020.108654

Hoban S, Archer FI, Bertola LD, Bragg JG, Breed MF, *et al.* (2022) Global genetic diversity status and trends: Towards a suite of Essential Biodiversity Variables (EBVs) for genetic composition. *Biological Reviews of the Cambridge Philosophical Society* **97**, 1511–1538.

Jamieson IG, Allendorf FW (2012) How does the 50/500 rule apply to MVPs? *Trends in Ecology & Evolution* **27**(10), 578–584.

Johri P, Aquadro CF, Beaumont M, Charlesworth B, Excoffier L, *et al.* (2022) Recommendations for improving statistical inference in population genomics. *PLoS Biology* **20**(5), e3001669.

Jorde PE (2012) Allele frequency covariance among cohorts and its use in estimating effective size of age-structured populations. *Molecular Ecology Resources* **12**, 476–480.

Jorde PE, Ryman N (1995) Temporal allele frequency change and estimation of effective size in populations with overlapping generations. *Genetics* **139**, 1077–1090.

Jorde PE, Ryman N (2007) Unbiased estimator for genetic drift and effective population size. *Genetics* **177**, 927–935.

Kardos M, Armstrong EE, Fitzpatrick SW, Hauser S, Hedrick PW, *et al.* (2021) The crucial role of genome-wide genetic variation in conservation. *Proceedings of the National Academy of Sciences* **118**(48), e2104642118. doi:10.1073/pnas.2104642118

Kardos M, Zhang Y, Parsons KM, Kang H, Xu X, *et al.* (2023) Inbreeding depression explains killer whale population dynamics. *Nature Ecology & Evolution* **7**, 675–686. doi:10.1038/s41559-023-01995-0

Kardos M, Luikart G (2021) The genetic architecture of fitness drives population viability during rapid environmental change. *The American Naturalist* **197**(5), 511–525. doi:10.1086/713469

Kardos M, Qvarnstrom A, Ellegren H (2017) Inferring individual inbreeding and demographic history from segments of identity by descent in flycatcher genome sequences. *Genetics* **205**(3), 1319–1334.

Khan A, Patel K, Shukla H, Viswanathan A, van der Valk T, *et al.* (2021) Genomic evidence for inbreeding depression and purging of deleterious genetic variation in Indian tigers. *Proceeding of the National Academy of Sciences USA* **118**(49), e2023018118. doi:10.1073/pnas.2023018118

Kidd KK, Pakstis AJ, Speed WC (2014) Current sequencing technology makes microhaplotypes a powerful new type of genetic marker for forensics. *Forensic Science International: Genetics* **12**, 215–224. doi:10.1016/j.fsigen.2014.06.014

Laikre L, Hoban S, Bruford MW, Segelbacher G, Allendorf FW, *et al.* (2020) Post-2020 goals overlook genetic diversity. *Science* **367**(6482), 1083.

Li H, Durbin R (2011) Inference of human population history from individual whole-genome sequences. *Nature* **475**, 493–496. doi:10.1038/nature10231

Luikart G, *et al.* (2018) Population genomics: advancing understanding of nature. In: *Population Genomics.* (Ed OP Rajora) pp. 3–79. Springer, Cham.

Luikart G, Antao T, Hand BK, Muhlfeld CC, Boyer MC, *et al.* (2021) Detecting population declines via monitoring the effective number of breeders (N_b). *Molecular Ecology Resources* **21**(2), 379–393. doi:10.1111/1755-0998.13251

Mazet O, Rodríguez W, Grusea S, Boitard S, Chikhi L (2016) On the importance of being structured: instantaneous coalescence rates and human evolution – lessons for ancestral population size inference? *Heredity* **116**(4), 362–371. doi:10.1038/hdy.2015.104

Miga KH, Wang T (2021) The need for a human pangenome reference sequence, *Annual Review of Genomics and Human Genetics* **22**(1), 81–102. doi:10.1146/annurev-genom-120120-081921

Morin PA, Archer FI, Avila CD (2021) Reference genome and demographic history of the most endangered marine mammal, the vaquita. *Molecular Ecology Resources* **21**(4), 1008–1020. doi:10.1111/1755-0998.13284

Nadachowska-Brzyska K, Dutoit L, Smeds L, Kardos M, Gustafsson L, *et al.* (2021) Genomic inference of contemporary effective population size in a large island population of collared flycatchers (*Ficedula albicollis*). *Molecular Ecology* **30**(16), 3965–3973. doi:10.1111/mec.16025

Nei M (1977) *F*-statistics and analysis of gene diversity in subdivided populations *Annals of Human Genetics* **41**, 225–233.

Palstra FP, Fraser DJ (2012) Effective/census population size ratio estimation: A compendium and appraisal. *Ecology and Evolution* **2**(9), 2357–2365. doi:10.1002/ece3.329

Pemberton JM (2008) Wild pedigrees: the way forward. *Proceedings of the Royal Society B: Biological Sciences* **275**(1635), 613–621. doi:10.1098/rspb.2007.1531

Petrou EL, Fuentes-Pardo AP, Rogers LA, Orobko M, Tarpey C, *et al.* (2021) Functional genetic diversity in an exploited marine species and its relevance to fisheries management. *Proceedings of the Royal Society B* **288**, 20202398.

Porubsky D, Ebert P, Audano PA, Vollger MR, Harvey WT, *et al.* (2021) Fully phased human genome assembly without parental data using single-cell strand sequencing and long reads. *Nature Biotechnology* **39**, 302–308.

Ryman N, Laikre L, Hössjer O (2019) Do estimates of contemporary effective population size tell us what we want to know? *Molecular Ecology* **28**(8), 1904–1918. doi:10.1111/mec.15027

Santiago E, Novo I, Pardinas AF (2020) Recent demographic history inferred by high-resolution analysis of linkage disequilibrium. *Molecular Biology and Evolution* **37**, 3642–3653.

Schwartz MK, Luikart G, Waples RS (2007) Genetic monitoring as a promising tool for conservation and management. *Trends in Ecology & Evolution* **22**, 25–33. doi:10.1016/j.tree.2006.08.009

Shaw RG (2019) From the past to the future: Considering the value and limits of evolutionary prediction. *American Naturalist* **193**(1), 1–10. doi:10.1086/700565

Soulé ME (Ed.) (1987) *Viable Populations for Conservation.* Cambridge University Press.

Thompson EA (2013) Identity by descent: variation in meiosis, across genomes, and in populations. *Genetics* **194**(2), 301–326. doi:10.1534/genetics.112.148825

Waples RK, Larson WA, Waples RS (2016) Estimating contemporary effective population size in non-model species using linkage disequilibrium across thousands of loci. *Heredity* **117**, 233–240.

Waples RS (1989) A generalized approach for estimating effective population size from temporal changes in allele frequency. *Genetics* **121**, 379–391.

Waples RS, Luikart G, Faulkner JR, Tallmon DA (2013) Simple life-history traits explain key effective population size ratios across diverse taxa. *Proceedings of the Royal Society B, Biological Sciences* **280**(1768), 20131339.

Waples RS (2016) Making sense of genetic estimates of effective population size. *Molecular Ecology* **25**(19), 4689–4691. doi:10.1111/mec.13814

Waples RS, Ford MJ, Nichols K, Kardos M, Myers J, *et al.* (2022) Implications of large-effect loci for conservation: A review and case study with Pacific salmon. *Journal of Heredity* **113**(2), 121–144. doi:10.1093/jhered/esab069

Waples RS, Antao T, Luikart G (2014) Effects of overlapping generations on linkage disequilibrium estimates of effective population size. *Genetics* **197**(2), 769–780. doi:10.1534/genetics.114.164822

Waples RS, Do C (2008) LDNE: a program for estimating effective population size from data on linkage disequilibrium. *Molecular Ecology Resources* **8**(4), 753–756.

Wellenreuther M, Bernatchez L (2018) Eco-evolutionary genomics of chromosomal inversions. *Trends in Ecology & Evolution* **33**, 427–440. doi:10.1016/j.tree.2018.04.002

Wold J, Koepfli KP, Galla SJ, Eccles D, Hogg CJ, Le Lec MF, *et al.* (2021) Expanding the conservation genomics toolbox: Incorporating structural variants to enhance genomic studies for species of conservation concern. *Molecular Ecology* **30**(23), 5949–5965. doi:10.1111/mec.16141

ADAPTATION AND CHANGE

14 Adaptive responses to the environment and environmental change

Orly Razgour, Jesse R. Lasky, Thibaut Capblancq and Brenna R. Forester

ABSTRACT

Identifying adaptive responses to the environment is key for understanding and predicting the ability of species to respond to human-induced global changes, such as climate change, land-use change, pollution and disease outbreaks. Adaptive responses can be studied using a variety of observational, experimental and modelling methods. The genomic revolution has led to the development of new approaches and refinement of existing approaches to identify the genomic basis of adaptive responses to the environment and environmental change. These methods often involve the application of statistical techniques that relate variation at the genomic level to environmental conditions or phenotypic variability in order to detect candidate adaptive genetic loci. The past decade has seen a proliferation of studies employing these tools in a variety of applications from informing conservation management, agricultural production and the management of invasive species, to understanding disease dynamics and modelling vulnerability to future global changes. Experimental and functional validation of these statistical inferences represents an area of increasing importance in this rapidly evolving field. Emerging approaches look beyond the organism's genome to its interactions with its associated bacterial metagenomes, at epigenetic variation and the structure of the genome itself.

INTRODUCTION

Identifying adaptive responses to the environment is key for understanding and predicting the ability of species to respond to human-induced global changes, such as climate change, land-use change, pollution and disease outbreaks. Shifts in phenotypic traits in response to local environmental conditions or environmental change can be the result of either short-term plastic responses, whereby the same genotype expresses different phenotypes within the lifetime of an individual (phenotypic plasticity), or longer-term changes in genotypes or allele frequencies in the population over generations (genetic adaptations or microevolution; Franks and Hoffmann 2012). Although phenotypic plasticity provides an important mechanism for rapid response and acclimatisation, genetic adaptations are essential for enabling populations to cope with extensive and continuing environmental changes (Gienapp *et al.* 2008).

Adaptive responses to the environment were traditionally studied by quantifying changes in phenotypes following controlled breeding, common garden, or reciprocal transplant experiments. The use of these methods has been limited, however, because they are logistically challenging and can be difficult or impossible to implement in species of conservation concern or those not amenable to experimental manipulation, like long-lived, long generation time species (Hohenlohe *et al.* 2021). The advent of high-throughput sequencing technologies opened the door to the use of genomic approaches to identify the genetic basis of adaptations and mechanisms of adaptive responses in wild populations and notably for species of conservation concern (Allendorf *et al.* 2010). Much of the focus has been on identifying local environmental adaptations, whereby resident genotypes have, on average, higher fitness in their local habitat than genotypes originating from other habitats. Local adaptations are manifested through phenotypic and genetic differentiation across contrasting environments or environmental gradients, and therefore can be studied using genetic and genomic tools. Genomic tools, which often analyse entire genomes or exomes, are particularly suitable given that local adaptations can arise from polygenic quantitative traits (Savolainen *et al.* 2013) and that good genome marker density is needed to detect the few genes associated with oligogenic traits (Box 14.1).

Evolutionary adaptations can be identified using different types of genomic approaches that are selected based on the research question and the species characteristics (Box 14.2). Genome scans are commonly used on large genomic datasets to relate individual genotypes or population allele frequencies to phenotypic traits associated with fitness (adaptive traits) or environmental conditions (Rellstab *et al.* 2015; Hoban *et al.* 2016). Other approaches, like **whole transcriptome sequencing**, can capture plastic gene expression responses to environmental variation within and between individuals (Todd *et al.* 2016).

Adaptive responses can be studied through comparing individuals or populations experiencing gradients of

---

Box 14.1: The effect of genetic architecture on the detection, validation, and application of environmental adaptations

The genetic architecture of adaptations plays a major role in facilitating or complicating the detection, validation, and application of environmental adaptations. Whether adaptation is driven by many genetic variants of small effect (polygenic), or a few variants of large effect (oligogenic) influences the nature of these challenges. In species where controlled crosses are possible, such as crops, livestock, or captive-bred species, environmentally adapted alleles can be introgressed into desired genotypic backgrounds using targeted crosses and backcrosses. Even when breeding is uncontrolled in nature, selection will favour the combination of newly introduced beneficial alleles (blue) and existing beneficial alleles (yellow). For some species, genetic engineering (e.g. transgenics, CRISPR) may be a more precise way to improve a given genetic background compared to recurrent backcrosses. If existing beneficial alleles are ignored or overlooked during introgression of environmentally adapted alleles, these existing beneficial alleles may be lost due to linkage drag and drift.

When adaptation is oligogenic (A), the detection challenge can be substantial, especially in species with large or poorly assembled genomes, where resource constraints can limit the density of genetic markers. In this case (C), a few large effect variants may be missed by a set of markers that do not cover a sufficient portion of the genome. In contrast, validating and applying the basis of oligogenic traits (E) is more straightforward. Introgression of one or a few loci into a desired genetic background requires relatively few recombination breakpoints, which are locations of crossing over between homologous chromosomes during meiosis. Alternatively, genetic engineering to alter one or a few loci is possible in some systems.

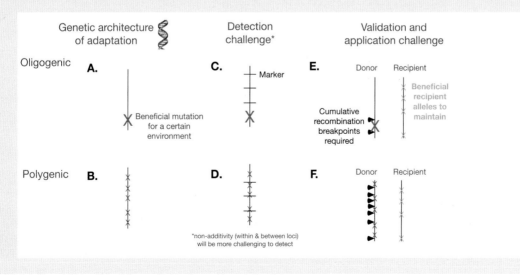

When adaptation is polygenic (B), detecting at least a subset of causal loci is much easier due to their greater abundance (D). However, polygenic adaptation faces greater constraints for validation and applications involving introgression or genetic engineering (F). When there are existing genotypes with a number of desirable alleles across the genome into which environmentally adapted alleles are to be introgressed, a large number of recombination events are required to achieve the desired end-product genotype. When species have long generation times or low outcrossing rates, the scarcity of these recombination events may limit adaptation. Similarly, engineering is more technically challenging because many loci must be targeted.

Population genetic theory provides guidance for where environmental adaptation may be oligogenic versus polygenic. For example, when existing polygenic variation results in local adaptation, local adaptation may retain a polygenic architecture for hundreds or thousands of generations (Polechová and Barton 2015). However, ongoing gene flow across environmental gradients will eventually favour more oligogenic architectures as only large effect polymorphisms can be maintained (Yeaman and Whitlock 2011). Yet, determining the true architecture of empirical environmental adaptation is challenging.

Box 14.2: Genomic methods to identify local adaptations

1. **Differentiation-based analyses**, which include the widely used Fst-outlier tests, identify candidate adaptive genetic markers that show high levels of genetic divergence between populations through differentiating locus-specific patterns (including selection) from genome-wide patterns (genetic drift, demographic processes, and gene flow; Luikart *et al.* 2003). Differentiation-based methods are especially useful for detecting strong divergent selection (Storz 2005). Most methods require population-level sampling and are based on theoretical population genetic models that are violated in many empirical systems (Lotterhos and Whitlock 2014), though individual-based model-free options are available (Luu *et al.* 2017). Recent approaches have improved on some previous problems of non-independence among populations (Lotterhos and Whitlock 2015) and of incorrectly identifying neutral markers as under selection due to failure to account for population structure (Gautier 2015).

2. **Genotype-environment associations (GEA)** methods are used to identify candidate adaptive genetic loci based on associations between allele distributions and environmental variables hypothesised to drive selection, with adaptive loci showing a pattern of selected alleles at higher frequency in certain environments (Rellstab *et al.* 2015). GEA methods are flexible (e.g. can be used with either individual- or population-based sampling), have high power to detect adaptive loci (de Villemereuil *et al.* 2014; Whitlock and Lotterhos 2015), and can detect both strong divergent selection and weaker selective signatures, such as selection on standing genetic variation (Forester *et al.* 2018). As with differentiation-based analyses, accounting for population structure can reduce false-positive rates, but can also reduce power (Forester *et al.* 2018). The design of sampling schemes, spatial population structure, and the geometry of selective gradients affect the genetic architecture of adaptation, as well as the power to detect local adaptation with GEA analysis and false-positive rates in GEA tests. These are important issues for study design and interpretation (Lotterhos and Whitlock 2015; Hoban *et al.* 2016).

3. An alternative approach is to study the genetic basis of traits under selection (Hoekstra *et al.* 2006) or components of fitness and their change across environments (Fournier-Level *et al.* 2011; Lasky *et al.* 2018). **Genome-wide association studies (GWAS)** and **linkage mapping** are used to identify the genetic basis of phenotypic variation. These approaches find markers (e.g. SNPs) that covary with a phenotype of interest, either in groups of related (linkage mapping) or unrelated (association mapping) individuals. They are commonly used in evolutionary biology to identify the genetic basis of adaptive traits (Hall *et al.* 2006; Atwell *et al.* 2010). GWAS can identify the genes responsible for trait variation with precision, but it requires dense genetic markers and phenotypic data on hundreds of individuals, ideally raised in a common environment (Korte and Farlow 2013). The statistical models underlying GWAS overlap with those used for GEAs and can also account for population structure (Hayes 2013).

4. Whole transcriptome sequencing through RNA sequencing (**RNAseq**) is a high-throughput sequencing approach for both characterising the sequence of all the RNAs in the sample (the transcriptome) and quantifying their abundance. RNAseq does not require a reference genome and is therefore particularly useful for non-model organisms (Wang *et al.* 2009). This approach is suitable for studies of local adaptation because, in addition to revealing sequence variation in the transcribed region, RNAseq directly quantifies levels of gene expression, which can be used to identify genes that are up- or down-regulated under different conditions or experimental treatments (Todd *et al.* 2016). **Differential expression**

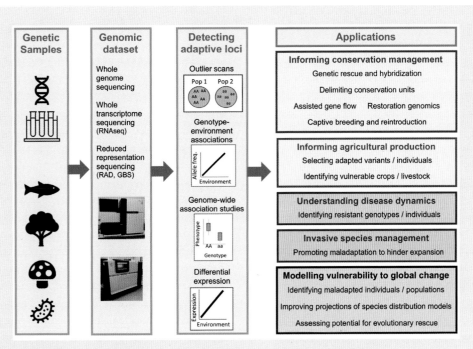

Fig. 14.1.   The process of detecting adaptive genetic variation and downstream applications.

analysis is used to statistically analyse quantitative changes in the expression levels of genes between conditions based on differences in the number of reads mapped to each locus (Rapaport *et al.* 2013). Differential expression analysis can provide insight into both plastic and evolutionary responses to environmental changes (DeBiasse and Kelly 2016). However, distinguishing between the two mechanisms is not straightforward and may require controlled experiments to identify genetic differences in expression (Fig. 14.1).

environmental conditions through space or time. For example, a comparison of urban versus rural populations of white-footed mice, *Peromyscus leucopus*, identified genetic adaptations to urbanisation that suggested selection on metabolic pathways related to novel diets in urban environments (Harris and Munshi-South 2017). Alternatively, a temporal approach can be adopted using evolve and resequence experiments (Long *et al.* 2015) or longitudinal studies, whereby the same population is sampled before and after an artificial (experimental manipulation) or natural selection event, such as the outbreak of sea star wasting disease in ochre sea stars, *Pisaster ochraceus* (Schiebelhut *et al.* 2018). Other studies combine experimental approaches with genomic datasets to identify genes involved in local climatic adaptations. For example, molecular genetic studies in the model plant *Arabidopsis thaliana* first identified CBF2, a transcription factor that turns on cold acclimation pathways (Thomashow 1999). CBF2 exhibits multiple independent loss-of-function mutations in warmer Mediterranean climates (Monroe *et al.* 2016). Reciprocal transplant experiments with crosses between Italian (warmer climate) and

Swedish (colder climate) individuals showed that winter cold was a main driver of differential selection between Italy and Sweden, and that CBF2 plays a key role in local adaptation to climates not experiencing freezing (Oakley *et al.* 2014).

In this chapter, we review the diversity of research on the genomics of environmental adaptation, including applications in conservation management, agriculture, disease and invasive species control, and vulnerability modelling. We conclude by highlighting outstanding questions and future directions for adaptive genomics research and applications.

APPLICATIONS

Application 1: Conservation management

The potential for adaptive genomics to inform conservation management has been recognised for over a decade (e.g. Allendorf *et al.* 2010; Sgrò *et al.* 2011). Applications have increased during this time as sequencing costs have declined, genotyping from poor-quality samples has improved, and annotated reference genomes have become more common. Adaptive genomics has been applied to a variety of conservation applications, from guiding conservation management and prioritisation to genomic monitoring (reviewed in Forester *et al.* 2018). It is important to note that although a focus on functional (adaptive) genetic variation is important for ensuring adaptive capacity and enabling evolutionary rescue, understanding locus-specific effects on a trait and fitness is challenging and focusing on a small number of loci can lead to other beneficial genetic variation being missed (Box 14.1). Therefore, it is essential to also conserve genome-wide genetic variation to prevent inbreeding depression, reduced growth and viability and lost ability to adapt to environmental change (Kardos *et al.* 2021).

Conservation unit delineation

Conservation unit (CU) is a general term for a large set of biological and legal categories used to delineate sub-specific population units for conservation management. The reasons for defining CUs include conserving intraspecific genetic and phenotypic diversity, informing effective management strategies, and identifying a unit's listing status under legislative jurisdictions (see Chapter 23). Genomic data can inform CU delineation through both increased resolution of neutral differentiation and the characterisation of adaptive differentiation (Funk *et al.* 2012). For example, a genomic study in Baltic Sea herring (*Clupea harengus*) identified population differentiation whereas previous research using smaller genetic datasets had found little evidence for genetic structuring (Guo *et al.* 2016). This study also identified local adaptation to salinity and temperature across populations, indicating that the existing management units were poorly aligned with neutral and adaptive differentiation, with potentially negative impacts on fisheries yields and stock abundance. The inclusion of genetic divergence at adaptive markers is particularly relevant for designing genetic rescue strategies between CUs (Coates *et al.* 2018).

Genomic monitoring

Genetic monitoring has traditionally focused on using neutral markers to track individuals or distinguish species for population monitoring (e.g. abundance, vital rates, site occupancy; Chapter 10), and monitor population genetic parameters over time, such as genetic diversity or effective population size (Schwartz *et al.* 2007). The use of genomics in species of conservation concern has expanded genetic monitoring to adaptive variation, providing opportunities to monitor adaptive responses to management actions such

as translocations, genetic rescue, or assisted gene flow (Flanagan *et al.* 2018; Van Rossum and Hardy 2021), as well as adaptive responses to environmental change (Hansen *et al.* 2012). Additionally, guidelines are increasingly available for effective genotyping and panel development with degraded or low-quality samples, such as those derived using non-invasive sampling methods (Carroll *et al.* 2018; von Thaden *et al.* 2020) or from museum specimens that can provide temporal genetic data to identify adaptive changes (Bi *et al.* 2013). A genetic monitoring panel that incorporates both neutral and candidate adaptive markers has been used in the management of declining Pacific lamprey (*Entosphenus tridentatus*) to assess the effectiveness of management actions including translocations and habitat restoration, as well as linking candidate adaptive markers to lamprey phenotypes, such as body size and migration timing (Hess *et al.* 2015). In another case, amplicon sequencing has been used to monitor neutral and functional loci in Tasmanian devil (*Sarcophilus harrisii*) insurance populations in response to devil facial tumor disease (Wright *et al.* 2015). In this case, adaptive loci are monitored to assess functional consequences of loss of allelic diversity due to captive breeding (Chapter 9).

Assisted gene flow (within historical range) and migration (outside historical range)

The fast pace of global warming is challenging species' natural capacity to adapt to new environments or migrate to follow suitable climates. To help them track this rapid change, some propose to artificially move, across space, individuals that are already preadapted to future local climates (Aitken and Whitlock 2013). The goal of these management actions is either to introduce new adaptive alleles into populations that will need these alleles to maintain their fitness in the future (i.e. assisted gene flow), or to move individuals beyond their current range to locations uncolonised by the species, but which will become suitable in the future (i.e. assisted migration). Potentially important to these actions is the identification of the genes involved in adaptation to local climate and the prediction of the optimal distribution of adaptive alleles across future climatic landscapes. Assisted gene flow and migration have been investigated and tested predominantly in trees (Milesi *et al.* 2019; Young *et al.* 2020), whose long generation times and strong local adaptations prevent rapid migration and make them particularly vulnerable to climate change (Aitken and Bemmels 2016). Because a poorly designed assisted gene flow strategy could induce a deleterious dilution of locally adapted alleles (outbreeding depression), and because the conservation community is nervous to introduce species outside their natural range, both measures are still contentious and have rarely been applied in animal conservation (McLachlan *et al.* 2007). However, the increasing threats to biodiversity posed by climate change and other anthropogenic stressors are likely to increase willingness to test these emerging conservation strategies in diverse systems (Kelly *et al.* 2021).

Restoration genomics

In some cases, current local adaptations are a higher priority for conservation actions than adaptation to future conditions (Breed *et al.* 2019). For example, rehabilitation of highly degraded sites, such as mined areas and salinised soils, is focused on identifying adaptations that best match site-specific characteristics to ensure the establishment of viable populations under challenging conditions. These site-adjusted provenancing strategies will often be focused on environmental characteristics beyond climate, including terrain and soil characteristics. For example, Carvalho *et al.* (2021) used genomic, environmental, and phenotypic data to predict provenances of two common native plant species that would be best suited to restoring a highly degraded mining site. Genotype-environment associations (GEA; Box 14.2) were used to identify local adaptations to climate and at-site soil characteristics, while genome-wide associations (GWAS; Box 14.2) identified genetic variation underlying leaf macro- and micronutrient levels and specific leaf area. Adaptive genotypes were then predicted for the degraded mine site; however, none of the genotypes sampled in natural habitats matched conditions at the site, likely due to the severely degraded soil conditions. The recommendation was to combine multiple locally adapted genotypes sampled across the region in order to maximise evolutionary potential and facilitate adaptation to the novel soil conditions (Lesica and Allendorf 1999).

Captive breeding and reintroduction programs

Captive breeding is an important conservation tool used to prevent the extinction of endangered species that are unable to survive in the wild, with the aim of eventual reintroduction to their historical range. The low success rate of reintroduction programs has been attributed in part to reduced fitness when reintroduced to the wild due to genetic adaptations to the captive environment, which, by relaxing natural selection, favours rare and partially recessive deleterious alleles (Frankham 2008). Genomic approaches can contribute to detecting adaptations to captivity based on rapid changes in allele frequencies (Allendorf *et al.* 2010).

Willoughby *et al.* (2017) used a **reduced-representation genome sequencing** dataset to identify SNPs under selection in experimental populations of white-footed mice, *Peromyscus leucopus,* under different captive breeding regimes. They show that the effect of adaptations to captivity can be reduced if the breeding program is designed to minimise overall levels of relatedness among individuals. Further contribution of genomic approaches is to inform the selection of suitable individuals for breeding and reintroduction based on their adaptive genetic variation (Allendorf *et al.* 2010). He *et al.* (2016) recommend that source individuals for reintroduction should be selected to maximise functional genetic variation, and consequently adaptive potential, based on their allele frequencies in SNPs associated with fitness related traits, their levels of heterozygosity in coding region SNPs and their transcription profile in genes involved in tolerance to environmental stress. However, these approaches have not been applied yet in reintroduction programs, and therefore their effectiveness is unknown.

Application 2: Agriculture

Adaptation to different environments is an essential aspect of agricultural biodiversity, allowing food production across dramatically different locations on earth. Cultivated plants and livestock have been models for understanding how organisms adapt to different conditions, given the applied importance of the systems and benefitting from existing collections of genetically diverse, local varieties. Understanding the genetic basis of environmental adaptation has long been a goal in crop and animal breeding, to adapt organisms to abiotic or biotic stressors that threaten agricultural production. Here we focus on three major goals of understanding the genomics of adaptation to environment in agricultural research: 1) identifying alleles and traits adapted to specific environments, 2) identifying optimal genotypes/individuals for specific environments, and 3) identifying genotypes vulnerable to future environmental change (Fig. 14.2).

First, for the purposes of breeding crop and livestock varieties that are resilient or adapted to specific environmental stressors, researchers often conduct genetic mapping for response to potentially stressful conditions, traits thought to be adaptive in the face of challenging conditions, or environment-associated loci. Once loci are identified, they can be introgressed into desired recipient genetic backgrounds through targeted crosses with donor genotypes, followed up with successive rounds of additional crosses to the original recipient (known as backcrosses) to reduce the introgression to the target region (Box 14.1).

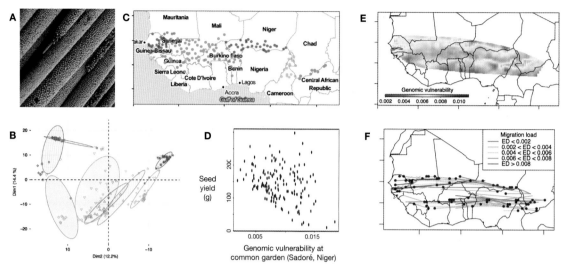

Fig. 14.2. Assessment of genomic vulnerability of local traditional varieties of pearl millet (*Pennisetum glaucum*), a staple cereal of smallholder farmers in West Africa (Rhoné *et al.* 2020). (A) Pearl millet panicles (seed heads). (B) PCA of ~140k SNPs shows genomic similarity among (C) 173 landraces from across West Africa. From these SNPs, gradient forest (GF) models were built relating climate to allele frequency to assess genomic vulnerability as the distance between the GF-predicted optimal genetic composition for a given environment and the genetic composition of a given individual or population. (D) Genomic vulnerability was validated at a single common garden in Niger where increased difference (genomic vulnerability) was associated with decreased yield. Genomic vulnerability was predicted across West Africa (E) comparing current and 2050 climates, highlighting two latitudinal bands of high vulnerability (yellow to red colours). (F) Lines connecting vulnerable regions (black circles) with the optimal current existing landrace for that region. The line colours represent the variation in the fit of the best landraces for a given location's future climate, i.e. the genomic vulnerability of the best landrace ('ED' = Euclidean distance between the genetic composition of the best available landrace versus the ideal genotype). Modified from Rhoné *et al.* 2020.

Mapping the genetic basis of adaptations to specific environments has traditionally used common garden experiments in target environments or experiments contrasting organismal performance across environments combined with association or linkage mapping (Malosetti *et al.* 2013). However, implementing such trials is logistically challenging, and so genotype-environment associations (GEA; Box 14.2) have also been implemented using traditional local crops, e.g. in sorghum (Lasky *et al.* 2015); in maize (Gates *et al.* 2019) and livestock (Lv *et al.* 2014) varieties.

The genomic basis of environmental adaptation can also be used for prediction purposes in breeding programs. In particular, when phenotypes are challenging to measure and heritability is low (which is often true of traits involved in environmental adaptation) genetic prediction can be valuable for breeding (Heffner *et al.* 2009). In these applications, the goal is to identify how a given stressor might impact a given genotype or to identify the optimal genotype for a given environment (Tiezzi *et al.* 2017). When substantial ecophysiological information exists, interactions among loci and traits can be incorporated into genetic predictions based on underlying mechanistic developmental and growth models, as in the so-called 'crop models' (Technow *et al.* 2015; Messina *et al.* 2018). Environmental associations can also be used for genetic prediction (Lasky *et al.* 2015; Gienapp *et al.* 2017) though

these genotype-environment predictions have yet to be integrated into real-world breeding programs.

A final major application of the genomic basis of environment adaptation in agriculture is to identify vulnerable crop or livestock genotypes and populations in the face of future environmental changes, such as those due to greenhouse gas based warming or cooling due to volcanic eruption. One of the few examples to be implemented was in pearl millet, relying on the fact that most pearl millet farmers in west Africa grow traditional local varieties (Rhoné *et al.* 2020). The authors estimated **genomic vulnerability** of sequenced landraces under future climates, and found that adaptation could be accomplished by geographic transfer of appropriate genotypes, but that this strategy could be hindered by national boundaries and exchange regulations (Rhoné *et al.* 2020; Fig. 14.2).

Application 3: Disease dynamics

Adaptive genomics can be used to identify disease related traits and genomic regions associated with response to the selection pressures imposed by disease outbreaks (Hohenlohe *et al.* 2021). Within this context, diseases are viewed as a novel environmental condition that populations need to rapidly adapt to. Alternatively, as some diseases or pathogens are endemic to certain regions within the species' range, diseases can be viewed as part of the local conditions to which populations are adapted to through evolving resistance and tolerance (Bellis *et al.* 2020).

Auteri and Knowles (2020) used differentiation-based genome scans (Box 14.2) on a reduced-representation genome dataset to study evolutionary changes in bats in response to white-nose syndrome, a disease that has decimated bat populations in North America and has been rapidly expanding across the continent since its introduction 15 years ago. Comparing the genomic makeup of little brown bat (*Myotis lucifugus*) survivors versus non-survivors, they identified putative adaptive shifts in allele frequencies in genes involved with regulating hibernation and arousal from hibernation, metabolism and echolocation (Auteri and Knowles 2020). Similarly, in a whole-genome sequencing study of little brown bats that survived white-nose syndrome, Gignoux-Wolfsohn *et al.* (2021) identified 63 candidate SNPs under selection located in genes associated with immunity, metabolism and hibernation, functions that are likely to contribute to hibernating bats surviving white-nose syndrome.

In another example of the rapid action of novel diseases, devil facial tumor disease (DFTD), a form of nearly universally lethal transmissible cancer, has caused rapid population declines in Tasmanian devils (*Sarcophilus harrisii*) since its identification in 1996, leading to the near extinction of this carnivorous marsupial. Adaptive genomics research has been pivotal in identifying the origins of DFTD, the genomics of susceptibility, and the adaptive evolutionary response conferring DFTD resistance (reviewed in Storfer *et al.* 2018). For example, Epstein *et al.* (2016) identified genomic regions showing extreme allele frequency changes in three populations of devils sampled before and after the identification of DFTD. They identified a rapid and parallel evolutionary response (within ~4 generations) to DFTD in these populations, with all three showing allele frequency shifts in the same two genomic regions associated with immune function and cancer risk (Fig. 14.3; Chapter 9).

In another case, Cassin-Sackett *et al.* (2019) used a suite of techniques including differentiation-based genome

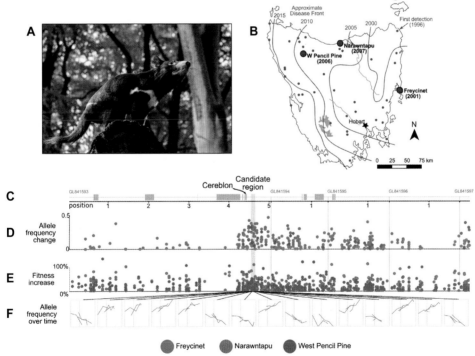

Fig. 14.3. (A) Tasmanian devil (photo by Mathias Appel). (B) The three focal populations (pink circles) sampled by Epstein *et al.* 2016, with grey points representing additional samples to assess genome-wide variation. Pink lines show devil facial tumor disease (DFTD) disease front expansion. (C) Location along a set of five scaffolds (i.e. parts of the genome sequence) on chromosome 2 of the Tasmanian devil genome: scaffolds are labeled starting with 'GL', scaffold 'Position' is shown in megabases from the start of each scaffold, and genes in the candidate region (marked by the wide vertical gray line) under strong selection in response to DFTD are shown as gray boxes. Cereblon is a myeloma therapy target in humans related to limb and brain development. (D) The location (*x*-axis) of SNPs with allele frequency changes (*y*-axis) in the top 2.5% pre- and post-disease across the three focal populations (colors). Note the peak in allele frequency change across multiple SNPs in the candidate region. (E) Estimates of the relative fitness advantage of the selected alleles in response to DFTD, which average 19%–29% across the three populations. (F) The directionality of allele frequency changes in specific SNPs (boxes) in the three populations over time (*x*-axis is time since DFTD detection, where grey vertical lines represent first detection of DFTD). Note that allele frequency changes are in the same direction in all three populations at many of the SNPs, indicating a parallel response to DFTD. All but (A) modified from Epstein *et al.* (2016).

scans to identify genetic regions conferring resistance to avian malaria in the Hawai'i 'amakihi (*Chlorodrepanis virens*). Avian malaria is a mosquito-transmitted protozoan parasite implicated in population declines and extinctions of Hawai'ian honeycreepers, including the 'amakihi, since its introduction in the 1930s. The 'amakihi is one of only a few species of honeycreeper to have exhibited adaptive responses to the parasite. Low elevation populations, where infected mosquitos are prevalent, have higher survivorship in response to infection compared to high elevation populations, where mosquitos are mostly absent. In contrast to DFTD, resistance to avian malaria in low-elevation populations was conferred by multiple changes in classes of genes related to pathogen defence and immune response, with different populations showing different adaptive pathways to resistance. In this case, selection may have been acting on differing standing variation in particular classes of genes among populations, but not on specific genes across all populations.

Application 4: Invasive species

In the case of invasive species, managers may seek to promote maladaptation to local environments and to hinder local adaptation (Allendorf and Lundquist 2003) to prevent or minimise invasion success. For biocontrol agents ('good' invasive species), managers may seek a mix of adaptive variation to enable establishment, with maladaptation to prevent unwanted spread (Bock *et al.* 2015). Additionally, managers may want to predict how genetically distinct (and possibly locally adapted) populations of an invasive species will respond to environmental change. Predicting maladaptation may help identify combinations of source populations pre-adapted to specific, still-uninvaded regions where successful invasion is most likely, in order to focus efforts on routes to stop the spread of propagules.

To date, these applications are mostly hypothetical. In invasive species, the genomics of environmental adaptation is mostly at an early descriptive phase (as opposed to applied), answering questions about where invasive populations trace their ancestry or identifying loci showing evidence of selection in invasive populations. For example, Calfee *et al.* (2020) studied the invasion history of honeybees, *Apis mellifera scutellata,* out of Brazil and showed that this invasion stalled at similar latitudes in North and South America, potentially due to selection against many loci of small effect in temperate zones. In the human commensal fruit fly *Drosophila melanogaster,* which has spread from Africa to much of the globe, diapause has apparently been selected in temperate regions. Schmidt *et al.* (2008)

identified the *cpo* gene as underlying much of the variation in diapause because allele frequencies showed strong latitudinal clines, suggesting mutations at this gene underlie adaptation to the novel temperate environments.

Application 5: Modelling vulnerability

Biodiversity vulnerability to future climate change is commonly assessed using predictive **species distribution models** (Box 14.3). These approaches have been criticised for being over-simplistic, failing to take into consideration local adaptations (Hällfors *et al.* 2016), and ignoring important mechanisms affecting species vulnerability, including evolutionary mechanisms and adaptive capacity (Urban *et al.* 2016). Climate change, by rapidly modifying local environments, will impact the distribution of adaptive alleles across species' ranges. If a local population is not able to track that change by modifying its genetic composition, it may lead to a decrease in fitness and eventually decline. New genomic tools can complement species distribution models through integrating this intraspecific adaptive component into predictive models that assess species' ability to adapt to future changes. In this section we review recent developments in the field in which genomic tools are applied to model vulnerability to climate change and assess species adaptive capacity. These tools can be applied to a broad range of species, including species with long generation time and species of conservation concern (Harrisson *et al.* 2014; Hoffmann *et al.* 2021)

Integrative approaches linking genomics, demography and modelling

Initial approaches to integrating genetics with species distribution models used neutral markers to either delimit genetic clusters for modelling (D'Amen *et al.* 2013), delimit climatic zones based on associations between genetic variables and climatic variables (Sork *et al.* 2010) or forecast changes in intraspecific genetic variation in response to climate change using ancestry distribution models (Jay *et al.* 2012). Although these approaches improved model projections, they focused on **neutral genetic variation** and did not include adaptive variation and adaptive potential. In contrast, Bush *et al.* (2016) incorporated adaptive capacity into a hybrid species distribution model that took into account physiological tolerance limits (critical thermal temperature tolerance) and dispersal dynamics in Australian fruit fly species. Using a quantitative genetic model to calculate evolutionary response, this study illustrated how incorporating adaptive capacity through genetic modelling of physiological traits could affect projections of species' distributions.

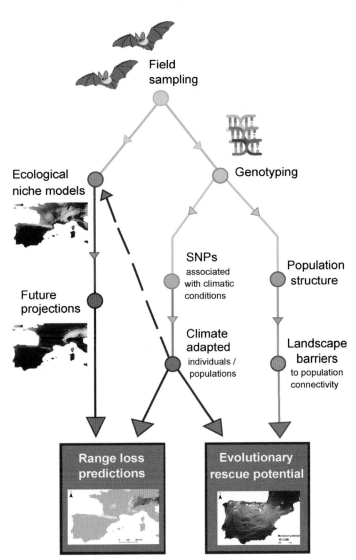

Fig. 14.4. Framework for modelling vulnerability to climate change through incorporating genomic data and climate adaptive variation into species distribution models and landscape connectivity analysis (taken from Razgour *et al.* 2019). The framework begins with field sampling to collect both samples for genomic analysis and information on the current distribution of the species. Samples are used to generate a genomic dataset that is divided into a neutral dataset, which is used to assess population structure and landscape barriers to movement using a landscape genetics approach, and an adaptive dataset, using a combination of GEA methods to identify SNPs associated with climatic conditions of interest. Based on their genomic makeup in these adaptive SNPs, individuals are divided into those potentially pre-adapted to future climatic conditions and those that are likely to be maladapted. This information is then used to assess the potential of evolutionary rescue in the form of gene flow from adapted to maladapted populations based on the identified landscape barriers to current patterns of genetic connectivity. Finally, two separate ecological niche (species distribution) model projections are generated for potentially adapted versus maladapted individuals to calculate extent of future range losses in comparison to models that do not include genomic information.

Razgour *et al.* (2019) developed an alternative framework for incorporating genomic data into species distribution models to forecast range changes under climate change and assess the potential for evolutionary rescue of maladapted populations (Fig. 14.4). This framework employs GEAs (Box 14.2) to identify putative SNPs under selection associated with climatic variables likely to affect species survival and predicted to change in the future. Then, individuals are divided into those associated with hot-dry versus cold-wet conditions based on their genomic makeup in these putative climate-adaptive SNPs. Intraspecific variation in local climatic adaptations is directly incorporated into species distribution models through generating separate predictive models for individuals adapted to different climatic conditions. Razgour *et al.* (2019) show that considering local climatic adaptations in species distribution models reduces future range loss projections for Mediterranean bat species. Moreover, they use the landscape genetics approach (Manel *et al.* 2003) to predict the potential for gene flow from populations adapted to warmer and drier conditions to populations likely to be maladapted under future conditions based on the effect of landscape permeability on current patterns of genetic connectivity.

'Genetic offset' and 'genomic vulnerability'

Other recent studies make use of genomic data to estimate the magnitude of change that will be required for local populations to track the future shift in climate, avoid maladaptation and maintain their fitness in the future (Capblancq *et al.* 2020). By modelling the relationship between environmental and genetic variation, these studies predict the genetic composition that would optimise species fitness at any combination of site-by-environment (Fitzpatrick and Keller 2015). Measuring the difference between genetic composition predicted under current and future climates then provides an estimate of potential maladaptation, which has been subsequently called 'genetic offset', 'risk of non-adaptedness' and 'genomic vulnerability' (Fig. 14.2). Different approaches have been developed to estimate this proxy for maladaptation, using either locus-based measure of change in allele frequency (Rellstab *et al.* 2015; Rochat *et al.* 2021), multi-locus genetic distance (Fitzpatrick and Keller 2015; Capblancq *et al.* 2020) or variation of the selection coefficients averaged across all adaptive loci (Exposito-Alonso *et al.* 2019). For example, Bay *et al.* (2018) used the gradient forest approach developed by Fitzpatrick and Keller (2015) to calculate genomic vulnerability in a widely distributed North American migratory bird, the yellow warbler, *Setophaga petechia*. They first identified and visualised climate-associated genetic variation across the species' breeding range. Then they calculated the extent of mismatch between current and predicted future genomic variation based on differences in allele frequencies in SNPs identified as associated with changing climatic conditions. Finally, they compared genomic vulnerability predictions to surveyed population trends over the past ~50 years and found that areas predicted to have higher genomic vulnerability under future conditions have already experienced the greatest population declines (Bay *et al.* 2018).

It is important to note that genetic offset estimates a gap between current and future optimal genetic compositions at a specific location; it does not give any information on the population's ability to fill this gap and avoid maladaptation. The ability to avoid maladaptation will depend on many species-specific parameters, including availability of adaptive alleles, generation time and population connectivity (Hoffmann *et al.* 2021). More work is needed to validate the potential of genetic offset for management and conservation applications. However, a recent study showed that genetic offset was a good predictor of fitness after a climate translocation in poplars (Fitzpatrick *et al.* 2021).

Risk and vulnerability assessment

Hoffmann *et al.* (2015) show how evolutionary genomics can be incorporated into a decision-making framework for biodiversity conservation under climate change. Genomic tools can inform decisions on whether populations have enough genetic diversity for an evolutionary response (based on levels of inbreeding and amount of standing genetic variation), are adapted to local climatic conditions (based on differentiation-based or genotype-environment associations analyses; Box 14.2), have adequate levels of gene flow (population structure and landscape genetics approaches), and whether hybridisation with closely related species can result in a favourable evolutionary response (Hoffmann *et al.* 2015). Assessment of genomic vulnerability and the extent of genomic change needed to track climate change are particularly relevant for predicting vulnerability and adaptive potential of populations. However, it is important to validate predictions with experimental approaches and distinguish between true signatures of environmental adaptations versus low genomic variation due to genetic drift in small populations, in particular when selecting populations for genetic mixing to increase the adaptive potential of threatened species (Hoffmann *et al.* 2021).

Razgour *et al.* (2018) developed an integrated framework to identify wildlife populations under threat from climate change based on exposure, sensitivity and range shift potential. They apply the framework to a long-lived limited-dispersal bat species, *Plecotus austriacus*. Genomic data are used to inform population sensitivity to future changes based on allele frequencies in loci identified as putatively associated with climatic conditions that have a strong impact on bat survival and reproductive success and are predicted to change in the future. Genomic data are also used to assess the effect of landscape connectivity on gene flow and project how changes in landscape connectivity will affect the ability of populations to shift their ranges to track future suitable climatic conditions. The three components of the framework are combined to assign levels of risk to populations, which can be used to inform conservation priorities and select appropriate management interventions under climate change (Razgour *et al.* 2018).

Simulations provide an alternative framework for risk assessment that can integrate demographic and evolutionary

---

Box 14.3: Methods to model vulnerability to environmental change

Vulnerability is the extent to which biodiversity is susceptible to environmental change due to an inability to accommodate or respond to changing conditions. It is often assessed in terms of a species' *exposure* and *sensitivity* to changing conditions, and its *adaptive capacity* in response to the environmental change (Foden *et al.* 2019). Exposure describes the magnitude of the disturbance, that is, the departure from levels that the species has evolved with. It is commonly assessed using species distribution models (also known as bioclimatic-envelope or niche models). Sensitivity is characterised by aspects of a species' life history, ecophysiology, and microhabitat preferences and defines how closely tied the persistence, performance, or fitness of a species is to changing conditions (Dawson *et al.* 2011). Adaptive capacity includes attributes that allow a population or species to cope with, accommodate, or evolve in response to environmental change. It is most commonly summarised by three features: dispersal and colonisation ability, phenotypic plasticity, and evolutionary potential (the capacity to evolve genetically based changes that increase fitness under changing conditions; Dawson *et al.* 2011). These components of adaptive capacity interact with the cumulative effects of exposure and sensitivity, reducing vulnerability and mitigating extinction risk. Despite the importance of adaptive capacity, it has rarely been incorporated in climate change vulnerability assessments because it is more difficult to measure than exposure and sensitivity. Yet, even studies that have incorporated proxies of adaptive capacity, such as neutral genetic diversity, population size, number of populations and body size as a surrogate for dispersal ability, found it influenced the outcome of the vulnerability assessment (Ofori *et al.* 2017; Wade *et al.* 2017). More recent approaches (Bay *et al.* 2017; Razgour *et al.* 2018, reviewed in the 'Risk and vulnerability assessment' section) have incorporated genomic data and local environmental adaptations as measures of sensitivity and adaptive capacity.

---

dynamics in response to shifting environmental conditions. For example, Bay *et al.* (2017) use simulation models to assess extinction risk in a population of corals (*Acropora hyacinthus*) in Rarotonga, Cook Islands, by integrating demographic data and future climate change scenarios with genomic data related to coral thermal tolerance (identified using genotype-environment associations and differentiation-based analyses; Box 14.2). Under low-emissions climate change scenarios, corals persisted through shifts in adaptive allele frequencies, while higher-emissions scenarios resulted in population extinction due to maladaptation and negative population growth rates. Assisted gene flow through movement of warm-tolerant corals at a rate of 1% per year accelerated evolutionary responses, and prevented extinction under a high-emissions scenario (Bay *et al.* 2017). Extending this work in a spatially explicit framework to incorporate dispersal and metapopulation dynamics will be an important next step in estimating regional or even species-wide extinction risk in response to increasing temperatures.

FUTURE DIRECTIONS AND OUTSTANDING QUESTIONS

Structural variants

To date, most genomic studies have investigated genetic variation through the genotyping and analysis of SNPs. However, an increasing number of studies show that another type of genetic variation – structural variation – is associated with functional changes and phenotype variation (Wellenreuther and Bernatchez 2018). As its name suggests, a structural variant is a region of DNA that experiences a change in structure across individuals. It can be a deletion or insertion of one or several nucleotides, the duplication or inversion of a DNA segment or even the translocation or fusion of genomic regions (Wellenreuther *et al.* 2019). Structural variants include transposable elements, copy number variation and all types of chromosomal rearrangements, all of which can play a major role in species adaptation and diversification (Mérot *et al.* 2020). In particular, inversions (i.e. chromosomal rearrangement where a segment of DNA is reversed compared to the ancestral state) can limit genomic recombination (Box 14.1) among lineages and protect specific allelic combinations. When these inversions host beneficial adaptive alleles, they help maintain local adaptation, even in the face of gene flow (Wellenreuther and Bernatchez 2018). The increasing availability of good quality whole-genome references and data together with recent improvements in long-read sequencing technologies have made it easier to detect structural variation and will greatly facilitate the use of these markers to better understand the genetic architecture of adaptation in the coming years.

Epigenetics

Epigenetic modifications are heritable changes in gene function that do not involve changes in the DNA sequence. For example, environmentally induced variation in DNA methylation can cause differential gene expression that changes phenotypes. Because epigenetic modifications are influenced by genotype-environment interactions, they can shape patterns of adaptive genomic variation across environments (Verhoeven *et al.* 2016; Whipple and Holeski 2016). Epigenetic variation can also allow for rapid adaptation to changing environmental conditions (via plasticity), potentially contributing to adaptive responses to climate change (McGuigan *et al.* 2021). Additionally, because epigenetic variation can be maintained in the face of small population sizes and low genetic diversity, it may contribute to the invasion success (Mounger *et al.* 2021) and the maintenance of evolutionary potential in species of conservation concern with otherwise low genetic diversity (Bernatchez 2016). Despite over a decade of research, our understanding of the importance of epigenetic processes in natural settings remains limited due to the need for transgenerational studies combined with the difficulty of quantifying the fitness effects of epigenetic variation and its interaction with genetic adaptations (Whipple and Holeski 2016; McGuigan *et al.* 2021). Careful study design is critical to improve our understanding of the adaptive significance of epigenetic variation in response to environmental change (McGuigan *et al.* 2021).

Hologenomics

Given the fundamental role played by symbiotic microorganisms in the form, function and fitness of their hosts, animals and plants cannot be considered as autonomous entities, but rather as biological units that include numerous microbial symbionts and their genomes – the 'holobiont' (Bordenstein and Theis 2015). Evolution can be the result of changes in the host genome and/or its associated microbial genomes (metagenome; Zilber-Rosenberg and Rosenberg 2008). Alberdi *et al.* (2016) propose that host acclimation and adaptation to rapid environmental change is likely to be facilitated by the plasticity of the gut microbiota. Therefore, the study of adaptive responses to the environment can benefit from adopting a 'hologenomic' perspective, i.e. considering the combined genetic information of the host and its microbiota (Zilber-Rosenberg and Rosenberg 2008). Hologenomics has potential far-reaching applications in agriculture, biotechnology and biomedical research, as well as ecology, evolution and conservation (Nyholm *et al.* 2020). Although applications, especially to wildlife, are still at their infancy, the Earth Hologenome Initiative (https://www.earthhologenome.org/) is currently generating paired vertebrate genomes and their gut microbial metagenomes to understand the hologenomic underpinnings of environmental adaptations, convergence evolution and ecological interactions.

Validating inference from genomics

Without experimental validation, statistical inferences about environmental adaptation must be interpreted with caution. Many of the above methods for identifying loci and genotypes adapted to specific environments are based on population genetic patterns, but not phenotypic variation. Even in the case of GWAS for adaptive phenotypes, population structure and limited characterisation of functional variants can limit the strength of inferences. Stronger evidence that a given genotype or allele is adapted to a specific environment can be obtained from several experimental approaches. For example, when adaptation is oligogenic, introgression of a putative adaptive allele can be used to create near isogenic lines, allowing one to directly test the allele's effects (Hepworth *et al.* 2020), though recombination limits how narrow the introgressed region is (Box 14.1). Alternatively, when transgenic or CRISPR mutants are made that replicate the putative causal natural allelic variation, the effect of the natural variation can be tested (Bellis *et al.* 2020). Nevertheless, in many systems adaptation is polygenic, preventing these types of locus-specific validation.

When adaptation is polygenic, the validation of genomic inferences can be done using experiments to test (out-of-sample) multi-locus predictions of adaptive traits in specific common garden environments. While this approach can validate inferences aggregated across loci, it does not allow for the identification or validation of specific causal loci. A less direct, but more relevant (for certain goals) validation approach is to test genetic predictions of environment-dependent individual performance or population growth rate in wild individuals (Gienapp *et al.* 2017; Bay *et al.* 2018; Gienapp *et al.* 2019). However, this approach is also subject to spurious associations when changes in genotypes across environments (genotype by environment interactions) are not accounted for. Hence, given the trade-off between efficiency, logistical challenges and depth of inference both experimental and population genomic inference have their place.

Reflections

As illustrated in this chapter, adaptive genomic techniques have an important role to play in the management and conservation of agricultural resources, natural ecosystems, and global biodiversity under changing environmental conditions. The genomic landscape of adaptation is often highly complex (Box 14.1), interacting with a species' environment, demographic history, life history, and evolutionary legacy. This complexity can lend uncertainty to management and conservation efforts that incorporate adaptive genomic data. For example, predicting evolutionary responses to climate change in the annual plant *Arabidopsis thaliana* has proven difficult, despite the wealth of genomic and experimental data available for this model species (Fournier-Level *et al.* 2016). Nevertheless, simple best practices for maintaining evolutionary potential and adaptive capacity, such as maximising genetic diversity, were found to be effective (Fournier-Level *et al.* 2016). This finding confirms the importance of conserving species across phenotypic, genetic, and environmental diversity and maintaining overall genomic diversity to conserve adaptive capacity and evolutionary resilience in response to known and unknown future threats (Sgrò *et al.* 2011; Kardos *et al.* 2021).

The *Arabidopsis* case illustrates why it will be important, where possible, to move away from sole reliance on statistical inference about the genomic basis of environmental adaptation. However, because experimental and functional validation may not always be possible due to the longevity, life history or conservation status of the species in question, it remains essential to develop new methods and best practices to guide the application of this emerging field. For example, statistical inferences could be better grounded in quantitative and population genetic theory, which lags behind the complexity we see in natural systems (Balkenhol *et al.* 2015). Another approach couples statistical inference with complementary data from simulations (Epperson *et al.* 2010), such as in the case of breeding plans for transgenic blight-tolerant American chestnut trees (*Castanea dentata*; Westbrook *et al.* 2020). American chestnut was a **keystone species** of eastern North American forests before the introduction of a fungal pathogen (*Cryphonectria parasitica*) in the early 1900s. This simulation study models the efficacy of crossing transgenic, blight-tolerant trees with susceptible wild-type trees to conserve the genetic diversity and evolutionary potential of wild-type chestnuts while improving resistance to the blight pathogen. In combination with genomic prediction to introgress polygenic resistance from *Castanea mollissima* (Westbrook *et al.* 2020), these efforts could facilitate the start of large-scale restoration of this species across its former range within a few decades. As this and several studies reviewed in this chapter show, improving our understanding of the genomics of environmental adaptation can inform a range of applications, from predictions of species responses to environmental change to crop improvements that increase resilience under climate change.

DISCUSSION TOPICS

1. Compare commonly used genomic methods to identify local environmental adaptations and discuss which applications they are most suitable for and why.
2. What genomic methods and/or experimental techniques would be required to fully assess the evolutionary potential of a population or species? Is this feasible?
3. Is it important to specifically identify and conserve adaptive variation, or should we focus instead on measures that will increase neutral genetic variation?

ACKNOWLEDGEMENTS

O. Razgour was supported by a Natural Environment Research Council Independent Research Fellowship (NE/M018660/1). J.R. Lasky acknowledges the support of the US NIH 1R35GM138300-01 and US NSF DEB-1927009. T. Capblancq was supported by a postdoctoral associate program awarded by the University of Vermont. B.R. Forester was supported by a David H. Smith Conservation Research Fellowship.

REFERENCES

Aitken SN, Bemmels JB (2016) Time to get moving: assisted gene flow of forest trees. In *Evolutionary Applications*. pp. 271–290. Wiley. doi:10.1111/eva.12293

Aitken SN, Whitlock MC (2013) Assisted gene flow to facilitate local adaptation to climate change. *Annual Review of Ecology, Evolution, and Systematics* **44**, 367–388. doi:10.1146/annurev-ecolsys-110512-135747

Alberdi A, Aizpurua O, Bohmann K, Zepeda-Mendoza ML. Gilbert MTP (2016) Do vertebrate gut metagenomes confer rapid ecological adaptation? *Trends in Ecology & Evolution* **31**, 689–699. doi:10.1016/j.tree.2016.06.008

Allendorf F, Lundquist L (2003) Population biology, evolution, and control of Invasive Species. *Conservation Biology* **17**(1), 24–30. doi:10.1046/j.1523-1739.2003.02365.x

Allendorf FW, Hohenlohe PA, Luikart G (2010) Genomics and the future of conservation genetics. *Nature Reviews Genetics* **11**, 697–709. doi:10.1038/nrg2844

Atwell S, Huang Y, Vilhjálmsson B (2010) Genome-wide association study of 107 phenotypes in *Arabidopsis thaliana* inbred lines. *Nature* **465**, 627–631. doi:10.1038/nature08800

Auteri GG, Knowles LL (2020) Decimated little brown bats show potential for adaptive change. *Scientific Reports* **10**, 3023. doi:10.1038/s41598-020-59797-4

Balkenhol N, Cushman SA, Waits LP, Storfer A (2015) Current status, future opportunities, and remaining challenges in landscape genetics. In *Landscape Genetics: Concepts, Methods, Applications*. (Eds Niko Balkenhol, SA Cushman, AT Storfer, LP Waits) pp. 247–255. John Wiley and Sons Ltd. doi:10.1002/9781118525258.ch14

Bay RA, Harrigan RJ, Le Underwood V, Gibbs HL, Smith TB, et al. (2018) Genomic signals of selection predict climate-driven population declines in a migratory bird. *Science* **359**, 83–86. doi:10.1126/science.aan4380

Bay RA, Rose NH, Logan CA, Palumbi SR (2017) Genomic models predict successful coral adaptation if future ocean warming rates are reduced. *Science Advances* **3**, 1701413. doi:10.1126/sciadv.1701413

Bellis ES, Kelly EA, Lorts CM, Gao H, DeLeo VL, et al. (2020) Genomics of sorghum local adaptation to a parasitic plant. *Proceedings of the National Academy of Sciences* **117**, 4243–4251. doi:10.1073/pnas.1908707117

Bernatchez L (2016) On the maintenance of genetic variation and adaptation to environmental change: considerations from population genomics in fishes. *Journal of Fish Biology* **89**, 2519–2556. doi:10.1111/jfb.13145

Bi K, Linderoth T, Vanderpool D, Good JM, Nielsen R, et al. (2013) Unlocking the vault: Next-generation museum population genomics. *Molecular Ecology* **22**, 6018–6032. doi:10.1111/mec.12516

Bock DG, Caseys C, Cousens RD, Hahn MA, Heredia SM, et al. (2015) What we still don't know about invasion genetics. *Molecular Ecology* **24**, 2277–2297. doi:10.1111/mec.13032

Bordenstein SR, Theis KR (2015) Host biology in light of the microbiome: ten principles of holobionts and hologenomes. *PLoS Biology* **13**, 1002226. doi:10.1371/journal.pbio.1002226

Breed MF, Harrison PA, Blyth C, Byrne M, Gaget V, et al. (2019) The potential of genomics for restoring ecosystems and biodiversity. *Nature Reviews Genetics* **20**, 615–628. doi:10.1038/s41576-019-0152-0

Bush A, Mokany K, Catullo R, Hoffmann A, Kellermann V, et al. (2016) Incorporating evolutionary adaptation in species distribution modelling reduces projected vulnerability to climate change. *Ecology Letters* **19**, 1468–1478. doi:10.1111/ele.12696

Calfee E, Agra MN, Palacio MA, Ramírez SR, Coop G (2020) Selection and hybridization shaped the rapid spread of African honey bee ancestry in the Americas. *PLoS Genetics* **16**, 1009038. doi:10.1371/journal.pgen.1009038

Capblancq T, Fitzpatrick MC, Bay RA, Exposito-Alonso M, Keller SR (2020) Genomic prediction of (mal)adaptation across current and future climatic landscapes. *Annual Review of Ecology, Evolution, and Systematics* **51**, 245–269. doi:10.1146/annurev-ecolsys-020720-042553

Carroll EL, Bruford MW, DeWoody JA, Leroy G, Strand A, et al. (2018) Genetic and genomic monitoring with minimally invasive sampling methods. *Evolutionary Applications* **11**, 1094–1119. doi:10.1111/eva.12600

Carvalho CS, Forester BR, Mitre SK, Alves R, Imperatriz-Fonseca VL, et al. (2021) Combining genotype, phenotype, and environmental data to delineate site-adjusted provenance strategies for ecological restoration. *Molecular Ecology Resources* **21**, 44–58. doi:10.1111/1755-0998.13191

Cassin-Sackett L, Callicrate TE, Fleischer RC (2019) Parallel evolution of gene classes, but not genes: Evidence from Hawai'ian honeycreeper populations exposed to avian malaria. *Molecular Ecology* **28**, 568–583. doi:10.1111/mec.14891

Coates DJ, Byrne M, Moritz C (2018) Genetic diversity and conservation units: Dealing With the species-population continuum in the age of genomics. *Frontiers in Ecology and Evolution* **6**, 165. doi:10.3389/fevo.2018.00165

D'Amen M, Zimmermann NE, Pearman PB (2013) Conservation of phylogeographic lineages under climate change. *Global Ecology and Biogeography* **22**, 93–104. doi:10.1111/j.1466-8238.2012.00774.x

Dawson TP, Jackson ST, House JI, Prentice IC, Mace GM (2011) Beyond predictions: biodiversity conservation in a changing climate. *Science* **332**, 53–58. doi:10.1126/science.1200303

de Villemereuil P, Frichot É, Bazin É, François O, Gaggiotti O (2014) Genome scan methods against more complex models: when and how much should we trust them? *Molecular Ecology* **23**, 2006–19. doi:10.1111/mec.12705

DeBiasse MB, Kelly MW (2016) Plastic and evolved responses to global change: what can we learn from comparative transcriptomics? *Journal of Heredity* **107**, 71–81. doi:10.1093/jhered/esv073

Epperson BK, McRae BH, Scribner KIM, Cushman SA, Rosenberg MS, et al. (2010) Utility of computer simulations in landscape genetics. *Molecular Ecology* **19**, 3549–3564. doi:10.1111/j.1365-294X.2010.04678.x

Epstein B, Jones M, Hamede R, Hendricks S, McCallum H, et al. (2016) Rapid evolutionary response to a transmissible cancer in Tasmanian devils. *Nature Communications* **7**(12684), 126–129. doi:10.1038/ncomms12684

Exposito-Alonso M, Team, 500 Genomes Field Experiment, Burbano HA, Bossdorf O, Nielsen R, et al. (2019) Natural selection on the *Arabidopsis thaliana* genome in present and future climates. *Nature* **573**, 126–129. doi:10.1038/s41586-019-1520-9

Fitzpatrick MC, Chhatre VE, Soolanayakanahally RY, Keller SR (2021) Experimental support for genomic prediction of climate maladaptation using the machine learning approach Gradient Forests. *Molecular Ecology Resources* **21**(8), 2749–2765. doi:10.1111/1755-0998.13374

Fitzpatrick MC, Keller SR (2015) Ecological genomics meets community-level modelling of biodiversity: Mapping the genomic landscape of current and future environmental adaptation. *Ecology Letters* **18**, 1–16. doi:10.1111/ele.12376

Flanagan SP, Forester BR, Latch EK, Aitken SN, Hoban SM (2018) Guidelines for planning genomic assessment and monitoring of locally adaptive variation to inform species conservation. *Evolutionary Applications* **11**, 1035–1052. doi:10.1111/eva.12569

Foden WB, Young BE, Akçakaya HR, Garcia RA, Hoffmann AA, et al. (2019) Climate change vulnerability assessment of species. *Wiley Interdisciplinary Reviews: Climate Change* **10**, 551. doi:10.1002/wcc.551

Forester BR, Landguth EL, Hand BK, Balkenhol N (2018) Landscape genomics for wildlife research. In *Population Genomics: Wildlife.* (Eds PA Hohenlohe, OP Rajora) pp. 145–184. Springer International Publishing. doi:10.1007/13836_2018_56

Forester BR, Lasky JR, Wagner HH, Urban DL (2018) Comparing methods for detecting multilocus adaptation with multivariate genotype-environment associations. *Molecular Ecology* **27**, 2215–33. doi:10.1111/mec.14584

Fournier-Level A, Korte A, Cooper MD, Nordborg M, Schmitt J, et al. (2011) A map of local adaptation in *Arabidopsis thaliana.* *Science* **334**, 86–89. doi:10.1126/science.1209271

Fournier-Level A, Perry EO, Wang JA, Braun PT, Migneault A, et al. (2016) Predicting the evolutionary dynamics of seasonal adaptation to novel climates in *Arabidopsis thaliana*. *Proceedings of the National Academy of Sciences* **113**, 2812–2821. doi:10.1073/pnas.1517456113

Frankham R (2008) Genetic adaptation to captivity in species conservation programs. *Molecular Ecology* **17**, 325–333. doi:10.1111/j.1365-294X.2007.03399.x

Franks SJ, Hoffmann AA (2012) Genetics of climate change adaptation. *Annual Review of Genetics* **46**, 185–208. doi:10.1146/annurev-genet-110711-155511

Funk WC, McKay JK, Hohenlohe PA, Allendorf FW (2012) Harnessing genomics for delineating conservation units. *Trends in Ecology & Evolution* **27**, 489–496. doi:10.1016/j.tree.2012.05.012

Gates DJ, Runcie D, Janzen GM (2019) Single-gene resolution of locally adaptive genetic variation in Mexican maize. *BioRxiv*, 706739. doi:10.1101/706739

Gautier M (2015) Genome-wide scan for adaptive divergence and association with population-specific covariates. *Genetics* **201**, 1555–1579. doi:10.1534/genetics.115.181453

Gienapp P, Calus MP, Laine VN, Visser ME (2019) Genomic selection on breeding time in a wild bird population. *Evolution Letters* **3**, 142–151. doi:10.1002/evl3.103

Gienapp P, Fior S, Guillaume F, Lasky JR, Sork VL, et al. (2017) Genomic quantitative genetics to study evolution in the wild. *Trends in Ecology & Evolution* **32**, 897–908. doi:10.1016/j.tree.2017.09.004

Gienapp P, Teplitsky C, Alho JS, Mills JA, Merilä J (2008) Climate change and evolution: disentangling environmental and genetic responses. *Molecular Ecology* **17**, 167–178. doi:10.1111/j.1365-294X.2007.03413.x

Gignoux-Wolfsohn SA, Pinsky ML, Kerwin K, Herzog C, Hall M, et al. (2021) Genomic signatures of selection in bats surviving white-nose syndrome. *Molecular Ecology* **30**, 5643–5657. doi:10.1111/mec.15813

Guo B, Li Z, Merilä J (2016) Population genomic evidence for adaptive differentiation in the Baltic Sea herring. *Molecular Ecology* **25**, 2833–2852. doi:10.1111/mec.13657

Hall MC, Basten CJ, Willis JH (2006) Pleiotropic quantitative trait loci contribute to population divergence in traits associated with life-history variation in Mimulus guttatus. *Genetics* **172**, 1829–1844. doi:10.1534/genetics.105.051227

Hällfors MH, Liao J, Dzurisin J, Grundel R, Hyvärinen M, et al. (2016) Addressing potential local adaptation in species distribution models: implications for conservation under climate change. *Ecological Applications* **26**, 1154–1169. doi:10.1890/15-0926

Hansen MM, Olivieri I, Waller DM, Nielsen EE, Group GW (2012) Monitoring adaptive genetic responses to environmental change. *Molecular Ecology* **21**, 1311–1329. doi:10.1111/j.1365-294X.2011.05463.x

Harris SE, Munshi-South J (2017) Signatures of positive selection and local adaptation to urbanization in white-footed mice (Peromyscus leucopus. *Molecular Ecology* **26**, 6336–6350. doi:10.1111/mec.14369

Harrisson KA, Pavlova A, Telonis-Scott M, Sunnucks P (2014) Using genomics to characterize evolutionary potential for conservation of wild populations. *Evolutionary Applications* **7**, 1008–1025. doi:10.1111/eva.12149

Hayes B (2013) Overview of statistical methods for Genome-Wide Association Studies (GWAS). In *Genome-Wide Association Studies and Genomic Prediction. Methods in Molecular Biology (Methods and Protocols), vol 1019*. (Eds C Gondro, J Werf, B Hayes) Humana Press. doi:10.1007/978-1-62703-447-0_6

He X, Johansson ML, Heath DD (2016) Role of genomics and transcriptomics in selection of reintroduction source populations. *Conservation Biology* **30**, 1010–1018. doi:10.1111/cobi.12674

Heffner EL, Sorrells ME, Jannink JL (2009) Genomic selection for crop improvement. *Crop Science* **49**, 1–12. doi:10.2135/cropsci2008.08.0512

Hepworth J, Antoniou-Kourounioti RL, Berggren K, Selga C, Tudor EH, et al. (2020) Natural variation in autumn expression is the major adaptive determinant distinguishing Arabidopsis FLC haplotypes. *ELife* **9**, e57671. doi:10.7554/eLife.57671

Hess JE, Campbell NR, Docker MF, Baker C, Jackson A, et al. (2015) Use of genotyping by sequencing data to develop a high-throughput and multifunctional SNP panel for conservation applications in Pacific lamprey. *Molecular Ecology Resources* **15**, 187–202. doi:10.1111/1755-0998.12283

Hoban S, Kelley JL, Lotterhos KE, Antolin MF, Bradburd G, et al. (2016) Finding the genomic basis of local adaptation: pitfalls, practical solutions, and future directions. *The American Naturalist* **188**, 379–397. doi:10.1086/688018

Hoekstra HE, Hirschmann RJ, Bundey RA, Insel PA, Crossland JP (2006) A single amino acid mutation contributes to adaptive beach mouse color pattern. *Science* **313**, 101–104. doi:10.1126/science.1126121

Hoffmann AA, Griffin P, Dillon S, Catullo R, Rane R, et al. (2015) A framework for incorporating evolutionary genomics into biodiversity conservation and management. *Climate Change Responses* **2**, 1–24. doi:10.1186/s40665-014-0009-x

Hoffmann AA, Weeks AR, Sgrò CM (2021) Opportunities and challenges in assessing climate change vulnerability through genomics. *Cell* **184**, 1420–1425. doi:10.1016/j.cell.2021.02.006

Hohenlohe PA, Funk WC, Rajora OP (2021) Population genomics for wildlife conservation and management. *Molecular Ecology* **30**, 62–82. doi:10.1111/mec.15720

Jay F, Manel S, Alvarez N, Durand EY, Thuiller W, et al. (2012) Forecasting changes in population genetic structure of alpine plants in response to global warming. *Molecular Ecology* **21**, 2354–2368. doi:10.1111/j.1365-294X.2012.05541.x

Kardos M, Armstrong E, Fitzpatrick S, Hauser S, Hedrick P, et al. (2021) The crucial role of genome-wide genetic variation in conservation. *Proceedings of the National Academy of Sciences* **118**(48), e2104642118. doi:10.1073/pnas.2104642118

Kelly E, Jolly CJ, Indigo N, Smart A, Webb J, et al. (2021) No outbreeding depression in a trial of targeted gene flow in an endangered Australian marsupial. *Conservation Genetics* **22**, 23–33. doi:10.1007/s10592-020-01316-z

Korte A, Farlow A (2013) The advantages and limitations of trait analysis with GWAS: a review. *Plant Methods* **9**, 1–9. doi:10.1186/1746-4811-9-29

Lasky JR, Forester BR, Reimherr M (2018) Coherent synthesis of genomic associations with phenotypes and home environments.

Molecular Ecology Resources **18**, 91–106. doi:10.1111/1755-0998.12714

Lasky JR, Upadhyaya HD, Ramu P, Deshpande S, Hash CT, *et al.* (2015) Genome-environment associations in sorghum landraces predict adaptive traits. *Science Advances* **1**, 1400218. doi:10.1126/sciadv.1400218

Lesica, P., & Allendorf, F. W. (1999) Ecological genetics and the restoration of plant communities: Mix or match? *Restoration Ecology*, 7, 42–50. doi:10.1046/j.1526-100X.1999.07105.x

Long A, Liti G, Luptak A, Tenaillon O (2015) Elucidating the molecular architecture of adaptation via evolve and resequence experiments. *Nature Reviews Genetics* **16**, 567–582. doi:10.1038/nrg3937

Lotterhos KE, Whitlock MC (2014) Evaluation of demographic history and neutral parameterization on the performance of FST outlier tests. *Molecular Ecology* **23**, 2178–2192. doi:10.1111/mec.12725

Lotterhos KE, Whitlock MC (2015) The relative power of genome scans to detect local adaptation depends on sampling design and statistical method. *Molecular Ecology* **24**, 1031–46. doi:10.1111/mec.13100

Luikart G, England P, Tallmon D, Jordan S, Taberlet P (2003) The power and promise of population genomics: from genotyping to genome typing. *Nature Reviews Genetics* **4**, 981–94. doi:10.1038/nrg1226

Luu K, Bazin E, Blum MGB (2017) pcadapt: An R package to perform genome scans for selection based on principal component analysis. *Molecular Ecology Resources* **17**, 67–77. doi:10.1111/1755-0998.12592

Lv FH, Agha S, Kantanen J, Colli L, Stucki S, *et al.* (2014) Adaptations to climate-mediated selective pressures in sheep. *Molecular Biology and Evolution* **31**, 3324–3343. doi:10.1093/molbev/msu264

Malosetti M, Ribaut JM, Eeuwijk FA (2013) The statistical analysis of multi-environment data: modeling genotype-by-environment interaction and its genetic basis. *Frontiers in Physiology* **4**, 44. doi:10.3389/fphys.2013.00044

Manel S, Schwartz MK, Luikart G, Taberlet P (2003) Landscape genetics: combining landscape ecology and population genetics. *Trends in Ecology & Evolution* **18**, 189–197. doi:10.1016/S0169-5347(03)00008-9

McGuigan K, Hoffmann AA, Sgrò CM (2021) How is epigenetics predicted to contribute to climate change adaptation? What evidence do we need? *Philosophical Transactions of the Royal Society B* **376**, 20200119. doi:10.1098/rstb.2020.0119

McLachlan JS, Hellmann JJ, Schwartz MW (2007) A framework for debate of assisted migration in an era of climate change. *Conservation Biology* **21**, 297–302. doi:10.1111/j.1523-1739.2007.00676.x

Mérot C, Oomen RA, Tigano A, Wellenreuther M (2020) A roadmap for understanding the evolutionary significance of structural genomic variation. *Trends in Ecology & Evolution* **35**, 561–572. doi:10.1016/j.tree.2020.03.002

Messina CD, Technow F, Tang T, Totir R, Gho C, *et al.* (2018) Leveraging biological insight and environmental variation to improve phenotypic prediction: Integrating crop growth models (CGM) with whole genome prediction (WGP). *European Journal of Agronomy* **100**, 151–162. doi:10.1016/j.eja.2018.01.007

Milesi P, Berlin M, Chen J, Orsucci M, Li L, *et al.* (2019) Assessing the potential for assisted gene flow using past introduction of Norway spruce in southern Sweden: Local adaptation and genetic basis of quantitative traits in trees. *Evolutionary Applications* **12**, 1946–1959. doi:10.1111/eva.12855

Monroe JG, McGovern C, Lasky JR, Grogan K, Beck J, *et al.* (2016) Adaptation to warmer climates by parallel functional evolution of CBF genes in Arabidopsis thaliana. *Molecular Ecology* **25**, 3632–3644. doi:10.1111/mec.13711

Mounger J, Ainouche ML, Bossdorf O, Cavé-Radet A, Li B, *et al.* (2021) Epigenetics and the success of invasive plants. *Philosophical Transactions of the Royal Society B* **376**, 20200117. doi:10.1098/rstb.2020.0117

Nyholm L, Koziol A, Marcos S, Botnen AB, Aizpurua O, *et al.* (2020) Holo-omics: integrated host-microbiota multi-omics for basic and applied biological research. *Iscience* **23**, 101414. doi:10.1016/j.isci.2020.101414

Oakley CG, Ågren J, Atchison RA, Schemske DW (2014) QTL mapping of freezing tolerance: links to fitness and adaptive trade-offs. *Molecular Ecology* **23**, 4304–4315. doi:10.1111/mec.12862

Ofori BY, Stow AJ, Baumgartner JB, Beaumont LJ (2017) Influence of adaptive capacity on the outcome of climate change vulnerability assessment. *Scientific Reports* **7**, 12979. doi:10.1038/s41598-017-13245-y

Polechová J, Barton NH (2015) Limits to adaptation along environmental gradients. *Proceedings of the National Academy of Sciences* **112**, 6401–6406. doi:10.1073/pnas.1421515112

Rapaport F, Khanin R, Liang Y (2013) Comprehensive evaluation of differential gene expression analysis methods for RNA-seq data. *Genome Biology* **14**, 3158. doi:10.1186/gb-2013-14-9-r95

Razgour O, Taggart JB, Manel S, Juste J, Ibanez C, *et al.* (2018) An integrated framework to identify wildlife populations under threat from climate change. *Molecular Ecology Resources* **18**, 18–31. doi:10.1111/1755-0998.12694

Razgour O, Forester B, Taggart JB, Bekaert M, Juste J, *et al.* (2019) Considering adaptive genetic variation in climate change vulnerability assessment reduces species range loss projections. *Proceedings of the National Academy of Sciences* **116**, 10418–10423. doi:10.1073/pnas.1820663116

Rellstab C, Gugerli F, Eckert AJ, Hancock AM, Holderegger R (2015) A practical guide to environmental association analysis in landscape genomics. *Molecular Ecology* **24**, 4348–4370. doi:10.1111/mec.13322

Rhoné B, Defrance D, Berthouly-Salazar C, Mariac C, Cubry P, *et al.* (2020) Pearl millet genomic vulnerability to climate change in West Africa highlights the need for regional collaboration. *Nature Communications* **11**, 1–9. doi:10.1038/s41467-020-19066-4

Rochat E, Selmoni O, Joost S (2021) Spatial areas of genotype probability: Predicting the spatial distribution of adaptive genetic variants under future climatic conditions. *Diversity and Distributions* **27**, 1076–1090. doi:10.1111/ddi.13256

Savolainen O, Lascoux M, Merilä J (2013) Ecological genomics of local adaptation. *Nature Reviews Genetics* **14**, 807–820. doi:10.1038/nrg3522

Schiebelhut LM, Puritz JB, Dawson MN (2018) Decimation by sea star wasting disease and rapid genetic change in a keystone species, Pisaster ochraceus. *Proceedings of the National*

Academy of Sciences **115**, 7069–7074. doi:10.1073/pnas. 1800285115

Schmidt PS, Zhu CT, Das J, Batavia M, Yang L, *et al.* (2008) An amino acid polymorphism in the couch potato gene forms the basis for climatic adaptation in Drosophila melanogaster. *Proceedings of the National Academy of Sciences* **105**, 16207–16211. doi:10.1073/pnas.0805485105

Schwartz MK, Luikart G, Waples RS (2007) Genetic monitoring as a promising tool for conservation and management. *Trends in Ecology & Evolution* **22**, 25–33. doi:10.1016/j.tree.2006.08.009

Sgrò C, Lowe A, Hoffmann A (2011) Building evolutionary resilience for conserving biodiversity under climate change. *Evolutionary Applications* **4**, 326–337. doi:10.1111/j.1752-4571.2010.00157.x

Sork VL, Davis FW, Westfall R, Flint A, Ikegami M, *et al.* (2010) Gene movement and genetic association with regional climate gradients in California valley oak (*Quercus lobata Née*) in the face of climate change. *Molecular Ecology* **19**, 3806–3823. doi:10.1111/j.1365-294X.2010.04726.x

Storfer A, Hohenlohe PA, Margres MJ, Patton A, Fraik AK, *et al.* (2018) The devil is in the details: Genomics of transmissible cancers in Tasmanian devils. *PLoS Pathogens* **14**, 1007098. doi:10.1371/journal.ppat.1007098

Storz JF (2005) Using genome scans of DNA polymorphism to infer adaptive population divergence. *Molecular Ecology* **14**, 671–88. doi:10.1111/j.1365-294X.2005.02437.x

Technow F, Messina CD, Totir LR, Cooper M (2015) Integrating crop growth models with whole genome prediction through approximate Bayesian computation. *PloS one* **10**, 130855. doi:10.1371/journal.pone.0130855

Thomashow MF (1999) Plant cold acclimation: freezing tolerance genes and regulatory mechanisms. *Annual Review of Plant Biology* **50**, 571–599. doi:10.1146/annurev.arplant.50.1.571

Tiezzi F, Los Campos G, Gaddis KP, Maltecca C (2017) Genotype by environment (climate) interaction improves genomic prediction for production traits in US Holstein cattle. *Journal of Dairy Science* **100**, 2042–2056. doi:10.3168/jds.2016-11543

Todd EV, Black MA, Gemmell NJ (2016) The power and promise of RNA-seq in ecology and evolution. *Molecular Ecology* **25**, 1224–1241. doi:10.1111/mec.13526

Urban MC, Bocedi G, Hendry AP, Mihoub JB, Pe'er G, *et al.* (2016) Improving the forecast for biodiversity under climate change. *Science* **353**, 8466. doi:10.1126/science.aad8466

Van Rossum F, Hardy OJ (2021) Guidelines for genetic monitoring of translocated plant populations. *Conservation Biology* doi:10.1111/cobi.13670

Verhoeven KJ, VonHoldt BM, Sork VL (2016) Epigenetics in ecology and evolution: what we know and what we need to know. *Molecular Ecology* **25**, 1631–1638. doi:10.1111/mec.13617

von Thaden A, Nowak C, Tiesmeyer A, Reiners TE, Alves PC, *et al.* (2020) Applying genomic data in wildlife monitoring: Development guidelines for genotyping degraded samples with reduced single nucleotide polymorphism panels. *Molecular Ecology Resources* **20**, 662–680. doi:10.1111/1755-0998.13136

Wade AA, Hand BK, Kovach RP, Luikart G, Whited DC, *et al.* (2017) Accounting for adaptive capacity and uncertainty in assessments of species' climate-change vulnerability. *Conservation Biology* **31**, 136–149. doi:10.1111/cobi.12764

Wang Z, Gerstein M, Snyder M (2009) RNA-Seq: A revolutionary tool for transcriptomics. *Nature Reviews Genetics* **10**(1), 57–63. doi:10.1038/nrg2484

Wellenreuther M, Bernatchez L (2018) Eco-evolutionary genomics of chromosomal inversions. *Trends in Ecology & Evolution* **33**, 427–440. doi:10.1016/j.tree.2018.04.002

Wellenreuther M, Mérot C, Berdan E, Bernatchez L (2019) Going beyond SNPs: The role of structural genomic variants in adaptive evolution and species diversification. *Molecular Ecology* **28**, 1203–1209. doi:10.1111/mec.15066

Westbrook JW, Holliday JA, Newhouse AE, Powell WA (2020) A plan to diversify a transgenic blight-tolerant American chestnut population using citizen science. *Plants, People, Planet* **2**, 84–95. doi:10.1002/ppp3.10061

Westbrook JW, Zhang Q, Mandal MK, Jenkins EV, Barth LE, *et al.* (2020) Optimizing genomic selection for blight resistance in American chestnut backcross populations: A trade-off with American chestnut ancestry implies resistance is polygenic. *Evolutionary Applications* **13**, 31–47. doi:10.1111/eva.12886

Whipple AV, Holeski LM (2016) Epigenetic inheritance across the landscape. *Frontiers in Genetics* **7**, 189. doi:10.3389/fgene.2016.00189

Whitlock MC, Lotterhos KE (2015) Reliable detection of loci responsible for local adaptation: Inference of a null model through trimming the distribution of FST. *The American Naturalist* **186**, 24–36. doi:10.1086/682949

Willoughby JR, Ivy JA, Lacy RC, Doyle JM, DeWoody JA (2017) Inbreeding and selection shape genomic diversity in captive populations: Implications for the conservation of endangered species. *PLoS One* **12**, 175996. doi:10.1371/journal.pone.0175996

Wright B, Morris K, Grueber CE, Willet CE, Gooley R, *et al.* (2015) Development of a SNP-based assay for measuring genetic diversity in the Tasmanian devil insurance population. *BMC Genomics* **16**, 791. doi:10.1186/s12864-015-2020-4

Yeaman S, Whitlock MC (2011) The genetic architecture of adaptation under migration–selection balance. *Evolution: International Journal of Organic Evolution* **65**, 1897–1911. doi:10.1111/j.1558-5646.2011.01269.x

Young DJ, Blush TD, Landram M, Wright JW, Latimer AM, *et al.* (2020) Assisted gene flow in the context of large-scale forest management in California, USA. *Ecosphere* **11**, e03001. doi:10.1002/ecs2.3001

Zilber-Rosenberg I, Rosenberg E (2008) Role of microorganisms in the evolution of animals and plants: the hologenome theory of evolution. *FEMS Microbiology Reviews* **32**, 723–735. doi:10.1111/j.1574-6976.2008.00123.x

15 Perspective – The power of genomics for guiding reintroductions

Helen Taylor, Conservation Programme Manager, Royal Zoological Society of Scotland, UK

I am obsessed with power. Not in the dictatorial sense (although that would sometimes be handy in conservation), but in the statistical sense. The power to measure and detect effects: effects like inbreeding depression in small populations with low genetic diversity. I started my research career at the cusp of the genomic revolution and was still using microsatellite markers. Even with a relatively large panel of microsatellite markers (e.g. 28), individuals in the severely bottlenecked populations I worked with looked very similar genetically (Taylor *et al.* 2017). This means that there was very little statistical power to accurately reconstruct pedigrees, or to estimate relatedness or inbreeding (Taylor 2015; Taylor *et al.* 2015) which, in turn, made detecting inbreeding depression relatively challenging.

Now, as a conservation manager, genomics represents increased power to estimate the relatedness of founders for translocated populations, the genetic differences between populations being considered as sources and recipients for genetic rescue translocations, and the genetic diversity and inbreeding present in a remnant population or reintroduced populations and the ability to track this over time. I have two examples of how the team I currently work with is using genomics to inform conservation management, and they come from opposite ends of the animal taxonomic spectrum: Eurasian beavers and pine hoverflies.

Eurasian beavers were hunted to extinction in Great Britain around 400 years ago. The Scottish Beaver Trial involved reintroducing a total of 16 beavers from Telemark in Norway to Knapdale Forest in Argyll on Scotland's west coast (Campbell-Pamer and Jones 2014). However, genomic work carried out after the release using a panel of 306 SNP markers revealed that Norwegian beavers were, in fact, the least genetically diverse of all Eurasian beaver populations (Senn *et al.* 2014) leaving the long-term future of the Knapdale population in doubt.

There was also another beaver population in Scotland. An unauthorised release into the Tayside river catchment in the east of the country had resulted in a large population of beavers that were, unfortunately, frequently coming into conflict with farmers and other landowners. As luck would have it, these beavers were shown to be of Bavarian origin (McEwing *et al.* 2015) and it was known from the genomic research above that Bavarian beavers have more and different genetic diversity to their Norwegian counterparts. Thus, the decision was made to translocate some of the animals involved in human wildlife conflict in Tayside to the Knapdale population over a 3-year period.

Following translocations from Tayside, the Knapdale population as a whole now holds more genetic diversity than many other beaver subpopulations in Eurasia (unpublished data). What we really need to see is admixture between Norwegian and Bavarian lineage animals and detecting this will require future genetic monitoring (Dowse *et al.* 2020). The publication of a North America Beaver genome (Zhang *et al.* 2020) has assisted this research, but North American and Eurasian beavers have different numbers of chromosomes. We are eagerly awaiting the publication of a Eurasian beaver genome to give future work even better resolution.

While the beaver example involves wild to wild translocations, our work with the Critically Endangered pine hoverfly is focused on managing conservation breeding for release. Although found throughout Europe, in Great Britain, pine hoverflies are restricted to just one small forest patch in the Cairngorms National Park in Scotland. Habitat loss driven by deforestation and land-use change had driven numbers of this species so low that, in 2019, the decision was taken to take some larvae from the wild and bring them into a new conservation breeding program at RZSS' Highland Wildlife Park.

We started with 25 pine hoverfly larvae in 2019 and, as of October 2021, we have managed to breed 8000 larvae in our 2020/2021 season. As I write, we are preparing to start releasing animals in an attempt to establish new populations of this important pollinator in the Cairngorms. However, the initial breeding season was challenging and we know that in that first season (2019/2020), a maximum of two females were responsible for all eggs laid. We have sourced two additional individuals from the dwindling wild population to increase genetic diversity, but the majority of the individuals in our breeding program are all likely extremely closely related.

As with many invertebrates, there are scant genetic resources for pine hoverflies. A panel of 12 microsatellite loci was developed in 2012 (Rotheray *et al.* 2012). Given the likely extremely low genetic diversity in both the much-reduced wild population, and our breeding population, these markers will not give us the power we need to genetically manage our breeding population, or monitor reintroduced populations. To address this issue, we have formed a partnership with the Welcome Sanger Darwin Tree of Life project, an initiative that aims to sequence the genomes of 70 000 UK native species. They are currently using samples from our breeding population to produce the first ever genome for the pine hoverfly. This will allow our genetics team to conduct skim resequencing to assess genetic diversity and relatedness in the breeding population and in the wild. Genome sequencing may also allow our team to examine differences between UK and Scandinavian pine hoverflies to establish whether Scandinavian individuals could be used to repopulate the UK in the event of extirpation.

The common factor in these two examples and, indeed, many conservation genetics applications, is that the timing of the management actions and the genetic/genomic data production are currently out of step. This is because the conservation of threatened species often requires action at a faster pace than genetic data can be produced and analysed. Additionally, genetic information or the need for it, is still missing from many conservation plans (Pierson *et al.* 2016). Genomic studies produce enormous amounts of data and this can cause bottlenecks in the production of results and recommendations. If genomic data collection is not factored in before a management plan commences, then this lag becomes even greater. To me, one of the biggest challenges for effectively integrating genomic data into conservation practice is synchronising data production with management action timelines. With that synchronisation in place, the true power of genomics for informing conservation with be unleashed.

REFERENCES

Campbell-Pamer R, Jones S (2014) *The Scottish Beaver Trial: The story of Britain's first licensed release into the wild.*

Dowse G, Taylor H, Girling S, Costanzi J, Robinson S, *et al.* (2020) *Beavers in Knapdale: Final report from the Scottish Beavers Reinforcement Project.* Scottish Beavers, Edinburgh, UK.

McEwing R, Senn H, Campbell-Palmer R (2015) Genetic assessment of free-living beavers in and around the River Tay catchment, east Scotland. *Scottish Natural Heritage Commissioned Report No. 682.*

Pierson JC, Coates DJ, Oostermeijer JGB, Beissinger SR, Bragg JG, *et al.* (2016) Genetic factors in threatened species recovery plans on three continents. *Frontiers in Ecology and the Environment* **14**(8), 433–440. doi:10.1002/fee.1323

Rotheray EL, Nater A, Goulson D (2012) Polymorphic microsatellite loci for the endangered pine hoverfly *Blera fallax* (Diptera: Syrphidae). *Conservation Genetics Resources* **4**, 117–120. doi:10.1007/s12686-011-9488-2

Senn H, Ogden R, Frosch C, Syrůčková A, Campbell-Palmer R, *et al.* (2014) Nuclear and mitochondrial genetic structure in the Eurasian beaver (*Castor fiber*) – implications for future reintroductions. *Evolutionary Applications* **7**(6), 645–662. doi:10.1111/eva.12162

Taylor HR (2015) The use and abuse of genetic marker-based estimates of relatedness and inbreeding. *Ecology and Evolution* **5**(15), 3140–3150. doi:10.1002/ece3.1541

Taylor HR, Colbourne RM, Robertson HA, Nelson NJ, Allendorf FW, *et al.* (2017) Cryptic inbreeding depression in a growing population of a long-lived species. *Molecular Ecology* **26**(3), 799–813. doi:10.1111/mec.13977

Taylor HR, Kardos MK, Ramstad KM, Allendorf FW (2015) Valid estimates of individual inbreeding coefficients from marker-based pedigrees are not feasible in wild populations with low allelic diversity. *Conservation Genetics* **16**, 901–913. doi:10.1007/s10592-015-0709-1

Zhang Q, Tombline G, Ablaeva J, Zhang L, Zhou X, *et al.* (2020) The genome of North American beaver provides insights into the mechanisms of its longevity and cancer resistance. *BioRxiv*, 2020.2006.2025.171322..

16   Palaeo- and museo-genomics: perspectives on modern species

Alicia Grealy, Lauren C. White, Emily Roycroft and Jeremy J. Austin

ABSTRACT

The onset of rapid environmental change in the 'Anthropocene' puts into context the value of understanding past environmental change to predict future consequences for global biodiversity. Ancient and degraded DNA (aDNA) from fossils or museum specimens plays an important role in establishing historic baselines. Improvements in molecular technology have made obtaining genomic data from such sources more affordable and accessible to researchers outside the field. With that in mind, this chapter is intended for environmental managers, policy makers, researchers and students who do not have a comprehensive background in genetics that are looking to understand how and why palaeo- and museo-genomic data should be integrated into their decision-making, or who are looking to incorporate aDNA data into their research. Here, we begin by providing a brief overview of the technical challenges of working with aDNA and the considerations that are needed when adopting this technology. We then illustrate how aDNA can be used to answer a myriad of contemporary ecological and conservation questions by describing several case studies. Finally, we discuss future avenues of research and remaining gaps in knowledge. We encourage all readers to openly discuss among their peers the questions raised under 'Discussion topics' and explore these further using the accompanying resources. While many advancements have been made towards using aDNA to provide new perspectives on modern species, there remains a disconnect in translating these data into practical outcomes or policy.

INTRODUCTION

Ancient DNA (aDNA) is genetic material derived from poorly preserved biological specimens ranging in age from decades to up to 1 million years (van der Valk *et al.* 2021), but is more broadly considered to be DNA extracted from any specimen that was not stored for the express purpose of DNA analysis, including historical/archival material (Raxworthy and Smith 2021) and some forensic specimen sample types (Young *et al.* 2019; Hofreiter *et al.* 2021). aDNA can be sourced from a single, typically taxonomically identifiable sample, which includes substrates such as bones and teeth (Adler *et al.* 2011), hair (Gilbert *et al.* 2008), artifacts (Teasdale *et al.* 2015), feathers (Rawlence *et al.* 2009), eggs (Oskam *et al.* 2010), shells (Villanea *et al.* 2016), and leaves (Palmer *et al.* 2012) (Box 16.1). Additionally, aDNA can be extracted from environmental samples containing mixtures of DNA from animals, plants and microbes. For example, mixed-sample substrates can include water, ice (Willerslev *et al.* 2007), sediment (Jørgensen *et al.* 2012), dental calculus (Warinner *et al.* 2015), and coprolites (Hofreiter *et al.* 2003) (Box 16.1). Such ancient substrates are typically recovered from palaeontological and archaeological material within caves (Massilani *et al.* 2022), **animal middens** (Murray *et al.*

Box 16.1: Ancient DNA perspectives on modern species

Ancient DNA (aDNA) provides a window to the past, allowing us to determine what, how, and why species have changed. This allows us to better predict and manage how species today will respond to future environmental change.

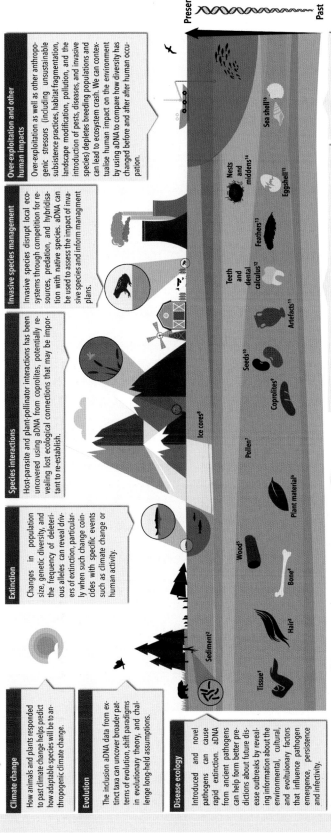

Climate change

How animals and plants responded to past climate change helps predict how adaptable species will be to anthropogenic climate change.

Evolution

The inclusion aDNA data from extinct taxa can uncover broader patterns of evolution, shift paradigms in evolutionary theory, and challenge long-held assumptions.

Disease ecology

Introduced and novel pathogens can cause rapid extinction. aDNA from ancient pathogens can help form better predictions about future disease outbreaks by revealing information about the environmental, cultural, and evolutionary factors that influence pathogen emergence, persistence and infectivity.

Conservation

aDNA can reveal historical ranges for species, identify populations that were formerly connected, and which populations would benefit from translocation or reintroductions.

Extinction

Changes in population size, genetic diversity, and the frequency of deleterious alleles can reveal drivers of extinction, particularly when such change coincides with specific events such as climate change or human activity.

Species interactions

Host-parasite and plant-pollinator interactions has been uncovered using aDNA from coprolites, potentially revealing lost ecological connections that may be important to re-establish.

Palaeodiet and palaeoenvironment

aDNA from coprolites, intestinal contents, and refuse middens can provide direct evidence of consumed food items, which allows us to reconstruct species interactions, food webs, and past ecosystems.

Invasive species management

Invasive species disrupt local ecosystems through competition for resources, predation, and hybridisation with native species. aDNA can be used to assess the impact of invasive species and inform managment plans.

Over-exploitation and other human impacts

Over-exploitation as well as other anthropogenic stressors (including unsustainable subsistence practices, habitat fragmentation, landscape modification, pollution, and the introduction of pests, diseases, and invasive species) depletes breeding populations and can lead to ecosystem crash. We can contextualise human impact on the environment by using aDNA to compare how diversity has changed before and after human occupation.

Domestication

aDNA from the remains of domesticated animals such as chickens, cattle, and dogs can reveal patterns of human migration, subsistence and breeding practices, and cultural exchange, as well as reveal how and when animals became domesticated. This may be particularly important in understanding susceptibility of domestic animals to zoonotic diseases today.

Phenotype and behaviour

Certain behaviours and phenotypes of extinct animals can be gleaned using aDNA, providing insights into adaptation and development.

Present

Past

Tissue[1] Hair[3] Sediment[2] Wood[5] Bone[4] Ice cores[8] Pollen[7] Plant material[6] Seeds[10] Coprolites[9] Teeth and dental calculus[12] Artefacts[11] Feathers[13] Nests and middens[14] Eggshell[15] Sea shell[16]

[1]Thomas et al. (1989) [2]Jørgensen et al. (2012) [3]Gilbert et al. (2008) [4]Adler et al. (2011) [5]Jiao et al. (2015) [6]Palmer et al. (2012) [7]Parducci et al. (2005) [8]Willerslev et al. (2007) [9]Hofreiter et al. (2003) [10]Gismondi et al. (2016) [11]Teasdale et al. (2015) [12]Warinner et al. (2015) [13]Rawlence et al. (2009) [14]Rinkert et al. (2021) [15]Oskam et al. (2010) [16]Villanea et al. (2016)

2012), archaeological sites (Ferrari *et al.* 2021), and permafrost (van der Valk *et al.* 2021). Samples may also be sourced from natural history collections in museums (Yeates *et al.* 2016) and herbaria (Taylor and Swann 1994): these typically span the last 300 years and include dry skins (Thomas, *et al.* 1989; Roycroft *et al.* 2022), tissues fixed in media (Hahn *et al.* 2021), pinned insects (Gilbert *et al.* 2007), pressed leaves (Gutaker *et al.* 2018), nests (Rinkert *et al.* 2021), and blown eggshells (Grealy *et al.* 2019). aDNA provides critical spatio-temporal genetic sampling of organisms to measure biodiversity change; assess species and ecosystem responses to environmental and anthropogenic change; identify the origin and spread of disease and invasive species; catalogue the process of animal and plant domestication; and provide a 'real-time' view of evolution across decades to hundreds of thousands of years (Box 16.1). aDNA data complement contemporary genomic surveys and traditional palaeo-environmental proxies, such as pollen (Parducci *et al.* 2013), insect, macrofossils (Lejzerowicz *et al.* 2013) and isotopes (Witt *et al.* 2021). The major advantages of aDNA for applied environmental genomics are that genetic data can be sampled from living and extinct populations across a range of time-scales and environmental transitions; they can provide insights across multiple levels of biodiversity from single genes, populations, species and whole ecosystems; they can incorporate a very broad range of samples (see Green and Speller 2017); and they are taxonomically unrestricted, delivering genetic information from a large array of species, many of which leave no physical trace in the fossil record. Critically, museums and herbaria contain large collections of fixed and preserved biological material that can provide genetic samples that span the major impacts of the **Anthropocene**, and may represent the only genetic material available for certain taxonomic groups (e.g. insects, soft-bodied organisms). Therefore, the field of palaeo- and museo-genomics offers enormous potential to solve modern problems in ecology, biosecurity, conservation, human health and climate change biology. In this chapter, we briefly review the challenges of working with aDNA, the geographic and temporal limits on aDNA survival, and the strategies used to mitigate these challenges and limitations (for a comprehensive review of methods and techniques see Orlando *et al.* 2021). We then discuss the types of modern environmental management questions that can be addressed using aDNA.

CHALLENGES AND LIMITATIONS OF WORKING WITH ANCIENT DNA

Compared with fresh DNA, there are several challenges and limitations that must be considered when working with aDNA (Box 16.2). DNA recovered from ancient samples can be extremely fragmented (often well below 100 bp in length), and chemically modified with single-stranded breaks, abasic sites, deaminated cytosines (which appear as C->T mutations) (Hofreiter *et al.* 2001), and molecular cross-links (Hoss *et al.* 1996). This post-mortem damage limits the amount of genetic information that can be obtained from a sample and introduces error and uncertainty into recovered sequences, which can be mistaken for *bona fide* genetic variation (Gilbert *et al.* 2003). The degradation of DNA post-mortem is influenced by the physical, chemical and biological properties of the microenvironment (Eglinton *et al.* 1991), with young age, low temperatures (Smith *et al.* 2003), low UV exposure, low water availability and neutral pH being the most favourable conditions for DNA preservation (Fig. 16.1; Box 16.2). For aDNA sourced from museum collections, the context of specimen preparation (e.g. collection location, length of post-mortem interval or decomposition), and storage (e.g. dry-preserved, fixation with formalin, ethanol, or other chemical preservatives) can also impact DNA preservation (Hahn *et al.* 2021). For instance, residual formaldehyde can oxidise to formic acid over time, leaving specimens in a low pH environment that degrades DNA (Koshiba *et al.* 1993). Furthermore, to extract DNA from fixed tissues, harsh digestion conditions are required to break intra- and intermolecular cross links introduced by fixation, which may further damage DNA (Hahn *et al.* 2021).

Thus, there is a strong bias in aDNA studies towards samples from natural history collections where DNA is typically much better preserved, or from high-latitude and high-elevation sites, including permafrost, caves and cold deserts (where the oldest record of aDNA recovery dates back ca. 1 million years; van der Valk *et al.* 2021). aDNA from tropical and hot environments is much more difficult to recover, and the temporal depth of DNA survival is shallower, in the range of hundreds to thousands of years at best (Gutiérrez-García *et al.* 2014; Schroeder *et al.* 2015; Grealy *et al.* 2017).

The proportion of endogenous, target aDNA recovered from a sample is typically orders of magnitude lower than the background DNA, which is largely derived from microbial contaminants in the depositional environment, or from decomposition (Gilbert *et al.* 2005). Furthermore, contamination with DNA derived from humans and other samples during handling, storage and analysis (Pruvost *et al.* 2007, 2008) pose a significant risk to the authenticity of recovered DNA sequences, requiring rigorous protocols to minimise contamination (Cooper and Poinar 2000; Bollongino *et al.*

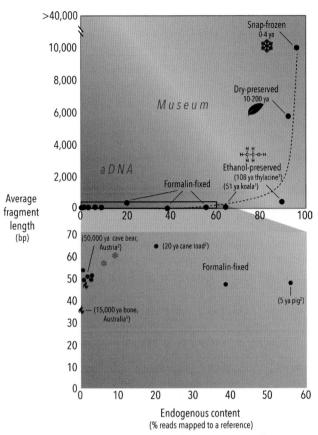

Fig. 16.1. The quality (fragmentation and target content) of ancient DNA compared with fresh tissue and museum specimens. aDNA is typically fragmented to below 100 bp in length while fresh DNA can be upwards of 40 kb. The majority of DNA recovered from ancient samples is non-endogenous contamination, with ca. 1% being the target of interest. Cold-preserved aDNA is typically less fragmented than aDNA from hot or tropical environments and therefore persists longer in the environment. For museum specimens, dry-preserved material (e.g. herbarium specimens) typically have less degraded DNA than ethanol-preserved or formalin-fixed tissues; DNA recovered from formalin-fixed tissue is typically the most degraded, in some cases comparably to aDNA. [1]Feigin *et al.* (2018). [2]Gansauge *et al.* (2017). [3]Hahn *et al.* (2021). [4]Grealy *et al.* (2016).

2008). For this reason, most aDNA studies target the high copy number **organellar** genomes (i.e. mitochondria and chloroplasts) as opposed to the nuclear genome (which only has two copies per cell in diploids) (see Discussion Topic 2). Organic contaminants, such as humic acids, phenols, and tannins, can also be co-purified with DNA, which (alongside the other molecular lesions previously mentioned) can inhibit the enzymatic reactions required in downstream processes (such as **PCR**, library generation, and sequencing) (Kemp *et al.* 2006). Finally, the amount of material available to be sampled for DNA is often limited, also resulting in poor yields (e.g. tiny, pinned insects, rare, difficult-to-obtain or precious specimens such as types or extinct species, or

where sampling may undermine the morphology or long-term integrity of specimen).

STRATEGIES FOR WORKING WITH ANCIENT DNA

Mitigating the challenges, limitations, and biases of aDNA requires optimised workflows that are more stringent than standard molecular biology workflows, and include specialised infrastructure, additional methodological considerations, and strict controls (detailed in Box 16.2). In addition, aDNA samples are rare and are a limited resource; care must be taken to ensure they are handled ethically and responsibly in the interest of maintaining important morphological features of specimens, retaining portions of samples for authentication or other analyses, and for accession within museums and herbaria for posterity. In response to this problem, minimally destructive techniques are being developed and have recently generated promising results (Scarsbrook *et al.* 2022). While methods will continue to improve with new developments in technology, these considerations remain the same.

Since the early studies in the 1980s, **cloning** or **PCR** amplification (Mullis and Faloona 1987) of short fragments (< 200 bp), followed by Sanger **sequencing** (Sanger *et al.* 1977) was the primary approach to targeted analysis of aDNA (Higuchi *et al.* 1984). However, using these methods only one DNA fragment can be sequenced at a time, making the process laborious, inefficient, and costly. Since the mid-2000s, high-throughput sequencing (**HTS**) – also known as next-generation sequencing (**NGS**) – has primarily been used instead because billions of fragments as short as 30 bp can be sequenced in parallel, making it ideal for sequencing mixed-source samples, such as aDNA (Margulies *et al.* 2005). The already degraded nature of aDNA can be leveraged for HTS, as there is no need to fragment aDNA prior to sequencing. There are three main approaches to generating aDNA sequence data from ancient samples and the choice of approach varies depending on the source material and the questions being asked, so it is important to establish clear aims and research questions early on in a project:

1. **Metabarcoding.** PCR is used to simultaneously amplify one or more specific 'barcode' loci from a wide range of organisms within a mixed sample (Taberlet *et al.* 2012). Barcodes are sequenced via HTS and compared with a genetic reference database to identify the taxonomic composition of the sample. The benefit of metabarcoding is that it is sensitive and relatively low cost. However, metabarcoding introduces unique biases (Murray *et al.* 2015), relies on the presence of a comprehensive

Box 16.2: aDNA method considerations

Ancient DNA workflows are optimised to accomodate the features of aDNA that makes it challenging. While methods can improve with new technology, these considerations will likely remain the same.

Challenges

1 Sampling

Collection of aDNA from the environment relies on interdisciplinary expertise

2 Low endogenous content

There are few target copies against a background of contamination

3 Inhibited

Compounds co-purified with aDNA such as humic acids can inhibit reactions

4 Damaged

UV radiation, temperature time, and exposure to water damage DNA; damage can be misinterpreted as true genetic variation

5 Fragmented

Damage includes fragmentation resulting in short strands, which are less informative than longer ones

Mitigation strategies

Experimental design

In additional to molecular biases, there are additional unique biases that should be considered including: replication vs pseudo-replication, sampling bias, taphonomic bias, time-averaging, agent of accumulation, and processing, transportation, or cooking by humans.[1,2]

Permissions and permits

Ensure appropriate permits and permissions are obtained from local, state, and/or federal government.

Specialised infrastructure, behaviour, and reagents

Pre-PCR aDNA workflows should be performed in designated spaces within a purpose-built ultra-clean environment.[10] Working surfaces are regularly decontaminated with bleach and/or UV irradiation. Reagents and consumables are purchased ultrapure.[11,12]

Controls

In order to identify laboratory contamination or cross-contamination, include no-template negative controls during extraction, library preparation, and PCR; these should be carried through to sequencing.

Positive controls and standards can be used to quantif targetly template concentration and reaction efficiency.

Collaboration and consultation

Liase with archaeologists, palaeontologists, museum curators, community, and traditional custodians. Dating and other analysis maybe necessary.

Repatriate culturally significant specimens where appropriate.

Sampling

Cold climates are most conducive to the preservation of aDNA.[3,4]

Age can influence DNA degradation[5]; with younger samples in a similar depositional content yielding more aDNA.

Freshly collected samples[6] where PPE can be worn during collection[7] yield more aDNA.

Avoid wet-sieving samples in the field.

Avoid temperature fluctuations to the sample post-excavation.

UV or bleach the exterior surface where appropriate.

Remove the exterior surface and discard where possible.

Target areas where aDNA is most likely to be preserved(e.g., teeth).[8,9]

Minimise impact on morphology, diagnostic chaters or overall appearence.

Optimised library preparation

Pre-treatment of extracts with specific enzymes can be used to repair damage (e.g. UDG / USER, endonuclease VIII).[13]

Some library preparation methods are better suited to retrieve short DNA fragments and/or recover the damaged fragments that would be lost by other methods: aDNA library preparation methods aim to minimise tube transfer, and clean-up steps to avoid sample loss.[18-24]

A dual indexing strategy, where index combinations are never be reused is ideal.[25,26]

Target high-copy number loci

The recovery of high copy-number loci (e.g., mitochondrial DNA) is most successful.[27] Target short stretches of informative DNA (ca. 60-250 bp), such as 'mini' barcodes.

Optimised DNA extractions

Pre-digestion can increase the proportion of endogenous DNA in the extract.[13]

Tailor-made buffers have been optimised to recover short DNA fragments which would be lost by traditional methods. Samples may require individual optimisation.[14,15,16]

Use qPCR

Use qPCR to observe reaction kinetics, quantify template, and estimate efficiency of library preparation.[28,18]

A dilution series of template can help assess inhibition and amplification efficiency.[1]

Independent replication

Perform replicates at each stage of the workflow where possible, experiments can be repeated by an independent laboratory.[27]

Specialised bioinformatic tools[35-37]

Some default programs and algorithms are less appropriate for aDNA. Parameters often equire optimisation or custom settings. Quality filtering and consensus calling is more conservative than usual. Consistent results from multiple bioinformatic methods confirms results are robust against bias.

The proportion of C-to-T transitions at the ends of reads can be used to confirm aDNA authenticity.[38,39]

Target enrichment

The use of blocking primers in PCR can prevent amplification of contaminants.[40]

aDNA targets can be enriched relative to background contamination using hybridisation capture.[31-34]

Use high-fidelity polymerases that can cope with uracils and other molecular lesions.[29]

PCR reaction enhancers may be necessary such as betaine, BSA, and DMSO.[30]

Next-generation sequencing

Millions of short fragments can be sequenced in parallel via NGS.[35]

Sequencing typically needs to be at a very high read depth to obtain adequate coverage per target locus.

[1]Murray et al. (2015) [2]Grealy et al. (2015) [3]Bollongino et al. (2008) [4]Keighley et al. (2021) [5]Esiner et al. (2015) [6]Pinhasi et al. (2015) [7]Fortea et al. (2008) [8]Pruvost et al. (2007) [9]Campos et al. (2012) [10]Knapp et al. (2012) [11]Fulton and Shapiro (2019) [12]Cooper and Poinar (2000) [13]Boessenkool et al. (2017) [14]Dabney et al. (2013) [15]Yang et al. (1998) [16]Glocke and Meyer (2017) [17]Briggs et al. (2010) [18]Gansauge and Meyer (2013) [19]Gansauge and Meyer (2010) [20]Li et al. (2013) [21]Meyer and Kircher (2010) [22]Carøe et al. (2018) [23]Wales et al. (2015) [24]Bennett et al. (2014) [25]Kircher et al. (2012) [26]MacConaill et al. (2018) [27]Shapiro and Hofreiter (2012) [28]Pruvost and Geigl (2004) [29]d'Abbadie et al. (2007) [30]Kreader (1996) [31]Carpenter et al. (2013) [32]Li et al. (2013) [33]Maricic et al. (2010) [34]Gansauge and Meyer (2014) [35]Margulies et al. (2005) [36]Hahn et al. (2013) [37]Schubert (2012) [38]Jonsson et al. (2013) [39]Ginolhac et al. (2011) [40]Boessenkool et al. (2012)

reference database (which is often lacking), and may have limited taxonomic resolution.

2. **Shotgun sequencing.** DNA fragments in a sample are indiscriminately sequenced allowing genomic data to be obtained from a single sample (Green *et al.* 2010), or the taxonomic composition of an environmental sample identified (metagenomics, e.g. Moore *et al.* 2020). This method allows authentication of true ancient templates based on damage patterns (Ginolhac *et al.* 2011), but is taxonomically limited as it requires representative reference genomes. For whole genome sequencing applications, only ca. 1–3% of data – the endogenous fraction – is typically of interest (Carpenter *et al.* 2013). Shotgun sequencing can therefore be prohibitively expensive because of the depth required to achieve sufficient coverage of endogenous targets. Library preparation for shotgun sequencing can also be expensive.

3. **Target capture enrichment.** Sequences of interest can be enriched, relative to background, by hybridising shotgun libraries to pre-designed DNA or RNA probes from a closely related modern species, which are then pulled out of solution, leaving non-target DNA behind (Maricic *et al.* 2010; Box 16.2). This method allows researchers to target taxonomic groups or loci (e.g. barcoding genes (Giebner *et al.* 2020), **organelle** genomes (Paijmans *et al.* 2017), nuclear genes (Castellano *et al.* 2014), nuclear **SNPs** (Lazaridis *et al.* 2014)) to address specific questions, while reducing the sequencing effort required to achieve high coverage of target aDNA (Box 16.2). This is particularly necessary for phylogenomics, where multiple orthologous loci need to be recovered from multiple taxa for comparison.

PRACTICAL APPLICATIONS OF ANCIENT DNA RESEARCH

aDNA opens a window into the past, and this ability can be used in practical environmental management applications in two main ways. First, examining how ecosystems and species have responded to environmental change in the past can help us predict how they will respond and cope during the current period of change. Second, understanding how the natural world was in the past, before anthropogenic impacts, can help us set conservation goals, and guide ecological restoration initiatives (Rick and Lockwood 2012).

Contextualising and predicting ecological change: the 'when' and 'why' and 'how' of biodiversity turnover

For millennia, human activity has placed significant pressure on the environment, culminating in an observable collapse of global ecosystems within the last 150 years that coincides with industrialisation. In this '**Anthropocene**', the rate of extinction is considered to be on par with other mass extinction events of the distant past (Barnosky *et al.* 2011) and is caused by anthropogenic stressors such as unsustainable subsistence practices (e.g. 'over-kill'), habitat fragmentation (e.g. deforestation), landscape modification (e.g. burning, farming), pollution, the introduction of pests, diseases, and invasive species and anthropogenic climate change (Box 16.1) (Pievani 2014). Studying how species and ecosystems have responded to periods of change in the past – or identifying why biodiversity has changed – using aDNA can help us predict how species may respond to current and future environmental pressures, and which species are – or will be – most vulnerable to extinction.

Extinction. aDNA can be used to better estimate when species became extinct. For instance, DNA extracted from a museum eggshell specimen purported to be from a paradise parrot some 40 years after their extinction identified the egg as belonging to a common extant parrot, putting to rest the controversy over late survival of the species (Grealy *et al.* 2021). Pinpointing when species became extinct is important if we want to determine why they became extinct, i.e. testing the relative impact of extinction drivers. This includes intrinsic drivers (genetic and population demographics) and extrinsic drivers (predominantly climatic, anthropogenic, or geological events) of extinction. aDNA enables researchers to detect changes in taxonomic diversity, genetic diversity or population size through time more accurately than can be achieved using modern data alone. The timing of these population changes can then be compared with that of specific ecological or anthropogenic events to implicate specific drivers of extinction. For instance, thanks to aDNA, we know that moa, an extinct order of giant (17–242 kg) flightless birds native to New Zealand, were not in decline prior to Polynesian colonisation. This suggests that their extinction soon after human arrival to New Zealand can be attributed to overexploitation by the first settlers (Allentoft *et al.* 2014). A similar approach has also been used to implicate climate change in the extinction of the Eurasian musk ox (Campos *et al.* 2010) and woolly rhinoceros (Lorenzen *et al.* 2011), and a combination of climatic and anthropogenic factors in the extinction of the steppe bison (Lorenzen *et al.* 2011), cave bears (Stiller *et al.* 2010), marsupial carnivore thylacines (White *et al.* 2018a, b), and the Australian mainland population of Tasmanian devils (Brüniche-Olsen *et al.* 2014, 2018).

aDNA has also been used to test for intrinsic threats that may have increased local population- and/or species-level

Box 16.3: Case study: Reconstructing the extinction of Australian rodents

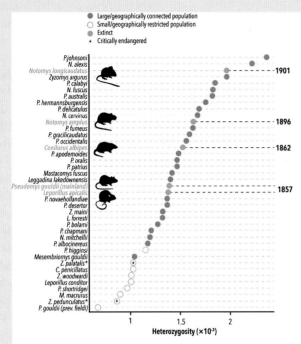

'Our results highlight the capacity of collections-based research to inform conservation and management of persisting species.'

Roycroft *et al.* (2021)

At least 36 Australian mammals have become extinct since European colonisation of Australia in 1788.[1] Native rodents have been disproportionately affected by this recent extinction, but due to limited historical specimens and an incomplete fossil record, it is unclear whether the onset of the decline in native rodents began prior to European colonisation. Historical accounts from early naturalists suggested that two species, the white-footed rabbit rat (*Conilurus albipes*) and the lesser stick-nest rat (*Leporillus apicalis*), may have had large populations during the 19th century.[2,3]

Using aDNA extracted from museum specimens collected shortly before their extinction, Roycroft *et al.* (2021) estimated genetic diversity in five species of now-extinct Australian rodents (*Conilurus albipes, Leporillus apicalis, Notomys amplus, Notomys longicaudatus* and *Pseudomys gouldii*), as well as extant species from the same clade. Their results showed that now-extinct species had high genetic diversity shortly before their extinction, indicating that their decline was extremely rapid. This demonstrates that Australian rodents were likely not in decline prior to European colonisation, and that genetic diversity does not necessarily protect species from catastrophic extinction events.

By comparing aDNA from extinct Australian rodents to living species, the study was also able to taxonomically 'resurrect' Gould's mouse (*Pseudomys gouldii*), which was found to be synonymous with the Shark Bay mouse, or Djoongari (*Pseudomys fieldi*). This result removes a species from the list of recent Australian extinctions, but further highlights the rapid pace of population collapse in Australian rodents since European colonisation: in less than 100 years, the distribution of this species went from spanning most of mainland Australia, to now only survivng on a single offshore island.

Figure adapted from Roycroft et al. (2021). Whole exome heterozygosity for extinct and extant Australian rodents. Extinct species had high genetic diversity prior to their extinction after European colonisation, showing that extinction risk is not necessarily predicted by levels of genetic diversity. Rather, body size and biome were better predictors of extinction risk in Australian rodents (Roycroft et al. 2021).

[1] Woinarski *et al.* (2015)   [2] Krefft (1866)   [3] Mackaness (1978)

susceptibility to extinction. For example, ancient mitochondrial DNA analyses from two extinct species of giant Malagasy lemur showed that both species had low genetic diversity and likely small population sizes prior to their extinction. The authors suggest that these characteristics made the species more vulnerable to extinction than the more genetically diverse lemurs that ultimately survived initial human colonisation of Madagascar (Kistler *et al.* 2015). Similarly, the genome of a 4300-year-old mammoth from Wrangel Island – a small, late-surviving population – showed an excess of putatively harmful mutations, which likely accumulated due to the small population size and may have reduced population sustainability (Pečnerová *et al.* 2017; Rogers and Slatkin 2017). **Genomic erosion** has also been observed in Grauer's gorillas using genomes from museum specimens, confirming a genetic contribution to this species' decline (van der Valk *et al.* 2019). Conversely, aDNA from museum specimens of Australian rodents collected shortly before their extinction in the 19th and early 20th centuries show that these species did not have low

genetic diversity prior to European colonisation, demonstrating how rapidly populations can collapse to extinction even where no intrinsic threat may be present (Roycroft *et al.* 2021; Box 16.3). aDNA can also be used to model population size over time. For example, Hung *et al.* (2014) found that population size of passenger pigeons fluctuated greatly over the previous one million years prior to their extinction in the 1800s, showing that even species with large populations can be vulnerable to extinction if their population size is unstable. These types of studies help to build predictions about how species will respond to stressors today and can assist in planning to prioritise finite conservation efforts and hopefully mitigate the risk of extinction in vulnerable species (see section below).

Human exploitation and impacts. aDNA can be used to increase our understanding of how and to what extent past peoples exploited certain environments to assist in establishing more sustainable industries and harvesting practices (see Oosting *et al.* 2019 and Hofman *et al.* 2015 for review). For instance, aDNA can be used to infer past subsistence practices (such as hunting, gathering, or farming, etc.; Box 16.1). Wide-spread geographic sampling of zooarchaeological aDNA (Seersholm *et al.* 2018) and artifacts (e.g. Māori feather cloaks, Hartnup *et al.* 2011) can also reveal the scale of human exploitation: Losey and Yang (2007) used aDNA from a bone attached to a spear head to prove native Americans actively hunted whales rather than only scavenging beached whales, as suggested by some studies. Likewise, Barrett *et al.* (2020) sex-typed ancient walrus remains to uncover a pattern of increased hunting pressure through time in the medieval European walrus ivory trade. Zooarchaeological aDNA can also be used to track human migration and pinpoint when invasive species were introduced to naïve environments (Hardy *et al.* 1994; Matisoo-Smith 2018). For example, the origin of wild chickens (*Gallus gallus*) on the Hawaiian island of Kauai was unclear until an analysis of ancient and modern chicken DNA showed recent introgression and near replacement of the red jungle fowl, a legacy species from Polynesian first colonisers, by feral domestic chickens (Thomson *et al.* 2014; Gering *et al.* 2015). This history complicates conservation decisions because, while domestic chickens are the world's most abundant bird and a common pathogen vector, red jungle fowl are a threatened species, and the Kauai population may contain unique genetic diversity.

Archaeological middens, fire pits, and other sites of past human occupation, provide direct evidence of the plants and animals humans were consuming (whether for food, shelter, clothing, or cultural purposes). Butchering, cooking, and modification often means that bones and artifacts cannot be identified by traditional means, and in these cases, aDNA becomes a particularly useful supplementary tool for taxonomic identification. For instance, Grealy *et al.* (2016) used aDNA extracted in bulk from morphologically ambiguous bone fragments retrieved from an archaeological midden to genetically identify marine prey targets of early Malagasy people and compare them to the diversity observed in the area today. They identified species that are currently extirpated from the area, as well as evidence of resource depletion over time: the presence of benthic and pelagic fish species suggested that past people were engaged in bottom-trawling and open-ocean net-fishing, which are large-scale technologies in comparison to more-sustainable, small-scale line-fishing. Other taxa, including plants, leave little trace or are under-represented in the macro-fossil record, and in many instances their presence at a site is known only from an examination of aDNA. For instance, Seersholm *et al.* (2016) used aDNA derived from archaeological sediments to

identify novel prey targets of palaeo-Inuit people that had not previously been described in the archaeological record. Other direct evidence of human exploitation of the environment can be gleaned through aDNA analysis of ancient faecal matter and gut contents, which is used to reconstruct human palaeodiet (Poinar *et al.* 2001). From palaeontological sites, human impact can be inferred from the coincidence in time of human presence with faunal and floral turnover. aDNA from fossil assemblages before and after initial human settlement or European colonisation can be compared to identify shifts in species presence/absence and abundance. For example, Boessenkool *et al.* (2009) used aDNA from modern and subfossil penguin bones in New Zealand to reveal extinction of a previously unknown species (*Megadyptes waitaha*) following Polynesian arrival. They also found that *M. waitaha* was replaced after a range expansion of the extant, yellow-eyed penguin (*M. antipodes*), which itself has subsequently become endangered following European arrival.

Furthermore, understanding the ecological shifts induced by historic introductions of invasive species and accurately assessing the success of restoration attempts may be difficult or impossible without a temporal perspective. Using chloroplast meta-barcoding of a lake sediment core (sedaDNA) at multiple chronological layers, Ficetola *et al.* (2018) described an abrupt and previously undocumented, change in the plant biota – from a previous 600-year stable state – after the introduction of rabbits (*Oryctolagus cuniculus*) to a subantarctic island. The authors also showed that, despite the decline of the rabbit population since the deliberate release of the myxomatosis virus in the 1950s, plant communities had not recovered to the pre-invasion stable state. This shows how the impact of introduced species can be extremely rapid, while recovery may be slow, heterogeneous across ecosystem features and, ultimately, incomplete.

Anthropogenic climate change is expected to drastically change global environments in the coming years and decades, and predicting how species are likely to respond is a common and vital use of aDNA. For instance, Seersholm *et al.* (2018) extracted aDNA from bulk bone and sediment collected from ice-aged deposits in southern Texas (USA) that span a cool period known as the Younger Dryas. They discovered a change in species assemblage that coincided with the Younger Dryas. From this information, we may be able to predict which plants and animals can tolerate a warmer environment, or indeed, which traits are associated with resilience. Similarly, Wood *et al.* (2018) used meta-barcoding of fossilised Chilean rodent middens spanning a 50 000-year period, which included a significant climate shift, to characterise the ancient community of plant pathogens. They found that rust fungus (*Pucciniaceae spp.*) significantly increased in abundance and diversity during a period of increased precipitation, highlighting how altered climates can favour certain pathogens. Finally, Crump *et al.* (2021) used aDNA metabarcoding from arctic lake sediment cores to examine floral community composition during the last interglacial, a time when temperatures were warmer than present day. Their results give an indication of how much Arctic greening we might expect in the future as the global climate continues to warm.

Speciation. Like extinction, understanding the forces governing the generation and maintenance of biodiversity will also help conserve biodiversity. aDNA can provide the 'missing links' to reveal relationships between extant and extinct species. Phylogenetic relationships between species derived solely from modern DNA can lead to erroneous conclusions about evolution, including the drivers of speciation and adaptation (Box 16.1). It also has implications for taxonomy, which in turn can impact conservation decisions as accurate designation of species limits/boundaries can affect biodiversity assessments and the definition of conservation units (see section below). Instead, the inclusion of data from aDNA, particularly extinct taxa, can uncover broader patterns of evolution, shift paradigms in evolutionary theory, and challenge long-held assumptions. One of the best examples comes from the inclusion of DNA from the extinct moa and elephant birds into the **palaeognath** phylogeny, which has re-written our view of avian evolution: the accuracy of molecular dating was improved by the addition of aDNA and showed that most major clades of flightless ratites diverged after the breakup of Gondwana, suggesting that continental **vicariance** did not play a role in the diversification of these flightless birds, as was previously thought (Phillips *et al.* 2010; Mitchell *et al.* 2014; Yonezawa *et al.* 2017; Grealy *et al.* 2017). This information couches our understanding of extant ratites and their adaptations (e.g. gigantism, flightlessness) in a new light.

GUIDING ECOLOGICAL RESTORATION AND CONSERVATION: PUTTING ANCIENT DNA TO WORK

Contextualising and predicting species' response to change can help us better evaluate actions that could reduce the risk of extinction in the future. Conservation decisions based solely on contemporary data have been shown to be biased (Leonard 2008), which can adversely affect the success of species and ecosystem recovery plans. aDNA helps inform

ecological restoration strategies primarily by providing **'baselines'** (i.e. the ecological state prior to disturbance; see Discussion Topic 1), which can act as a goal towards which conservation initiatives work. The nature of these baselines is varied – for example, they may describe genetic diversity, taxonomic groupings, species composition, migration and gene-flow, or ecosystem function – as are their applications. In this section we describe a range of examples of how aDNA has been used to establish baselines for ecological restoration, and how these have been practically applied, predominantly in the assisted movement of animals for conservation (i.e. reintroduction and translocation; Box 16.4). Reintroduction and translocations are now common practice around the world, but deciding whether it would benefit a species or environment at all, what the best source populations would be, where the recipient site should be, and how many individuals are needed for such programs can be difficult without ancient and historical perspectives that aDNA can provide.

Identifying former connectivity between currently isolated populations

Populations of threatened species are becoming increasingly fragmented and isolated, which can increase their vulnerability to extinction. However, using modern genetic data alone, we may be unable to distinguish between recent genetic drift and long-term differentiation (see Leonard 2008 for a comprehensive review), two scenarios that would be managed very differently. In the former case, gene flow between populations should be re-established to boost genetic diversity and effective population size, while in the latter case, admixture between isolated populations that have evolved local adaptations should be avoided to prevent outbreeding depression. aDNA can be an effective means of distinguishing between these two cases. For example, although modern DNA was unable to determine whether the four remaining wild populations of the Western Australian woylies (*Bettongia penicillata ogilbyi*) had been connected prior to the species population collapse, aDNA data revealed that these isolated groups were once part of a large panmictic population (Pacioni *et al.* 2015; Haouchar *et al.* 2016). These results provided a precedent for re-establishing gene flow between the extant populations, for example by creating habitat corridors. In contrast, an aDNA investigation into the historical population structure of the vulnerable short-tailed albatross (*Phoebastria albatrus*) found that the contemporary population structure of this species was not due to drastic population declines in the 20th century, but had been in place for at least 1000 years (Eda *et al.* 2012).

Box 16.4: Case study: Beaver reintroduction planning

The Eurasian beaver (*Castor fiber*) was near extinction at the beginning of the twentieth century due to human hunting pressure. At this time there were thought to be only around 1200 animals surviving in eight isolated populations[1] and numerous conservation initiatives and policies were enacted to save the species.[2] Across Scotland, and most of Britain, paleontological and archaeological evidence suggests that beavers were once widespread but became locally extinct in the early 16th century.[3] To restore lost ecosystem functions, increase biodiversity and contribute to beaver conservation efforts, a trial reintroduction of Eurasian beavers to Scotland was begun in 2009 and reviewed in 2014.[4] This review drew on numerous lines of evidence, including ancient DNA, to evaluate the trial and make recommendations on the future of beavers in Scotland.[4] For example, a genetic study of ancient beaver specimens across Europe confirmed that the eight contemporary subpopulations were isolated recently as a result of human hunting pressure (Horn *et al.* 2014). This is in contrast to previous studies that were limited to modern DNA, some of which went as far as calling for the subpopulations to be taxonomically designated as subspecies.[5,6] The review of Scottish beaver reintroductions concluded from the results of Horn *et al.* (2014) that there is no reason to preserve the subpopulation boundaries when sourcing for future reintroductions and that mixing the subpopulations may have positive genetic benefits.[4] In 2015 the Scottish government announced that beavers would remain in Scotland and in 2017, reinforcement of the trial population was undertaken using animals sourced from the Norwegian and Bavarian subpopulations.[7]

'Our data suggest that [the subspecies] classification is an artefact of recent population decline, rather than the consequence of long-term genetic isolation.'

Horn *et al.* (2014)

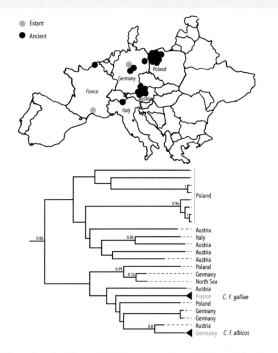

Figure adapted from Horn *et al.* (2014). Bayesian posterior probabilities over 0.5 are shown above nodes. There is little to no phylogeographic structure in the former range of the Eurasian beaver (*Castor fiber*) in western Europe, suggesting that 'the relict populations from Germany and France are descendents of the same western Eurpopean beaver population and therefore do not warrant separate subspecies assignment' (Horn *et al.* 2014).

[1]Nolet and Rosell (1998) [2]Halley and Rosell (2002) [3]Kitchener and Conroy (1997) [4]Gaywood (2018) [5]Durka *et al.* (2005) [6]Ducroz *et al.* (2005) [7]Dowse *et al.* (2020)

Identifying historical ranges for extant species

Knowledge of the past distribution of species can be uncovered using aDNA to identify refuges (such as islands), or areas for reintroduction of species to their former ranges, the argument being that this is a crucial component of ecosystem restoration. For example, aDNA has been used to identify historical ranges for extant species to identify habitats that could likely sustain and benefit from a reintroduced population of particular species. In the case of the Laysan duck, aDNA showed they were extirpated from the Hawaiian islands (Cooper *et al.* 1996), and this information has been incorporated into their recovery plan, where ducks are being considered for translocation to Hawai'i (U.S. Fish and Wildlife Service 2009). aDNA also identified the pre-human distribution of the kiwi (*Apteryx australis;* Shepherd and Lambert 2008; Shepherd *et al.* 2012), allowing translocations of this endangered species into its former range to take place as part of its conservation management.

Identifying which extant populations are the most appropriate candidates from which to draw stock for reintroductions, translocations, or captive breeding

Suitability of populations as genetic stock usually relies on a combination of factors, including a genetic resemblance to past populations, and enough genetic diversity to maintain heterozygosity, minimise kinship and mitigate inbreeding depression, but not so much as to cause outbreeding depression through the creation of unfit hybrids (Nakahama 2021). aDNA identification of an unknown rock wallaby bone from Depuch Island, Western Australia, showed that the most appropriate species for reintroduction to the Island was *Petrogale lateralis* rather than *P. rothschildi* (Haouchar *et al.* 2013). Robinson and Matthee (1999) also argue that the close affiliation between *Struthio camelus* and another extinct subspecies of ostrich (*Struthio camelus syriacus*) supports the conservation decision to reintroduce *S. camelus* to Saudi Arabia.

Uncovering past taxonomic affiliations

If a functionally important species is now extinct, conservation practitioners may seek the most closely related species to translocate into a habitat to restore lost ecosystem functions. aDNA can help establish which extant species may be most appropriate in these instances by assisting in species delimitation or in the identification of evolutionary significant units (or conservation units). For example, Grealy *et al.* (2020) extracted aDNA from ca. 1000-year-old fossil dentaries of the spotted-tailed quoll (*Dasyurus maculatus*) to uncover which extant sub-species (mainland or Tasmanian) are most closely related to the extirpated Kangaroo Island population. They found that the Kangaroo Island population was most closely related to the Tasmanian sub-species but belongs to a distinct **evolutionary significant unit (ESU)**, and suggest that such information be considered when discussing the potential for reintroductions of spotted-tailed quolls to Kangaroo Island. aDNA can also be used to synonymise taxa, which has implications for their conservation. In the case of Preble's Meadow jumping mouse (*Zapus hudsonius preblei),* aDNA was used to argue against its listing as a distinct subspecies (Ramey *et al.* 2005; Malaney and Cook 2013), resulting in a petition to delist the taxon from the federal register of threatened and endangered species (however, see Carolan 2008). Conversely, aDNA helped show that the Norfolk Island Robin (*Petroica multicolor multicolor*) constitutes a distinct species, and the authors advocate for it to be recognised as endangered (Kearns *et al.* 2016).

Estimating past population size

Welch *et al.* (2012) used museum specimens alongside modern specimens to examine temporal changes in population size in the Hawaiian petrel (*Pterodroma sandwichensis*): they found that over the last 3000 years population size was stable but has been observed to be declining in recent years. Despite this, genetic diversity has been maintained. Studies like this allow us to answer questions like: how many individuals are required to maintain genetic diversity, or maintain a stable population? Answers to these questions are important for setting population size targets and deciding what conservation strategies funding should be directed towards (Leonard 2008), as each species case differs.

Identifying suitable habitats

aDNA from sediments, gut contents, and coprolites (Box 16.1) can be used to reconstruct the palaeoenvironment and identify the crucial factors in the habitat that are needed for species survival. For instance, the decline in the plant *Dactylanthus taylorii* in recent years may be linked to the decline of New Zealand's flightless parrot, the kākāpō (*Strigops habroptilus*). Wood *et al.* (2012c) used aDNA and pollen from coprolites to show that kākāpō may have been an historic pollinator of *Dactylanthus*. Restoration of *Dactylanthus* may rely on the reintroduction of kākāpō or other native pollinators to its current range. Alternatively, translocations of organisms may fare better if they are introduced to environments that most closely resemble their past habitat, whether that overlaps with the historic range or not: in the case of *Dactylanthus*, it may benefit from introduction to offshore islands that are inhabited by putative pollinators.

Determining ecological roles

The most appropriate species for restoring ecological function may not always be the extinct species' closest living relative, and reconstructing the diet of extinct animals can help clarify this. Reconstructing the diet of ancient animals can provide clues to lost ecosystem functions of extinct species or populations, and increase our understanding of ecosystem change over time. aDNA is an important component of many multi-proxy investigations that aim to uncover the composition of consumed material remains found in sub-fossil coprolites (Hofreiter *et al.* 2000, 2003; Bon *et al.* 2012; Witt *et al.* 2021), intestinal contents (van Geel *et al.* 2011, 2014; Gravendeel *et al.* 2014), and archaeological refuse middens (Evans *et al.* 2016). The main benefits of the aDNA approach, in comparison to macrofossil and pollen identification or stable isotope analyses, is that it can provide direct evidence of consumed food items, without the need for visually identifiable remains to be present. For example, the extinct moa played a significant role in shaping the structure and composition of New Zealand vegetation (Wood *et al.* 2020), and some have suggested that their ecological function could be replaced by extant ratites such as emu or ostriches (Bond *et al.* 2004) or introduced deer (Caughley 1983). However, aDNA meta-barcoding of moa coprolites (preserved ancient faeces) has contributed to detailed assessments of moa diet and niche partitioning (Wood *et al.* 2012a, b, 2013; Rawlence *et al.* 2016; Boast *et al.* 2018), showing that neither introduced ungulates nor extant large flightless birds have dietary overlap with the moa and thus should not be considered as ecological replacements.

MANAGING OTHER BIOTIC THREATS
Invasive species

The spread of non-native species is a major driver of biological change globally. Their impacts have significant economic costs and contribute to the loss and decline of endemic biota (Diagne *et al.* 2021). Thus, how to mitigate, manage and prevent invasive species introduction and spread is the subject of much ongoing research and interest. aDNA has revealed complex processes and implications surrounding past introductions, and can inform management and prevention plans. For example, determining whether a species is invasive or endemic may not be possible without an ancient or historical perspective. Arctic ground squirrels (*Urocitellus parryii*) on islands within the Alaskan Maritime National Wildlife Refuge negatively impact native bird species through egg predation and were presumed to have been introduced by colonisers, leading to calls for their eradication. However, West *et al.* (2017) used aDNA and radiocarbon dating to show that native people on one island interacted with ground squirrels for at least 2000 years before Russian or American occupation. The authors suggest that the negative impact of the squirrels on native birds may be part of wider and more complex ecological change in the region rather than due to the naiveté of the birds to novel predators. Similarly, Campbell *et al.* (2018) used historical records and molecular data generated from museum specimens to demonstrate that sugar gliders (*Petaurus breviceps*) are not endemic to Tasmania, but rather, a recent post-European introduction. This result has implications for sugar glider management in Tasmania, where they are impacting an endangered parrot species. aDNA of pathogens from museum specimens has also implicated a disease in the extinction of an Australian endemic rat (Christmas Island rat, *Rattus macleari*) (Wyatt *et al.* 2008), after the introduction of black rats (*Rattus rattus*). This example speaks to how aDNA can be used to track the impacts of both invasive species and disease (see below) on biodiversity.

Pests, pathogens and disease

Global leadership is, more than ever, asking itself how infectious disease outbreaks – which impact global health, food security and ecological sustainability – can be better managed or avoided (see Chapter 25 for details on how contemporary genomics are used for disease surveillance). Time-stamped genomes from ancient pathogens can provide important calibration points for phylogenetic reconstructions used for testing hypotheses on the timing of disease emergence and outbreaks, providing insights into epidemiology (Søe *et al.* 2018). How environmental, cultural and evolutionary factors have influenced pathogen emergence, persistence, and infectivity in the past is crucial information that can help us form better predictions about future disease outbreaks. Extraction and sequencing of ancient pathogen genomes can assist in this effort in a variety of ways. For example, the barley mosaic virus (*Hordeivirus* sp.) is an economically important virus, which causes disease in wheat and barley crops. Based on the earliest record of symptoms and phylogenies built from contemporary genomes, it was hypothesised to have emerged and spread extremely recently (~100 years ago), which influenced policy decisions regarding the movement of plant materials. However, the sequencing of the barley mosaic virus genome extracted from ~750-year-old Egyptian barley grain falsifies this hypothesis and alters our understanding of the evolutionary history of this virus (Smith *et al.* 2014). Museum specimens are a viable source of endogenous retroviral genomic data and may even preserve information about historical DNA and RNA virus diversity (Speer *et al.* 2022).

Ancient and historic pathogen genomics can also help us better understand the evolution of important disease traits. Since the discovery of antibiotic medicine in 1928, antibiotic resistance in bacteria has become an increasing problem that threatens global health and food security. Ancient pathogen genomes with antibiotic resistance genes from 30 000-year-old permafrost sediment (D'Costa *et al.* 2011), medieval human dental calculus (Warinner *et al.* 2014), and coprolites (Appelt *et al.* 2014) show conclusively that antibiotic resistance predates the modern selective pressure of clinical antibiotic use. The reality of wide-spread and ancient antibiotic resistance in a variety of microbial communities has implications for antibiotic use guidelines.

Biosecurity and wildlife forensics

aDNA techniques are being used to identify confiscated biological material, such as illegally trafficked bird's eggs. Eggs are difficult to distinguish morphologically and rely on DNA barcoding to identify them to species; however, often eggs are autoclaved by customs because they present a biosecurity risk, which can damage DNA, requiring aDNA methods to recover and sequence the DNA (Coghlan, White *et al.* 2012). aDNA methods can also help discover the provenance of elephant tusks seized from the illegal ivory trade (Wasser *et al.* 2007) or even shipwrecks (de Flamingh *et al.* 2021), as well as help identify endangered species present in traditional medicines (Coghlan, Haile *et al.* 2012).

FUTURE DEVELOPMENTS

Technical advances in aDNA analysis over the last 20 years (including improved DNA extraction, library preparation, and hybridisation-capture), combined with advances in bioinformatic analysis of degraded, multi-source DNA sequence data, and the rapidly decreasing costs of high-throughput sequencing, have allowed researchers to explore the temporal, geographic and biological-source limits of aDNA recovery. Harnessing these new methodological advances has provided powerful insights into evolutionary and ecological change across the globe over the last million years, and the methods developed for aDNA contribute to scientific advancement in other fields, such as modern eDNA. However, there remain several gaps in knowledge, the most pressing of which are expanded upon below.

First, there is a bias in the distribution of studies, which mostly focus on terrestrial, northern-hemisphere species and sites because these are typically cold locations, and the DNA is well-preserved. Though this is unsurprising, most biodiversity is concentrated in the latitudes closer to the equator, which experience hot, wet climates – conditions that are unfavourable for long-term DNA survival. There is also more attention placed on 'charismatic' megafauna over small-bodied animals (especially reptiles, amphibians, fish and invertebrates), and plants, even though these organisms are more so the 'sentinels' of ecosystem change (e.g. Woods et al. 2017; der Sarkissian et al. 2020). As methods improve, we are seeing an increase in the number of studies recovering aDNA from warm-climate ecosystems, however, there is more to be done in this area.

Second, particularly in Australia, there has been limited integration of aDNA data into species recovery plans, many of which have not been updated in the past decade despite the progress that has been made in the aDNA space during that time. We need collaborative initiatives connecting researchers, practitioners, and policy makers, to translate what we learn from aDNA into concrete outcomes for conservation. This requires concerted outreach and active engagement with conservation proposals on the behalf of palaeo-geneticists (see Dietl and Flessa 2011 and Dietl 2019), and vice versa.

Finally, as the generation of aDNA data becomes more accessible, a greater challenge is meeting the unprecedented computational demands, including the bioinformatic expertise to analyse vast quantities of genomic data. This is further hindered by the incompleteness of genomic reference databases, which continues to remain a bottle neck. Yet another way that the scientific community benefits from aDNA extracted from vouchered or type specimens housed in research collections is through the provision of highly curated reference genomes. There are many initiatives focused on collecting genetic references from different groups of organisms, including the Plant and Fungal Tree of Life (PAFTOL), Genomics for Australian Plants (GAP), Barcode Of Life (BOL), the Bird 10 000 Genomes (B10K) Project, Oz Mammals Genomics (OMG), and CSIRO's National Biodiversity DNA Library (NBDL), to name a few. To this end, aDNA is becoming an increasingly useful tool in routine collection management, being used to verify the identity and provenance of specimens to ensure that the integrity of historical records is maintained. Taxonomy (Boubli et al. 2021), historic distributions of species, extinction times (Grealy et al. 2021), and numbers of observations, can be impacted by erroneous data – some of which is deliberately falsified – but can be corrected using DNA data (Boessenkool et al. 2010; Rawlence et al. 2014; Verry et al. 2019).

In terms of future directions, we are beginning to see a movement beyond ancient genomics into ancient phenomics: what genes are being expressed (i.e. translated into protein) and how genes interact with the environment to produce an organism's **phenotype**. This encompasses the emerging fields of ancient and museum **epigenetics** (Gokhman et al. 2016, 2017; Hahn et al. 2020) and ancient **RNA** (Fordyce, Avila-Arcos et al. 2013; Fordyce, Kampmann et al. 2013; Guy 2014). Importantly, changes in gene regulation through epigenetic modifications may occur over short time scales and precede changes in DNA sequence variation. Thus, epigenetic signals in ancient and museum samples may document species' phenotypic responses to environmental change over decadal time scales. When integrated with modern epigenomics and transcriptomics, ancient epigenomics can potentially provide a very powerful view of adaptive response versus phenotypic plasticity.

In parallel, modern eDNA surveys of terrestrial, freshwater, marine and sedimentary biological diversity have rapidly expanded in scope and sensitivity. For biodiversity surveys there is a desire to see methods developed to quantify species abundance as well as richness. Such quantitative approaches may be possible with the advent of direct sequencing (mitigating bias introduced by PCR and library preparation) and single-cell sequencing technology. As anthropological impacts continue to affect species and ecosystems, it will be critical for a DNA researchers studying subfossil samples and museum/herbarium material to collaborate with eDNA researchers to collect and analyse comparable datasets to address applied environmental genomics problems. Areas of potential future benefit could include ancient sedimentary DNA analysis in temperate and lower-latitude regions to document pre-European biodiversity.

After more than 30 years, aDNA has become a well-established field of evolutionary and ecological research, contributing new, and often unexpected, insights into species and ecosystem responses to environmental change and anthropogenic impacts. Environmental managers and policy makers should take every opportunity to harness the unique temporal perspective that aDNA can provide to better understand historical baselines and make more accurate predictions of future ecological responses to change.

DISCUSSION TOPICS

1. It has been said that aDNA information can provide a measure of **baseline** diversity for an ecosystem. Discuss how we define what (or when) 'baseline' diversity was.
   a. Guiding questions: Is a baseline an 'absolute' or 'relative' concept? What assumptions are being made? Why is it important to define a historical baseline? What is a 'shifting baseline'?
2. One limitation of aDNA is that it is often difficult to recover nuclear DNA. Discuss how this could bias our 'perspective on modern species'.
   a. Guiding questions: Why is recovering organellar aDNA (mitochondrial and chloroplast) typically more successful? How does the rate of mitochondrial evolution differ from nuclear? What other caveats and biases of aDNA need to be considered when designing experiments that aim to provide an ancient or historical perspective?
3. Historical specimens of the same species or population collected over decades or centuries can provide snapshots of genetic diversity through time. Discuss what we might learn from such data, and the importance for continuing to collect specimens into the future.
   a. Guiding questions: What questions might we be able to answer with temporal genetic data that we cannot answer with isolated specimens? What are some practical limitations for such studies? How might specimen collection be better targeted in the future so that museum collections have maximum value and utility for studying the genomics of adaptation and change?
4. Often the study of extinct organisms is funded more heavily or garners more attention in high impact journals than their extant counterparts because of the novelty and mystery surrounding something that can no longer be observed directly, as well as the technical challenges to retrieve the DNA. Discuss some of the ethical considerations of aDNA research.
   a. Guiding questions: Who owns ancient DNA? Are there any examples where what we know about an extant taxonomic group is derived largely from studies on their extinct relatives? Do you think this is beneficial or detrimental for extant species?
5. **De-extinction** efforts have been spear-headed by organisations such as The Genetic Rescue Foundation (www.geneticrescue.science), and Revive and Restore (reviverestore.org), but the concept remains controversial. Discuss the advantages and disadvantages of such a pursuit.
   a. Guiding questions: What is the aim of de-extinction? How might de-extinction be achieved? What are the logistical and ethical challenges? Would the resources required be better directed toward preventing future extinctions? How might the development of de-extinction technologies improve conservation outcomes for modern species?
   b. For examples of recent/ongoing de-extinction attempts see: Clarke S (2013) 'Bizarre extinct frog brought back to life.' ABCNews. (https://www.abc.net.au/news/2013-03-16/bizarre-extinct-frog-brought-back-to-life/4575916), and Kilvert N (2022) 'De-extinction: Is it really possible to bring animals back from the dead?' ABCNews (https://www.abc.net.au/news/science/2022-03-19/de-extinction-thylacine-tasmanian-tiger-woolly-mammoth/100913846). Note that these attempts have not been peer-reviewed or published as of 2022.

RESOURCES AND FURTHER READING

Bennett JR, Maloney RF, Steeves TE, Brazill-Boast J, Possingham HP, *et al.* (2017) Spending limited resources on de-extinction could lead to net biodiversity loss. *Nature Ecology and Evolution* **1**, 53.

Bi K, Linderoth T, Vanderpool D, Good JM, Nielsen R *et al.* (2013) Unlocking the vault: Next-generation museum population genomics. *Molecular Ecology* **22**, 6018–6032.

Bi K, Linderoth T, Singhal S, Vanderpool D, Patton JL, *et al.* (2019) Temporal genomic contrasts reveal rapid evolutionary responses in an alpine mammal during recent climate change. *PLOS Genetics* **15**(5), e1008119.

Bollongino R, Tresset A, Vigne J-D (2008) Environment and excavation: Pre-lab impacts on ancient DNA analyses. *Palevol* **7**, 91–98.

Cortex AD, Bolnick DA, Nicholas G, Bardill J, Colwell C (2021) An ethical crisis in ancient DNA research: Insights from the Chaco Canyon controversy as a case study. *Journal of Social Archaeology* **21**(2), 157–178.

Genovesi P, Simberloff D (2020) 'De-extinction' in conservation: assessing risks of releasing "resurrected" species. *Journal for Nature Conservation* **56**, 125838.

Higgs E, Falk DA, Guerrini A, Hall M, Harris J, *et al.* (2014) The changing role of history in restoration ecology. *Frontiers in Ecology and the Environment* **12**(9), 499–506.

Ladoukakis ED, Zouros E (2017) Evolution and inheritance of animal mitochondrial DNA: Rules and exceptions. *Journal of BiologicalResearch(Thessalon)***24**(2),doi:10.1186/s40709-017-0060-

Makarewicz C, Marom N, Bar-Oz G (2017) Ensure equal access to ancient DNA. *Nature* **548**, 158.

Rick TC, Lockwood R (2012) Integrating palaeobiology, archaeology, and history to inform biological conservation. *Conservation Biology* **27**(1), 45–54.

Rodrigues ASL, Monsarrat S, Charpentier A, Brooks TM, Hoffmann M, *et al.* (2019) Unshifting the baseline: a framework for documenting historical population changes and assessing long-term anthropogenic impacts. *Philosophical Transactions of the Royal Society B* **374**, 20190220. *This article appears in a discussion meeting issue 'The past is a foreign country: how much can the fossil record actually inform conservation?' Turvey ST, Saupe (eds). There are several articles in this issue that are relevant and recommended reading.*

Seddon PJ (eds) (2017) Special feature: The ecology of de-extinction. *Functional Ecology* **31**, 987–1172.

Wagner JK, Colwell C, Claw KG, Stone AC, Bolnick DA, *et al.* (2020) Fostering responsible research on ancient DNA. *The American Journal of Human Genetics* **107**(2), 183–195.

REFERENCES

Adler CJ Haak W, Donlon D, Cooper A, The Genographic Consortium (2011) Survival and recovery of DNA from ancient teeth and bones. *Journal of Archaeological Science* **38**(5), 956–964.

Allentoft ME, Heller R, Oskam CL, Lorenzen ED, Hale ML, *et al.* (2014) Extinct New Zealand megafauna were not in decline before human colonization. *Proceedings of the National Academy of Sciences* **111**, 4922–4927.

Appelt S, Fancello L, Le Bailly M, Raoult D, Drancourt M, *et al.* (2014) Viruses in a 14th-century coprolite. *Applied and Environmental Microbiology* **80**, 2648–2655.

Barnosky A, Matzke N, Tomiya S *et al.* (2011) Has the Earth's sixth mass extinction already arrived? *Nature* **471**, 51–57.

Barrett JH, Boessenkool S, Kneale CJ, O'Connell TC, Star B (2020) Ecological globalisation, serial depletion and the medieval trade of walrus rostra. *Quaternary Science Reviews* **229**, 106122.

Bennett EA, Massilani D, Lizzo G, Daligault J, Geigl EM, *et al.* (2014) Library construction for ancient genomics: single strand or double strand? *Biotechniques* **56**(6), 289–300.

Boast AP, Weyrich LS, Wood JR, Metcalf JL, Knight R, *et al.* (2018) Coprolites reveal ecological interactions lost with the extinction of New Zealand birds. *Proceedings of the National Academy of Sciences* **115**(7), 1546–1551.

Boessenkool S, Austin JJ, Worthy TH, Scofield P, Cooper A, *et al.* (2009) Relict or colonizer? Extinction and range expansion of penguins in southern New Zealand. *Proceedings of the Royal Society B: Biological Sciences* **276**(1658), 815–821.

Boessenkool S, Star B, Scofield RP, Seddon PJ, Waters JM (2010) Lost in translation or deliberate falsification? Genetic analyses reveal erroneous museum data for historic penguin specimens. *Proceedings of the Royal Society B: Biological Sciences* **277**(1684), 1057–1064.

Boessenkool S, Epp LS, Haile J, Bellemain E, Edwards M, *et al.* (2012) Blocking human contaminant DNA during PCR allows amplification of rare mammal species from sedimentary ancient DNA. *Molecular Ecology* **21**, 1806–1815.

Boessenkool S, Hanghøj K, Nistelberger HM, Der Sarkissian C, Gondek AT, *et al.* (2017) Combining bleach and mild predigestion improves ancient DNA recovery from bones. *Molecular Ecology Resources* **17**(4), 742–751.

Bollongino R, Tresset A, Vigne JD (2008) Environment and excavation: Pre-lab impacts on ancient DNA analyses. *Comptes Rendus Palevol* **7**, 91–98.

Bon C, Berthonaud V, Maksud F, Labadie K, Poulain J, *et al.* (2012) Coprolites as a source of information on the genome and diet of the cave hyena. *Proceedings of the Royal Society B: Biological Sciences* **279**(1739), 2825–2830.

Bond WJ, Lee WG, Craine JM, (2004) Plant structural defences against browsing birds: A legacy of New Zealand's extinct moas. *Oikos* **104**(3), 500–508.

Boubli JP, Janiak MC, Porter LM, De la Torre S, Cortés-Ortiz L, *et al.* (2021) Ancient DNA of the pygmy marmoset type specimen *Cebuella pygmaea* (Spix, 1823) resolves a taxonomic conundrum. *Zoological Research* **42**(6), 761.

Briggs AW, Stenzel U, Meyer M, Krause J, Kircher M *et al.* (2010) Removal of deaminated cytosines and detection of in vivo methylation in ancient DNA. *Nucleic Acids Research*, 38, e87.

Brüniche-Olsen A, Jones ME, Austin JJ, Burridge CP, Holland BR (2014) Extensive population decline in the Tasmanian devil predates European settlement and devil facial tumour disease. *Biology Letters* **10**, 20140619.

Brüniche-Olsen A, Jones ME, Burridge CP, Murchison EP, Holland BR, *et al.* (2018) Ancient DNA tracks the mainland extinction and island survival of the Tasmanian Devil. *Journal of Biogeography* **45**(5), 963–976.

Campbell CD, Sarre SD, Stojanovic D, Gruber B, Medlock K, *et al.* (2018) When is a native species invasive? Incursion of a novel predatory marsupial detected using molecular and historical data. *Diversity & Distributions* **24**(6), 831–840.

Campos PF, Willerslev E, Sher A, Orlando L, Axelsson E, *et al.* (2010) Ancient DNA analyses exclude humans as the driving force behind late Pleistocene musk ox (Ovibos moschatus) population dynamics. *Proceedings of the National Academy of Sciences* **107**(12), 5675–5680.

Campos PF, Craig OE, Turner-Walker G, Peacock E, Willerslev E, *et al.* (2012) DNA in ancient bone – Where is it located and how should we extract it? *Annals of Anatomy-Anatomischer Anzeiger* **194**, 7–16.

Carolan MS (2008) The politics in environmental science: The endangered species act and the Preble's mouse controversy. *Environmental Politics* **17**(3), 449–465.

Carøe C, Gopalakrishnan S, Vinner L, Mak SS, Sinding MHS, *et al.* (2018) Single-tube library preparation for degraded DNA. *Methods in Ecology and Evol*ution **9**(2), 410–419.

Carpenter ML, Buenrostro JD, Valdiosera C, Schroeder H, Allentoft ME, *et al.* (2013) Pulling out the 1%: Whole-genome capture for the targeted enrichment of ancient DNA sequencing libraries. *American Journal of Human Genetics* **93**, 852–864.

Castellano S, Parra G, Sanchez-Quinto FA, Racimo F, Kuhlwilm M, *et al.* (2014) Patterns of coding variation in the complete exomes of three Neandertals. *Proceedings of the National Academy* **111**, 6666–6671.

Caughley G (1983) *The Deer Wars*. Heinemann, Auckland, pg 187.

Coghlan ML, Haile J, Houston J, Murray DC, White NE, *et al.* (2012) Deep sequencing of plant and animal DNA contained within traditional Chinese medicines reveals legality issues and health safety concerns. *PLoS genetics* **8**(4), e1002657.

Coghlan ML, White NE, Parkinson L, Haile J, Spencer PBS, *et al.* (2012) Egg forensics: An appraisal of DNA sequencing to assist in species identification of illegally smuggled eggs. *Forensic Science International: Genetics* **6**(2), 268–273.

Cooper A, Rhymer J, James HF, Olson SL, McIntosh CE, *et al.* (1996) Ancient DNA and island endemics. *Nature* **381**, 484–484.

Cooper A, Poinar HN (2000) Ancient DNA: Do it right or not at ALL. *Science* **289**, 1139–1139.

Crump SE, Fréchette B, Power M, Cutler S, de Wet G, *et al.* (2021) Ancient plant DNA reveals High Arctic greening during the Last Interglacial. *Proceedings of the National Academy of Sciences* **118**(13), e2019069118.

Dabney J, Knapp M, Glocke I, Gansauge MT, Weihmann A, *et al.* (2013) Complete mitochondrial genome sequence of a Middle Pleistocene cave bear reconstructed from ultrashort DNA fragments. *Proceedings of the National Academy of Sciences* **110**, 15758–15763.

d'Abbadie M, Hofreiter M, Vaisman A, Loakes D, Gasparutto D, *et al.* (2007) Molecular breeding of polymerases for amplification of ancient DNA. *Nature Biotechnology* **25**, 939–943.

D'Costa VM, King CE, Kalan L, Morar M, Sung WW, *et al.* (2011) Antibiotic resistance is ancient. *Nature* **477**(7365), 457–461.

de Flamingh A, Coutu A, Sealy J, Chirikure S, Bastos AD, *et al.* (2021) Sourcing elephant ivory from a sixteenth-century Portuguese shipwreck. *Current Biology* **31**(3), 621–628.

der Sarkissian C, Möller P, Hofman CA, Ilsøe P, Rick TC, *et al.* (2020) Unveiling the ecological applications of ancient DNA from mollusk shells. *Frontiers in Ecology and Evolution* **8**, 37.

Diagne C, Leroy B, Vaissière AC, Gozlan RE, Roiz D, *et al.* (2021) High and rising economic costs of biological invasions worldwide. *Nature* **592**, 571–576.

Dietl GP, Flessa KW (2011) Conservation paleobiology: putting the dead to work. *Trends in Ecology and Evolution* **26**(1), 30–37.

Dietl GP (2019) Conservation palaeobiology and the shape of things to come. *Philosophical Transactions of the Royal Society B* **374**(1788), 20190294.

Dowse G, Taylor HR, Girling S, Costanzi JM, Robinson S, *et al.* (2020) Beavers in Knapdale: final report from the Scottish Beavers Reinforcement Project. Published by Scottish Beavers, Edinburgh, UK.

Ducroz J-F, Stubbe M, Saveljev AP, Heidecke D, Samjaa R, *et al.* (2005) Genetic variation and population structure of the Eurasian beaver Castor fiber in Eastern Europe and Asia. *Journal of Mammalogy* **86**, 1059–1067.

Durka W, Babik W, Ducroz J-F, Heidecke D, Rosell F (2005) Mitochondrial phylogeography of the Eurasian beaver *Castor fiber* L. *Molecular Ecology* **14**, 3843–3856.

Eda M, Koike H, Kuro-o M, Mihara S, Hasegawa H, *et al.* (2012) Inferring the ancient population structure of the vulnerable albatross *Phoebastria albatrus*, combining ancient DNA, stable isotope, and morphometric analyses of archaeological samples. *Conservation Genetics* **13**(1), 143–151.

Eglinton G, Logan GA, Ambler RP, Boon JJ, Perizonius WRK (1991) Molecular preservation [and discussion]. *Philosophical Transactions of the Royal Society B: Biological Sciences* **333**, 315–328.

Elsner J, Schibler J, Hofreiter M, Schlumbaum A (2015) Burial condition is the most important factor for mtDNA PCR amplification success in Palaeolithic equid remains from the Alpine foreland. *Archaeological and Anthropological Sciences* **7**, 505–515.

Evans S, i Godino IB, Álvarez M, Rowsell K, Collier P, *et al.* (2016) Using combined biomolecular methods to explore whale exploitation and social aggregation in hunter–gatherer–fisher society in Tierra del Fuego. *Journal of Archaeological Science: Reports* **6**, 757–767.

Ficetola GF, Poulenard J, Sabatier P, Messager E, Gielly L, *et al.* (2018) DNA from lake sediments reveals long-term ecosystem changes after a biological invasion. *Science Advances* **4**(5), eaar4292.

Feigin CY, Newton AH, Doronina L, Schmitz J, Hipsley CA, *et al.* (2018) Genome of the Tasmanian tiger provides insights into the evolution and demography of an extinct marsupial carnivore. *Nature Ecology & Evolution* **2**(1), 182–192.

Ferrari G, Cuevas A, Gondek-Wyrozemska AT, Ballantyne R, Kersten O, *et al.* (2021) The preservation of ancient DNA in archaeological fish bone. *Journal of Archaeological Science* **126**, 105317.

Fordyce SL, Avila-Arcos MC, Rasmussen M, Cappellini E, Romero-Navarro JA, *et al.* (2013) Deep Sequencing of RNA from Ancient Maize Kernels. *PLOS One*, **8**, e50961.

Fordyce SL, Kampmann ML, van Doorn NL, Gilbert MT (2013) Long-term RNA persistence in postmortem contexts. *Investigative Genetics*, **4**, 1–7.

Fortea J, de la Rasilla M, García-Tabernero A, Gigli E, Rosas A, *et al.* (2008) Excavation protocol of bone remains for Neandertal DNA analysis in El Sidron Cave (Asturias, Spain). *Journal of Human Evolution* **55**, 353–357.

Fulton TL, Shapiro B (2019) Setting up an ancient DNA laboratory. In *Ancient DNA*. pp. 1–13. Humana Press, New York, NY.

Gansauge MT, Meyer M (2013) Single-stranded DNA library preparation for the sequencing of ancient or damaged DNA. *Nature Protocols* **8**, 737–748.

Gansauge MT, Meyer M (2014) Selective enrichment of damaged DNA molecules for ancient genome sequencing. *Genome Research* **24**(9), 1543–1549.

Gansauge MT, Gerber T, Glocke I, Korlević P, Lippik L, *et al.* (2017) Single-stranded DNA library preparation from highly degraded DNA using T4 DNA ligase. *Nucleic Acids Research* **45**(10), e79–e79.

Gaywood MJ (2018) Reintroducing the Eurasian beaver Castor fiber to Scotland. *Mammal Review* **48**(1), 48–61.

Gering E, Johnsson M, Willis P, Getty T, Wright D (2015) Mixed ancestry and admixture in Kauai's feral chickens: invasion of domestic genes into ancient Red Junglefowl reservoirs. *Molecular Ecology* **24**(9), 2112–2124.

Giebner H, Langen K, Bourlat SJ, Kukowka S, Mayer C, *et al.* (2020) Comparing diversity levels in environmental samples: DNA sequence capture and metabarcoding approaches using 18S and COI genes. *Molecular Ecology Resources* **20**(5), 1333–1345.

Gilbert MTP, Willerslev E, Hansen AJ, Barnes I, Rudbeck L, *et al.* (2003) Distribution patterns of postmortem damage in human mitochondrial DNA. *American Journal of Human Genetics* **72**, 32–47.

Gilbert MTP, Rudbeck L, Willerslev E, Hansen AJ, Smith C, *et al.* (2005) Biochemical and physical correlates of DNA contamination in archaeological human bones and teeth excavated at Matera, Italy. *Journal of Archaeological Science* **32**, 785–793.

Gilbert MTP, Mo ore W, Melchior L, Worobey M (2007) DNA extraction from dry museum beetles without conferring external morphological damage. *PloS one* **2**(3), e272.

Gilbert MTP, Grønnow B, Andersen PK, Metspalu E, Reidla M, *et al.* (2008) Paleo- Eskimo mtDNA genome reveals matrilineal discontinuity in Greenland. *Science* **320**, 1787–1789.

Ginolhac A, Rasmussen M, Gilbert MTP, Willerslev E, Orlando L (2011) mapDamage: testing for damage patterns in ancient DNA sequences. *Bioinformatics* **27**, 2153–2155.

Gismondi A, Di Marco G, Martini F, Sarti L, Crespan M, *et al.* (2016) Grapevine carpological remains revealed the existence of a Neolithic domesticated *Vitis vinifera* L. specimen containing ancient DNA partially preserved in modern ecotypes. *Journal of Archaeological Science* **69**, 75–84.

Glocke I, Meyer M (2017) Extending the spectrum of DNA sequences retrieved from ancient bones and teeth. *Genome Research* **27**(7), 1230–1237.

Gokhman D, Meshorer E, Carmel L (2016) Epigenetics: It's getting old. Past meets future in paleoepigenetics. *Trends in Ecology and Evolution* **31**, 290–300.

Gokhman D, Malul A, Carmel L (2017) Inferring past environments from ancient epigenomes. *Molecular Biology and Evolution* **34**(10), 2429–2438,

Gravendeel B, Protopopov A, Bull I, Duijm E, Gill F, *et al.* (2014) Multiproxy study of the last meal of a mid-Holocene Oyogos Yar horse, Sakha Republic, Russia. *The Holocene* **24**(10), 1288–1296.

Grealy A, McDowell MC, Scofield P, Murray DC, Fusco DA, *et al.* (2015) A critical evaluation of how ancient DNA bulk bone metabarcoding complements traditional morphological analysis of fossil assemblages. *Quaternary Science Reviews* **128**, 37–47.

Grealy A, Macken A, Allentoft ME, Rawlence NJ, Reed E, *et al.* (2016) An assessment of ancient DNA preservation in Holocene-Pleistocene fossil bone excavated from the world heritage Naracoorte Caves, South Australia. *Journal of Quaternary Science* **31**, 33–45.

Grealy A, Douglass K, Haile J, Bruwer C, Gough C, *et al.* (2016) Tropical ancient DNA from bulk archaeological fish bone reveals the subsistence practices of a historic coastal community in southwest Madagascar. *Journal of Archaeological Science* **75**, 82–88.

Grealy A, Phillips M, Miller G, Gilbert MTP, Rouillard J, *et al.* (2017) Eggshell palaeogenomics: palaeognath evolutionary history revealed through ancient nuclear and mitochondrial DNA from Madagascan elephant bird (*Aepyornis* sp.) eggshell. *Molecular Phylogenetics and Evolution* **109**, 151–163.

Grealy A, Bunce M, Holleley CE (2019) Avian mitochondrial genomes retrieved from museum eggshell. *Molecular Ecology Resources* **19**(4), 1052–1062.

Grealy A, McDowell M, Retallick C, Bunce M Peacock D (2020) Novel mitochondrial haplotype of spotted-tailed quoll (*Dasyurus maculatus*) present on Kangaroo Island (South Australia) prior to extirpation. *The Holocene* **30**(1), 136–144.

Grealy A, Langmore NE, Joseph L, Holleley CE (2021) Genetic barcoding of museum eggshell improves data integrity of avian biological collections. *Scientific Reports* **11**, 1605.

Green RE, Krause J, Briggs AW, Maricic T, Stenzel U, *et al.* (2010) A draft sequence of the neandertal genome. *Science* **328**, 710–722.

Green EJ, Speller CF (2017) Novel substrates as sources of ancient DNA: prospects and hurdles. *Genes* **8**(7), 180.

Gutaker RM, Reiter E, Furtwängler A, Schuenemann V, Burbano HA (2018) Extraction of ultrashort DNA molecules from herbarium specimens. *Biotechniques* **62**(2), 76–79.

Gutiérrez-García TA, Vázquez-Domínguez E, Arroyo-Cabrales J, Kuch M, Enk J, *et al.* (2014) Ancient DNA and the tropics: a rodent's tale. *Biology Letters* **10**, 20140224.

Guy PL (2014) Prospects for analyzing ancient RNA in preserved materials. *Wiley Interdisciplinary Reviews-RNA* **5**, 87–94.

Hahn C, Bachmann L, Chevreux B (2013) Reconstructing mitochondrial genomes directly from genomic next-generation sequencing reads-a baiting and iterative mapping approach. *Nucleic Acids Research* 41, e129.

Hahn EE, Grealy A, Alexander M, Holleley CE (2020) Museum epigenomics: charting the future by unlocking the past. *Trends in Ecology & Evolution* **35**(4), 295–300.

Hahn EE, Alexander MR, Grealy A, Stiller J, Gardiner DM, *et al.* (2021) Unlocking inaccessible historical genomes preserved in formalin. *Molecular Ecology Resources*, doi: 10.1111/1755-0998.13505

Halley DJ, Rosell F (2002) The beaver's reconquest of Eurasia: Status, population development and management of a conservation success. *Mammal Review* **32**, 153–178.

Haouchar D, Haile J, Spencer PBS, Bunce M (2013) The identity of the Depuch Island rock wallaby revealed through ancient DNA. *Australian Mammalogy* **35,** 101–106.

Haouchar D, Pacioni C, Haile J, McDowell MC, Baynes A, *et al.* (2016) Ancient DNA reveals complexity in the evolutionary history and taxonomy of the endangered Australian brush-tailed bettongs (*Bettongia*: Marsupialia: Macropodidae: Potoroinae). *Biodiversity and Conservation* **25**(14), 2097–2927.

Hardy C, Vigne JD, Casañe D, Dennebouy N, Mounolou JC, *et al.* (1994) Origin of European rabbit (*Oryctolagus cuniculus*) in a Mediterranean island: zooarchaeology and ancient DNA examination. *Journal of Evolutionary Biology* **7**(2), 217–226.

Hartnup K, Huynen L, Te Kanawa R, Shepherd LD, Millar CD, *et al.* (2011) Ancient DNA recovers the origins of Māori feather cloaks. *Molecular Biology and Evolution* **28**(10), 2741–2750.

Higuchi R, Bowman B, Freiberger M, Ryder OA, Wilson AC (1984) DNA sequences from the quagga, an extinct member of the horse family. *Nature* **312**, 282–284.

Hofman CA, Rick TC, Fleischer RC, Maldonado JE (2015) Conservation archaeogenomics: Ancient DNA and biodiversity in the Anthropocene. *Trends in Ecology and Evolution* **30**, 540–549.

Hofreiter M, Poinar HN, Spaulding WG, Bauer K, Martin PS, *et al.* (2000) A molecular analysis of ground sloth diet through the last glaciation. *Molecular Ecology* **9**, 1975–1984.

Hofreiter M, Jaenicke V, Serre D, Haeseler AV, Pääbo S (2001) DNA sequences from multiple amplifications reveal artifacts induced by cytosine deamination in ancient DNA. *Nucleic Acids Research* **29**, 4793–4799.

Hofreiter M, Betancourt JL, Sbriller AP, Markgraf V, McDonald HG (2003) Phylogeny, diet, and habitat of an extinct ground sloth from Cuchillo Cura, Neuquen Province, southwest Argentina. *Quaternary Research* **59**, 364–378.

Hofreiter M, Sneberger J, Pospisek M, Vanek D (2021) Progress in forensic bone DNA analysis: Lessons learned from ancient DNA. *Forensic Science International: Genetics* **54**, 102538.

Horn S, Prost S, Stiller M, Makowiecki D, Kuznetsova T, *et al.* (2014) Ancient mitochondrial DNA and the genetic history of Eurasian beaver (*Castor fiber*) in Europe. *Molecular Ecology* **7**, 1717–1729.

Hoss M, Jaruga P, Zastawny TH, Dizdaroglu M, Paabo S (1996) DNA damage and DNA sequence retrieval from ancient tissues. *Nucleic Acids Research* **24**, 1304–1307.

Hung C-M, Shaner P-J, Zink R M, Liu W-C, Chu T-C, *et al.* (2014) Drastic population fluctuations explain the rapid extinction of the passenger pigeon. *Proceedings of the National Academy of Sciences* **111**(29), 10636–10641.

Jiao L, Liu X, Jiang X, Yin Y (2015) Extraction and amplification of DNA from aged and archaeological *Populus euphratica* wood for species identification. *Holzforschung* **69**(8), 925–931.

Jonsson H, Ginolhac A, Schubert M, Johnson PLF, Orlando L (2013) mapDamage2.0: fast approximate Bayesian estimates of ancient DNA damage parameters. *Bioinformatics* **29**, 1682–1684.

Jørgensen T, Haile J, Möller P, Andreev A, Boessenkool S, *et al.* (2012) A comparative study of ancient sedimentary DNA, pollen and macrofossils from permafrost sediments of northern Siberia reveals long-term vegetational stability. *Molecular Ecology* **21**, 1989–2003.

Kapp JD, Green RE, Shapiro B (2021) A fast and efficient single-stranded genomic library preparation method optimized for ancient DNA. *Journal of Heredity* **112**(3), 241–249.

Kearns AM, Joseph L, White LC, *et al.* (2016) Norfolk Island Robins are a distinct endangered species: ancient DNA unlocks surprising relationships and phenotypic discordance within the Australo-Pacific Robins. *Conservation Genetics* **17**, 321–335.

Keighley X, Bro-Jørgensen MH, Ahlgren H, Szpak P, Ciucani MM, *et al.* (2021) Predicting sample success for large-scale ancient DNA studies on marine mammals. *Molecular Ecology Resources* **21**(4), 1149–1166.

Kemp BM, Monroe C, Smith DG (2006) Repeat silica extraction: a simple technique for the removal of PCR inhibitors from DNA extracts. *Journal of Archaeological Science* **33**, 1680–1689.

Kircher M, Sawyer S, Meyer M (2012) Double indexing overcomes inaccuracies in multiplex sequencing on the Illumina platform. *Nucleic Acids Research* **40**(1), e3–e3.

Kistler L, Ratan A, Godfrey LR, Crowley BE, Hughes CE, *et al.* (2015) Comparative and population mitogenomic analyses of Madagascar's extinct, giant 'subfossil' lemurs. *Journal of Human Evolution* **79**, 45–54.

Kitchener AC, Conroy JWH (1997) The history of the Eurasian beaver Castor fiber in Scotland. *Mammal Review* **27**(2), 95–108.

Knapp M, Clarke AC, Horsburgh KA, Matisoo-Smith EA (2012) Setting the stage – Building and working in an ancient DNA laboratory. *Annals of Anatomy- Anatomischer Anzeiger* **194**, 3–6.

Koshiba M, Ogawa K, Hamazaki S, Sugiyama T, Ogawa O, *et al.* (1993) The effect of formalin fixation on DNA and the extraction of high-molecular-weight DNA from fixed and embedded tissues. *Pathology, Research and Practice* **189**(1), 66–72.

Kreader CA (1996) Relief of amplification inhibition in PCR with bovine serum albumin or T4 gene 32 protein. *Applied and Environmental Microbiology* **62**, 1102–1106.

Krefft G (1866) On vertebrate animals of the Lower Murray and Darling, their habits, economy and geographical distribution. *Philosophical Society of New South Wales, 1862–1865*, 1–33.

Lazaridis I, Patterson N, Mittnik A, Renaud G, Mallick S, *et al.* (2014) Ancient human genomes suggest three ancestral populations for present-day Europeans. *Nature* **513**, 409–413.

Lejzerowicz F, Esling P, Majewski W, Szczuciński W, Decelle J, *et al.* (2013) Ancient DNA complements microfossil record in deep-sea subsurface sediments. *Biology Letters* **9**, 20130283.

Leonard JA (2008) Ancient DNA applications for wildlife conservation. *Molecular Ecology* **19**, 4186–4196.

Li C, Hofreiter M, Straube N, Corrigan S, Naylor GJ (2013) Capturing protein-coding genes across highly divergent species. *Biotechniques* **54**(6), 321–326.

Lorenzen E, Nogués-Bravo D, Orlando L, Weinstock J, Binladen J (2011) Species-specific responses of Late Quaternary megafauna to climate and humans. *Nature* **479**, 359–364.

Losey RJ, Yang DY (2007) Opportunistic whale hunting on the southern northwest coast: Ancient DNA, artifact, and ethnographic evidence. *American Antiquity* **72**(4), 657–676.

MacConaill LE, Burns RT, Nag A, Coleman HA, Slevin MK, *et al.* (2018) Unique, dual-indexed sequencing adapters with UMIs effectively eliminate index cross-talk and significantly improve sensitivity of massively parallel sequencing. *BMC Genomics* **19**(1),1–10.

Mackaness G (1978) The Correspondence of John Cotton, Victorian Pioneer, 1842–1849. Part 2 (Review Publications).

Malaney JL, Cook JA (2013) Using biogeographical history to inform conservation: the case of Preble's meadow jumping mouse. *Molecular Ecology* **22**(24), 6000–6017.

Margulies M, Egholm M, Altman WE, Attiya S, Bader JS, *et al.* (2005) Genome sequencing in microfabricated high-density picolitre reactors. *Nature* **437**, 376–380.

Maricic T, Whitten M, Pääbo S (2010) Multiplexed DNA sequence capture of mitochondrial genomes using PCR products. *PLOS One* **5**, e14004.

Massilani D, Morley MW, Mentzer SM, Aldeias V, Vernot B, *et al.* (2022) Microstratigraphic preservation of ancient faunal and hominin DNA in Pleistocene cave sediments. *Proceedings of the National Academy of Sciences* **119**(1), e2113666118.

Matisoo-Smith E (2018) Ancient DNA in zooarchaeology: New methods, new questions and settling old debates in pacific commensal studies. In *Zooarchaeology in Practice*. (Eds C Giovas, M LeFebvre) pp. 209–224. Springer, Cham.

Meyer M, Kircher M (2010) Illumina sequencing library preparation for highly multiplexed target capture and sequencing. *Cold Spring Harbour Protocols* 6, pdb-prot5448.

Mitchell KJ, Llamas B, Soubrier J, Rawlence NJ, Worthy TH, *et al.* (2014) Ancient DNA reveals elephant birds and kiwi are sister taxa and clarifies ratite bird evolution. *Science* **344**, 898–900.

Moore G, Tessler M, Cunningham SW, Betancourt J, Harbert R (2020) Paleo-metagenomics of North American fossil packrat middens: Past biodiversity revealed by ancient DNA. *Ecology and Evolution* **10**(5), 2530–2544.

Mullis KB, Faloona FA (1987) Specific synthesis of DNA *in vitro* via a polymerase-catalyzed chain-reaction. *Methods in Enzymology* **155**, 335–350.

Murray DC, Pearson SG, Fullagar R, Chase BM, Houston J, *et al.* (2012) High-throughput sequencing of ancient plant and mammal DNA preserved in herbivore middens. *Quaternary Science Reviews* **58**, 135–145.

Murray DC, Coghlan M, Bunce M (2015) From benchtop to desktop: important considerations when designing amplicon sequencing workflows. *PLOS One* **10**, e0124671.

Nakahama N (2021) Museum specimens: An overlooked and valuable material for conservation genetics. *Ecological Research* **36**, 13–23.

Nolet BA, Rosell F (1998) Comeback of the beaver Castor fiber: An overview of old and new conservation problems. *Biological Conservation* **83**, 165–173.

Oosting T, Star B, Barrett JH, Wellenreuther M, Ritchie PA, *et al.* (2019) Unlocking the potential of ancient fish DNA in the genomic era. *Evolutionary Applications* **12**(8), 1513–1522.

Orlando L, Allaby R, Skoglund P, Der Sarkissian C, Stockhammer PW, *et al.* (2021) Ancient DNA analysis. *Nature Review Methods Primers* **1**, 14.

Oskam CL, Haile J, McLay E, Rigby P, Allentoft ME, *et al.* (2010) Fossil avian eggshell preserves ancient DNA. *Proceedings of the Royal Society B- Biological Sciences* **277**, 1991–2000.

Pacioni C, Hunt H, Allentoft ME, Vaughan TG, Wayne AF, *et al.* (2015) Genetic diversity loss in a biodiversity hotspot: Ancient DNA quantifies genetic decline and former connectivity in a critically endangered marsupial. *Molecular Ecology* **24**, 5813–5828.

Palmer S, Smith O, Allaby RG (2012) The blossoming of plant archaeogenetics. *Annals of Anatomy* **194**, 146–156.

Paijmans JLA, Barnett R, Gilbert MTP, Zepeda-Mendoza ML, Reumer JWF, *et al.* (2017) Evolutionary history of Saber-toothed cats based on ancient mitogenomics. *Current Biology* **27**, 3330–3336.

Parducci L, Suyama Y, Lascoux M, Bennett KD (2005) Ancient DNA from pollen: a genetic record of population history in Scots pine. *Molecular Ecology* **14**(9), 2873–2882.

Parducci L, Matetovici I, Fontana SL, Bennett KD, Suyama Y, *et al.* (2013) Molecular and pollen based vegetation analysis in lake sediments from central Scandinavia. *Molecular Ecology* **22**, 3511–3524.

Pečnerová P, Palkopoulou E, Wheat CW, Skoglund P, Vartanyan S, *et al.* (2017) Mitogenome evolution in the last surviving woolly mammoth population reveals neutral and functional

consequences of small population size. *Evolution Letters* **1**(6), 292–303.

Phillips MJ, Gibb GC, Crimp EA, Penny D (2010) Tinamous and moa flock together: Mitochondrial genome sequence analysis reveals independent losses of flight among ratites. *Systematic Biology* **59**, 90–107.

Pievani T (2014) The sixth mass extinction: Anthropocene and the human impact on biodiversity. *Rendiconti Lincei* **25**, 85–93.

Pinhasi R, Fernandes D, Sirak K, Novak M, Connell S, *et al.* (2015) Optimal ancient DNA yields from the inner ear part of the human petrous bone. *PloS one* **10**, e0129102.

Poinar HN, Kuch M, Sobolik KD, Barnes I, Stankiewicz AB, *et al.* (2001) A molecular analysis of dietary diversity for three archaic Native Americans. *Proceedings of the National Academy of Sciences* **98**, 4317–4322.

Pruvost M, Geigl EM (2004) Real-time quantitative PCR to assess the authenticity of ancient DNA amplification. *Journal of Archaeological Science* **31**, 1191–1197.

Pruvost M, Schwarz R, Correia VB, Champlot S, Braguier S, *et al.* (2007) Freshly excavated fossil bones are best for amplification of ancient DNA. *Proceedings of the National Academy of Sciences* **104**, 739–744.

Pruvost M, Schwarz R, Correia VB, Champlot S, Grange T, *et al.* (2008) DNA diagenesis and palaeogenetic analysis: Critical assessment and methodological progress. *Palaeogeography Palaeoclimatology Palaeoecology* **266**, 211–219.

Ramey RR, Liu H-P, Epps CW, Carpenter LM, Wehausen JD (2005) Genetic relatedness of the Preble's meadow jumping mouse (*Zapus hudsonius preblei*) to nearby subspecies of *Z. hudsonius* as inferred from variation in cranial morphology, mitochondrial DNA, and microsatellite DNA: implications for taxonomy and conservation. *Animal Conservation Forum* **8**(3), 329–346.

Rawlence NJ, Wood JR, Armstrong KN, Cooper A. (2009) DNA content and distribution in ancient feathers and potential to reconstruct the plumage of extinct avian taxa. *Proceedings of the Royal Society B-Biological Sciences* **276**, 3395–3402.

Rawlence NJ, Kennedy M, Waters JM, Scofield RP (2014) Morphological and ancient DNA analyses reveal inaccurate labels on two of Buller's bird specimens. *Journal of the Royal Society of New Zealand* **44**(4), 163–169.

Rawlence NJ, Wood JR, Bocherens H, Rogers KM (2016) Dietary interpretations for extinct megafauna using coprolites, intestinal contents and stable isotopes: Complimentary or contradictory? *Quaternary Science Reviews* **142**, 173–178.

Raxworthy CJ, Smith BT (2021) Mining museums for historical DNA: advances and challenges in museomics. *Trends in Ecology and Evolution* **36**(11), 1049–1060.

Rick TC, Lockwood R (2012) Integrating palaeobiology, archaeology, and history to inform biological conservation. *Conservation Biology* **27**(1), 45–54.

Rinkert A, Misiewicz TM, Carter BE, Salmaan A, Whittall JB (2021) Bird nests as botanical time capsules: DNA barcoding identifies the contents of contemporary and historical nests. *Plos one*, **16**(10), e0257624.

Robinson TJ, Matthee CA (1999) Molecular genetic relationships of the extinct ostrich, Struthio camelus syriacus: Consequences for ostrich introductions into Saudi Arabia. *Animal Conservation* **2**, 165–171.

Rogers RL, Slatkin M (2017) Excess of genomic defects in a woolly mammoth on Wrangel island. *PLoS Genetics* **13**(3), e1006601.

Roycroft E, MacDonald AJ, Moritz C, Moussalli A, Portela Miguez R, *et al.* (2021) Museum genomics reveals the rapid decline and extinction of Australian rodents since European settlement. *Proceedings of the National Academy of Sciences* **118**(27), e2021390118.

Roycroft E, Moritz C, Rowe KC, Moussalli A, Eldridge MDB, *et al.* (2022) Sequence capture from historical museum specimens: Maximizing value for population and phylogenomic studies. *Frontiers in Ecology and Evolution* **10**, 1–12.

Sanger F, Nicklen S, Coulson AR (1977) DNA sequencing with chain-terminating inhibitors. *Proceedings of the National Academy of Sciences* **74**, 5463–5467.

Scarsbrook L, Verry AJF, Walton K, Hitchmough RA, Rawlence NJ (2022) Ancient mitochondrial genomes recovered from small vertebrate bones through minimally destructive DNA extraction: Phylogeography of the New Zealand gecko genus *Hoplodactylus. Molecular Ecology* [Online early].

Schroeder H, Ávila-Arcos M, Malaspinas A, Poznik, GD, Sandoval-Velasco M, *et al.* (2015) Genome-wide ancestry of 17th-century enslaved Africans from the Caribbean. *Proceedings of the National Academy Sciences of the United States of America* **112**, 3669–3673.

Schubert M, Ginolhac A, Lindgreen S, Thompson JF, Al-Rasheid KAS, *et al.* (2012) Improving ancient DNA read mapping against modern reference genomes. *BMC Genomics* **13**, 178.

Seersholm FV, Pedersen MW, Søe MJ, Shokry H, Mak SST, *et al.* (2016) DNA evidence of bowhead whale exploitation by Greenlandic Paleo-Inuit 4,000 years ago. *Nature Communications* **7**(1), 1–9.

Seersholm FV, Cole TL, Grealy A, Rawlence NJ, Greig K, *et al.* (2018) Subsistence practices, past biodiversity, and anthropogenic impacts revealed by New Zealand-wide ancient DNA survey. *Proceedings of the National Academy of Sciences* **115**(30), 7771–7776.

Shapiro B, Hofreiter M (2012) *Ancient DNA: Methods and Protocols.* Humana Press, New York (Springer Science).

Shepherd LD, Lambert DM (2008) Ancient DNA and conservation: lessons from the endangered kiwi of New Zealand. *Molecular Ecology* **17**(9), 2174–2184.

Shepherd LD, Worthy TH, Tennyson AJD, Scofield RP, Randstad KM, *et al.* (2012) Ancient DNA analyses reveal contrasting phylogeographic patterns amongst kiwi (*Apteryx* spp.) and a recently extinct lineage of spotted kiwi. *Plos One* **7**, e42384. doi:10.1371/journal.pone.0042384

Smith CI, Chamberlain AT, Riley MS, Stringer C, Collins MJ (2003) The thermal history of human fossils and the likelihood of successful DNA amplification. *Journal of Human Evolution* **45**, 203–217.

Smith O, Clapham A, Rose P, Liu Y, Wang J, *et al.* (2014) A complete ancient RNA genome: identification, reconstruction and evolutionary history of archaeological Barley Stripe Mosaic Virus. *Scientific Reports* **4**, 4003.

Speer KA, Hawkins MTR, Flores MFC, McGowen MR, Fleischer RC, *et al.* (2022) A comparative study of RNA yields from museum specimens, including an optimized protocol for extracting RNA from formalin-fixed specimens. *Frontiers in Ecology and Evolution* **10**, 953131.

Søe MJ, Nejsum P, Seersholm FV, Fredensborg BL, Habraken R, *et al.* (2018) Ancient DNA from latrines in Northern Europe and the Middle East (500 BC–1700 AD) reveals past parasites and diet. *PloS one* **13**(4), e0195481.

Stiller M, Baryshnikov G, Bocherens H, Grandal d'Anglade A, Hilpert B, *et al.* (2010) Withering away-25,000 years of genetic decline preceded cave bear extinction. *Molecular Biology Evolution* **27**, 975–978.

Taberlet P, Coissac E, Pompanon F, Brochmann C, Willerslev E (2012) Towards next-generation biodiversity assessment using DNA metabarcoding. *Molecular Ecology* **21**, 2045–2050.

Taylor JW, Swann EC (1994) DNA from Herbarium Specimens. In *Ancient DNA.* (Eds B Herrmann, S Hummel) Springer, New York, NY.

Teasdale MD, van Doorn NL, Fiddyment S, Webb CC, O'Connor T, *et al.* (2015) Paging through history: Parchment as a reservoir of ancient DNA for next generation sequencing. *Philosophical Transactions of the Royal Society B: Biological Sciences* **370**, 20130379.

Thomas R, Schaffner W, Wilson A, Pääbo S (1989) DNA phylogeny of the extinct marsupial wolf. *Nature* **340**, 465–467.

Thomson VA, Lebrasseur O, Austin JJ, Hunt TL, Burney DA, *et al.* (2014) Using ancient DNA to study the origins and dispersal of ancestral Polynesian chickens across the Pacific. *Proceedings of the National Academy of Sciences* **111**, 4826–4831.

U.S. Fish and Wildlife Service (2009) Revised Recovery Plan for the Laysan Duck (*Anas laysanensis*). U.S. Fish and Wildlife Service, Portland, Oregon. ix + 114 pp.

van der Valk T, Díez-del-Molino D, Marques-Bonet T, Guschanski K, Dalén L (2019) Historical genomes reveal the genomic consequences of recent population decline in eastern gorillas. *Current Biology* **29**(1), 165–170.

van der Valk T, Pečnerová P, Díez-del-Molino D *et al.* (2021) Million-year-old DNA sheds light on the genomic history of mammoths. *Nature* **591**, 265–269.

van Geel B, Fisher DC, Rountrey AN, van Arkel J, Duivenvoorden JF, *et al.* (2011) Palaeo-environmental and dietary analysis of intestinal contents of a mammoth calf (Yamal Peninsula, northwest Siberia). *Quaternary Science Reviews* **30**(27–28), 3935–3946.

van Geel B, Protopopov A, Bull I, Duijm E, Gill F, *et al.* (2014) Multiproxy diet analysis of the last meal of an early Holocene Yakutian bison. *Journal of Quaternary Science* **29**(3), 261–268.

Verry AJ, Scarsbrook L, Scofield RP, Tennyson AJ, Weston KA, *et al.* (2019) Who, where, what, wren? Using ancient DNA to examine the veracity of museum specimen data: a case study of the New Zealand rock wren (*Xenicus gilviventris*). *Frontiers in Ecology and Evolution* **7**, 496.

Villanea FA, Parent CE, Kemp BM (2016) Reviving Galapagos snails: ancient DNA extraction and amplification from shells of probably extinct endemic land snails. *Journal of Molluscan Studies* **82**, 449–456.

Wales N, Carøe C, Sandoval-Velasco M, Gamba C, Barnett R, *et al.* (2015) New insights on single-stranded versus double-stranded DNA library preparation for ancient DNA. *Biotechniques* **59**(6), 368–371.

Wasser SK, Mailand C, Booth R, Mutayoba B, Kisamo E, *et al.* (2007) Using DNA to track the origin of the largest ivory seizure since the 1989 trade ban. *Proceedings of the National Academy of Sciences* **104**(10), 4228–4233.

Warinner C, Rodrigues JFM, Vyas R, Trachsel C, Shved N, *et al.* (2014) Pathogens and host immunity in the ancient human oral cavity. *Nature Genetics* **46**(4), 336–344.

Warinner C, Speller C, Collins MJ (2015) A new era in palaeomicrobiology: prospects for ancient dental calculus as a long-term record of the human oral microbiome. *Philosophical Transactions of the Royal Society B* **370**, 20130376.

Welch AJ, Wiley AE, James HF, Ostrom PH, Stafford Jr TW, *et al.* (2012) Ancient DNA reveals genetic stability despite demographic decline: 3,000 years of population history in the endemic Hawaiian petrel. *Molecular Biology and Evolution* **29**(12), 3729–3740.

West C, Hofman CA, Ebbert S, Martin J, Shirazi S, *et al.* (2017) Integrating archaeology and ancient DNA analysis to address invasive species colonization in the Gulf of Alaska. *Conservation Biology* **31**(5), 1163–1172.

White LC, Saltré F, Bradshaw CJ, Austin JJ (2018a) High-quality fossil dates support a synchronous, Late Holocene extinction of devils and thylacines in mainland Australia. *Biology Letters* **14**(1), 20170642.

White LC, Mitchell KJ, Austin JJ (2018b) Ancient mitochondrial genomes reveal the demographic history and phylogeography of the extinct, enigmatic thylacine (*Thylacinus cynocephalus*). *Journal of Biogeography* **45**(1), 1–13.

Willerslev E, Cappellini E, Boomsma W, Nielsen R, Hebsgaard MB, *et al.* (2007) Ancient biomolecules from deep ice cores reveal a forested southern Greenland. *Science* **317**(5834), 111–114.

Witt KE, Yarlagadda K, Allen JM, Bader AC, Simon ML, *et al.* (2021) Integrative analysis of DNA, macroscopic remains and stable isotopes of dog coprolites to reconstruct community diet. *Scientific Reports* **11**, 3113.

Woinarski JCZ, Burbidge AA, Harrison PL (2015) Ongoing unraveling of a continental fauna: Decline and extinction of Australian mammals since European settlement. *Proceedings of the National Academy of Sciences* **112**, 4531–4540.

Wood JR, Wilmshurst JM, Wagstaff SJ, Worthy TH, Rawlence NJ *et al.* (2012a) High-resolution coproecology: Using coprolites to reconstruct habits and habitats of New Zealand's extinct upland moa (*Megalapteryx didinus*). *PLoS ONE* **7**, e40025.

Wood JR, Wilmshurst JM, Worthy TH, Cooper A (2012b) First coprolite evidence for the diet of *Anomalopteryx didiformis*, an extinct forest ratite from New Zealand. *N. Z. Journal of Ecology* **36**, 164–170.

Wood JR, Wilmshurst JM, Worthy TH, Holzapfel AS, Cooper A (2012c) A lost link between a flightless parrot and a parasitic plant and the potential role of coprolites in conservation palaeobiology. *Conservation Biology* **26**(6), 1091–1099.

Wood JR, Wilmshurst JM, Richardson SJ, Rawlence NJ, Wagstaff SJ, *et al.* (2013) Resolving lost herbivore community structure using coprolites of four sympatric moa species (Aves: Dinornithiformes). *Proceedings of the National Academy of Sciences* **110**, 16910–16915.

Wood JR, Díaz FP, Latorre C, Wilmshurst JM, Burge OR, *et al.* (2018) Plant pathogen responses to Late Pleistocene and Holocene climate change in the central Atacama Desert, Chile. *Scientific Reports* **8**(1), 1–8.

Wood JR, Richardson SJ, McGlone MS, Wilmshurst JM (2020) The diets of moa (Aves: Dinornithiformes). *New Zealand Journal of Ecology* **44**(1), 1–21.

Woods R, Marr MM, Brace S, Barnes I (2017) The small and the dead: A review of ancient DNA studies analysing micromammal species. *Genes* **8**, 312.

Wyatt KB, Campos PF, Gilbert MTP, Kolokotronis S-O, Hynes WH, *et al.* (2008) Historical mammal extinction on Christmas Island (Indian Ocean) correlates with introduced infectious disease. *PLoS One* **3**(11), e3602.

Yang DY, Eng B, Waye JS, Dudar JC, Saunders SR (1998) Technical note: Improved DNA extraction from ancient bones using silica-based spin columns. *American Journal of Physical Anthropology* **105**, 539–543.

Yeates DK, Zwick A, Mikheyev AS (2016) Museums are biobanks: Unlocking the genetic potential of the three billion specimens in the world's biological collections. *Current Opinion in Insect Science* **18**, 83–88.

Yonezawa T, Segawa T, Mori H, Campos PF, Hongoh Y, *et al.* (2017) Phylogenomics and morphology of extinct paleognaths reveal the origin and evolution of ratites. *Current Biology* **27**, 68–77.

Young JM, Higgins D, Austin J (2019) Hybridization enrichment to improve forensic mitochondrial DNA analysis of highly degraded human remains. *Frontiers in Ecology and Evolution* **7**, doi:10.3389/fevo.2019.00450.

17 Perspective – Genomics and the prioritisation of taxa and populations for conservation

Catherine Darst, U.S. Fish and Wildlife Service, Ventura, California

Up to one million plant and animal species face extinction, many within decades, because of human activities (Sage 2020). Several countries have laws that try to address the extinction problem, including the Endangered Species Act in the United States (US Endangered Species Act 1988), the Biodiversity Law of Costa Rica (passed in 1992), the Endangered Species Protection Act of Australia (passed in 2002), Canada's Species at Risk Act (passed in 2002), and the South African National Environmental Management Biodiversity Act (passed in 2004) (Waples *et al.* 2013).

One of the most pressing problems in understanding the biological status of a species as it relates to legislated conservation status is 'What is the appropriate entity to be assessing?', followed closely by 'For that entity, what is its current and future extinction risk?' It sounds so simple but continually plagues conservation practitioners trying to conserve species under the ESA. The revolution in genetic techniques has transformed our understanding of the amount and distribution of genetic variation in natural populations (Allendorf *et al.* 2010). Thus, ESA practitioners rely increasingly on genetics and genomics in defining species (USFWS and NMFS 1996, see chapter 4), and are working to use this information in assessing extinction risk (Smith *et al.* 2018). Scientists' conclusions about whether populations are genetically distinct have become extremely important in decision making (Brosi *et al.* 2009). However, debate continues about how best to use increasingly detailed genomic information to identify species for implementation of the ESA and assessment of their risk of extinction (e.g. Haig and D'elia 2010; Regan *et al.* 2013; Keith *et al.* 2015; Boyd *et al.* 2017; Gallego-García *et al.* 2021).

The ESA defines species broadly to include species, subspecies, varieties, and, for vertebrates, distinct population segments (DPS), defined as a population or group of populations that is discrete and significant in relation to the entire species. Identifying and discriminating these entities has been the primary use of genomic information under the ESA. Once we've determined what the entity is that we're assessing, we are faced with evaluating the distribution of genetic and ecological variation within the entity and how that relates to extinction risk. A species can be listed as either an endangered or threatened species under the ESA depending on the degree of threat it faces (ESA 1973, Sect. 3, 4a). An endangered species is one that is in danger of extinction throughout all or a significant portion of its range. A threatened species is one that is likely to become endangered in the foreseeable future throughout all or a significant portion of its range.

Incorporating information on adaptive potential into models of extinction risk can improve ESA implementation by increasing the accuracy of these assessments (Forester and Lama 2022). On the one hand, if we do not allow for the possibility of adaptation in response to novel environmental stressors, then extinction estimates might be biased high, which could result in ESA listing of a species that has the capacity to evolve and persist in the face of environmental change. On the other hand, if the possibility that threats (e.g. habitat loss, invasive species, overexploitation, etc.) have decreased or are decreasing adaptive potential is not considered, then extinction estimates may be biased low, resulting in not listing a species for which listing is warranted. In the context of recovering endangered species, an understanding of how to exploit available adaptive potential, or be conservative in the face of a lack of adaptive potential, could be beneficial in choosing optimal actions (see Chapter 14).

Given the past difficulty of quantifying adaptive potential, little information has typically been available for most species that are candidates for listing. Because genomics greatly increases the feasibility of characterising adaptive potential in non-model species, for example using genome-wide or functional gene-centric variation, it can improve ESA implementation by moving us closer to estimation and integration of adaptive potential into assessments of extinction risk (Funk *et al.* 2019; Kardos *et al.* 2021; Forester *et al.* 2022).

Conservation practitioners must make effective and timely decisions. And yet, our challenge is that these decisions are made in a highly dynamic context. As indicated above, technologies like genomics are advancing fast and constantly providing new insights into genetic distinctiveness and adaptive potential that could enhance the accuracy of our ESA decisions. While we welcome these advances, we are also faced with an increasing number of species facing extinction. Given this, now is a critical time to bring the academics and conservation practitioners together to determine how to most effectively use genomics to directly information extinction risk assessments and plans for recovering endangered species.

REFERENCES

Allendorf FW, Hohenlohe PA, Luikart G (2010) Genomics and the future of conservation genetics. *Nature Reviews Genetics* **11**(10), 697–709.

Boyd C, DeMaster DP, Waples RS, Ward EJ, Taylor BL (2017) Consistent extinction risk assessment under the US Endangered Species Act. *Conservation Letters* **10**(3), 328–336.

Brosi BJ, Biber EG (2009) Statistical inference, Type II error, and decision making under the US Endangered Species Act. *Frontiers in Ecology and the Environment* **7**(9), 487–494.

Forester BR, Lama T (2022) The role of genomics in the future of ESA decision-making. *EcoRxiv*, doi:10.32942/osf.io/b6rf4

Forester BR, Beever EA, Darst C, Szymanski J, Funk WC, *et al.* (2022) Linking evolutionary potential to extinction risk: Applications and future directions. *Frontiers in Ecology and the Environment* **20**(9), 507–515.

Funk W, Forester BR, Converse SJ, Darst C, Morey S (2019) Improving conservation policy with genomics: a guide to integrating adaptive potential into US Endangered Species Act decisions for conservation practitioners and geneticists. *Conservation Genetics* **20**(1), 115–134.

Gallego-García N, Caballero S, Shaffer HB (2021) Are genomic updates of well-studied species worth the investment for conservation? a case study of the Critically Endangered Magdalena river turtle. *Journal of Heredity* **112**(7), 575–589.

Haig SM, D'elia J (2010) Avian subspecies and the US Endangered Species Act. *Ornithological Monographs* **67**(1), 24–34.

Kardos M, Armstrong EE, Fitzpatrick SW, Hauser S, Hedrick PW, *et al.* (2021) The crucial role of genome-wide genetic variation in conservation. *Proceedings of the National Academy of Sciences* **118**(48), e2104642118.

Keith D, Akçakaya HR, Butchart SH, Collen B, Dulvy NK, *et al.* (2015) Temporal correlations in population trends: Conservation implications from time-series analysis of diverse animal taxa. *Biological Conservation* **192**, 247–257.

Regan TJ, Taylor BL, Thompson GG, Cochrane JF, Ralls K, *et al.* (2013) Testing decision rules for categorizing species' extinction risk to help develop quantitative listing criteria for the US Endangered Species Act. *Conservation Biology* **27**(4), 821–831.

Sage RF (2020) Global change biology: A primer. *Global Change Biology* **26**(1), 3–30.

Smith DR, Allan NL, McGowan CP, Szymanski JA, Oetker SR, *et al.* (2018) Development of a species status assessment process for decisions under the US Endangered Species Act. *Journal of Fish and Wildlife Management* **9**(1), 302–320.

US Endangered Species Act (1988) *Endangered Species Act of 1973*. Retrieved from https://www.fws.gov/law/endangered-species-act

USFWS and NMFS (1996) Endangered Species Habitat Conservation Planning Handbook. United States Fish and Wildlife Service and National Marine Fisheries Service, Washington, DC, USA.

Waples RS, Nammack M, Cochrane JF, Hutchings JA (2013) A tale of two acts: endangered species listing practices in Canada and the United States. *Bioscience* **63**(9), 723–734.

ENVIRONMENTAL MOLECULAR PHYSIOLOGY

18   Applied epigenomics in a rapidly changing world

M. Teresa Boquete, Sabrina M. McNew and Christina L. Richards

ABSTRACT

The field of epigenetics has developed rapidly over the past 10 years based on three main ideas: 1) information encoded in the **epigenome** might explain phenotypic variation that cannot be explained by DNA sequence variation; 2) this information could be more labile than genetic information, that is, more susceptible to changes in response to internal/external environmental stimuli; and 3) such changes could be transmitted across generations allowing organisms to respond more efficiently to environmental challenges. Insights gained from ecological studies in natural populations as well as experimental studies in the laboratory have supported these ideas, opening promising research avenues in applied fields that would help us tackle some of the most pressing challenges associated with rapid global change. In this chapter, we (1) present evidence of the potential of the epigenome to shape organisms' ecological interactions and evolutionary trajectories; (2) review the literature that demonstrates the phenotypic implications of natural or artificially induced epigenetic variation; and (3) discuss how all this information can be leveraged under the current context of human-driven global environmental change in ecological risk assessment programs, crop and livestock breeding programs, and conservation of biodiversity programs. Finally, we discuss technologies such as 'epigenome editing' which have exciting potential to engineer the epigenome to improve conservation, food production, and more.

THE EPIGENOME AT THE INTERFACE BETWEEN ORGANISMS AND THE ENVIRONMENT

As a result of overexploitation of natural resources, mining, urbanisation, extraction and burning of fossil fuels, pollution, and development of transportation networks and industries, humans are profoundly altering the structure and functioning of the Earth's ecosystems (Vitousek 1994; Camill 2010; Malhi 2017). In turn, all other organisms must face new environmental challenges such as the spread of invasive species, urbanisation, pollution, new parasite/pathogen emergence and climate change (Arim *et al.* 2006; Crowl *et al.* 2008; Elmqvist *et al.* 2013; Poloczanska *et al.* 2013; Brei *et al.* 2016; Walsh *et al.* 2016). An organism's phenotype determines its fitness within a given set of environmental conditions. Hence, the chances of survival under future anthropogenic conditions will depend partly on the ability to adjust phenotypes to altered biotic or abiotic factors, i.e. their capacity for phenotypic change (Jump and Peñuelas 2005; Hendry *et al.* 2008; Chevin *et al.* 2010; Forsman and Wennersten 2016; Snell-Rood *et al.* 2018). The phenotype is encoded in two main layers of information, the genome and the epigenome, and it is shaped by the interaction between them, and between each of them and the environment (Maher 2008; Rahim *et al.* 2008; Herrera and Bazaga 2013; Li *et al.* 2018; Wojciechowski *et al.* 2018; Angers *et al.* 2020). The capacity of organisms to succeed under new environmental contexts is thus ultimately determined by the amount of genetic and epigenetic variation at the population and/or species level (Jump and Peñuelas 2005; Münzbergová *et al.* 2019). Similarly, our ability to intervene and alleviate the impact of human activities on natural ecosystems and their services depends on our mechanistic understanding of how such variation shapes phenotypes.

Through different epigenetic mechanisms, that is, DNA methylation, histone modifications and histone variants, and non-coding RNAs (Box 18.1), the epigenome can modify the way genes are expressed within the cells by controlling the chromatin structure and accessibility of the DNA molecule (**'chromatin accessibility'**) to macromolecules including RNA polymerases (Li *et al.* 2007; Bartee *et al.* 2017). This information allows organisms to efficiently respond to internal and external environmental stimuli. Experimental evidence suggests that epigenetic information is more dynamic than DNA sequence and structural variation in DNA (Rando and Verstrepen 2007). For example, point epimutations (i.e. spontaneous changes in the methylation status of single nucleotides) for cytosines followed by guanines (CG context) occur at a rate that is five orders of magnitude more frequent than sequence mutations in the model plant *Arabidopsis thaliana* (Becker *et al.* 2011; Graaf *et al.* 2015). While there is little evidence that such point epimutation can translate into functional differences in plants, changes in methylation across larger genomic regions have been associated with phenotypic changes in several species (Cortijo *et al.* 2014; Gallusci *et al.* 2016; Shen *et al.* 2018). Moreover, a recent study indicated that changes in these differentially methylated regions (DMRs) arise at the same rate as point epimutations (Denkena *et al.* 2021). In bacteria, environmentally induced ON and OFF phase transitions of the pili-adhesion complexes (that mediate cell-cell and cell-host adhesion) (Epler Barbercheck *et al.* 2018) is dependent on DNA methylation (Casadesús and Low 2013). These transitions can happen very fast, at a rate of $\sim 10^{-4}$ (OFF to ON) and $\sim 10^{-2}$ (ON to OFF) per cell per generation (Holden *et al.* 2007). Additionally, epigenomes seem to be more responsive than DNA sequence to a variety of environmental cues in both plants and animals (Verhoeven *et al.* 2010; Dowen *et al.* 2012; Richards *et al.* 2012; Foust *et al.* 2016; Putnam *et al.* 2016; McNew *et al.* 2017; Hu *et al.* 2018; Furlong *et al.* 2020; Sagonas *et al.* 2020; Lim *et al.* 2021). Epigenetic modifications are thought to be generally stable through mitosis – allowing dividing cells of the same tissue to preserve patterns of gene expression and phenotype – but largely erased in germ cells and early embryos – i.e. **epigenetic reprogramming** (Feng *et al.* 2010b). However, at least a fraction of environmentally induced epigenetic changes can be transmitted to subsequent generations (Verhoeven *et al.* 2010; Rubenstein *et al.* 2016; Weyrich *et al.* 2016). The processes that prevent reprogramming of certain epigenetic marks are not well understood. Nevertheless, the potential for environmentally induced epimutations to be inherited across organismal generations has brought increasing attention to the potential ecological and evolutionary implications of epigenetic variation (Richards *et al.* 2017; Eirin-Lopez and Putnam 2019; Ashe *et al.* 2021; Mounger, Ainouche *et al.* 2021). The contribution of the epigenome to organisms' success might be instrumental, especially for those with presumably low levels of genetic variation (e.g. in clonal and predominantly asexually reproducing organisms, after population bottlenecks, or during the invasion of new habitats) (Raj *et al.* 2011; Liebl *et al.* 2015; Jueterbock *et al.* 2020; Mounger, Boquete *et al.* 2021).

Box 18.1: Epigenetic regulation in plants and animals

The activity of eukaryotic genomes is regulated by epigenetic mechanisms, that is, the epigenome, that drive changes in chromatin conformation, that is, the access of the transcriptional machinery to genes (Jaenisch and Bird 2003; Li *et al.* 2007; Bartee *et al.* 2017). There are three main types of epigenetic mechanisms, namely DNA methylation, histone variants and histone post-translational modifications (PTMs), and non-coding RNAs (ncRNA) (see Fig. 18.1).

- DNA methylation refers to the addition of a methyl group (CH_3) to the carbon 5 position of the cytosine bases in the genome (but see methylation in carbon 4 in liverworts (Walker *et al.* 2021) and in adenine in *Caenorhabditis elegans* (Greer *et al.* 2015) and several bacteria (Casadesús and Low 2013; Val *et al.* 2014)). The deposition is catalysed by DNA methyltransferase enzymes (DNMTs) or DNA adenine methylase (Dam). There are two main types of DNMTs: *de novo* DNMTs, which methylate cytosines that were previously unmethylated, and maintenance DNMTs, which maintain methylation during DNA replication.
- Histone variants have changes to the amino acids of one of the four core histone proteins (H2A, H2B, H3, and H4), resulting in changes to chromatin architecture and function (Henikoff and Smith 2015). Histone PTMs, on the other hand,

consist of chemical modifications to the amino-terminal histone tails. Such modifications can directly alter how nucleosomes interact with each other and with the DNA leading to changes in the chromatin conformational structure (i.e. condensation) and, consequently, in gene expression (Bannister and Kouzarides 2011). Histone PTMs can also recruit/repel other regulatory proteins and indirectly cause changes in chromatin conformation and genome function (Jenuwein and Allis 2001). The main histone PTMs include acetylation, phosphorylation, methylation, ubiquitylation, and sumolynation (but see Bannister and Kouzarides 2011 for additional histone PTMs); their functional effects depend on the type of post-translational modifications (PTM) and its location.

- ncRNAs are short (~20–30 nucleotides) or long (>200 nucleotides) RNA molecules that do not code for proteins. Instead, these molecules alter gene expression patterns at the translational (through interactions with the DNA, RNA, and protein molecules) or post-translational (through direct splicing of messenger RNAs – mRNAs) levels (Peschansky and Wahlestedt 2014).

The epigenetic toolkit is relatively conserved across the eukaryotic tree of life (Goll and Bestor 2005; Law and Jacobsen 2010; Schmitz *et al.* 2019; Weiner *et al.* 2020). Genome-wide patterns of epigenetic variation (epigenomic landscape), however, differ greatly across taxa (Schmitz *et al.* 2019). By far, the most studied epigenetic mark is DNA methylation implying that most comparative examples are limited to this mechanism. For example, DNA methylation in animal genomes is found predominately in the CG sequence context, while plant genomes can be methylated in CG, CHG, and CHH contexts (where H = A, C, or T). Specifically, unlike animals, non-CG methylation in plants is targeted to silence transposable elements and repetitive elements. Vertebrate genomes are heavily methylated genome-wide whereas invertebrate, plant, and fungi show interspersed methylated and unmethylated regions across their genomes (Suzuki and Bird 2008; Feng *et al.* 2010a; Law and Jacobsen 2010; Schmitz *et al.* 2019). Epigenetic alterations throughout an organism's lifetime are more likely transmitted to offspring in plants whose germline cells are not segregated early in development as in animals (Hu and Barrett 2017).

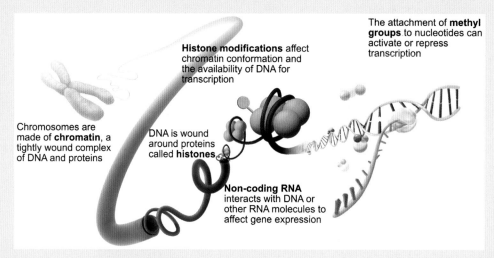

The attachment of **methyl groups** to nucleotides can activate or repress transcription

Histone modifications affect chromatin conformation and the availability of DNA for transcription

Chromosomes are made of **chromatin**, a tightly wound complex of DNA and proteins

DNA is wound around proteins called **histones**

Non-coding RNA interacts with DNA or other RNA molecules to affect gene expression

Fig. 18.1. Epigenetic mechanisms determining chromatin conformation in eukaryotic cells. Illustration by Charlotte W. Holden.

Recent research in ecological and evolutionary epigenetics has focused on understanding the contribution of epigenetic variation to functional variation, as well as the extent of inheritance of environmentally induced epigenetic changes (reviewed in Verhoeven *et al.* 2016; Richards *et al.* 2017; Herrel *et al.* 2020; Richards and Pigliucci 2020). Some of these studies have found a clear link between epigenetic and phenotypic change. For example, one of the first important studies showed that the switch from bilateral to radial floral symmetry in *Linaria vulgaris* is the result of extensive methylation and consequent silencing of the *Lyc* gene (Cubas *et al.* 1999). More recently, genome-wide changes in methylation and histone modifications have been shown to drive the green to albino transition of genetically identical *Agave angustifolia* plants (Us-Camas *et al.* 2017). DNA methylation and histone modifications have also long been associated with nutrition-dependent development of queen/worker adult phenotypes in honeybees (Kucharski *et al.* 2008; Wojciechowski *et al.* 2018). Recent studies show methylation is also involved in caste-specific expression of genes associated with phenotypic traits of castes and developmental stages in ants (Morandin *et al.* 2019). The temperature-sensitive expression of a histone demethylase controls the expression of the sex-determining gene, *DMRT1*, in red-eared slider turtles (*Trachemys scripta elegans*), demonstrating how epigenetic mechanisms can mediate environmentally dependent sex determination (Ge *et al.* 2018).

Other studies have found support for the potential contribution of epigenetic variation to evolutionary change (Niederhuth and Schmitz 2017). In *A. thaliana*, DMRs accounted for 60–90% of the heritability in flowering time and root length variation in isogenic (i.e. possess the same genotype) lines (Cortijo *et al.* 2014) suggesting that natural selection can act on epigenetic variants. Such variants can also arise through hybridisation, even between lines within

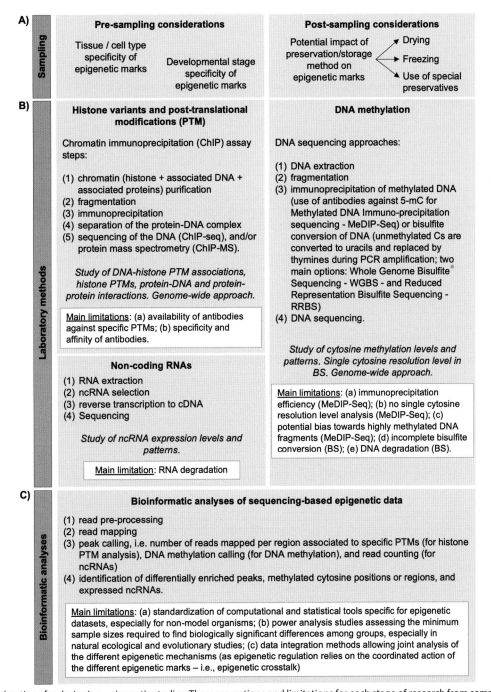

Fig. 18.2. Considerations for designing epigenetic studies. There are options and limitations for each stage of research from sample collection (A) to laboratory methods (B) and bioinformatic analysis (C).

species (Schmid *et al.* 2018). In other cases, **epigenetic imprinting** of genes could lead to reproductive isolation and speciation through parent-of-origin defects in hybrids (Vrana 2007). For example, hybrids of the deer mouse *Peromyscus maniculatus* and *P. polionotus* showed altered growth and development associated with the loss of DNA methylation and altered expression of gene clusters located within imprinted regions (Wiley *et al.* 2008).

To date, most of our mechanistic understanding of the functional role of the epigenome is based on the study of only a few representatives of the tree of life (e.g. model organisms or species of economic importance), and a limited number of ecological contexts even though the epigenomic landscape varies greatly across taxa (Schmitz *et al.* 2019) (Box 18.1). Similarly, our knowledge of the different epigenetic mechanisms is strongly biased towards DNA methylation, and not as much is known about histone modifications and non-coding RNAs. Each of these epigenetic mechanisms has generally been studied in isolation even though they engage in complex interactions that shape genome structure and functioning (Ben-Porath and Cedar 2001; Winter and Fischle 2010). As a result, we currently have an incomplete and potentially distorted view of the epigenome and its effect on genome function. These limitations create barriers to the practical implementation of epigenetics, especially in fields like the conservation of biodiversity (Fig. 18.2). Still, insights and technologies developed so far are promising.

In this chapter, we review the evidence for human-driven, environmentally induced epigenetic changes in plants and animals. We discuss the potential application of this knowledge in the fields of ecotoxicology, food production, and conservation. As with genomic applications more generally, the application of these approaches aims to mitigate some of the most urgent challenges derived from the current situation of global environmental change.

PRACTICAL APPLICATIONS OF EPIGENETIC RESEARCH

Two key characteristics of the epigenome suggest that such information could be useful for practical applications: it is sensitive to the environment (e.g. Dowen *et al.* 2012; Foust *et al.* 2016; McNew *et al.* 2017; Hu *et al.* 2018; Furlong *et al.* 2020; Sagonas *et al.* 2020; Lim *et al.* 2021) and its partially stable within and between generations (i.e. **epigenetic memory** (Verhoeven *et al.* 2010; Rubenstein *et al.* 2016; Weyrich *et al.* 2016). These characteristics provide both a signal of the environment, or 'epigenetic footprint', in the

genome of individuals, as well as a target to engineer the phenotypes of interest. The responsiveness of the epigenome can be used for environmental biomonitoring and ecotoxicology, since exposure to environmental stressors and toxicants can leave behind characteristic signatures or epigenetic biomarkers (Suarez-Ulloa *et al.* 2015). Similarly, epigenomic signals may be useful for monitoring wildlife populations or captive-reared plants and animals, allowing us to 'fingerprint' and delimit populations of conservation interest (Beal *et al.* 2020; Rey *et al.* 2020). In the future, targeted manipulation of epigenetic marks could be used to improve crop and livestock productivity, quality, and biotic and abiotic stress resistance (Ibeagha-Awemu and Zhao 2015; Álvarez-Venegas and De-la-Peña 2016; Ibeagha-Awemu and Khatib 2017). Although current technologies may not yet permit immediate application of these ideas, the growing expansion of epigenetics in many different taxa, including non-model organisms, hints at a burgeoning number of possibilities.

Epigenetic responses in toxicological research

The 'epigenetic footprint' induced by the environment in an organism's epigenome could be used in the future to retrace the specific environmental stressors that the organism has experienced throughout its lifetime (Mirbahai and Chipman 2014). Clear evidence of this footprint comes from environmental epigenetics studies that document stable epigenetic effects, and associated phenotypic consequences, as a result of chemical and toxicant exposure (Eirin-Lopez and Putnam 2019). For example, chronic exposure to heavy metals and organic pollutants induced **hypermethylation** of genes involved in oocyte development and maturation in wild females of the European eel (*Anguilla anguilla*) (Pierron *et al.* 2014). Such alterations may impact the reproductive capacity through changes in gonadal development in the affected eels. Abnormal liver development in rats after short-term exposure to hepatotoxicants has been associated with histone modifications, DNA **hypomethylation** of a long interspersed element-1 (LINE-1) transposable element, and changes in micro RNA (miRNA) abundances in the liver tissues in a dose-dependent manner (Miousse *et al.* 2017). Other studies in rats identified toxicant-specific heritable epigenetic signatures (i.e. DMRs as well as differential histone retention sites) and associated pathologies developed in offspring of parents exposed to fungicides, herbicides and pesticides (Manikkam *et al.* 2012; McBirney *et al.* 2017; King *et al.* 2019; Maamar *et al.* 2020). These studies across vertebrate taxa highlight a broad range of negative consequences of pollutant exposure. The fact that many of these epigenetic effects are linked to endocrine function and gonadal development (Soubry *et al.* 2014; Aulsebrook *et al.* 2020) has consequences for fertility of humans and wildlife. Moreover, these effects have disturbing implications for long-term consequences – the inheritance of some epigenetic changes means that future generations could suffer phenotypic consequences of toxicant exposure in parents or grandparents.

In plants, Wang *et al.* (2016) found significant, genome-wide DNA methylation alterations in seedlings of *A. thaliana* exposed to cadmium even before growth effects were observed. In another study, Boquete *et al.* (2022) found single cytosine methylation changes in response to cadmium and copper exposure in plants of the moss *Scopelophila cataractae* (Boquete *et al.* 2021). A considerable proportion of these changes in *S. cataractae* were common to both metals; however, almost none of them was shared among the four populations compared. This finding raises an important issue for biomarker development that it may be difficult to identify consistent changes across individuals even within the same species.

Epigenetic modifications that signal pollutant exposure during the lifetime of the individual could be used in environmental protection and ecological risk assessment programs through, for example, screening for biomarkers of exposure (Miousse *et al.* 2015; Chung and Herceg 2020). The potential for this application of research is promising. However, there is still a long road ahead, as important factors such as stress-specific and dose-dependent epigenetic modifications, tissue-specific effects, the stability of the epigenetic patterns over time and across generations, the phenotypic effects of epigenetic modifications, and the potential population-level consequences are mostly unexplored (Vandegehuchte and Janssen 2014). In addition, our capacity to implement the use of epigenetic modifications depends on the development of large databases of modifications that are stress-specific, like those already developed for biomedical molecular markers in humans (e.g. MarkerDB, https://markerdb.ca/).

EPIGENETIC MODIFICATIONS IN FOOD PRODUCTION

Insights gained from studying the effects of stressors on epigenetic modifications and phenotypes may be leveraged to improve livestock and crop health and productivity (Karavolias *et al.* 2021). The incorporation of epigenetic research into food improvement programs could help researchers manipulate phenotypic traits of interest in livestock and crops such as productivity, nutritional value,

immunity or abiotic stress resistance. Epigenetic changes have been shown to mediate the effects of nutritional imbalance on increased disease susceptibility in pigs (Cong *et al.* 2012) and altered expression of metabolic genes in the pigs' offspring (Altmann *et al.* 2013). Milk production in dairy cows is epigenetically regulated (Singh *et al.* 2010; Li *et al.* 2012), and so is fat formation in muscle tissue (Baik *et al.* 2014; Romao *et al.* 2014). As a result, targeted dietary strategies could be used to modify the expression status of epigenetically regulated genes to obtain the desired phenotype for both dairy and meat production (Doherty *et al.* 2014). For example, the expression of the myostatin gene (involved in muscle generation in cattle) could be manipulated through diet and used to enhance muscle production in livestock (Doherty *et al.* 2014). Similarly, zinc supplementation of laying hens has been used to improve the gut health and innate immune function of chicks through the epigenetic reprogramming of gene ***A20*** (Li *et al.* 2015). The link between nutrition and epigenetics is strong in part because of the interlinked pathways that are collectively referred to as 'one-carbon (1C) metabolism' (Clare *et al.* 2019). 1C metabolism refers to the biochemical reactions involved in molecular biosynthesis and maintenance, and regulation of gene expression. These cellular processes involve transfer of methenyl, formyl, and methyl groups and are mediated by dietary sources of vitamins (B2, B6, B9 and B12), methionine, and choline (betaine) (Anderson *et al.* 2012; Clare *et al.* 2019).

In plants, agronomically important traits such as flowering, fruit development, stress response and immunity are also epigenetically regulated (Tsuji *et al.* 2006; Mlynárová *et al.* 2007; Zhong *et al.* 2013; Liu *et al.* 2015; Lee *et al.* 2016; Ramirez-Prado *et al.* 2018). Hence, knowledge of the epigenetic modifications responsible for specific traits of interest could also be used to perform targeted crosses and further selection of the variants of interest (Springer and Schmitz 2017). More generally, genetic information has long been central to artificial selection in crop and livestock breeding programs. Incorporating epigenetic information in models of individuals' **true breeding value** could improve their accuracy in predicting the best candidates for the phenotypic traits of interest (Slatkin 2009; Banta and Richards 2018). Several studies have supported the idea that epigenetic variation is a source of phenotypic variance and can be selected on (Hauben *et al.* 2009; Ji *et al.* 2015; Gallusci *et al.* 2017; Shen *et al.* 2018). With this line of reasoning, David and Ricard (2019) recently developed a 'transmissibility model' that incorporates both genetic and non-genetic sources of inheritance (including epigenetic information) to improve selection in livestock. Nonetheless, we still lack information about what epigenetic modifications are functionally relevant and transgenerationally stable for domestic breeding programs (Doherty *et al.* 2014; Ibeagha-Awemu and Zhao 2015). Since sophisticated genomic toolkits are typically available for crop plants and livestock, these species can provide productive models for studying the phenotypic effects of epigenetic modifications and their inheritance patterns. Specifically, epigenome-wide association studies (EWAS) could be used to identify epimutations associated with particular phenotypes. Similar studies are commonly used to develop epigenetic biomarkers of disease in humans (e.g. Paul and Beck 2014; Campagna *et al.* 2021) and are currently being considered in crop (Gahlaut *et al.* 2020) and livestock (Ibeagha-Awemu and Zhao 2015) improvement programs.

Developing resources to manipulate plant epigenomes could be particularly useful as many commercial crops are isogenic, and are grown in dense monocultures. The absence of genetic diversity means that crops are vulnerable to pathogen infection, especially to host-adapted pathogens, and disease can quickly spread in such monocultures (Zhi and Chang 2021). Literature on crop disease resistance has demonstrated that epigenetic mechanisms play key roles in the transcriptional activation of defense-response genes (Ding *et al.* 2012; Johnson *et al.* 2015; Geng *et al.* 2019; Atighi *et al.* 2020). Hence, the substantial epigenetic and phenotypic diversity found among isogenic or near-isogenic plants (Busconi *et al.* 2015; Kitavi *et al.* 2020) could be used in crop resistance improvement through selection of resistant epigenetic variants. Additionally, studies performing targeted transformation and gene knockout of epigenetic machinery in crops have made some progress in this field. For example, silencing of histone deacetylase 701 led to enhanced resistance to two rice pathogens, the fungus *Magnaporthe oryzae* and the bacterium *Xanthomonas oryzae* pv *oryzae*, in transgenic rice (Ding *et al.* 2012). Similarly, knockout of a domains rearranged methylase 2 homolog in the wheat progenitor *Aegilops tauschii* enhanced its resistance to the fungus *Blumeria graminis* through the increased expression of genes involved in defense against this pathogen (Geng *et al.* 2019). Finally, non-targeted approaches like chemical inhibition of DNA methylation resulted in the generation of a rice line with hypomethylation and constitutive expression of the Xa21G gene, involved in rice resistance against *X. oryzae* pv *oryzae*. This line showed high resistance against this bacterium even after 10 generations (Akimoto *et al.* 2007; Box 18.2).

Box 18.2: Plant case study

Several studies demonstrated that manipulation of epigenetic mechanisms can result in increased resistance of crops to biotic and abiotic stresses, which can be leveraged to improve crop production in the face of global change without the need for the controversial genetic manipulation. One such example resulted from the manipulation of genome wide DNA methylation that produced a line of rice (*Oryza sativa* ssp. *japonica*) that was highly resistant to the bacterium *Xanthomonas oryzae* pv *oryzae* (Akimoto *et al.* 2007). Importantly, resistance to this pathogen was maintained in this line for at least 10 generations after the experimental manipulation (see Fig. 18.3).

In this research, Akimoto *et al.* (2007) exposed around 1000 rice seeds to 5-azadeoxycytidine (5-azadC), a DNA methyltransferase inhibitor that causes DNA hypomethylation. Only 35 seedlings survived this treatment, suggesting that either 5-azadC exposure was lethal for most of the plants, or random DNA hypomethylation affected loci essential for survival, or both of them. The surviving lines were grown in the laboratory until seed production. The seeds were collected and subsequently propagated in the field for nine generations (F1 to F9).

Both parent and offspring from one of these lines (L2) showed a marked phenotypic change (dwarfism) compared to the other lines and the wild-type. Further molecular analyses of DNA methylation changes in L2 identified six significantly hypomethylated DNA fragments whose sequences could be mapped to the rice genome. One of these fragments mapped to a disease resistance gene, *Xa21G*, involved in rice resistance against *X. oryzae* pv *oryzae*. This gene was consistently demethylated in F3–F9 offspring of L2, whereas it was heavily methylated in the promoter region in the wild type. While silenced in the wild type, transcripts of *Xa21G* accumulated in plants from L2 even in the absence of infection, suggesting that hypomethylation led to constitutive expression of this gene in the newly generated L2. Upon infection with *X. oryzae* pv *oryzae*, L2 plants accumulated high transcript levels of *Xa21G*, and showed increased resistance against this pathogen compared to the wild type.

These results provide an excellent example of how manipulation of epigenetic information can give rise to epigenetic variants with desirable agricultural traits. The molecular analyses carried out here enabled the authors to unravel the molecular mechanism behind this beneficial trait. This piece of information is crucial to develop tools for the targeted manipulation of epigenomes in search of increased disease resistance in this and other crops.

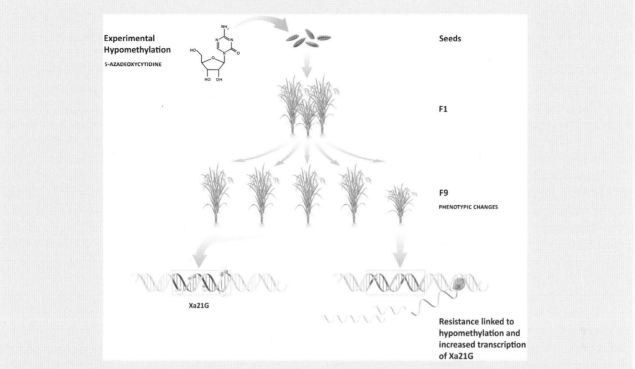

Fig. 18.3. Experimental design of the artificial epigenetic manipulation of rice (*Oryza sativa* ssp. *japonica*) resulting in a line highly resistant to the bacterium *Xanthomonas oryzae* pv *oryzae*. Illustration by Charlotte W. Holden.

Finally, crops that are propagated clonally often cannot be preserved in seed banks, meaning that conservation of these strains relies on germplasm accessions and/or cryopreservation. Tolerance to cryopreservation varies among genotypes and may be mediated by *de novo* DNA methylation (Johnston *et al.* 2009). Cryopreservation may also alter DNA methylation patterns (Kaczmarczyk *et al.* 2010). Thus, epigenetic variation may need to be considered when selecting cultivars of plants in germplasm accessions (Kitavi *et al.* 2020). A recent study found very different patterns of genetic and epigenetic variation in clonally propagated *Corydalis yanhusuo* compared to wild populations, supporting the importance of epigenetic variation in cultivation of this medicinal plant (Chen *et al.* 2020). Future studies could look for effects of cryopreservation and different preservation techniques on methylation, which would provide useful guidelines for preservation of economically important crops or plants of conservation importance.

THE IMPORTANCE OF EPIGENETIC MODIFICATIONS IN CONSERVATION

Epigenetics has been regarded as a promising field to complement genetic information in advising conservation strategies (Rey *et al.* 2020). The goal of biological conservation is to prevent the loss of biodiversity. Inherent in this goal is the challenge of determining which populations or groups of populations are 'evolutionarily significant' (Fraser and Bernatchez 2001). A variety of criteria is currently used to determine whether a group is evolutionarily distinct including phenotypic and behavioral traits, geographic distribution, and genetic information (Fraser and Bernatchez 2001). To our knowledge, epigenetic variation has not been considered in conservation or management decisions so far. However, identifying specific epigenetic modifications could prove valuable for future determinations (Ouborg *et al.* 2010). Epigenetic differences may be linked to local adaptation to the environment, and/or incipient population structure (Ouborg *et al.* 2010; McNew *et al.* 2017; Meröndun *et al.* 2019). Epigenetic variation may be particularly important for small populations and/or inbred populations, or those that have recently gone through a population bottleneck, and have little genetic variation (Medrano *et al.* 2020; Mounger, Boquete *et al.* 2021). Thus, studying epigenetic variation in genetically depauperate species may help prioritise populations for management and conservation and could even reveal cryptic species within groups with little genetic variation.

Epigenetic effects of captive rearing

In addition to delimiting groups of interest, keeping or breeding individuals in captivity may be essential interventions for critically endangered species (Cunninghame *et al.* 2015; Zhang *et al.* 2019). However, environmental changes, stress, and other effects of *ex situ* conservation may have unintended consequences on the physiology and behavior of the animals. Changes in DNA methylation may indicate both the positive and negative effects of the captive rearing environment (Zhang *et al.* 2019; Berbel-Filho *et al.* 2020). Changes to diet have specifically been associated with epigenetic effects in this context. For example, there were significant differences in the DNA methylation and transcriptomic profiles of golden snub-nosed monkeys *Rhinopithecus roxellana* living in the wild vs. under two different feeding regimes in captivity (Zhang *et al.* 2019). Even less-intensive interventions, such as supplemental feeding, could have epigenetic implications. Free-living baboons (*Papio cynocephalus*) that had access to human food had significantly different DNA methylation levels compared to free-living baboons foraging naturally in a savannah environment (Lea *et al.* 2016). More research on the phenotypic consequences of epigenetic modifications induced by captive rearing and their reversibility before or after reintroduction should allow us to better predict the potential of species reintroduction programs to succeed.

In fish, several studies have now reported inheritance of epigenetic changes in captive-raised compared to wild-born individuals (Gavery *et al.* 2018; Rodriguez Barreto *et al.* 2019; Nilsson *et al.* 2021). Epigenetic differences between hatchery and wild-born fish have been found in a variety of genes including those linked to behaviors such as responses to social stress and aggression as well as cellular processes such as nucleic acid binding (Gavery *et al.* 2018; Rodriguez Barreto *et al.* 2019). These changes are important to identify because captive-raised fish may inadvertently escape aquaculture facilities or may be intentionally released into the wild to bolster populations (Rodriguez Barreto *et al.* 2019). Epigenetic studies may prove useful in identifying why many captive-born fish have lower fitness than wild-bred ones and identifying the molecular basis of other phenotypic changes in hatchery fish (Tave and Hutson 2019; O'Sullivan *et al.* 2020; Nilsson *et al.* 2021). In addition, these epigenetic modifications could potentially be used alongside morphological, genetic and physiological signs to identify and track the spread of fish escaped from hatcheries (Fiske *et al.* 2005).

Ex situ conservation programs have long worked to minimise deleterious genetic consequences of keeping animals in captivity (Williams and Hoffman 2009; Lynch and O'Hely 2001). However, given the sensitivity of epigenetic mechanisms to the external environment, we suggest that management strategies also plan to monitor for epimutations and associated phenotypic consequences of captivity. At the same time, 'epigenetic programming' presents an intriguing possibility for leveraging epigenetic variation to improve aquaculture, crops, and/or wildlife breeding programs (Moghadam *et al.* 2015; Springer and Schmitz 2017). Although we do not yet have the ability to induce epimutations in wild animals (see 'epigenetic engineering' below), one idea involves using specific diets to manipulate DNA methylation and/or histone modifications thereby influencing phenotypes (Moghadam *et al.* 2015). Advances in our ability to understand and manipulate epigenetic mutations may therefore be used to promote species conservation.

Epigenetic modifications through ageing

Methylation of certain cytosines changes predictably over the lifetime of an individual, making 'epigenetic clocks' a potentially valuable tool for ageing animals (Chapter 7). In humans, a limited panel of cytosines showed a 73% association with age (Bocklandt *et al.* 2011; Horvath 2013; Fei *et al.* 2021). Epigenetic clocks have recently been developed for species that are difficult to age non-invasively including chimpanzees (Ito *et al.* 2018), cetaceans (Polanowski *et al.* 2014; Bors *et al.* 2021), seabirds (De Paoli-Iseppi *et al.* 2019), canids (Thompson *et al.* 2017), and fish (Mayne *et al.* 2021). These studies report the ability to estimate the age of individuals very precisely by interrogating just a handful of cytosines (~ e.g. <30; Ito *et al.* 2018; Bors *et al.* 2021; Mayne *et al.* 2021). The utility of non-destructive biomarkers for age is immense; accurate age data from a population aid in demography studies and estimations of population growth (Fig. 18.4). For individuals of known chronological age, epigenetic clocks may also be used to identify individuals at advanced 'biological age' who may be at heightened risk for age-related disorders (Bocklandt *et al.* 2011). Epigenetic clocks thus have applications for fisheries management (Anastasiadi and Piferrer 2020; Mayne *et al.* 2021) and wildlife conservation (Polanowski *et al.* 2014; Bors *et al.* 2021). For the moment, epigenetic clocks appear to require species-specific calibration (Mayne *et al.* 2021). However, as more useful loci are discovered, these modifications could be used for broad-ranging studies of age structure in communities using non-invasive sampling techniques such as faecal metabarcoding and environmental DNA sampling. For example, an epigenetic clock could be used to estimate

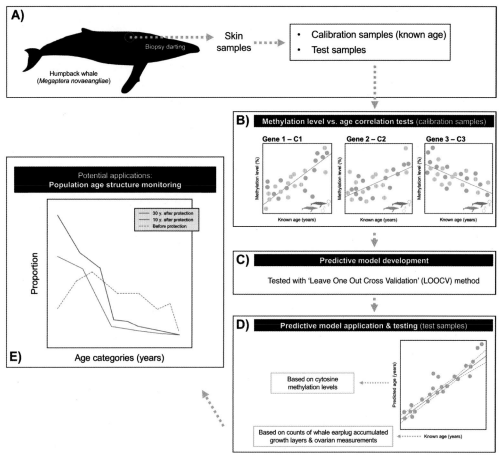

Fig. 18.4. Example of the development and application of non-destructive epigenetic biomarkers of age in population monitoring programs, based on the Humpback Epigenetic Age Assay (HEAA) developed by Polanowski *et al.* (Polanowski *et al.* 2014). Skin tissue is collected from wild humpback whales using biopsy darting (A). A set of samples of known age, 'calibration samples', are used to perform regression tests between the methylation level of a selection of cytosine positions and the age of the samples (B). These positions were selected based on their location in genes with known age-related epigenetic changes in humans and mice. Cytosine positions with the strongest significant correlation with age are selected and used to build a model to predict the age of the samples according to their methylation status in those positions (C). The predictive capacity of this model is tested against a set of 'test samples' whose actual age had been previously estimated using destructive methods like earplug growth layer counting and ovarian measurements (D). Finally, the model is hypothetically applied to describe population age structure changes over time before and after a population of humpback whales were protected from fishing (E). See also Chapter 7.

demography of fish populations sampled through faecal metabarcoding of seabirds (McInnes *et al.* 2017). Faecal metabarcoding of piscivorous birds provides an efficient way of monitoring temporal and spatial variation in fish diversity and thus has applications for wildlife conservation as well as management of economically important fisheries. However, unlike traditional methods of fisheries monitoring, metabarcoding does not provide information on the size of fish, age structure, or other demographic parameters. Applying an epigenetic clock to studies of metabarcoding could amplify the utility of this method by efficiently characterising not only fish diversity, but also the age structure of those populations. Implementation of this technique will require the identification of modifications that can be used as a 'common clock' for multiple fish

species of interest, as well as 'metaepigenomic' bioinformatic methods that can separate individuals within a pooled sample.

Epigenetic modifications in invasive species

Invasive species can be demographically similar to threatened populations: they often have small population sizes that have experienced a population bottleneck and resulting loss of genetic variation (Allendorf and Lundquist 2003). How can invasive species be so successful despite the apparent negative consequences of founder effects and population bottlenecks? This so-called 'invasive species paradox' is not as common as we once thought thanks to multiple introductions, novel genomic interactions or reduced diversity following rapid selection in the invaded

Box 18.3: Animal case study

Recent research is providing insights into how epigenetic mechanisms mediate rapid adaptation of wild animals to environmental change. These studies have applications for anticipating the consequences of climate change on animal and plant populations as well as understanding how invasive species successfully spread in novel environments. In one experiment, researchers transplanted brown anole lizards *Anolis sagrei* from a larger island to eight smaller lizard-free islands (Hu *et al.* 2019). The experimental islands varied in vegetation cover and climate and half were considered 'high quality' habitat while others were 'low quality'.

After just 4 days on the islands, the researchers documented significant changes in liver methylation of lizards that were transplanted to low-quality islands. They identified 29 significant differentially methylated cytosines between the source population and lizards transplanted to low-quality islands. Moreover, across all individuals, average daily temperature was a significant predictor of variation in methylation. However, translocation is not always correlated with epigenetic change. Lizards moved to high-quality islands had minimal methylation differences compared with the source population. These results suggest that the extent of epigenetic changes that individuals undergo may be related to the degree of environmental stress that they experience.

These results are striking because they demonstrate that epigenetic changes associated with environmental change can occur within days. Methylation changes in lizards transplanted to low-quality islands were associated with genes with potentially relevant functional roles including the immune response, cellular signalling and the circadian rhythm. However, whether these changes are permanent, or even heritable, is not yet known. Further work in this area is also needed to understand how these epigenetic changes affect gene expression and phenotype, and whether the changes are adaptive.

Fig. 18.5. Brown anole (*Anolis sagrei*). Wikimedia Commons.

habitat (Estoup *et al.* 2016). However, some invasive species truly have limited genetic diversity and several studies have shown that epigenetic diversity may provide an important source of phenotypic variation (Baumel *et al.* 2001; Gao *et al.* 2010; Richards *et al.* 2012; Zhang *et al.* 2016; Sarma *et al.* 2020, 2021). Moreover, introduced populations may have increased epigenetic diversity compared to native populations (Schrey *et al.* 2012; Liebl *et al.* 2015; Hawes *et al.* 2018). For example, Ardura *et al.* (2017) documented differences in global DNA methylation in two different species of mussels between each species' native and invasive ranges. Differences were associated with stress factors such as changes to salinity and anthropogenic pressures, suggesting that environmental stress associated with a new environment can induce epigenetic change, and that perhaps these changes may help introduced species establish in novel environments. Similarly, experimental evidence using wild animals demonstrates that epigenetic profiles can shift rapidly in response to a novel environment. An experimental study followed colonisation of small Caribbean Islands with brown anole lizards (*Anolis sagrei*) (Hu *et al.* 2019) (Box 18.3). After just 4 days on the islands,

variation in DNA methylation in the livers of recaptured lizards was significantly associated with temperature of the new island. Some differentially methylated cytosines were identified among lizards that were translocated to islands of poorer quality. These insights into the mechanisms of rapid adaptation of invasive species may help anticipate the effects of climate change and other anthropogenic sources of environmental change. The development of tools to manipulate the epigenome (below) may also provide ways to curb the spread of harmful invasive species.

TECHNOLOGICAL OPPORTUNITIES AND LIMITATIONS

Advances in laboratory techniques and bioinformatic analyses have greatly expanded our abilities to interrogate epigenetic polymorphisms in model and non-model organisms. Currently, most epigenetic research focuses on DNA methylation. DNA methylation is appealing for study because it does not require special preservation of the sample; protocols typically start with extracted, purified DNA from any source. However, sample storage technique and time do appear to affect methylation, so researchers should consider these potential confounding effects when designing sequencing experiments (Husby 2022). Common techniques for identifying methylation polymorphisms are bisulfite sequencing, immunoprecipitation (MeDIP), and methylation-sensitive amplification length polymorphism (MS-AFLP) (Sepers *et al.* 2019). Bisulfite sequencing has emerged as the gold standard in this arena; however, whole-genome bisulfite sequencing (WGBS) is still expensive. Consequently, many studies opt for reduced-representation bisulfite sequencing (RRBS or **epiGBS**), which allows for genome-wide, albeit sparse characterisation of the methylome (Paun *et al.* 2019; Husby 2022). Also, bisulfite conversion severely degrades DNA. Wherefore, newer methods are being developed that rely on the enzymatic conversion of unmethylated cytosines to uracils without affecting the integrity of the DNA (Feng *et al.* 2020). New technologies in long-read (nanopore) sequencing have the exciting potential to cost-effectively interrogate many more positions in the methylome (Amarasinghe *et al.* 2020). This technology is also exciting because it may allow for faster, portable sequencing options that would facilitate epigenetic profiling of individuals in the field.

A currently unresolved issue in studies of ecological epigenetics is how much sequencing is required to detect meaningful differences between groups. Many studies are potentially underpowered (Lea *et al.* 2017) and publishing bias for significant results may give the impression that epigenetic variation is more important than it actually is. Unlike genomic variation, it is difficult to know what degree of epigenomic differentiation is functionally relevant, and few studies use simulated data or randomisation approaches to determine whether observed epigenetic differences between groups could have occurred by chance (McNew *et al.* 2021).

Another important consideration for studies of wild populations is the choice of sample tissue. Many epigenetic modifications are expected to be tissue-specific (Horvath 2013; Gutierrez-Arcelus *et al.* 2015); however, in wild or protected populations it is often not possible to destructively sample individuals, or take samples from particular tissues. In addition, samples from long-term studies and museum collections may be powerful troves of studies of epigenetic variation over time, as long as their sample types are appropriate to the question at hand (Taff *et al.* 2019; Hahn *et al.* 2020). Studies in wild animals do show differences in methylation between somatic and germ cells (McNew *et al.* 2017); however, some evidence suggests that commonly available tissues (e.g. blood) may be useful

proxies for detecting epigenetic effects (Husby 2020; McNew *et al.* 2021). In a study of nestling birds, McNew *et al.* (2021) found methylation differences in blood of zebra finches (*Taeniopygia guttata*) exposed to a pyrethroid insecticide in the nest. Even though this insecticide probably had more direct effects on other tissues (e.g. skin during exposure, liver during detoxification), methylation changes in genes associated with pyrethroid detoxification were visible in the blood. This result suggests that easily sampled tissues including blood may still be useful for epigenetic studies where individuals cannot be sampled destructively.

Leveraging non-destructive samples and existing collections is a powerful way to investigate epigenetic variation over time (Hahn *et al.* 2020). Recent advances in the extraction of DNA from fixed tissues, dried specimens, and other 'ancient' samples opens the opportunity to test how events such as urbanisation, species introductions, or changes in climate have affected the epigenome. However, not all epigenetic techniques are available for these studies. Although DNA methylation may be preserved in a wide array of tissue types, it may also change over time in storage (Husby 2022). Histone modifications and small RNAs are more sensitive to degradation and thus may only be assayed in fresh or specially preserved samples (Hahn *et al.* 2020).

FUTURE DIRECTIONS AND OUTSTANDING QUESTIONS
Epigenetic editing

It is becoming clear that epigenetic variation underlies phenotypic differences and can be involved in rapid adaptation to environmental change. These insights present exciting possibilities for 'epigenetic editing' to improve biotic and abiotic stress resistance, control pests and invasive species, or for the conservation of threatened populations. Currently, we lack the ability to manipulate DNA methylation or other epigenetic markers in a predictable manner in natural populations. However, several tools are being developed that may eventually prove useful for management and conservation (Cano-Rodriguez and Rots 2016). Methods currently in development for epigenomic editing include zinc-finger proteins, transcriptional activator-like effectors and clustered regularly interspaced short palindromic repeats (CRISPR) (Thakore *et al.* 2016; Yim *et al.* 2020). While many of these tools were developed to alter DNA sequence at specific loci, they have recently been adapted to control transcription of particular genes instead (Yim *et al.* 2020).

CRISPR/Cas9 systems are particularly promising for epigenetic editing (Nakamura *et al.* 2021). CRISPR gene editing was adapted from a bacterial immune system which recognises and cleaves specific DNA sequences (Yim *et al.* 2020). The Cas9 endonuclease is bound to a guide RNA that allows the complex to be guided to specific sites in the genome. This system has been expanded to specifically manipulate transcription of genes through the fusion of Cas9 with various proteins, modifications that are referred to as CRISPR activation (CRISPRa) and CRISPR interference (CRISPRi) (Yim *et al.* 2020). Fusion with the transcriptional activator VP64 increases chromatin accessibility, increasing transcription at targeted sites, while fusion with the **Krüppel associated box (KRAB)** repressor recruits heterochromatin-modifying enzymes to the transcription start site (TSS) region, inhibiting transcription (Thakore *et al.* 2016).

This technology also may be used to test hypotheses about the functional effects of methylation and/or manipulate methylation for clinical or conservation purposes. For example, CRISPR-Cas9 has been adapted to manipulate DNA methylation by fusing a Cas9 to the catalytic domain of DNA methyltransferase 3A (DNMT3A), the most active methyltransferase in humans (Vojta *et al.* 2016). This complex allowed the researchers to combine the genomic targeting abilities of Cas9 with the methyltransferase activity of DNMT3A and successfully manipulate CpG methylation in the promoter regions of two targeted genes (Vojta *et al.* 2016). Although these technologies are exciting, more work is needed to identify genomic regions where editing can have a specific phenotypic effect. In addition, CRISPR-Cas9 gene editing can have non-target effects, which presents risk for application in a clinical or wild setting. Although strategies are being developed to avoid non-target edits (Naeem *et al.* 2020), it is unclear when the precision of epigenomic editing will be safe enough for use in a clinical or wild population setting.

These technologies have the exciting potential to engineer the epigenome to improve conservation, food production, and human health. However, these tools are still in development and there are several outstanding questions about their utility. For instance, it is unclear whether epigenetic edits are stable within the lifetime of the individual and/or are heritable to offspring. The stability of epigenetic edits is particularly important to understand because stability will affect how often, and at what point(s) editing interventions will be needed. In addition, it is unknown whether edits can be targeted to specific tissues, and to what degree epigenetic reprogramming is affected by the chromatin microenvironment and/or expression of genes in interacting networks (Cano-Rodriguez and Rots 2016).

DISCUSSION TOPICS

1. Can functional epigenetic variation arise independent of genetic variation? Even though some studies reported the occurrence of pure epigenetic variants (i.e. independent of any genetic variants) (Shen *et al.* 2018; Xu *et al.* 2019), evidence suggests that a significant proportion of epigenetic variation can be attributed to genetic variation in the epigenetic machinery (Dubin *et al.* 2015; Sasaki *et al.* 2019). This effect, however, is not unidirectional. Epigenetic mechanisms can also affect genome evolution for instance because of a higher frequency of cytosine to thymine mutations when cytosines are methylated (Coulondre *et al.* 1978; Duncan and Miller 1980), and because epigenetically mediated chromatin conformation alters access of the DNA repair machinery (Yi and Goodisman 2021).

2. Are stress/environmentally induced epigenetic changes inherited? Evidence is still mixed about the extent to which epigenetic changes accumulated during an organism's lifetime can escape epigenetic reprogramming. The majority of epigenetic modifications are thought to be erased during early development (Feng *et al.* 2010b); however, various laboratory and observational studies have documented inheritance of epigenetic changes (Akimoto *et al.* 2007; Heijmans *et al.* 2008; Guerrero-Bosagna *et al.* 2010; Serpeloni *et al.* 2017; Legoff *et al.* 2019). To what extent are epigenetic changes heritable, and how should future studies consider 'epigenetic evolution'?

3. What is the role of DNA methylation in genome function? The effect of DNA methylation on gene expression is still unclear as it differs depending on the sequence context, the genic region, and varies tremendously across taxa (Schmitz *et al.* 2019). Ecological epigenetics studies commonly report differences in DNA methylation between treatment groups or taxa (e.g. Watson *et al.* 2020; McNew *et al.* 2021). Do we have the ability to infer the functional effects of these differences on phenotype?

REFERENCES

Akimoto K, Katakami H, Kim H-J, Ogawa E, Sano CM *et al.* (2007) Epigenetic inheritance in rice plants. *Annals of Botany* **100**, 205–217. doi:10.1093/aob/mcm110

Allendorf FW, Lundquist LL (2003) Introduction: Population biology, evolution, and control of invasive species. *Conservation Biology* **17**, 24–30

Altmann S, Murani E, Schwerin M, Metges CC, Wimmers K *et al.* (2013) Dietary protein restriction and excess of pregnant German Landrace sows induce changes in hepatic gene expression and promoter methylation of key metabolic genes in the offspring. *The Journal of Nutritional Biochemistry* **24**, 484–495. doi:10.1016/j.jnutbio.2012.01.011

Álvarez-Venegas R, De-la-Peña C (2016) Editorial: Recent advances of epigenetics in crop biotechnology. *Frontiers in Plant Science* **7**, 413. doi:10.3389/fpls.2016.00413

Amarasinghe SL, Su S, Dong X, Zappia L, Ritchie ME, *et al.* (2020) Opportunities and challenges in long-read sequencing data analysis. *Genome Biology* **21**, 30. doi:10.1186/s13059-020-1935-5

Anastasiadi D, Piferrer F (2020) A clockwork fish: Age prediction using DNA methylation-based biomarkers in the European seabass. *Molecular Ecology Resources* **20**, 387–397. doi:10.1111/1755-0998.13111

Anderson OS, Sant KE, Dolinoy DC (2012) Nutrition and epigenetics: an interplay of dietary methyl donors, one-carbon metabolism and DNA methylation. *The Journal of Nutritional Biochemistry* **23**, 853–859. doi:10.1016/j.jnutbio.2012.03.003

Angers B, Perez M, Menicucci T, Leung C (2020) Sources of epigenetic variation and their applications in natural populations. *Evolutionary Applications* **13**, 1262–1278. doi:10.1111/eva.12946

Ardura A, Zaiko A, Morán P, Planes S, Garcia-Vazquez E *et al.* (2017) Epigenetic signatures of invasive status in populations of marine invertebrates. *Scientific Reports* **7**, 42193. doi:10.1038/srep42193

Arim M, Abades SR, Neill PE, Lima M, Marquet PA *et al.* (2006) Spread dynamics of invasive species. *Proceedings of the National Academy of Sciences* **103**, 374–378. doi:10.1073/pnas.0504272102

Ashe A, Colot V, Oldroyd BP (2021) How does epigenetics influence the course of evolution? *Philosophical Transactions of the Royal Society B: Biological Sciences* **376**, 20200111. doi:10.1098/rstb.2020.0111

Atighi MR, Verstraeten B, De Meyer T, Kyndt T (2020) Genome-wide DNA hypomethylation shapes nematode pattern-triggered immunity in plants. *New Phytologist* **227**, 545–558. doi:10.1111/nph.16532

Aulsebrook LC, Bertram MG, Martin JM, Aulsebrook AE, Brodin T, *et al.* (2020) Reproduction in a polluted world: implications for wildlife. *Reproduction* **160**, R13–R23. doi:10.1530/REP-20-0154

Baik M, Vu TTT, Piao MY, Kang HJ (2014) Association of DNA methylation levels with tissue-specific expression of adipogenic and lipogenic genes in longissimus dorsi muscle of Korean cattle. *Asian-Australasian Journal of Animal Sciences* **27**, 1493–1498. doi:10.5713/ajas.2014.14283

Bannister AJ, Kouzarides T (2011) Regulation of chromatin by histone modifications. *Cell Research* **21**, 381–395. doi:10.1038/cr.2011.22

Banta JA, Richards CL (2018) Quantitative epigenetics and evolution. *Heredity* **121**, 210–224. doi:10.1038/s41437-018-0114-x

Bartee L, Shriner W, Creech C (2017) Eukaryotic epigenetic regulation. In: *Principles of Biology.* Open Oregon Educational Resources, Oregon, USA.

Baumel A, Ainouche ML, Levasseur JE (2001) Molecular investigations in populations of *Spartina anglica* C.E. Hubbard (Poaceae) invading coastal Brittany (France). *Molecular Ecology* **10**, 1689–1701. doi:10.1046/j.1365-294X.2001.01299.x

Beal A, Rodriguez-Casariego J, Rivera-Casas C, Suarez-Ulloa V, Eirin-Lopez JM, *et al.* (2020) Environmental Epigenomics and Its Applications in Marine Organisms. In: *Population Genomics: Marine Organisms.* (Eds Oleksiak MF, Rajora OP) pp. 325–359. Springer International Publishing, Cham.

Becker C, Hagmann J, Müller J, Koenig D, Stegle O, *et al.* (2011) Spontaneous epigenetic variation in the *Arabidopsis thaliana* methylome. *Nature* **480**, 245–249. doi:10.1038/nature10555

Ben-Porath I, Cedar H (2001) Epigenetic Crosstalk. *Molecular Cell* **8**, 933–935. doi:10.1016/S1097-2765(01)00399-9

Berbel-Filho WM, Berry N, Rodríguez-Barreto D, Rodrigues Teixeira S, Garcia de Leaniz C, *et al.* (2020) Environmental enrichment induces intergenerational behavioural and epigenetic effects on fish. *Molecular Ecology* **29**, 2288–2299. doi:10.1111/mec.15481

Bocklandt S, Lin W, Sehl ME, Sánchez FJ, Sinsheimer JS, *et al.* (2011) Epigenetic Predictor of Age. *PLOS ONE* **6**, e14821. doi:10.1371/journal.pone.0014821

Boquete MT, Lang I, Weidinger M, Richards CL, Alonso C (2021) Patterns and mechanisms of heavy metal accumulation and tolerance in two terrestrial moss species with contrasting habitat specialization. *Environmental and Experimental Botany* **182**, 104336. doi:10.1016/j.envexpbot.2020.104336

Boquete MT, Schmid MW, Wagemaker NCAM, Carey SB, McDaniel SF, *et al.* (2022) Molecular basis of intraspecific differentiation for heavy metal tolerance in the copper moss *Scopelophila cataractae. Environmental and Experimental Botany* **201**, 104970. doi:10.1016/j.envexpbot.2022.104970

Bors EK, Baker CS, Wade PR, O'Neill KB, Shelden KE, *et al.* (2021) An epigenetic clock to estimate the age of living beluga whales. *Evolutionary Applications* **14**, 1263–1273. doi:10.1111/eva.13195

Brei M, Pérez-Barahona A, Strobl E (2016) Environmental pollution and biodiversity: Light pollution and sea turtles in the Caribbean. *Journal of Environmental Economics and Management* **77**, 95–116. doi:10.1016/j.jeem.2016.02.003

Busconi M, Colli L, Sánchez RA, Santaella M, De-Los-Mozos Pascual M, *et al.* (2015) AFLP and MS-AFLP analysis of the variation within Saffron Crocus (*Crocus sativus* L.) Germplasm. *PLOS ONE* **10**, e0123434. doi:10.1371/journal.pone.0123434

Camill P (2010) Global Change: An Overview. https://www.nature.com/scitable/knowledge/library/global-change-an-overview-13255365/. Accessed 22 Jan 2021

Campagna MP, Xavier A, Lechner-Scott J, Maltby V, Scott RJ, *et al.* (2021) Epigenome-wide association studies: Current knowledge, strategies and recommendations. *Clinical Epigenetics* **13**, 214. doi:10.1186/s13148-021-01200-8

Cano-Rodriguez D, Rots MG (2016) Epigenetic editing: On the verge of reprogramming gene expression at will. *Current Genetic Medicine Reports* **4**, 170–179. doi:10.1007/s40142-016-0104-3

Casadesús J, Low DA (2013) Programmed heterogeneity: Epigenetic mechanisms in bacteria. *Journal of Biological Chemistry* **288**, 13929–13935. doi:10.1074/jbc.R113.472274

Chen C, Zheng Z, Bao Y, Zhang H, Richards CL, *et al.* (2020) Comparisons of natural and cultivated populations of *Corydalis yanhusuo* indicate divergent patterns of genetic and epigenetic variation. *Frontiers in Plant Science* **11**, 985. doi:10.3389/fpls.2020.00985

Chevin L-M, Lande R, Mace GM (2010) Adaptation, plasticity, and extinction in a changing environment: Towards a predictive theory. *PLOS Biology* **8**, e1000357. doi:10.1371/journal.pbio.1000357

Chung FF-L, Herceg Z (2020) The promises and challenges of toxico-epigenomics: Environmental chemicals and their impacts on the epigenome. *Environmental Health Perspectives* **128**, 015001. doi:10.1289/EHP6104

Clare CE, Brassington AH, Kwong WY, Sinclair KD (2019) One-carbon metabolism: Linking nutritional biochemistry to epigenetic programming of long-term development. *Annual Review of Animal Biosciences* **7**, 263–287. doi:10.1146/annurev-animal-020518-115206

Cong R, Jia Y, Li R, Ni Y, Yang X, et al. (2012) Maternal low-protein diet causes epigenetic deregulation of HMGCR and CYP7α1 in the liver of weaning piglets. *Journal of Nutritional Biochemistry* **23**, 1647–1654. doi:10.1016/j.jnutbio.2011.11.007

Cortijo S, Wardenaar R, Colomé-Tatché M, Gilly A, Etcheverry M, et al. (2014) Mapping the epigenetic basis of complex traits. *Science* **343**, 1145–1148. doi:10.1126/science.1248127

Coulondre C, Miller JH, Farabaugh PJ, Gilbert W (1978) Molecular basis of base substitution hotspots in Escherichia coli. *Nature* **274**, 775–780. doi:10.1038/274775a0

Crowl TA, Crist TO, Parmenter RR, Belovsky G, Lugo AE, et al. (2008) The spread of invasive species and infectious disease as drivers of ecosystem change. *Frontiers in Ecology and the Environment* **6**, 238–246. doi:10.1890/070151

Cubas P, Vincent C, Coen E (1999) An epigenetic mutation responsible for natural variation in floral symmetry. *Nature* **401**, 157–161. doi:10.1038/43657

Cunninghame F, Switzer R, Parks B, Young G, Carrión A, et al. (2015) Conserving the critically endangered mangrove finch: Head-starting to increase population size. Galapagos Report 2013-2014. pp. 151–157. GNPD, GCREG, CDF and GC. Puerto Ayora, Galapagos, Ecuador.

David I, Ricard A (2019) A unified model for inclusive inheritance in livestock species. *Genetics* **212**, 1075–1099. doi:10.1534/genetics.119.302375

De Paoli-Iseppi R, Deagle BE, Polanowski AM, McMahon CR, Dickinson JL, et al. (2019) Age estimation in a long-lived seabird (*Ardenna tenuirostris*) using DNA methylation-based biomarkers. *Molecular Ecology Resources* **19**, 411–425. doi:10.1111/1755-0998.12981

Denkena J, Johannes F, Colomé-Tatché M (2021) Region-level epimutation rates in *Arabidopsis thaliana*. *Heredity* **127**, 190–202. doi:10.1038/s41437-021-00441-w

Ding B, Bellizzi M del R, Ning Y, Meyers BC, Wang GL (2012) HDT701, a histone H4 deacetylase, negatively regulates plant innate immunity by modulating histone H4 acetylation of defense-related genes in rice. *Plant Cell* **24**, 3783–3794. doi:10.1105/tpc.112.101972

Doherty R, Farrelly CO, Meade KG (2014) Comparative epigenetics: Relevance to the regulation of production and health traits in cattle. *Animal Genetics* **45**, 3–14. doi:10.1111/age.12140

Dowen RH, Pelizzola M, Schmitz RJ, Lister R, Dowen JM, et al. (2012) Widespread dynamic DNA methylation in response to

biotic stress. *Proceedings of the National Academy of Sciences of the United States of America* **109**, E2183–E2191. doi:10.1073/pnas.1209329109

Dubin MJ, Zhang P, Meng D, Remigereau MS, Osborne EJ, et al. (2015) DNA methylation in Arabidopsis has a genetic basis and shows evidence of local adaptation. *eLife* **4**, e05255. doi:10.7554/eLife.05255

Duncan BK, Miller JH (1980) Mutagenic deamination of cytosine residues in DNA. *Nature* **287**, 560–561. doi:10.1038/287560a0

Eirin-Lopez JM, Putnam HM (2019) Marine environmental epigenetics. *Annual Review of Marine Science* **11**, 335–368. doi:10.1146/annurev-marine-010318-095114

Elmqvist T, Fragkias M, Goodness J, Güneralp B, Marcotullio PJ, et al. (eds) (2013) *Urbanization, Biodiversity and Ecosystem Services: Challenges and Opportunities: A Global Assessment.* Springer, Netherlands.

Epler Barbercheck CR, Bullitt E, Andersson M (2018) Bacterial Adhesion Pili. In *Membrane Protein Complexes: Structure and Function.* (Eds JR Harris, EJ Boekema) pp. 1–18. Springer, Singapore.

Estoup A, Ravigné V, Hufbauer R, Vitalis R, Gautier M, et al. (2016) Is there a genetic paradox of biological invasion? *Annual Review of Ecology, Evolution, and Systematics* **47**, 51–72. doi:10.1146/annurev-ecolsys-121415-032116

Fei Z, Raj K, Horvath S, Lu A (2021) Universal DNA methylation age across mammalian tissues. *Innovation in Aging* **5**, 412. doi:10.1093/geroni/igab046.1588

Feng S, Jacobsen SE, Reik W (2010a) Conservation and divergence of methylation patterning in plants and animals. *Proceedings of the National Academy of Sciences* **107**, 8689–8694. doi:10.1073/pnas.1002720107

Feng S, Jacobsen SE, Reik W (2010b) Epigenetic reprogramming in plant and animal development. *Science* **330**, 622–627. doi:10.1126/science.1190614

Feng S, Zhong Z, Wang M, Jacobsen SE (2020) Efficient and accurate determination of genome-wide DNA methylation patterns in *Arabidopsis thaliana* with enzymatic methyl sequencing. *Epigenetics & Chromatin* **13**, 42. doi:10.1186/s13072-020-00361-9

Fiske P, Lund RA, Hansen LP (2005) Chapter 31 – Identifying fish farm escapees. In *Stock Identification Methods.* (Eds SX Cadrin, KD Friedland, JR Waldman) pp. 659–680. Academic Press, Burlington.

Forsman A, Wennersten L (2016) Inter-individual variation promotes ecological success of populations and species: evidence from experimental and comparative studies. *Ecography* **39**, 630–648. doi:10.1111/ecog.01357

Foust CM, Preite V, Robertson MH (2016) Genetic and epigenetic differences associated with environmental gradients in replicate populations of two salt marsh perennials. *Molecular Ecology* **25**, 1639–1652. doi:10.1111/mec.13522

Fraser DJ, Bernatchez L (2001) Adaptive evolutionary conservation: towards a unified concept for defining conservation units. *Molecular Ecology* **10**, 2741–2752. doi:10.1046/j.0962-1083.2001.01411.x

Furlong MA, Paul KC, Yan Q, Chuang YH, Cockburn MG, et al. (2020) An epigenome-wide association study of ambient pyrethroid pesticide exposures in California's central valley.

International Journal of Hygiene and Environmental Health **229**, 113569. doi:10.1016/j.ijheh.2020.113569

Gahlaut V, Zinta G, Jaiswal V, Kumar S (2020) Quantitative epigenetics: A new avenue for crop improvement. *Epigenomes* **4**, 25. doi:10.3390/epigenomes4040025

Gallusci P, Dai Z, Génard M, Gauffretau A, Leblanc-Fournier N, *et al.* (2017) Epigenetics for plant improvement: Current knowledge and modeling avenues. *Trends in Plant Science* **22**, 610–623. doi:10.1016/j.tplants.2017.04.009

Gallusci P, Hodgman C, Teyssier E, Seymour GB (2016) DNA methylation and chromatin regulation during fleshy fruit development and ripening. *Frontiers in Plant Science* **7**, 807. doi:10.3389/fpls.2016.00807

Gao L, Geng Y, Li B, Chen J, Yang JI (2010) Genome-wide DNA methylation alterations of *Alternanthera philoxeroides* in natural and manipulated habitats: implications for epigenetic regulation of rapid responses to environmental fluctuation and phenotypic variation. *Plant, Cell & Environment* **33**, 1820–1827. doi:10.1111/j.1365-3040.2010.02186.x

Gavery MR, Nichols KM, Goetz GW, Middleton MA, Swanson P, *et al.* (2018) Characterization of genetic and epigenetic variation in sperm and red blood cells from adult hatchery and natural-origin steelhead. *Oncorhynchus mykiss* G3 Genes|Genomes|Genetics **8**, 3723–3736. doi:10.1534/g3.118.200458

Ge C, Ye J, Weber C, Sun W, Zhang H, *et al.* (2018) The histone demethylase KDM6B regulates temperature-dependent sex determination in a turtle species. *Science* **360**, 645–648. doi:10.1126/science.aap8328

Geng S, Kong X, Song G, Jia M, Guan J, *et al.* (2019) DNA methylation dynamics during the interaction of wheat progenitor *Aegilops tauschii* with the obligate biotrophic fungus *Blumeria graminis* f. sp. *tritici*. *New Phytologist* **221**, 1023–1035. doi:10.1111/nph.15432

Goll MG, Bestor TH (2005) Eukaryotic cytosine methyltransferases. *Annual Review of Biochemistry* **74**, 481–514.

Greer EL, Blanco MA, Gu L, Sendinc E, Liu J, *et al.* (2015) DNA methylation on N6-adenine in *C. elegans*. *Cell* **161**, 868–878.

Guerrero-Bosagna C, Settles M, Lucker B, Skinner MK (2010) Epigenetic transgenerational actions of vinclozolin on promoter regions of the sperm epigenome. *PLOS ONE* **5**, e13100. doi:10.1371/journal.pone.0013100

Gutierrez-Arcelus M, Ongen H, Lappalainen T, Montgomery SB, Buil A, *et al.* (2015) Tissue-specific effects of genetic and epigenetic variation on gene regulation and splicing. *PLOS Genetics* **11**, e1004958. doi:10.1371/journal.pgen.1004958

Hahn EE, Grealy A, Alexander M, Holleley CE (2020) Museum epigenomics: Charting the future by unlocking the past. *Trends in Ecology & Evolution* **35**, 295–300. doi:10.1016/j.tree.2019.12.005

Hauben M, Haesendonckx B, Standaert E, Van Der Kelen K, Azmi A, *et al.* (2009) Energy use efficiency is characterized by an epigenetic component that can be directed through artificial selection to increase yield. *Proceedings of the National Academy of Sciences* **106**, 20109–20114. doi:10.1073/pnas.0908755106

Hawes NA, Fidler AE, Tremblay LA, Pochon X, Dunphy BJ, *et al.* (2018) Understanding the role of DNA methylation in successful biological invasions: a review. *Biological Invasions* **20**, 2285–2300. doi:10.1007/s10530-018-1703-6

Heijmans BT, Tobi EW, Stein AD, Putter H, Blauw GJ, *et al.* (2008) Persistent epigenetic differences associated with prenatal exposure to famine in humans. *Proceedings of the National Academy of Sciences* **105**, 17046–17049. doi:10.1073/pnas.0806560105

Hendry AP, Farrugia TJ, Kinnison MT (2008) Human influences on rates of phenotypic change in wild animal populations. *Molecular Ecology* **17**, 20–29. doi:10.1111/j.1365-294X.2007.03428.x

Henikoff S, Smith MM (2015) Histone variants and epigenetics. *Cold Spring Harbor Perspectives in Biology* **7**, a019364.

Herrel A, Joly D, Danchin E (2020) Epigenetics in ecology and evolution. *Functional Ecology* **34**, 381–384. doi:10.1111/1365-2435.13494

Herrera CM, Bazaga P (2013) Epigenetic correlates of plant phenotypic plasticity: DNA methylation differs between prickly and nonprickly leaves in heterophyllous *Ilex aquifolium* (Aquifoliaceae) trees. *Botanical Journal of the Linnean Society* **171**, 441–452. doi:10.1111/boj.12007

Holden N, Totsika M, Dixon L, Catherwood K, Gally DL, *et al.* (2007) Regulation of P-fimbrial phase variation frequencies in Escherichia coli CFT073. *Infect Immun* **75**, 3325–3334. doi:10.1128/IAI.01989-06

Horvath S (2013) DNA methylation age of human tissues and cell types. *Genome Biology* **14**, R115. doi:10.1186/gb-2013-14-10-r115

Hu J, Barrett RDH (2017) Epigenetics in natural animal populations. *Journal of Evolutionary Biology* **30**, 1612–1632. doi:10.1111/jeb.13184

Hu J, Askary AM, Thurman TJ, Spiller DA, Palmer TM, *et al.* (2019) The epigenetic signature of colonizing new environments in *Anolis* lizards. *Molecular Biology and Evolution* **36**, 2165–2170. doi:10.1093/molbev/msz133

Hu J, Pérez-Jvostov F, Blondel L, Barrett RDH (2018) Genome-wide DNA methylation signatures of infection status in Trinidadian guppies (*Poecilia reticulata*). *Molecular Ecology* **27**, 3087–3102. doi:10.1111/mec.14771

Husby A (2022) Wild epigenetics: insights from epigenetic studies on natural populations. *Proceedings of the Royal Society B* **289**, 20211633. doi:10.1098/rspb.2021.1633

Husby A (2020) On the use of blood samples for measuring DNA methylation in ecological epigenetic studies. *Integrative and Comparative Biology* **60**, 1558–1566. doi:10.1093/icb/icaa123

Ibeagha-Awemu EM, Khatib H (2017) Chapter 29 – Epigenetics of livestock breeding. In *Handbook of Epigenetics*. 2nd edn. (Ed TO Tollefsbol) pp. 441–463. Academic Press, Cambridge, MA, USA.

Ibeagha-Awemu EM, Zhao X (2015) Epigenetic marks: regulators of livestock phenotypes and conceivable sources of missing variation in livestock improvement programs. *Frontiers in Genetics* **6**, 302. doi:10.3389/fgene.2015.00302

Ito H, Udono T, Hirata S, Inoue-Murayama M (2018) Estimation of chimpanzee age based on DNA methylation. *Scientific Reports* **8**, 9998. doi:10.1038/s41598-018-28318-9

Jaenisch R, Bird A (2003) Epigenetic regulation of gene expression: how the genome integrates intrinsic and environmental signals. *Nature Genetics* **33**, 245–254.

Jenuwein T, Allis CD (2001) Translating the histone code. *Science* **293**, 1074–1080.

Ji L, Neumann DA, Schmitz RJ (2015) Crop epigenomics: Identifying, unlocking, and harnessing cryptic variation in crop genomes. *Molecular Plant* **8**, 860–870. doi:10.1016/j.molp.2015.01.021

Johnson KCM, Xia S, Feng X, Li X (2015) The chromatin remodeler SPLAYED negatively regulates SNC1-mediated immunity. *Plant and Cell Physiology* **56**, 1616–1623. doi:10.1093/pcp/pcv087

Johnston JW, Benson EE, Harding K (2009) Cryopreservation induces temporal DNA methylation epigenetic changes and differential transcriptional activity in Ribes germplasm. *Plant Physiology and Biochemistry* **47**, 123–131. doi:10.1016/j.plaphy.2008.10.008

Jueterbock A, Boström C, Coyer JA, Olsen JL, Kopp M, *et al.* (2020) The seagrass methylome is associated with variation in photosynthetic performance among clonal shoots. *Frontiers in Plant Science* **11**, . doi:10.3389/fpls.2020.571646

Jump AS, Peñuelas J (2005) Running to stand still: adaptation and the response of plants to rapid climate change. *Ecology Letters* **8**, 1010–1020. doi:10.1111/j.1461-0248.2005.00796.x

Kaczmarczyk A, Houben A, Keller ERJ, Mette MF (2010) Influence of cryopreservation on the cytosine methylation state of potato genomic DNA. *Cryoletters* **31**, 380–391.

Karavolias NG, Horner W, Abugu MN, Evanega SN (2021) Application of gene editing for climate change in agriculture. *Frontiers in Sustainable Food Systems* **5**, 296. doi:10.3389/fsufs.2021.685801

King SE, McBirney M, Beck D, Sadler-Riggleman I, Nilsson E, *et al.* (2019) Sperm epimutation biomarkers of obesity and pathologies following DDT induced epigenetic transgenerational inheritance of disease. *Environmental Epigenetics* **5**, dvz008. doi:10.1093/eep/dvz008

Kitavi M, Cashell R, Ferguson M, Lorenzen J, Nyine M, *et al.* (2020) Heritable epigenetic diversity for conservation and utilization of epigenetic germplasm resources of clonal East African Highland banana (EAHB) accessions. *Theoretical and Applied Genetics* **133**, 2605–2625. doi:10.1007/s00122-020-03620-1

Kucharski R, Maleszka J, Foret S, Maleszka R (2008) Nutritional control of reproductive status in honeybees via DNA methylation. *Science* **319**, 1827–1830. doi:10.1126/science.1153069

Law JA, Jacobsen SE (2010) Establishing, maintaining and modifying DNA methylation patterns in plants and animals. *Nature Reviews Genetics* **11**, 204–220.

Lea AJ, Altmann J, Alberts SC, Tung J (2016) Resource base influences genome-wide DNA methylation levels in wild baboons (*Papio cynocephalus*). *Molecular Ecology* **25**, 1681–1696. doi:10.1111/mec.13436

Lea AJ, Vilgalys TP, Durst PAP, Tung J (2017) Maximizing ecological and evolutionary insight in bisulfite sequencing data sets. *Nature Ecology & Evolution* **1**, 1074–1083. doi:10.1038/s41559-017-0229-0

Lee S, Fu F, Xu S, Lee SY, Yun DJ, *et al.* (2016) Global regulation of plant immunity by histone lysine methyl transferases. *The Plant Cell* **28**, 1640–1661. doi:10.1105/tpc.16.00012

Legoff L, D'Cruz SC, Tevosian S, Primig M, Smagulova F, *et al.* (2019) Transgenerational inheritance of environmentally induced epigenetic alterations during mammalian development. *Cells* **8**, 1559. doi:10.3390/cells8121559

Li B, Carey M, Workman JL (2007) The role of chromatin during transcription. *Cell* **128**, 707–719. doi:10.1016/j.cell.2007.01.015

Li C, Guo S, Gao J, Guo Y, Du E, *et al.* (2015) Maternal high-zinc diet attenuates intestinal inflammation by reducing DNA methylation and elevating H3K9 acetylation in the A20 promoter of offspring chicks. *The Journal of Nutritional Biochemistry* **26**, 173–183. doi:10.1016/j.jnutbio.2014.10.005

Li X, Guo T, Mu Q, Li X, Yu J, *et al.* (2018) Genomic and environmental determinants and their interplay underlying phenotypic plasticity. *Proceedings of the National Academy of Sciences* **115**, 6679–6684. doi:10.1073/pnas.1718326115

Li Z, Liu H, Jin X, Lo L, Liu J, *et al.* (2012) Expression profiles of microRNAs from lactating and non-lactating bovine mammary glands and identification of miRNA related to lactation. *BMC Genomics* **13**, 731. doi:10.1186/1471-2164-13-731

Liebl AL, Schrey AW, Andrew SC, Sheldon EL, Griffith SC, *et al.* (2015) Invasion genetics: Lessons from a ubiquitous bird, the house sparrow *Passer domesticus*. *Current Zoology* **61**, 465–476.

Lim Y-K, Cheung K, Dang X, Roberts SB, Wang X, *et al.* (2021) DNA methylation changes in response to ocean acidification at the time of larval metamorphosis in the edible oyster, *Crassostrea hongkongensis*. *Marine Environmental Research* **163**, 105214. doi:10.1016/j.marenvres.2020.105214

Liu R, How-Kit A, Stammitti L, Teyssier E, Rolin D, *et al.* (2015) A DEMETER-like DNA demethylase governs tomato fruit ripening. *Proceedings of the National Academy of Sciences* **112**, 10804–10809. doi:10.1073/pnas.1503362112

Lynch M, O'Hely M (2001) Captive breeding and the genetic fitness of natural populations. *Conservation Genetics* **2**, 363–378.

Maamar MB, Beck D, Nilsson EE, Kubsad D, Skinner MK, *et al.* (2020) Epigenome-wide association study for glyphosate induced transgenerational sperm DNA methylation and histone retention epigenetic biomarkers for disease. *Epigenetics* **0**, 1–18. doi:10.1080/15592294.2020.1853319

Maher B (2008) Personal genomes: The case of the missing heritability. *Nature* **456**, 18–21. doi:10.1038/456018a

Malhi Y (2017) The concept of the Anthropocene. *Annual Review of Environment and Resources* **42**, 77–104. doi:10.1146/annurev-environ-102016-060854

Manikkam M, Guerrero-Bosagna C, Tracey R, Haque MM, Skinner MK, *et al.* (2012) Transgenerational actions of environmental compounds on reproductive disease and identification of epigenetic biomarkers of ancestral exposures. *PLOS ONE* **7**, e31901. doi:10.1371/journal.pone.0031901

Mayne B, Espinoza T, Roberts D, Butler GL, Brooks S, *et al.* (2021) Nonlethal age estimation of three threatened fish species using DNA methylation: Australian lungfish, Murray cod and Mary River cod. *Molecular Ecology Resources* **21**, 2324–2332. doi:10.1111/1755-0998.13440

McBirney M, King SE, Pappalardo M, Houser E, Unkefer M, *et al.* (2017) Atrazine induced epigenetic transgenerational inheritance of disease, lean phenotype and sperm epimutation pathology biomarkers. *PLOS ONE* **12**, e0184306. doi:10.1371/journal.pone.0184306

McInnes JC, Jarman SN, Lea M-A, Raymond B, Deagle BE, *et al.* (2017) DNA metabarcoding as a marine conservation and management tool: A circumpolar examination of fishery discards in the diet of threatened albatrosses. *Frontiers in Marine Science* **4**, 277.

McNew SM, Beck D, Sadler-Riggleman I, Knutie SA, Koop JA, *et al.* (2017) Epigenetic variation between urban and rural populations of Darwin's finches. *BMC Evolutionary Biology* **17**, 183.

McNew SM, Boquete MT, Espinoza-Ulloa S, Andres JA, Wagemaker NC, *et al.* (2021) Epigenetic effects of parasites and pesticides on captive and wild nestling birds. *Ecology and Evolution* **11**, 7713–7729. doi:10.1002/ece3.7606

Medrano M, Alonso C, Bazaga P, López E, Herrera CM, *et al.* (2020) Comparative genetic and epigenetic diversity in pairs of sympatric, closely related plants with contrasting distribution ranges in south-eastern Iberian mountains. *AoB PLANTS* **12**, plaa013. doi:10.1093/aobpla/plaa013

Meröndun J, Murray DL, Shafer ABA (2019) Genome-scale sampling suggests cryptic epigenetic structuring and insular divergence in Canada lynx. *Molecular Ecology* **28**, 3186–3196. doi:10.1111/mec.15131

Miousse IR, Currie R, Datta K, Ellinger-Ziegelbauer H, French JE, *et al.* (2015) Importance of investigating epigenetic alterations for industry and regulators: An appraisal of current efforts by the Health and Environmental Sciences Institute. *Toxicology* **335**, 11–19. doi:10.1016/j.tox.2015.06.009

Miousse IR, Murphy LA, Lin H, Schisler MR, Sun J, *et al.* (2017) Dose-response analysis of epigenetic, metabolic, and apical endpoints after short-term exposure to experimental hepatotoxicants. *Food and Chemical Toxicology* **109**, 690–702. doi:10.1016/j.fct.2017.05.013

Mirbahai L, Chipman JK (2014) Epigenetic memory of environmental organisms: A reflection of lifetime stressor exposures. *Mutation Research/Genetic Toxicology and Environmental Mutagenesis* **764–765**, 10–17. doi:10.1016/j.mrgentox.2013.10.003

Mlynárová L, Nap J-P, Bisseling T (2007) The SWI/SNF chromatin-remodeling gene AtCHR12 mediates temporary growth arrest in *Arabidopsis thaliana* upon perceiving environmental stress. *The Plant Journal* **51**, 874–885. doi:10.1111/j.1365-313X.2007.03185.x

Moghadam H, Mørkøre T, Robinson N (2015) Epigenetics – Potential for programming fish for aquaculture? *Journal of Marine Science and Engineering* **3**, 175–192. doi:10.3390/jmse3020175

Morandin C, Brendel VP, Sundström L, Helanterä H, Mikheyev AS, *et al.* (2019) Changes in gene DNA methylation and expression networks accompany caste specialization and age-related physiological changes in a social insect. *Molecular Ecology* **28**, 1975–1993. doi:10.1111/mec.15062

Mounger J, Ainouche ML, Bossdorf O, Cavé-Radet A, Li B, *et al.* (2021) Epigenetics and the success of invasive plants. *Philosophical Transactions of the Royal Society B: Biological Sciences* **376**, 20200117. doi:10.1098/rstb.2020.0117

Mounger J, Boquete MT, Schmid MW, Granado R, Robertson MH, *et al.* (2021) Inheritance of DNA methylation differences in the mangrove Rhizophora mangle. *Evolution & Development* **23**, 351–374. doi:10.1111/ede.12388

Münzbergová Z, Latzel V, Šurinová M, Hadincová V (2019) DNA methylation as a possible mechanism affecting ability of natural populations to adapt to changing climate. *Oikos* **128**, 124–134. doi:10.1111/oik.05591

Naeem M, Majeed S, Hoque MZ, Ahmad I (2020) Latest developed strategies to minimize the off-target effects in CRISPR-Cas-mediated genome editing. *Cells* **9**, 1608. doi:10.3390/cells9071608

Nakamura M, Gao Y, Dominguez AA, Qi LS (2021) CRISPR technologies for precise epigenome editing. *Nature Cell Biology* **23**, 11–22. doi:10.1038/s41556-020-00620-7

Niederhuth CE, Schmitz RJ (2017) Putting DNA methylation in context: from genomes to gene expression in plants. *Biochimica et Biophysica Acta (BBA) – Gene Regulatory Mechanisms* **1860**, 149–156. doi:10.1016/j.bbagrm.2016.08.009

Nilsson E, Sadler-Riggleman I, Beck D, Skinner MK (2021) Differential DNA methylation in somatic and sperm cells of hatchery vs wild (natural-origin) steelhead trout populations. *Environmental Epigenetics* **7**, dvab002. doi:10.1093/eep/dvab002

O'Sullivan RJ, Aykanat T, Johnston SE, Rogan G, Poole R, *et al.* (2020) Captive-bred Atlantic salmon released into the wild have fewer offspring than wild-bred fish and decrease population productivity. *Proceedings of the Royal Society B: Biological Sciences* **287**, 20201671. doi:10.1098/rspb.2020.1671

Ouborg NJ, Pertoldi C, Loeschcke V, Hedrick PW (2010) Conservation genetics in transition to conservation genomics. *Trends in Genetics* **26**, 177–187

Paul DS, Beck S (2014) Advances in epigenome-wide association studies for common diseases. *Trends in Molecular Medicine* **20**, 541–543. doi:10.1016/j.molmed.2014.07.002

Paun O, Verhoeven KJF, Richards CL (2019) Opportunities and limitations of reduced representation bisulfite sequencing in plant ecological epigenomics. *New Phytologist* **221**, 738–742. doi:10.1111/nph.15388

Peschansky VJ, Wahlestedt C (2014) Non-coding RNAs as direct and indirect modulators of epigenetic regulation. *Epigenetics* **9**, 3–12. doi:10.4161/epi.27472

Pierron F, Bureau du Colombier S, Moffett A, Caron A, Peluhet L, *et al.* (2014) Abnormal ovarian DNA methylation programming during gonad maturation in wild contaminated fish. *Environmental Science & Technology* **48**, 11688–11695. doi:10.1021/es503712c

Polanowski AM, Robbins J, Chandler D, Jarman SN (2014) Epigenetic estimation of age in humpback whales. *Molecular Ecology Resources* **14**, 976–987. doi:10.1111/1755-0998.12247

Poloczanska ES, Brown CJ, Sydeman WJ, Kiessling W, Schoeman DS, *et al.* (2013) Global imprint of climate change on marine life. *Nature Climate Change* **3**, 919–925. doi:10.1038/nclimate1958

Putnam HM, Davidson JM, Gates RD (2016) Ocean acidification influences host DNA methylation and phenotypic plasticity in environmentally susceptible corals. *Evolutionary Applications* **9**, 1165–1178. doi:10.1111/eva.12408

Rahim NG, Harismendy O, Topol EJ, Frazer KA (2008) Genetic determinants of phenotypic diversity in humans. *Genome Biology* **9**, 215. doi:10.1186/gb-2008-9-4-215

Raj S, Bräutigam K, Hamanishi ET, Wilkins O, Thomas BR, *et al.* (2011) Clone history shapes Populus drought responses.

Proceedings of the National Academy of Sciences **108**, 12521–12526. doi:10.1073/pnas.1103341108

Ramirez-Prado JS, Abulfaraj AA, Rayapuram N, Benhamed M, Hirt H, *et al.* (2018) Plant immunity: From signaling to epigenetic control of defense. *Trends in Plant Science* **23**, 833–844. doi:10.1016/j.tplants.2018.06.004

Rando OJ, Verstrepen KJ (2007) Timescales of genetic and epigenetic Inheritance. *Cell* **128**, 655–668. doi:10.1016/j.cell.2007.01.023

Rey O, Eizaguirre C, Angers B, Baltazar-Soares M, Sagonas K, *et al.* (2020) Linking epigenetics and biological conservation: Towards a conservation epigenetics perspective. *Functional Ecology* **34**, 414–427. doi:10.1111/1365-2435.13429

Richards CL, Alonso C, Becker C, Bossdorf O, Bucher E, *et al.* (2017) Ecological plant epigenetics: Evidence from model and non-model species, and the way forward. *Ecology Letters* **20**, 1576–1590. doi:10.1111/ele.12858

Richards CL, Pigliucci M (2020) Epigenetic Inheritance. A Decade into the Extended Evolutionary Synthesis. PG. doi:10.30460/99624

Richards CL, Schrey AW, Pigliucci M (2012) Invasion of diverse habitats by few Japanese knotweed genotypes is correlated with epigenetic differentiation. *Ecology Letters* **15**, 1016–1025. doi:10.1111/j.1461-0248.2012.01824.x

Rodriguez Barreto D, Garcia de Leaniz C, Verspoor E, Sobolewska H, Coulson M, *et al.* (2019) DNA methylation changes in the sperm of captive-reared fish: A route to epigenetic introgression in wild populations. *Molecular Biology and Evolution* **36**, 2205–2211. doi:10.1093/molbev/msz135

Romao JM, Jin W, He M, McAllister T, Guan LL, *et al.* (2014) MicroRNAs in bovine adipogenesis: genomic context, expression and function. *BMC Genomics* **15**, 137. doi:10.1186/1471-2164-15-137

Rubenstein DR, Skolnik H, Berrio A, Champagne FA, Phelps S, *et al.* (2016) Sex-specific fitness effects of unpredictable early life conditions are associated with DNA methylation in the avian glucocorticoid receptor. *Molecular Ecology* **25**, 1714–1728. doi:10.1111/mec.13483

Sagonas K, Meyer BS, Kaufmann J, Lenz TL, Häsler R, *et al.* (2020) Experimental parasite infection causes genome-wide changes in DNA methylation. *Molecular Biology and Evolution*. doi:10.1093/molbev/msaa084

Sarma RR, Crossland MR, Eyck HJF, DeVore JL, Edwards RJ, *et al.* (2021) Intergenerational effects of manipulating DNA methylation in the early life of an iconic invader. *Philosophical Transactions of the Royal Society B: Biological Sciences* **376**, 20200125. doi:10.1098/rstb.2020.0125

Sarma RR, Edwards RJ, Crino OL, Eyck HJ, Waters PD, *et al.* (2020) Do epigenetic changes drive corticosterone responses to alarm cues in larvae of an invasive amphibian? *Integrative and Comparative Biology* **60**, 1481–1494. doi:10.1093/icb/icaa082

Sasaki E, Kawakatsu T, Ecker JR, Nordborg M (2019) Common alleles of CMT2 and NRPE1 are major determinants of CHH methylation variation in *Arabidopsis thaliana*. *PLOS Genetics* **15**, e1008492. doi:10.1371/journal.pgen.1008492

Schmid MW, Heichinger C, Coman Schmid D, Guthorl D, Gagliardini V, *et al.* (2018) Contribution of epigenetic variation to adaptation in *Arabidopsis*. *Nature Communications* **9**, 4446. doi:10.1038/s41467-018-06932-5

Schmitz RJ, Lewis ZA, Goll MG (2019) DNA methylation: shared and divergent features across eukaryotes. *Trends in Genetics* **35**, 818–827. doi:10.1016/j.tig.2019.07.007

Schrey AW, Coon C a C, Grispo MT, Awad M, Imboma T, *et al.* (2012) Epigenetic variation may compensate for decreased genetic variation with introductions: A case study using house sparrows (*Passer domesticus*) on two continents. *Genetics Research International* **2012**, 979751. doi:10.1155/2012/979751

Sepers B, van den Heuvel K, Lindner M, Viitaniemi H, Husby A, *et al.* (2019) Avian ecological epigenetics: pitfalls and promises. *Journal of Ornithology*. doi:10.1007/s10336-019-01684-5

Serpeloni F, Radtke K, de Assis SG, Henning F, Nätt D, *et al.* (2017) Grandmaternal stress during pregnancy and DNA methylation of the third generation: an epigenome-wide association study. *Translational Psychiatry* **7**, e1202. doi:10.1038/tp.2017.153

Shen Y, Zhang J, Liu Y, Liu S, Liu Z, *et al.* (2018) DNA methylation footprints during soybean domestication and improvement. *Genome Biology* **19**, 1–14. doi:10.1186/s13059-018-1516-z

Singh K, Erdman RA, Swanson KM, Molenaar AJ, Maqbool NJ, *et al.* (2010) Epigenetic regulation of milk production in dairy cows. *Journal of Mammary Gland Biology and Neoplasia* **15**, 101–112. doi:10.1007/s10911-010-9164-2

Slatkin M (2009) Epigenetic inheritance and the missing heritability problem. *Genetics* **182**, 845–850. doi:10.1534/genetics.109.102798

Snell-Rood EC, Kobiela Megan E, Sikkink Kristin L, Shephard AM (2018) Mechanisms of plastic rescue in novel environments. *Annual Review of Ecology, Evolution, and Systematics* **49**, 331–354. doi:10.1146/annurev-ecolsys-110617-062622

Soubry A, Hoyo C, Jirtle RL, Murphy SK (2014) A paternal environmental legacy: Evidence for epigenetic inheritance through the male germ line. *BioEssays* **36**, 359–371. doi:10.1002/bies.201300113

Springer NM, Schmitz RJ (2017) Exploiting induced and natural epigenetic variation for crop improvement. *Nature Reviews Genetics* **18**, 563–575. doi:10.1038/nrg.2017.45

Suarez-Ulloa V, Gonzalez-Romero R, Eirin-Lopez JM (2015) Environmental epigenetics: A promising venue for developing next-generation pollution biomonitoring tools in marine invertebrates. *Marine Pollution Bulletin* **98**, 5–13. doi:10.1016/j.marpolbul.2015.06.020

Suzuki MM, Bird A (2008) DNA methylation landscapes: provocative insights from epigenomics. *Nature Reviews Genetics* **9**, 465–476. doi:10.1038/nrg2341

Taff CC, Campagna L, Vitousek MN (2019) Genome-wide variation in DNA methylation is associated with stress resilience and plumage brightness in a wild bird. *Molecular Ecology* **28**, 3722–3737. doi:10.1111/mec.15186

Tave D, Hutson AM (2019) Is good fish culture management harming recovery efforts in aquaculture-assisted fisheries? *North American Journal of Aquaculture* **81**, 333–339. doi:10.1002/naaq.10107

Thakore PI, Black JB, Hilton IB, Gersbach CA (2016) Editing the epigenome: technologies for programmable transcription and epigenetic modulation. *Nature Methods* **13**, 127–137. doi:10.1038/nmeth.3733

Thompson MJ, vonHoldt B, Horvath S, Pellegrini M (2017) An epigenetic aging clock for dogs and wolves. *Aging (Albany NY)* **9**, 1055–1068. doi:10.18632/aging.101211

Tsuji H, Saika H, Tsutsumi N, Hirai A, Nakazono M (2006) Dynamic and reversible changes in histone H3-Lys4 methylation and H3 acetylation occurring at submergence-inducible genes in rice. *Plant and Cell Physiology* **47**, 995–1003. doi:10.1093/pcp/pcj072

Us-Camas R, Castillo-Castro E, Aguilar-Espinosa M, Limones-Briones V, Rivera-Madrid R, *et al.* (2017) Assessment of molecular and epigenetic changes in the albinism of *Agave angustifolia* Haw. *Plant Science* **263**, 156–167. doi:10.1016/j.plantsci.2017.07.010

Val ME, Kennedy SP, Soler-Bistué AJ, Barbe V, Bouchier C, *et al.* (2014) Fuse or die: how to survive the loss of Dam in *Vibrio cholerae. Molecular Microbiology* **91**, 665–678.

Vandegehuchte MB, Janssen CR (2014) Epigenetics in an ecotoxicological context. *Mutation Research/Genetic Toxicology and Environmental Mutagenesis* **764–765**, 36–45. doi:10.1016/j.mrgentox.2013.08.008

Van Der Graaf A, Wardenaar R, Neumann DA, Taudt A, Shaw RG, *et al.* (2015) Rate, spectrum, and evolutionary dynamics of spontaneous epimutations. *PNAS* **112**, 6676–6681. doi:10.1073/pnas.1424254112

Verhoeven KJF, Jansen JJ, van Dijk PJ, Biere A (2010) Stress-induced DNA methylation changes and their heritability in asexual dandelions. *New Phytologist* **185**, 1108–1118. doi:10.1111/j.1469-8137.2009.03121.x

Verhoeven KJF, vonHoldt BM, Sork VL (2016) Epigenetics in ecology and evolution: what we know and what we need to know. *Molecular Ecology* **25**, 1631–1638. doi:10.1111/mec.13617

Vitousek PM (1994) Beyond global warming: Ecology and global change. *Ecology* **75**, 1861–1876. doi:10.2307/1941591

Vojta A, Dobrinić P, Tadić V, Bočkor L, Korać P, *et al.* (2016) Repurposing the CRISPR-Cas9 system for targeted DNA methylation. *Nucleic Acids Research* **44**, 5615–5628. doi:10.1093/nar/gkw159

Vrana PB (2007) Genomic imprinting as a mechanism of reproductive isolation in mammals. *Journal of Mammalogy* **88**, 5–23. doi:10.1644/06-MAMM-S-013R1.1

Walker J, Zhang J, Liu Y, Vickers M, Dolan L, *et al.* (2021) Extensive N4 cytosine methylation is essential for *Marchantia* sperm function. [Preprint]. *bioRxiv*. doi:10.1101/2021.02.12.428880

Walsh RE, Assis APA, Patton JL, Marroig G, Dawson TE, *et al.* (2016) Morphological and dietary responses of chipmunks to a century of climate change. *Global Change Biology* **22**, 3233–3252. doi:10.1111/gcb.13216

Wang H, He L, Song J, Cui W, Zhang Y, *et al.* (2016) Cadmium-induced genomic instability in *Arabidopsis*: Molecular toxicological biomarkers for early diagnosis of cadmium stress. *Chemosphere* **150**, 258–265. doi:10.1016/j.chemosphere.2016.02.042

Watson H, Powell D, Salmón P, Jacobs A, Isaksson C, *et al.* (2020) Urbanization is associated with modifications in DNA methylation in a small passerine bird. *Evolutionary Applications* **14**, 85–98. doi:10.1111/eva.13160

Weiner AKM, Cerón-Romero MA, Yan Y, Katz LA (2020) Phylogenomics of the epigenetic toolkit reveals punctate retention of genes across eukaryotes. *Genome Biology and Evolution* **12**, 2196–2210. doi:10.1093/gbe/evaa198

Weyrich A, Lenz D, Jeschek M, Chung TH, Rübensam K, *et al.* (2016) Paternal intergenerational epigenetic response to heat exposure in male Wild guinea pigs. *Molecular Ecology* **25**, 1729–1740. doi:10.1111/mec.13494

Wiley CD, Matundan HH, Duselis AR, Isaacs AT, Vrana PB, *et al.* (2008) Patterns of hybrid loss of imprinting reveal tissue- and cluster-specific regulation. *PLOS ONE* **3**, e3572. doi:10.1371/journal.pone.0003572

Williams SE, Hoffman EA (2009) Minimizing genetic adaptation in captive breeding programs: A review. *Biological Conservation* **142**, 2388–2400. doi:10.1016/j.biocon.2009.05.034

Winter S, Fischle W (2010) Epigenetic markers and their crosstalk. *Essays in Biochemistry* **48**, 45–61. doi:10.1042/bse0480045

Wojciechowski M, Lowe R, Maleszka J, Conn D, Maleszka R, *et al.* (2018) Phenotypically distinct female castes in honey bees are defined by alternative chromatin states during larval development. *Genome Research* **28**, 1532–1542. doi:10.1101/gr.236497.118

Xu J, Chen G, Hermanson PJ, Xu Q, Sun C, *et al.* (2019) Population-level analysis reveals the widespread occurrence and phenotypic consequence of DNA methylation variation not tagged by genetic variation in maize. *Genome Biology* **20**, 243. doi:10.1186/s13059-019-1859-0

Yi SV, Goodisman MAD (2021) The impact of epigenetic information on genome evolution. *Philosophical Transactions of the Royal Society B: Biological Sciences* **376**, 20200114. doi:10.1098/rstb.2020.0114

Yim YY, Teague CD, Nestler EJ (2020) In vivo locus-specific editing of the neuroepigenome. *Nature Reviews Neuroscience* **21**, 471–484. doi:10.1038/s41583-020-0334-y

Zhang D, Hu Q, Hu Y, Zhang Y, Zhang Y, *et al.* (2019) Epigenetic and transcriptional signatures of ex situ conserved golden snub-nosed monkeys (*Rhinopithecus roxellana*). *Biological Conservation* **237**, 175–184. doi:10.1016/j.biocon.2019.06.021

Zhang Y-Y, Parepa M, Fischer M, Bossdorf O (2016) Epigenetics of colonizing species? A study of Japanese knotweed in Central Europe. In *Invasion Genetics*. pp. 328–340. John Wiley & Sons, Ltd, Hoboken, NJ, USA.

Zhi P, Chang C (2021) Exploiting epigenetic variations for crop disease resistance improvement. *Frontiers in Plant Science* **12**, 953. doi:10.3389/fpls.2021.692328

Zhong S, Fei Z, Chen Y-R, Zheng Y, Huang M, *et al.* (2013) Single-base resolution methylomes of tomato fruit development reveal epigenome modifications associated with ripening. *Nature Biotechnology* **31**, 154–159. doi:10.1038/nbt.2462

19 DNA-based microbial bioindication of environmental state

Jodie van de Kamp, Ángel Borja and Andrew Bissett

ABSTRACT

Global ecosystems are subjected to anthropogenic pressures at an unprecedented scale, threatening the provision of valuable ecosystem services that society relies upon. Thus, there is an urgent need to have effective tools to monitor and predict the impacts of these pressures. Microbes underpin biogeochemical processes and nutrient cycling, sustain the base of food webs, and are key in determining ecosystem responses to environmental change. Their short generation times, variable sensitivity to environmental pressures, and prevalence in all environments, make them excellent candidates for bioindication of ecosystem state. Advances in environmental genomics and current sequence-based approaches have allowed us to provide information on the taxonomic and functional repertoires of microbial communities at a much greater level of resolution than ever before. For these reasons, DNA-based microbial bioindication offers great opportunities to improve ecosystem surveillance strategies and monitoring programs, particularly the ability to upscale to much higher temporal and spatial scales, which will ultimately aid environmental management decisions. Rapid technological advances and focused research efforts over the past decade have resulted in many works detailing and reviewing the use of DNA-based methodologies for microbial bioindication, yet the uptake and implementation of these approaches in routine biomonitoring has been slow. In this chapter, we give an overview of some of the recent approaches to DNA-based microbial bioindication of ecosystem state, outlining the strengths and limitations of these approaches and the current state of the field.

INTRODUCTION

Ecosystems are subject to substantial anthropogenic pressures including habitat modification and loss, nutrient and other contaminant loading, degraded water quality, introduction of invasive species and biodiversity loss, as well as the global effects of increasing temperatures, sea level rise and ocean acidification (Pörtner *et al.* 2021). These pressures are drastically altering the composition of ecological communities with cascading impacts on ecological functioning and, thus, ecosystem service provision (Borja *et al.* 2020; United Nations 2021): those fundamental services that make human life possible such as providing clean water, nutritious food, regulating climate and disease, and providing recreational and cultural benefits (Haines-Young and Potschin-Young 2018). The World Wildlife Foundation Living Planet Index 2018 observed that nature underpins all economic activity, presently worth an estimated US$125 trillion per annum (W.W.F. 2018). As such, governmental and nongovernmental agencies, scientists, conservationists, managers, regulators and the public are increasingly interested in assessing the health and trajectory of ecosystems and their components (species, populations, communities; Borja *et al.* 2008; Reker *et al.* 2019;

United Nations 2021). Assessment of all organisms in an ecosystem is impossible, so approaches to their assessment and management generally require the development of indicators to describe the state of different ecosystem components and to track their trends, that is, changes to state over time and space, and in response to disturbance (Birk *et al.* 2012).

Bioindicators are defined as individual organisms or communities of organisms, or biological processes that are used as a surrogate measure to assess the quality of an environment (Woodiwiss 1964; and as defined in Markert *et al.* 2003), though for the purposes of this chapter we will discuss only bioindicator organisms or communities. All organisms and assemblages are able to tolerate specific ranges of chemical, physical and biological conditions and this information can be used to evaluate the environmental state, that is, bioindication (Holt and Miller 2010). The development and application of bioindicators have been steadily growing since the 1960s. Traditionally, bioindicators have relied on direct observations, or counts, of organisms to calculate biotic indices and thus have focused on easily observed taxa (Díaz *et al.* 2004). Of 536 articles, containing the search terms 'indicator' or 'bioindicator', published between 1970 and 2005, the most prominently published bioindicator organisms were plants (40%), invertebrates (25%), and fish (12%) (reviewed in Burger 2006). Arguably, one of the most widely known biotic indices, AZTI's Marine Biotic Index (AMBI; Borja *et al.* 2000), uses marine benthic macroinvertebrate sensitivity to human pressures as an indicator of ecosystem health and has been applied in different geographical and environmental settings globally (reviewed in detail in Borja *et al.* 2019).

Though bioindicator indices are used extensively, and successfully, for ecosystem monitoring (Díaz *et al.* 2004; Birk *et al.* 2012; Borja *et al.* 2012, 2015; Poikane *et al.* 2020), there are major, and widely recognised, limitations to the direct observation methods including high cost due to labour requirements, a general requirement for high-level taxonomic expertise, methodological diversity across taxonomic groups, and the difficulty of upscaling methodology in time and space (Lear *et al.* 2009). Environmental genomics, in particular metabarcoding, offers a rapid, accurate and cost-effective alternative to upscale monitoring and assessment programs (Aylagas *et al.* 2018). Instead of identification based on direct observation of organisms and their morphologies, metabarcoding is the observation of DNA sequences from environmental samples, to indicate the presence of organisms. The high resolution of community characterisation and no requirement for whole specimens for identification via metabarcoding overcome further limitations of traditional morphology-based monitoring including the inability to reveal rare or cryptic (organisms that are difficult to distinguish morphologically) biodiversity, or identify early-life stages and/or damaged specimens. Combined with advances in bioinformatic methodologies and data analytics, environmental genomics is an attractive proposition to increase the spatial and temporal resolution of biomonitoring programs. In a *Molecular Ecology* special issue on eDNA, Baird and Hajibabaei (2012) introduced the idea of Biomonitoring 2.0, where they describe metabarcoding as a new paradigm in ecosystem assessment allowing biodiversity observation on a significantly greater scale, an increasing ability to develop insights into cause and effect of disturbances, as well as addressing the limitations of traditional assessments. In the scientific literature, the use of genomics for bioindication is neither new nor restricted to high-throughput sequencing datasets (e.g. reviewed in Bourlat *et al.* 2013; Leese *et al.* 2018; Pawlowski *et al.* 2018). For example, prior to the development of next generation sequencing technologies, DNA-based identification of microbes through clone library analysis of prokaryotic ribosomal RNA (16S rRNA) gene was used to assess the effects of organic enrichment on microbial diversity and community structure in fish farm sediments (Bissett *et al.* 2006). While the first reported use of high-throughput sequencing for bioindication was more than a decade ago when Chariton *et al.* (2010) demonstrated the sensitivity of eukaryotic ribosomal RNA (18S rRNA) gene metabarcoding to discriminate between reference and affected locations along a human impact gradient in Sydney Harbour, Australia.

The selection of informative bioindicator species or communities is critical in biomonitoring programs and is largely based on their perceived/inferred sensitivity to environmental change (Astudillo-García *et al.* 2019). Desirable characteristics of organisms for bioindication include a rapid, predictable and detectable response to disturbance, relative abundance in the environment and ease of sampling. Microbes are the most ancient, the most phylogenetically diverse (Hug *et al.* 2016) and most widespread life form on Earth occupying every conceivable niche. The term 'microbe' is historically a catch-all phrase to describe any organism only visible with the help of a microscope (formed from two Greek words, 'mikros' and 'bios' meaning 'small life'), including viruses, bacteria, archaea, protists and some fungi (Hariharan 2021). For the purposes of this text, 'microbial bioindication' refers to bioindicators based on bacterial, archaeal, and/or microeukaryote (such as diatom and dinoflagellate) communities. We recognise that other microbial taxa (e.g. viruses, fungi) and gene families (e.g. resistance genes) also offer valuable insight into ecosystem state and the concepts below are easily applied to these potential indicators.

Microbial communities drive key ecosystem processes in natural, managed and engineered environments (Konopka 2009) and are, therefore, intrinsically linked to the ecosystem state. The fundamental importance of microbes for ecosystem function, their environmental prevalence, sensitivity to environmental changes, and rapid replication rates, all point to the likelihood that microbial communities could offer an earlier indication of ecosystem state changes than organisms at higher trophic levels, not possessing these characteristics. Traditionally, microbial indicators were based on detecting the presence and/or abundance of single organisms, most often pathogenic organisms, via direct observations through culturing or microscopy in relatively closed systems: human microbiome and medical diagnostics, food safety (e.g. Jay 1995), agriculture site disease load, and measures of water quality for drinking or recreational purposes (reviewed in Mesquita and Noble 2013; Wen *et al.* 2020). However, ecosystems are complex and dynamic, with many parts (both biotic and abiotic) that interact, either directly or indirectly, to function and provide the services we rely upon. The pressures ecosystems are exposed to are also complex, from multiple sources and/or consisting of multiple stressors. Single species biomonitoring may not accurately reflect this complexity and there is a growing body of research recognising the importance of monitoring community composition and structure as a proxy for monitoring changes in whole ecosystem status/health and tracking longer-term trends, for example water quality (reviewed in Sagova-Mareckova *et al.* 2021), aquaculture impacts (Pochon *et al.* 2015; Keeley *et al.* 2018), coral reef health (reviewed in Glasl *et al.* 2017), oil operations (e.g. Laroche *et al.* 2016, 2018; Kostka *et al.* 2020), land-river-lagoon continuum (Bourhane *et al.* 2022), soil health (e.g. Dang *et al.* 2019; Fierer *et al.* 2021), and restoration success (e.g. Liddicoat *et al.* 2019; Yan *et al.* 2020).

Microbial ecologists pioneered the use of metabarcoding approaches for biodiversity discovery from a wide range of environmental and clinical settings, beginning with random shotgun sequencing of DNA from entire microbial communities, such as acid mine drainage (Tyson *et al.* 2004), seawater from the Sargasso Sea (Venter *et al.* 2004) and human gut microbiome (Gill *et al.* 2006), to metabarcoding approaches using the 16S rRNA gene (e.g. human gut microbiome, Eckburg *et al.* 2005; deep sea, Sogin *et al.* 2006 and Brown *et al.*

2009). Somewhat paradoxically, greater advances in the use of environmental genomics for bioindication have been made in the metazoan domain. Traditional observation-based metazoan bioindicators have been utilised extensively for ecosystem assessments (detailed previously) and it was a relatively straightforward next step to replace direct observation methodology with DNA-based observations which could be validated against traditional indices. Conversely, where microbiologists have relied heavily on DNA-based approaches to broad community assessments due to the inability to grow and characterise greater than 99% of microbes in the laboratory, the identification and use of microbial bioindicators have been relatively limited and are thus more difficult to validate against existing ecosystem assessments (reviewed in Astudillo-García *et al.* 2019). That said, microbes meet a number of criteria that make them amenable to widespread adoption as described by Fierer *et al.* (2021) in relation to soil health, but which hold true across any biome: reasonably cheap, fast and high throughput; temporally variable and responsive to change; and highly diverse thus allowing exploration of many aspects of the ecosystem.

THE APPLICATION – DNA-BASED MICROBIAL BIOINDICATION

There are several active areas of research in DNA-based microbial community bioindication which we define here as belonging to two pathways: 1) methods based on bioindicator microbes; and 2) methods based on community structure metrics (outlined below). Methods based on specific indicator microbes fall into a further two branches: those requiring classification and enumeration of taxonomically described (either formally or informally) microbes, and those that are independent of formal taxonomic information, here-in referred to as taxonomy-based and taxonomy-free, respectively. Community structure metrics are independent of any classification of individual taxa and focus on discovering and understanding the ecological processes shaping whole communities (Cordier 2020). In this chapter we take a detailed look at the application of DNA-based microbial bioindication via specific indicator organisms (both the taxonomy-based and taxonomy-free methods), and touch briefly on community structure-based metrics.

Bioindicator microbes – taxonomy-based

Biotic indices are widely used for indicating ecosystem state and are based on the relative abundances of bioindicator organisms which have been weighted by their ecological value (e.g. Borja *et al.* 2000; AMBI). This requires taxonomic identification of organisms and the assignment of identified taxa to an ecological grouping based on a known response of taxa to environmental stressors. This information, along with the relative abundances of taxa/ecological groupings, is used to calculate the biotic index of choice and provide an indication of ecosystem state. Much of the initial progress in bioindication via metabarcoding has been developing genomic versions of existing, successful, biotic indices (where sequenced-based observations replace direct observations) for metazoans (e.g. genomic AMBI 'gAMBI'; Aylagas *et al.* 2014), but also for microbes and we provide some examples of these below.

Diatom observations are widely used in aquatic environments, particularly rivers and streams, for water quality assessment because of their high sensitivity to environmental change and well-established taxon-specific ecological tolerances and preferences. Several diatom indices based on traditional, morphological taxonomic identifications exist (reviewed in Steveson 2014). The main limitation of these diatom indices is the inherent difficulty in diatom taxonomic identification based on morphology due to their diverse morphologies with high levels of intraspecific variability, their small size (<50 μM) and identification via microscopy requires specific sample preparation and expert taxonomic knowledge (Kermarrec *et al.* 2014). In response to these limitations, diatom metabarcoding data for morphospecies identification has been substituted in the calculation of, for example, the Specific Pollution Sensitivity Index (Indice de Pollusensibilité Spécifique – IPS; Kermarrec *et al.* 2014; Vasselon *et al.* 2017); a derived IPS index (IPSp) using clustering of diatom taxa based on phylogeny and traits (Keck *et al.* 2016) and the Swiss Diatom Index (DI-CH; Visco *et al.* 2015). While there was a large degree of divergence between the DNA-based and morphological taxa identifications and calculations of relative abundances (discussed below), the water quality rankings assigned to sites were generally consistent regardless of whether DNA-based or morphological data were used. While the methods were successfully applied in the above example, uptake of DNA based methods for calculation of diatom-based indices has not always been successful, highlighting the need for methodological validation in novel situations. For example, when the ecological status of a freshwater lake in France was assessed using three diatom indices – IPS; Eutrophication Pollution Index for littoral diatoms (EPI-L; Marchetto *et al.* 2013); and the Diatom Quality Index (S; Sgro *et al.* 2009) – based on both morphological and DNA-based approaches, the authors found that

the results differed between the indices and between the two methods (Rivera *et al.* 2018). The authors note that there are several potential reasons for this discrepancy, including the use of inappropriate diatom indices for the environment (e.g. lake vs. estuarine), incomplete reference library, presence of dead dells and non-diatom DNA in the samples and differences in the estimation of species abundances (for a detailed discussion see Rivera *et al.* 2018).

Bacterial assemblages have largely been ignored in biomonitoring for effects of perturbation due to their high complexity and difficulty of observation. Environmental genomics tools address this challenge, and one could argue that the reliance of microbial ecologists on DNA-based taxonomy has led to more complete and better curated sequence reference databases than other potential bioindicator taxa. The first taxonomy-based biotic index using bacterial community composition data for ecosystem assessment was the microgAMBI (Aylagas *et al.* 2017), the development and use of which we describe in detail in Box 19.1. MicrogAMBI is a further extension of the previously described AMBI and gAMBI, in that it is an index calculated based on the relative abundances of bacteria that have been taxonomically identified at the family level and assigned to an ecological grouping, that is, a known response of those bacteria to perturbation. This represented a major step forward for the potential inclusion of bacterial biotic indices in the management toolbox for biomonitoring and assessment (Pawlowski *et al.* 2018). While microgAMBI was developed with a view to broad application across a range of environments and pressure types (see Box 19.1), there are examples of other, bacteria-based indices, e.g. the bacteria-based index of biotic integrity (Ba-IBI; Li *et al.* 2018) and the microbial community-based index of biotic integrity (MC-IBI; Niu *et al.* 2018) that were developed for site-specific assessments of the Three Gorges Reservoir and Taihu Basin, respectively. These indices don't explicitly use taxonomic data that have been linked to an ecosystem state (as with the microgAMBI), but rather a combination of metrics describing taxonomic composition (relative abundance of taxa calculated from 16S rRNA sequencing data, e.g. relative abundances of Acidobacteria, or combined relative abundance of Firmicutes, Chloroflexi and Acidobacteria), gene abundances (calculated from real-time PCR data, e.g. log of gene abundance ratios 16S rRNA:antibiotic resistance genes) and trait information (e.g. relative abundance of methanotrophs or phototrophs). In both cases, the authors demonstrated the site-specific utility of indices based on a combination of taxonomic, functional and trait information to accurately identify reference versus disturbed sites, though the five core metrics used in the calculation of each index differed (Li *et al.* 2018; Niu *et al.* 2018). It is unknown if these measures would be more broadly transferrable or if new applications would require the investigation and validation of other appropriate core metrics most suited to each new case.

What data do you need?

A known bioindicator for your question/system, that is, an organism with a known response or association with an ecosystem state or contaminant; a marker gene that provides taxonomic information for your bioindicator taxa of choice (e.g. 16S rRNA – bacteria, archaea; 18S rRNA – eukaryotes; ribulose-1, 5-biphosphate carboxylase (*rbcL*) – diatoms; cytochrome oxidase I (COI) – micro and macro-eukaryotes); a reference database providing taxonomy for the bioindicator and marker gene of choice.

Considerations and limitations of taxonomy-based bioindication

Taxonomy-based strategies are de facto limited to the characterised fraction of biodiversity (Cordier 2020), that is, those taxa for which we have a known identification and

known association with an ecological state. Thus, potentially large proportions of community data, which remain unidentified or belong to taxa of unknown ecology, are ignored in subsequent index calculation. There are two widely recognised and fundamental caveats to this approach: taxonomic resolution of the dataset and assignment of taxa to ecological groupings (Weigand *et al.* 2019). Taxonomic resolution relies on our ability to accurately classify taxa, which is dependent on several variables including choice of marker gene and marker gene region, and completeness of the marker gene reference database used to classify sequence data. 'Completeness' in relation to bioindication as described here is really about whether the known morphology-based bioindicators are represented in DNA reference databases. In this case, the problem is reasonably easy to fix by filling these gaps. However, there are issues with the divergence between DNA-based and morphological taxa identifications; for example, the low congruence (15–28%) between DNA-based and morphologically-based calculation of diatom bioindices was mostly due to inadequate taxonomic coverage in DNA reference libraries (Kermarrec *et al.* 2014; Visco *et al.* 2015; Keck *et al.* 2016; Vasselon *et al.* 2017; Rivera *et al.* 2018). In addition, reference databases are curated or

---

Box 19.1: microgAMBI – a bacterial community-based biotic index to assess ecological status

MicrogAMBI is a biotic index calculated from 16S rRNA metabarcoding data, developed to indicate the health of coastal and estuarine locations, under a range of anthropogenic pressures, on the north coast of Spain. Bacterial taxa are identified via the taxonomic classification of sequences to family level and then assigned to ecological groups based on surveyed literature: those bacteria that are not associated with pollution inputs, including sensitive and indifferent taxa (Ecological Group I; EGI) and those bacteria that are associated with pollution inputs, including tolerant and opportunistic taxa (EGIII). The ratio of the relative abundance of EGI and EGIII in a sample is used to calculate the index which in turn provides an ecological classification of, high, good, moderate, poor, or bad status (Fig. 19.1). Taxa of unknown ecological function (EGII) are not included in calculation of the index. Aylagas *et al.* (2017) demonstrated that microgAMBI was significantly correlated (thus providing an accurate assessment of ecosystem state), with a pressure index calculated as a proxy of sediment quality and degree of anthropogenic disturbance and also with AMBI, known for its successful assessment of ecosystem status (Borja *et al.* 2019). MicrogAMBI has been demonstrated to work reasonably well under different environmental conditions and pressures. Case studies include a variety of sample types (sediment, water column, coral), pollution sources (wastewater, eutrophication, hydrocarbons), levels of anthropogenic disturbance (non-impacted vs. impacted), and geographical settings (polar, tropical, temperate; Borja 2018); anthropogenic impacts in oligotrophic coastal waters of the Red Sea (Pearman *et al.* 2018); impacts of increased nutrient loading in in situ experiments (Clark *et al.* 2021); assessing aquaculture impacts (Aylagas *et al.* 2021); tracking historical water quality changes in sediment profiles taken from a polluted, then remediated, reservoir in China (Sun *et al.* 2021); pressure gradients in estuarine and coastal sediments from the Bay of Biscay (Lanzen *et al.* 2021); and a pollution gradient in a land-river-lagoon continuum (Bourhane *et al.* 2022). It should be noted, though, that microgAMBI failed to detect a difference between the impacted Bay of Bengal and the non-impacted Barren Island, likely due to volcanic activity on Barren Island resulting in a high abundance of acidophilic and extremophile taxa, which are generally classified as pollution tolerant (Borja 2018). This serves as an important reminder that natural microbial communities can resemble an impacted microbial community and thus it is important to 'know your system'. Continued application of the microgAMBI to different systems under varied pressures will ultimately assist in expanding and refining the assignment of taxa to ecological groupings. The above-mentioned studies have resulted in the number of taxa in the microgAMBI list assigned to an ecological group increasing from the initial 226 taxa to the current 1564 taxa (updated from Borja 2018, and available upon request).

'quality-controlled' to differing degrees which can impact the accuracy and validity of classification (Rimet *et al.* 2021); this is especially true for microbiome reference databases where many taxonomy annotations are based on sequence predictions (denoised sequence clusters) rather than characterisation of cultured type strains (Edgar 2018a, b). Lastly, microbial taxonomy changes rapidly (see Sanford *et al.* 2021) leading to potential problems when a biotic index is bound to a specific taxonomy.

Assignment of taxa to ecological groupings can be difficult, particularly for microbes due to their variability of response and rapid adaptation under changing environmental conditions, the irony being that these features also make them good candidates for bioindication. Mis-classification to ecological groups can occur due to difficulties in assigning each taxon to a specific ecological response (Astudillo-García *et al.* 2019), or no ecological classification at all due to the presence of taxa with an unknown response to perturbation. In the latter case, as stated above, microbes with an unknown response to perturbation would be excluded from calculation of traditional biotic indices potentially ignoring an important bioindicator of

change. Notably, the majority of microbes remain uncultured and often with unknown function. Overmann *et al.* (2019) determined that 85 out of 118 phyla established at the time had not had a single species formally described. Advances in DNA-based techniques, such as whole metagenome sequencing and single cell sequencing, are bridging this gap; however, conflicts in nomenclature or the adoption of unvalidated classifications with little review still occur (Sanford *et al.* 2021). Another consideration is the level of taxonomic resolution available for any given taxon and its relationship to ecological function; in cases where response to perturbation is not known at the species or genus level, it has been assigned at the family level or higher (Borja 2018) and different organisms within a family, for example, can exhibit very different functions. Increasing the taxonomic resolution of the taxa list and the associated responses to perturbation will likely improve classifications of ecological status.

The calculation of taxa abundances (relative or other) from metabarcoding data is another area of contention. The number of sequence reads attributed to an individual taxon is a function of several things, including the

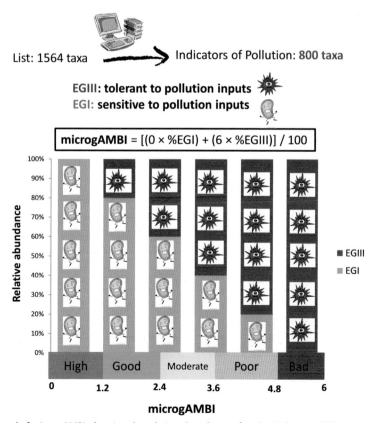

Fig. 19.1. Theoretical background of microgAMBI, showing the relative abundance of ecological group (EG) taxa tolerant (EGIII) and sensitive (EGI) to pollution, the equation to calculate the index and the boundary values determining the five quality classes (modified and updated from Aylagas *et al.* 2017). The current number of taxa has been updated from Borja (2018).

number of individuals, the biomass of individuals, the variable copy number of marker genes in the genome, variations in extraction efficiency, primer-specific amplification bias, sequence composition (e.g. GC content), sequence length, potential biases based on the bioinformatic methods chosen, and the compositional nature of data generated by next generation sequencing technology (Edgar 2017). Nevertheless, regardless of the considerations and limitations outlined above, the scientific community/literature is in general agreement that taxonomy-based bioindication via metabarcoding is promising, and, in some cases, the number of reads can be related to the biomass, as in the case of macroinvertebrates (Aylagas *et al.* 2018).

Bioindicator microbes – taxonomy-free discovery

Taxonomy-free (referred to as *de novo* in some literature) bioindication approaches allow the identification of bioindicators without prior taxonomic assignment. One of the fundamental lines of enquiry by microbial ecologists is to look for correlations between microbial community composition and environmental features (e.g. temperature, pH, grainsize distributions). While this type of approach is based on direct sequence-based observations correlated to environmental gradients, more recently the science has moved towards predictive outputs using cross-validated models, for example machine learning, whereby we attempt to identify groups of organisms best indicative of, or varying according to, specific environmental perturbations or conditions. Machine learning is the study of computer algorithms that improve automatically through experience and by the use of data (Mitchell 1997). For a comprehensive review of machine learning methodologies please see Namkung (2020) and Ghannam and Techtmann (2021). Machine learning approaches to predict 'state' from microbial community data have been utilised for more than a decade, for example using culture-based enumeration of faecal bacteria and chemical parameters to develop models predicting faecal sources in waters polluted by sewage (Belanche-Muñoz and Blanch 2008), and utilising metabarcoding data in human microbiome research to predict host phenotype (Knights *et al.* 2011; Knights *et al.* 2011), and environmental research to classify sites with differing geochemical characteristics e.g. uranium contamination (Smith *et al.* 2015). Generally, to explore the relationship between microbial community profiles and environmental 'state', supervised machine learning is used. Here we focus on two supervised machine learning approaches that are

being actively researched for taxonomy-free bioindication: regression analysis and random forest classification.

Environmental correlation through regression analysis can be utilised to assign taxa or sequences to ecological groupings without prior knowledge of their ecological function. These *de novo* generated ecological groupings can then be used to calculate biotic indices, similar to the taxonomy-based approach, to measure ecosystem state (Anderson 2008; Keeley *et al.* 2012; Keeley *et al.* 2018; Aylagas *et al.* 2021; Lanzen *et al.* 2021). One such method to identify *de novo* ecological groupings, uses quantile regression splines (QRS) to correlate an ecological state or environmental variable to changes in taxa distributions. Individual sequence abundances are plotted as a function of, for example, an impact gradient, and QRS models are constructed for the 95th percentile: the value below which 95% of a sequence abundance is expected to occur along the environmental gradient (Koenker and Schorfheide 1994; Koenker *et al.* 1994; Anderson 2008). Splines (curves of best fit) are fitted to the resulting models and a vertical line is added to the plot indicating the point along the *x*-axis that the maximum abundance of a taxon or OTU was predicted (Fig. 19.2). This point of maximum abundance represents the optimum conditions along the environmental gradient for each sequence/taxon. This allows predictions of sequence/taxon range, or assemblage change, along the environmental gradient and thus *de novo* ecological groupings are selected as the group of sequences/taxa whose distributions are closest to the peak of the fitted spline. Case studies applying this approach are detailed in Box 19.2. Complete community profiles (i.e. all sequences/taxa) can be input, though this is computationally expensive/prohibitive and may introduce spurious correlations with rare species. Prior to the use of QRS to calculate ecological groupings, the input sequence data can be further curated, for example including only the 'X' most abundant sequences/taxa (Keeley *et al.* 2018; Aylagas *et al.* 2021) or only validated indicator sequences/taxa selected based on their relationship to your variable of interest using a method such as threshold indicator taxa analysis (TITAN; Baker and King 2010; Lanzen *et al.* 2021). Other approaches to *de novo* identification of ecological groupings to calculate biotic indices have been proposed, for example modelling the relative abundances of OTUs in a sample along principal components axes of environmental parameters (Lau *et al.* 2015; Tapolczai, Keck, *et al.* 2019; Tapolczai, Vasselon, *et al.* 2019) or multivariate generalised linear modelling (Simonin *et al.* 2019; Frühe, Cordier, *et al.* 2021), though these are not described here.

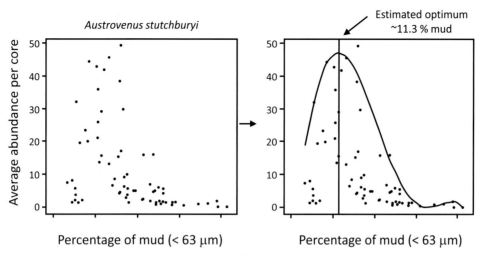

Fig. 19.2. Simplified representation of using quantile regression splines (QRS) to correlate changes in taxa distributions to an ecological state or environmental variable. The abundance of *Austrovenus stutchburyi* (cockles) was plotted against the percentage of mud in sediment. The regression spline model is shown for the 95th percentile with the maximum from the model (the estimated optimum for cockles being 11.3% mud) indicated by the vertical line. Source: Anderson (2008).

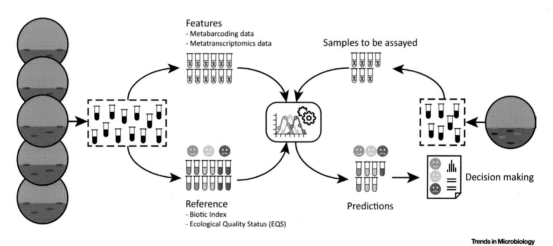

Trends in Microbiology

Fig. 19.3. Proposed workflow using a predictive model to make ecological quality status (EQS) assessment from environmental genomics data. The predictive model is built from training data that include both reference diagnostics and metabarcoding data using a supervised machine learning algorithm. Source: Cordier *et al.* (2019).

Supervised machine learning includes various computational and statistical data analysis methods that build and adapt models based on sample or observation data, known as 'training data', in order to make predictions or decisions without being explicitly programmed to do so (Namkung 2020); that is, identify a discriminative variable or combination of variables with the highest predictive power to classify new samples or data. For example, a training dataset consisting of microbial community sequence data collected from contaminated and uncontaminated sites could be used to create a model which can classify new sites as contaminated or not, based on the microbes present (illustrated in Fig. 19.3; Cordier *et al.* 2019). Research has been largely focused on demonstrating the efficacy of supervised machine learning to develop predictive models which infer an ecological classification without relying on taxonomic classification or assignment to ecological groups, and to test the limitations of these methods. Random forests are an increasingly used supervised machine learning method that works on the premise of building a decision tree that uses features and threshold values, for example metabarcoding community profiles of a sample (feature) associated with a reference disturbance level (threshold value), to successively split samples into groups that have similar values (Breiman 2001). This process is repeated by performing bootstrapping on the dataset, resulting in a 'forest' of trees and eventually a trained model which can be used to classify new data or samples. The random forest approach has been shown to be superior to other supervised machine learning algorithms (e.g. support vector machine, self-organising maps) to assess the impacts of marine aquaculture, and congruent with assessments produced by four different traditional morphological biotic indices (Cordier *et al.* 2018; Frühe *et al.* 2021). Furthermore, the random forest algorithm was shown to outperform taxonomy-based biotic indices constructed from a range of different marker genes of both microbial and eukaryote origin (detailed in Box 19.3; Cordier *et al.* 2018). It should be noted, however, that studies have also demonstrated the validity of other supervised machine learning methods for bioindication (e.g. Feio *et al.* 2020).

What data do you need?

When taxonomy-free supervised machine learning approaches are applied as described above for the classification of ecosystem state, they do not require taxonomic reference databases or known ecological classifications of taxa. You do need an extensive metabarcoding dataset with samples representative of all reference and impact states. Comprehensive environmental measurements across a gradient of impact (or natural variation) and/or ecological knowledge in the form of a classification of state or impact of your study region (e.g. sites classified as good, fair, poor) is essential. This combination of data is required to: 1) identify de novo ecological groupings to generate biotic indices in the case of the regression approach, or 2) infer the connection between ecosystem state and community composition necessary to train predictive models that will be able to assign a classification of ecosystem state to new samples or data.

Considerations and limitations of taxonomy-free bioindication

While taxonomy-free approaches show significant promise for biomonitoring, they are not without their limitations. The goal of supervised machine learning is to build predictive models, where the objective is not how well the model fits our study or dataset, but how well it will generalise to new studies or datasets (Namkung 2020). Both approaches outlined above require a training dataset consisting of samples from which both metabarcoding data and associated pressure or environmental measurement data are known and results are highly dependent on the balanced coverage of sites with contrasting ecological status. Therefore, training data at high resolution, both spatial and temporal, and representative of all impact states or the entire environmental/impact gradient, is required to generate accurate

predictive models (as discussed by Gerhard and Gunsch (2019).

Metabarcoding data are characterised by high dimensionality, a much higher number of features or 'taxa' (sequences in the form of OTUs or ASVs) than in samples, and this can lead to 'overfitting' of the predictive model thus decreasing its accuracy (Libbrecht and Noble 2015). Too many features can result in sparse data, where a single data point (sample) can be identified by a single feature (sequence); the probability of observing a perfect correlation between OTUs and an ecological classification or environmental state by chance, increases with the number of OTUs in the dataset. When a model is trained on overly sparse or noisy datasets it is less likely to perform well on new data or in a more generalised setting. The number of features can be reduced by grouping features, for example aggregating sequence data from an ASV to a clustered OTU (e.g. 97%), though a recent study using supervised machine learning to predict measures of soil health demonstrated that the most accurate models were those trained on data at the highest taxonomic resolution (ASVs; Wilhelm *et al.* 2022). Feature selection methods such as filtering datasets prior to modelling (using a univariate or multivariate statistic to score features based on correlation to some relevant criteria), wrapper methods (repeatedly constructing models using forward, backward or recursive selection of features), or embedded methods (feature selection methods built into modelling procedures) can be employed to identify fewer and more discriminative features that will maximise model performance (Ghannam and Techtmann 2021).

Rarely does a single study have a large enough sample set to be able to provide enough training data, validation data, and 'new' data to test model outcomes potentially leading to models that are too specific to the training dataset. The converse can also be true resulting in 'underfitting' of models – where a model is too simple or general, not capturing important information about the variables. Therefore, there is a trade-off between high OTU dimensionality and providing enough data to separate ecologically relevant units. Cross-validation techniques are used to control for under- or overfitting of models. Importantly, random forest models, most often chosen for microbiome research and in particular the bioindication space, are less prone to overfitting (Breiman 2001).

While traditional methods of bioindication based on morphological identification are expensive, the costs (both financial and computational) of producing metabarcoding datasets and associated environmental metadata at the scale and resolution required for effective bioindication are not insignificant. Assessing the relationship between sequencing depth in several microbial datasets and success of random forest classifications of environmental status demonstrated that 5000 sequences per sample (even as low as 50 sequences/sample in one dataset) were sufficient with no substantial improvements achieved in the random forest classification performance with greater sequencing depth (Dully *et al.* 2021). Indeed, the authors suggest that where random forest classification is used for bioindication of ecosystem state, as well as guiding future sampling designs to save financial and computational resources, the results of their study may also assist in avoiding the possible biases of overfitting and reducing noise due to too large datasets. Ultimately, this study could represent an important step towards minimum guidelines and standardising methodology in the design of biomonitoring programs.

Lanzen *et al.* (2021) provide a nice summary of the conceptual differences between the random forest and environmental correlation via QRS approaches – random forest analysis takes advantage of the non-linear and multivariate properties of community composition data, including the associations between taxa, whereas the QRS approach is based on auto-ecology, in that each sequence/taxon is treated individually and assigned an ecological grouping to calculate a biotic index. Thus, correlative QRS approaches are not able to identify the complex interactions between individuals and the possibility that large groups of microbes may respond to a stressor (Ghannam and Techtmann 2021). Conversely, while SML methods, such as random forest analysis, can potentially identify complex relationships, there are some pit falls around the interpretability of the data, particularly in a management setting (Cordier *et al.* 2021). For example, while a model may be shown to accurately classify or predict the state of an ecosystem it can be more challenging to understand the 'why' – the taxa associations that underlie the predictions or why certain observations have been grouped to a particular response (Ghannam and Techtmann 2021). In a management setting where intervention is required, this information might be critical. Thus, using QRS as a robust means to assign ecological groupings and calculate biotic indices is likely a more realistic shorter term goal for bioindication (Aylagas *et al.* 2021).

Box 19.2: Quantile regression splines (QRS) to develop de novo ecological groups for taxonomy-free biotic indices

Perhaps the most advanced application of DNA-based tools for biomonitoring has been undertaken in monitoring benthic impacts of aquaculture in New Zealand where, traditional and DNA-based monitoring was conducted in parallel for 7 years of sampling at sea-cage-based fish farms (reviewed in Aylagas *et al.* 2020; Pochon *et al.* 2020). Traditional macrofauna and biochemical analyses were undertaken to calculate a benthic Enrichment Stage (ES) index (Keeley *et al.* 2012) as a proxy for disturbance. In parallel, metabarcoding of bacteria, foraminifera, and eukaryote marker genes from eDNA and eRNA was conducted. Keeley *et al.* (2012) used QRS to identify and validate ecological groupings for benthic macrofaunal responses to organic ES, and subsequently developing a multi-trophic biotic index for monitoring benthic organic enrichment (Keeley *et al.* 2018). In brief, individual OTU abundances were plotted against ES values to correlate enrichment to taxa distributions, QRS models were constructed and ecological groups of OTUs identified. The Metabarcoding Biotic Index (MBI; development detailed in Keeley *et al.* 2018) is a modified version of the established AMBI (Borja *et al.* 2000) and was calculated for each taxonomic group individually (bacteria, foraminifera, eukaryotes) and in combination (multi-trophic MBI). Strong correlations were observed between the multi-trophic MBI, the bacterial and eukaryotic MBI, and ES. Regression splines were able to distinguish the response of OTUs whose tolerance of enrichment was unknown or poorly understood; one-third of taxa in Keeley *et al.* (2018) had no organic enrichment tolerance previously defined and thus would not have been included in a traditional taxonomy-based index. However, the authors found the approach was less robust when applied to low abundance and/or rare taxa, or taxa whose distributions were poorly correlated with the explanatory variables. Additionally, the authors found strong agreement in splines distribution between eDNA and eRNA datasets, suggesting eDNA data (cheaper, simpler to produce) can provide comparable results to eRNA (Keeley *et al.* 2018). Finally, an ASV-based bacterial (b-MBI) index validated for routine monitoring of New Zealand fish farms (Pochon *et al.* 2020) showed great potential for use in remote Norwegian fish farm environments (Keeley *et al.* 2021) and was recently adapted to freshwater environments for measuring the trophic state of 259 New Zealand lakes (Pearman *et al.* 2022).

Aylagas *et al.* (2021) used the same approach to develop a stressor-specific ecological grouping by correlating bacterial community structure with acid volatile sulphides (AVS) in sediments, a stressor directly related to intensive finfish production. While both the taxonomy-based microgAMBI and QRS-based biotic indices were able to identify an organically enriched gradient, the QRS biotic index outperformed microgAMBI by providing a higher discriminatory power between subtle shifts in other abiotic factors directly related to finfish production and allowing the identification of new bacterial bioindicators. It is noted that the identification of new bacterial bioindicators via QRS could represent a pathway to further expand and refine the microgAMBI taxa list. These case studies demonstrate the use of environmental correlation using a broad suite of stressors (ES index from a range of parameters) or a single stressor (AVS concentration gradient) to produce *de novo* biotic indices capable of elucidating impacts of marine aquaculture. It is likely that these techniques would translate successfully to measure the impacts of other anthropogenic stressors, multiple or single, across a broad range of environmental settings (e.g. Pearman *et al.* 2022).

Box 19.3: Supervised machine learning for biomonitoring: some examples and lessons

To our knowledge, the first use of microbial DNA-based data and supervised machine learning (SML) to identify environmental contaminants was the work of Smith *et al.* (2015). The authors trialled nine algorithms to classify sites with differing geochemical characteristics, demonstrating that bacterial community data (both metabarcoding and microarray data) could identify a range of geochemical signatures including, uranium and nitrate contamination at a nuclear waste site and hydrocarbon contamination from the Deepwater Horizon oil spill. This work identified a 'legacy' effect of contamination, whereby sites impacted by the DWH oil spill contained altered bacterial communities 'encoding a memory of prior contamination' even after the contaminants had been degraded and returned to baseline levels of hydrocarbon signatures (Smith *et al.* 2015). These results illustrated that ecological impacts may persist beyond the depletion of physico-chemical signals, the longevity of perturbation in an ecological context and the ability of bacterial community composition to reflect this (Smith *et al.* 2015; Frühe *et al.* 2021). The flip side is that we should be cautious in our interpretation of a site classified as 'contaminated', recognising that the contamination might no longer exist, but the ecological impacts perhaps do. Since that initial study, biomonitoring scientists have sought to demonstrate the use of metabarcoding data and SML in the prediction of biotic indices (e.g. AMBI) within the framework of impacts of marine aquaculture activities. Earlier work by Cordier *et al.* (2017, 2018) demonstrated the efficacy of SML to build predictive models from benthic foraminifera metabarcoding data using either composition or diversity metrics as features (Cordier *et al.* 2017) and the superiority of SML to taxonomy-based biotic indices (both derived from metabarcoding data; Cordier *et al.* 2018) to accurately identify impacts. SML has also been shown to be superior to indicator value approaches, for example IndVal and/or QRS methods, for predicting impacts of salmon aquaculture (Frühe, Dully, *et al.* 2021) and, more broadly, the impacts of multiple stressors in estuarine and coastal ecosystems (Lanzen *et al.* 2021).

Through these studies, the authors have suggested several important validations or qualifications around the use of these methods for bioindication. Where multiple SML algorithms have been trialled, random forests have proven superior to other approaches (Smith *et al.* 2015; Cordier *et al.* 2017; Frühe, Cordier, *et al.* 2021). Predictive models perform better when a larger taxonomic spectrum is targeted (metabarcoding utilising universal or broad-spectrum primers); furthermore, targeting smaller organisms, for example meiofauna or microbes, improves the required representativeness of community profiles, likely due to the inherent difficulties of capturing large-sized organisms in the small sample sizes used to produce metabarcoding datasets (Cordier *et al.* 2018). Most of these studies have relied upon the existence of traditional biotic indices, almost exclusively derived from traditional macroinvertebrate monitoring, to first classify samples in training datasets and to validate the accuracy of predictions (Cordier *et al.* 2017, 2018; Frühe, Cordier, *et al.* 2021; Lanzen *et al.* 2021). While this provides a convenient test bed it also has its flaws: macroinvertebrate-based assessments may be error prone for several reasons (e.g. methodological diversity, rare or cryptic biodiversity, difficulty identifying early-life stages and/or damaged specimens) and SML predictive models can only be as good as the data that they are trained upon. It also raises the question of how we can classify samples and/or validate predictions in ecosystems where these data are unavailable. There are still relatively few published SML case studies targeting biomonitoring and these have largely focused on the impacts of marine aquaculture; thus there are also questions on the broader applicability of the methodology, though more recently Lanzen *et al.* (2021) did successfully demonstrate a wider application predicting multiple impacts in estuarine and coastal ecosystems. Smith *et al.* (2015) also highlighted the need to demonstrate the geographical generalisability of predictive models generated from specific case studies, something that is still lacking today (Aylagas *et al.* 2021; Lanzen *et al.* 2021).

Community-based structural metrics

As opposed to indicator strategies based on specific organisms (whether classified taxonomically or not), community-based indicators rely on information pertaining to the whole community structure. Community-based indicators include measures of microbial biomass, ratios of organisms (e.g. fungi:bacteria), **alpha diversity**, beta diversity, and properties of co-occurrence networks (Laroche *et al.* 2018; Cordier *et al.* 2021; Fierer *et al.* 2021; Lopes *et al.* 2021). This strategy has resulted from the many studies that have sought to understand the processes determining microbial community responses to perturbation, and as result generally incorporate some temporal or space and time reference component. Alpha diversity, or the number of taxa within a particular area or ecosystem, has been used at various times to assess community response to disturbance (Liao *et al.* 2020; Seitz *et al.* 2022), with often contrasting results. It has been shown, for example, that bacterial diversity might increase (Seitz *et al.* 2022) or decrease (Liao *et al.* 2020) following disturbance. There also remains difficulty in standardising alpha diversity metrics between all studies (Bissett and Brown 2018). As a result, it is unlikely that alpha diversity, whether based on phylogeny or not, will be useful as an instantaneous indicator metric, but when put into context via temporal monitoring at specific locations or with the use of appropriate reference sites, it may be a useful indicator of change.

Beta diversity, or the extent of compositional change between communities, is useful for investigation of patterns of diversity change at varying scales of space and time. Like other community-based metrics there is considerable variation in the beta diversity response to disturbance, thereby likely making it most useful in an indicator sense when considered in context of a trajectory or in relation to some reference state. As reviewed in Socolar *et al.* (2016), for example, maximising beta-diversity is not necessarily desirable. Patterns in beta diversity through space and time can shed light on ecosystem response to change, ecosystem stability and predicted trajectory, as well as aid in the development of mechanistic understandings of these when coupled with organismal and functional approaches (Bowd *et al.* 2021; Laroche *et al.* 2021). Beta diversity has been used to indicate and monitor change in various systems, and its utilisation for ecological indication and monitoring is still under active development, in both macro (Azaele *et al.* 2014; Hui and Mcgeoch 2014; Mori *et al.* 2015; Mori *et al.* 2018) and micro (Glasl *et al.* 2017; Liddicoat *et al.* 2019; Su 2021) ecology. There has also been recent interest in the use of ecological and co-occurrence networks to indicate ecosystem state (reviewed in Cordier *et al.* (2021). These methods also show considerable variation in their response to system change and ability to indicate ecosystem status.

FUTURE DIRECTIONS AND OUTSTANDING QUESTIONS

Bioindicators derived from microbial metabarcoding data can provide an accurate assessment of the ecological status of an environment. However, the array of different methodologies that are currently being explored suggests that we may still be some ways from reaching a consensus regarding the most reliable approach (Hering *et al.* 2018; Pawlowski *et al.* 2018, 2021). In general, the scientific community seems to be placing greater emphasis on indicator organism-based, taxonomy-free approaches (e.g. Cordier *et al.* 2017, 2018; Keeley *et al.* 2018; Cordier 2020; Aylagas *et al.* 2021; Frühe, Cordier, *et al.* 2021; Frühe, Dully, *et al.* 2021; Lanzen *et al.* 2021). A direct comparison of organism indicator approaches outlined in this chapter (taxonomy-based, taxonomy-free *de novo* identification of ecological groupings, and taxonomy-free SML) found that both of the taxonomy-free approaches were more closely aligned with the classical morphologically derived diatom index to assess river state (Apotheloz-Perret-Gentil *et al.* 2021). However, it is important to remember that both taxonomy-based and taxonomy-free bioindication represent a step forward in our ability to effectively monitor the environment at greater scales (spatial and temporal), that both approaches have strengths and limitations, and that perhaps both have a place in the world of biomonitoring. The real power in these techniques is likely our ability to track change and/or predict trajectories of change; ecosystem assessment of a single point in time may not be considered robust due to some of the limitations outlined above whereas demonstrating a change in community composition and/or structure over time is a reliable indication that there has been a change in ecosystem state.

There is a critical need to sustain ongoing efforts to build comprehensive reference databases: databases composed of curated reference sequences for taxonomy-based approaches, as well as databases composed of datasets containing both metabarcoding data and comprehensive environmental measurements for taxonomy-free approaches (Apotheloz-Perret-Gentil *et al.* 2021). Improving databases should take into account both 'vertical' and 'horizontal' coverage, the addition of more taxa and the inclusion of more habitats and geographic regions, respectively

(Cordier *et al.* 2021). As sequencing technology continues to advance and costs continue to drop, large-scale (both spatial and temporal) microbial datasets are emerging (e.g. Australian Microbiome Initiative; National Microbiome Data Collaborative; Ocean Sampling Day; TARA Oceans). The growth of these standardised national and international sequence datasets in conjunction with a drive to provide comprehensive sample metadata will enable the further identification of relationships between bioindicators and ecosystem properties.

Bioindication science has largely focused on taxonomic observations of organisms. Even in the taxonomy-free methodologies detailed above, most current cases use data derived from taxonomic marker genes. There is a large body of research demonstrating that changes in microbial community structure due to disturbance can directly affect ecosystem process which is a result of changes in the metabolic functioning of the community (Kimes *et al.* 2014; Galand *et al.* 2016; Chen *et al.* 2021). Metabolic capabilities can be decoupled from the taxonomic identity of microorganisms due to convergent evolution, gene loss and/or horizontal gene transfer (Martiny *et al.* 2013). In addition, a single microbial taxon can exhibit a broad repertoire of functional capabilities, switching between different metabolic strategies depending on the environmental conditions at the time (Carbonero *et al.* 2010; Chen *et al.* 2021). As such, for microorganisms, the relationship between taxonomy and function is still largely undefined. Taxonomic composition can change more rapidly and at greater magnitude than the functional structure of a community in response to environmental change (Li *et al.* 2018), implying that the perceived environmental change, while affecting taxonomic community structure, may not necessarily have affected ecosystem processes or function (Allison and Martiny 2008). This functional redundancy implies a level of stability or resilience of ecosystem processes to change. Therefore, one might expect that biomonitoring via functional profiles might provide a better proxy to detect disturbance; both taxonomic and predicted functional microbial community profiles accurately predicted the impact of aquaculture on marine benthic biodiversity (Cordier 2020; Laroche *et al.* 2021). Certainly, the role that functional approaches supported by other omics technologies (e.g. metagenomics, metatranscriptomics, metaproteomics and metabolomics) could play in bioindication is an area of active research (Fig. 19.4; Sagova-Mareckova *et al.* 2021; Shah *et al.* 2021).

An important consideration regardless of the approach is the potential biases introduced at all stages of a metabarcoding workflow – from sample collection to the chosen bioinformatics workflow and data analytics. To use metabarcoding workflows for routine bioindication, standardisation and interoperability of methodology is required (Rimet *et al.* 2021), particularly if the goal is to be able to compare assessments across space and time. DNAaqua-Net is arguably the most advanced initiative in the bioindication space, with the objective to bring together researchers across disciplines to '*identify gold-standard genomic tools and novel eco-genomic indices and metrics for routine application for biodiversity assessments and biomonitoring of European water bodies*' (Leese *et al.* 2016). Working groups have been established to address challenges related to barcode reference databases (Weigand *et al.* 2019; Rimet *et al.* 2021); biotic indices and metrics (Pawlowski *et al.* 2018); field and

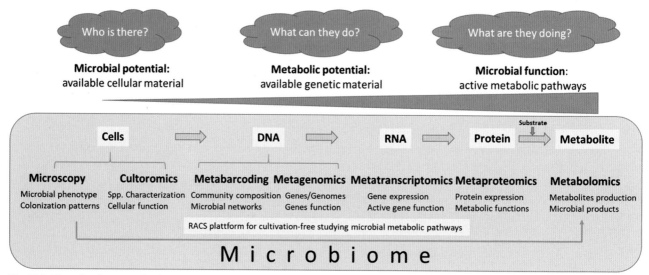

Fig. 19.4. The role of omics technologies in microbial research. RACS – Raman-activated cell sorting (Lee *et al.* 2019). Source: Berg *et al.* (2020).

laboratory protocols; data analysis and storage; and implementation strategy and legal issues; resulting in a large body of research and training opportunities in Europe. More recently, other initiatives supporting the development and sharing of best practise for omic technologies have been emerging (e.g. Ocean Best Practises System Task Team 21-03: OMICs/eDNA Protocol Management (Samuel *et al.* 2021); OMIC Biodiversity Observation Network (Omic-BON); and the UN endorsed Ocean Decade Action – Ocean Biomolecular Observing Network (OBON)) and are gaining more widespread traction in the scientific community.

For the potential of DNA-based bioindication to be fully realised it requires more than novel and strong science, it requires buy in and coordination among practitioners and end-users and ultimately to fit within regulatory frameworks. Despite the rapid advances, the uptake and implementation of these approaches in routine biomonitoring has been slow. Though not covered in this chapter, there are several excellent reviews on the reasons for this and potential pathways for implementation in a regulatory setting (Pawlowski *et al.* 2018, 2021; Aylagas *et al.* 2020; Cordier 2020). Regardless of the domain of life from which bioindicators based on metabarcoding data arise, most of the challenges and priority areas of future research to be addressed are the same. Makiola *et al.* (2020) pose key questions in their review paper 'Key questions for next-generation biomonitoring'; paraphrased, these are: How can benefits be communicated to citizens, scientists and policymakers? What are appropriate spatio-temporal scales for bioindication? What is the best balance between generic and case- or site-specific best practise methodologies? What are appropriate indicators of change? What is the benefit from machine learning approaches? What are the key technical challenges? How can these approaches be applied to risk management? What are the most promising advancements in genomics tools, computing and bioinformatics, and modelling in addressing target questions? While we direct the reader to the Makiola *et al.* (2020) review for robust discussion of these questions, it is clear that DNA metabarcoding has the potential to revolutionise biomonitoring and assessment across all habitats. However broad uptake of any of the proposed methodologies will require robust validation and bench-marking across a range of biomonitoring scenarios (Aylagas *et al.* 2020).

DISCUSSION TOPICS

1. While assessing and tracking the state of an ecosystem is of clear importance, can the data or methodologies described above inform us on the resistance or resilience of an ecosystem? How can we identify thresholds or tipping points of an ecosystem in response to disturbance?

2. How can we incorporate environmental data into more causative models of ecosystem trajectory to enable management interventions?

3. How can we 'globalise' efforts to build and deploy widely applicable (in space and time) ecosystem status models?

4. How best can we include future data (i.e. modelled data of future environmental conditions) in assessments of trajectories and states?

RESOURCES

There are several excellent reviews referenced in this chapter that we recommend for the reader interested in more detail on environmental genomics and bioindication across all domains of life including but not limited to:

Astudillo-García C, Hermans SM, Stevenson B, Buckley HL, Lear G (2019) Microbial assemblages and bioindicators as proxies for ecosystem health status: Potential and limitations. *Applied Microbiology and Biotechnology* **103**, 6407–6421. doi:10.1007/s00253-019-09963-0

Aylagas E, Borja A, Pochon X, Zaiko A, Keeley N, *et al.* (2020) Translational molecular ecology in practice: Linking DNA-based methods to actionable marine environmental management. *Science of The Total Environment* **744**, 140780. doi:10.1016/j.scitotenv.2020.140780

Baird DJ, Hajibabaei M (2012) Biomonitoring 2.0: A new paradigm in ecosystem assessment made possible by next-generation DNA sequencing. *Molecular Ecology* **21**, 2039–2044. doi:10.1111/j.1365-294X.2012.05519.x

Namkung J (2020) Machine learning methods for microbiome studies. *Journal of Microbiology* **58**, 206–216. doi:10.1007/s12275-020-0066-8

Pawlowski J, Kelly-Quinn M, Altermatt F, Apothéloz-Perret-Gentil L, Beja P, *et al.* (2018) The future of biotic indices in the ecogenomic era: Integrating (e)DNA metabarcoding in biological assessment of aquatic ecosystems. *Science of The Total Environment* **637–638**, 1295–1310. doi:10.1016/j.scitotenv.2018.05.002

Many of the recent articles referenced in this chapter were published in a *Molecular Ecology* special issue:

Pawlowski J, Bonin A, Boyer F, Cordier T, Taberlet, P (eds) (2021) Environmental DNA for biodiversity and ecosystem monitoring. [Special Issue]. *Molecular Ecology* **30**(13), 2931–3389.

Websites for some global initiatives aimed at enabling Biomonitoring 2.0 (Baird and Hajibabaei 2012):
1. https://dnaqua.net
2. https://stream-dna.com
3. https://lakes380.com/
4. https://www.biosecurity-toolbox.org.nz/

REFERENCES

Allison SD, Martiny JBH (2008) Resistance, resilience, and redundancy in microbial communities. *Proceeding1s of the National Academy of Sciences of the United States of America* **105**, 11512–11519. doi:10.1073/pnas.0801925105

Anderson MJ (2008) Animal-sediment relationships re-visited: Characterising species' distributions along an environmental gradient using canonical analysis and quantile regression splines. *Journal of Experimental Marine Biology and Ecology* **366**(1–2), 16–27. doi:10.1016/j.jembe.2008.07.006

Apotheloz-Perret-Gentil L, Bouchez A, Cordier T, Cordonier A, Guéguen J, *et al.* (2021) Monitoring the ecological status of rivers with diatom eDNA metabarcoding: A comparison of taxonomic markers and analytical approaches for the inference of a molecular diatom index. *Molecular Ecology* **30**, 2959–2968.

Astudillo-García C, Hermans SM, Stevenson B, Buckley HL, Lear G (2019) Microbial assemblages and bioindicators as proxies for ecosystem health status: potential and limitations. *Applied Microbiology and Biotechnology* **103**, 6407–6421.

Aylagas E, Borja Á, Tangherlini M, Dell'Anno A, Corinaldesi C, *et al.* (2017) A bacterial community-based index to assess the ecological status of estuarine and coastal environments. *Marine Pollution Bulletin* **114**, 679–688.

Aylagas E, Borja Á, Muxika I, Rodríguez-Ezpeleta N (2018) Adapting metabarcoding-based benthic biomonitoring into routine marine ecological status assessment networks. *Ecological Indicators* **95**, 194–202.

Aylagas E, Borja A, Pochon X, Zaiko A, Keeley N (2020) Translational molecular ecology in practice: Linking DNA-based methods to actionable marine environmental management. *Science of The Total Environment* **744**, 140780.

Aylagas E, Atalah J, Sánchez-Jerez P, Pearman JK, Casado N (2021) A step towards the validation of bacteria biotic indices using DNA metabarcoding for benthic monitoring. *Molecular Ecology Resources* **21**, 1889–1903.

Aylagas E, Borja Á, Rodríguez-Ezpeleta N (2014) Environmental status assessment using DNA metabarcoding: Towards a genetics based marine biotic index (Gambi). *PLoS One* **9**, 90529.

Azaele S, Maritan A, Cornell SJ, Suweis S, Banavar JR, *et al.* (2014) Towards a unified descriptive theory for spatial ecology: Predicting biodiversity patterns across spatial scales. *Methods in Ecology and Evolution* **6**(3), 324–332.

Baird DJ, Hajibabaei M (2012) Biomonitoring 2.0: a new paradigm in ecosystem assessment made possible by next-generation DNA sequencing. *Molecular Ecology* **21**, 2039–2044.

Baker ME, King RS (2010) A new method for detecting and interpreting biodiversity and ecological community thresholds. *Methods in Ecology and Evolution* **1**, 25–37.

Belanche-Muñoz L, Blanch AR (2008) Machine learning methods for microbial source tracking. *Environmental Modelling & Software* **23**, 741–750.

Berg G, Rybakova D, Fischer D, Cernava T, Vergès MC, *et al.* (2020) Microbiome definition re-visited: old concepts and new challenges. *Microbiome* **8**, 119.

Birk S, Bonne W, Borja A, Brucet S, Courrat A, *et al.* (2012) Three hundred ways to assess Europe's surface waters: An almost complete overview of biological methods to implement the Water Framework Directive. *Ecological Indicators* **18**, 31–41.

Bissett A, Bowman J, Burke C (2006) Bacterial diversity in organically-enriched fish farm sediments. *FEMS Microbiology Ecology* **55**, 48–56.

Bissett A, Brown M (2018) Alpha-diversity is strongly influenced by the composition of other samples when using multiplexed sequencing approaches. *Soil Biology and Biochemistry* **127**, 79–81.

Borja A, Chust G, Muxika I (2019) Forever young: The successful story of a marine biotic index. In *Advances in Marine Biology*. (Ed C Sheppard) pp. 93–127. Academic Press, Cambridge.

Borja A, Bricker SB, Dauer DM, Demetriades NT, Ferreira JG, *et al.* (2008) Overview of integrative tools and methods in assessing ecological integrity in estuarine and coastal systems worldwide. *Marine Pollution Bulletin* **56**(9), 1519–1537. doi10.1016/j.marpolbul.2008.07.005

Borja A, Basset A, Bricker S, Dauvin JC, Elliot M, *et al.* (2012) Classifying Ecological Quality and Integrity of Estuaries. In *Treatise on Estuarine and Coastal Science*. (Eds E Wolanski, DS Mclusky) pp. 125–162. Academic Press, Waltham.

Borja A (2018) Testing the efficiency of a bacterial community-based index (microgAMBI) to assess distinct impact sources in six locations around the world. *Ecological Indicators* **85**, 594–602.

Borja A, Andersen JH, Arvanitidis CD, Basset A, Buhl-Mortensen L, *et al.* (2020) Past and future grand challenges in marine ecosystem ecology. *Frontiers in Marine Science* **7**, 1–9.

Borja Á, Marín SL, Muxika I, Pino L, Rodríguez JG (2015) Is there a possibility of ranking benthic quality assessment indices to select the most responsive to different human pressures? *Marine Pollution Bulletin* **97**, 85–94.

Borja A, Franco J, Pérez V (2000) A marine biotic index to establish the ecological quality of soft-bottom benthos within European estuarine and coastal environments. *Marine Pollution Bulletin* **40**, 1100–1114.

Bourhane Z, Lanzén A, Cagnon C, Said OB, Mahmoudi E, *et al.* (2022) Microbial diversity alteration reveals biomarkers of contamination in soil-river-lake continuum. *Journal of Hazardous Materials* **421**, 126789.

Bourlat SJ, Borja A, Gilbert J, Taylor MI, Davies N, *et al.* (2013) Genomics in marine monitoring: New opportunities for assessing marine health status. *Marine Pollution Bulletin* **74**, 19–31.

Bowd EJ, Banks SC, Bissett A, May TW, Lindenmayer DB (2021) Direct and indirect disturbance impacts in forests. *Ecology Letters* **24**, 1225–1236.

Breiman L (2001) Random forests. *Machine Learning* **45**, 5–32.

Brown MV, Philip GK, Bunge JA, Smith MC, Bissett A, *et al.* (2009) Microbial community structure in the North Pacific Ocean. *The ISME Journal* **3**, 1374–1386.

Burger J (2006) Bioindicators: A review of their use in the environmental literature 1970–2005. *Environmental Bioindicators* **1**, 136–144.

Carbonero F, Oakley BB, Purdy KJ (2010) Metabolic flexibility as a major predictor of spatial distribution in microbial communities. *PLoS One* **9**, 85105–85105.

Chariton AA, Court LN, Hartley DM, Colloff MJ, Hardy CM, *et al.* (2010) Ecological assessment of estuarine sediments by pyrosequencing eukaryotic ribosomal DNA. *Frontiers in Ecology and the Environment* **8**, 233–238.

Chen Y-J, Leung PM, Wood JL, Bay SK, Hugenholtz P, *et al.* (2021) Metabolic flexibility allows bacterial habitat generalists to become dominant in a frequently disturbed ecosystem. *The ISME Journal* **15**, 2986–3004.

Clark DE, Pilditch C, Ellis J, Borja A, Atalah J, *et al.* (2021) eDNA reveals estuarine benthic community response to nutrient enrichment – evidence from an in-situ experiment. *ARPHA Conference Abstracts*, 4, p. 65403.

Cordier T, Esling P, Lejzerowicz F, Visco J, Ouadahi A, *et al.* (2017) Predicting the ecological quality status of marine environments from eDNA metabarcoding data using supervised machine learning. *Environmental Science & Technology* **51**, 9118–9126.

Cordier T, Forster D, Dufresne Y, Martins CI, Stoeck T, *et al.* (2018) Supervised machine learning outperforms taxonomy-based environmental DNA metabarcoding applied to biomonitoring. *Molecular Ecology Resources* **18**, 1381–1391.

Cordier T, Lanzén A, Apothéloz-Perret-Gentil L, Stoeck T, Pawlowski J (2019) Embracing environmental genomics and machine learning for routine biomonitoring. *Trends in Microbiology* **27**, 387–397.

Cordier T (2020) Bacterial communities' taxonomic and functional turnovers both accurately predict marine benthic ecological quality status. *Environmental DNA* **2**, 175–183.

Cordier T, Alonso-Sáez L, Apothéloz-Perret-Gentil L, Aylagas E, Bohan DA, *et al.* (2021) Ecosystems monitoring powered by environmental genomics: A review of current strategies with an implementation roadmap. *Molecular Ecology* **30**, 2937–2958.

Dang QL, Tan W, Zhao X, Li D, Li Y, *et al.* (2019) Linking the response of soil microbial community structure in soils to long-term wastewater irrigation and soil depth. *Science of The Total Environment* **688**, 26–36.

Díaz RJ, Solan M, Valente RM (2004) A review of approaches for classifying benthic habitats and evaluating habitat quality. *Journal of Environmental Management* **73**, 165–181.

Dully V, Wilding TA, Mühlhaus T, Stoeck T, *et al.* (2021) Identifying the minimum amplicon sequence depth to adequately predict classes in eDNA-based marine biomonitoring using supervised machine learning. *Computational and Structural Biotechnology Journal* **19**, 2256–2268.

Eckburg PB, Bik EM, Bernstein CN, Sargent M, Gill SR, *et al.* (2005) Multi-site culture-independent analysis of the normal human intestinal microflora using large-scale 16s Rdna sequence analysis. *Gastroenterology* **128**, 194–194.

Edgar R (2017) UNBIAS: An attempt to correct abundance bias in 16S sequencing, with limited success. *bioRxiv*, doi:10.1101/124149.

Edgar R (2018a) Accuracy of taxonomy prediction for 16S rRNA and fungal ITS sequences. *PeerJ* **6**, 4652–4652.

Edgar R (2018b) Taxonomy annotation and guide tree errors in 16S rRNA databases. *PeerJ* **6**, 5030.

Feio MJ, Serra SR, Mortágua A, Bouchez A, Rimet F, *et al.* (2020) A taxonomy-free approach based on machine learning to assess the quality of rivers with diatoms. *Science of The Total Environment* **722**, 137900.

Fierer N, Wood SA, Bueno De Mesquita CP (2021) How microbes can, and cannot, be used to assess soil health. *Soil Biology and Biochemistry* **153**, 108111.

Frühe L, Dully V, Forster D, Keeley NB, Laroche O, *et al.* (2021) Global trends of benthic bacterial diversity and community composition along organic enrichment gradients of salmon farms. *Frontiers in Microbiology* **12**, 853.

Frühe L, Cordier T, Dully V, Breiner HW, Lentendu G, *et al.* (2021) Supervised machine learning is superior to indicator value inference in monitoring the environmental impacts of salmon aquaculture using eDNA metabarcodes. *Molecular Ecology* **30**, 2988–3006.

Galand PE, Lucas S, Fagervold SK, Peru E, Pruski AM, *et al.* (2016) Disturbance increases microbial community diversity and production in marine sediments. *Frontiers in Microbiology* **7**, doi:10.3389/fmicb.2016.01950

Gerhard WA, Gunsch CK (2019) Microbiome composition and implications for ballast water classification using machine learning. *Science of The Total Environment* **691**, 810–818.

Ghannam RB, Techtmann SM (2021) Machine learning applications in microbial ecology, human microbiome studies, and environmental monitoring. *Computational and Structural Biotechnology Journal* **19**, 1092–1107.

Gill SR, Pop M, DeBoy RT, Eckburg PB, Turnbaugh PJ, *et al.* (2006) Metagenomic analysis of the human distal gut microbiome. *Science* **312**, 1355–1359.

Glasl B, Webster NS, Bourne DG (2017) Microbial indicators as a diagnostic tool for assessing water quality and climate stress in coral reef ecosystems. *Marine Biology* **164**, 91.

Haines-Young R, Potschin-Young M (2018) Revision of the Common International Classification for Ecosystem Services (CICES V5.1): A Policy Brief. *One Ecosystem* **3**, 27108.

Hariharan J (2021) What Counts as a Microbe. American Society for Microbiology. <https://asm.org/Articles/2021/April/What-Counts-as-a-Microbe>. Accessed 28 April 2023.

Hering D, Borja A, Jones JI, Pont D, Boets P, *et al.* (2018) Implementation options for DNA-based identification into ecological status assessment under the European Water Framework Directive. *Water Research* **138**, 192–205. doi:10.1016/j.watres.2018.03.003

Holt EA, Miller SW (2010) Bioindicators: Using Organisms to Measure Environmental Impacts. *Nature Education Knowledge* **3**, 8.

Hug LA, Baker BJ, Anantharaman K, Brown CT, Probst AJ, *et al.* (2016) A new view of the tree of life. *Nature Microbiology* **1**, 16048.

Hui C, Mcgeoch MA (2014) Zeta diversity as a concept and metric that unifies incidence-based biodiversity patterns. *The American Naturalist* **184**, 684–694.

Jay JM (1995) Indicators of Food Microbial Quality and Safety. In *Modern Food Microbiology*. (Ed JM Jay) pp. 387–407. Springer US, Boston.

Keck F, Bouchez A, Franc A, Rimet F (2016) Linking phylogenetic similarity and pollution sensitivity to develop ecological assessment methods: a test with river diatoms. *Journal of Applied Ecology* **53**, 856–864.

Keeley N, Wood SA, Pochon X (2018) Development and preliminary validation of a multi-trophic metabarcoding biotic index for monitoring benthic organic enrichment. *Ecological Indicators* **85**, 1044–1057.

Keeley NB, Macleod CK, Forrest BM (2012) Combining best professional judgement and quantile regression splines to improve characterisation of macrofaunal responses to enrichment. *Ecological Indicators* **12**, 154–166.

Kermarrec L, Franc A, Rimet F, Chaumeil P, Frigerio JM (2014) A next-generation sequencing approach to river biomonitoring using benthic diatoms. *Freshwater Science* **33**, 349–363.

Kimes NE, Callaghan AV, Suflita JM, Morris PJ (2014) Microbial transformation of the Deepwater Horizon oil spill—past, present, and future perspectives. *Frontiers in Microbiology* **5**, doi:10.3389/fmicb.2014.00603

Knights D, Parfrey LW, Zaneveld J, Lozupone C, Knight R (2011) Human-associated microbial signatures: Examining their predictive value. *Cell Host & Microbe* **10**, 292–296.

Knights D, Costello EK, Knight R (2011) Supervised classification of human microbiota. *FEMS Microbiology Reviews* **35**, 343–359.

Koenker R, Ng P, Portnoy S (1994) Quantile smoothing splines. *Biometrika* **81**, 673–680.

Koenker R, Schorfheide F (1994) Quantile spline models for global temperature-change. *Climatic Change* **28**, 395–404.

Konopka A (2009) What is microbial community ecology? *The ISME Journal* **3**, 1223–30.

Kostka J, Joye BS, Colwell RR (2020) Deepwater Horizon and the rise of the omics. *Eos – Science News by AGU*, 28.

Lanzen A, Mendibil I, Borja A, Alonso-Sáez L (2021) A microbial mandala for environmental monitoring: Predicting multiple impacts on estuarine prokaryote communities of the Bay of Biscay. *Molecular Ecology* **30**, 2969–2987.

Laroche O, Wood SA, Tremblay LA, Ellis JI, Lejzerowicz F (2016) First evaluation of foraminiferal metabarcoding for monitoring environmental impact from an offshore oil drilling site. *Marine Environmental Research* **120**, 225–235.

Laroche O, Wood SA, Tremblay LA, Ellis JI, Lear G, et al. (2018) A cross-taxa study using environmental DNA/RNA metabarcoding to measure biological impacts of offshore oil and gas drilling and production operations. *Marine Pollution Bulletin* **127**, 97–107.

Laroche O, Pochon X, Wood SA, Keeley N (2021) Beyond taxonomy: Validating functional inference approaches in the context of fish-farm impact assessments. *Molecular Ecology Resources* **21**, 2264–2277.

Lau KEM, Washington VJ, Fan V, Neale MW, Lear G, et al. (2015) A novel bacterial community index to assess stream ecological health. *Freshwater Biology* **60**, 1988–2002.

Lear G, Boothroyd IK, Turner SJ, Roberts K, Lewis GD, et al. (2009) A comparison of bacteria and benthic invertebrates as indicators of ecological health in streams. *Freshwater Biology* **54**, 1532–1543.

Lee KS, Palatinszky M, Pereira FC, Nguyen J, Fernandez VI, et al. (2019) An automated Raman-based platform for the sorting of live cells by functional properties. *Nature Microbiology* **4**(6), 1035–1048.

Leese F, Altermatt F, Bouchez A, Ekrem T, Hering D, et al. (2016) DNAqua-Net: Developing new genetic tools for bioassessment and monitoring of aquatic ecosystems in Europe. *Research Ideas and Outcomes* **2**, e11321.

Leese F, Bouchez A, Abarenkov K, Altermatt F, Borja Á, et al. (2018) Why We Need Sustainable Networks Bridging Countries, Disciplines, Cultures and Generations For Aquatic Biomonitoring 2.0: A Perspective Derived From The Dnaqua-Net Cost Action. In *Advances In Ecological Research*. (Eds DA Bohan, et al.) pp. 63–99. Academic Press, Cambridge.

Li Y, Yang N, Qian B, Yang Z, Liu D, et al. (2018) Development of a bacteria-based index of biotic integrity (Ba-IBI) for assessing ecological health of the Three Gorges Reservoir in different operation periods. *Science of The Total Environment* **640–641**, 255–263.

Liao H, Yen JY, Guan Y, Ke D, Liu C (2020) Differential responses of stream water and bed sediment microbial communities to watershed degradation. *Environment International* **134**, 105198.

Libbrecht MW, Noble WS (2015) Machine learning applications in genetics and genomics. *Nature Reviews Genetics* **16**, 321–32.

Liddicoat C, Weinstein P, Bissett A, Gellie NJ, Mills JG, et al. (2019) Can bacterial indicators of a grassy woodland restoration inform ecosystem assessment and microbiota-mediated human health? *Environment International* **129**, 105–117.

Lopes VG, Branco CW, Kozlowsky-Suzuki B, Bini LM (2021) The reliability of low taxonomic and numerical resolutions for biodiversity monitoring is site specific and dependent on the statistical method. *Ecological Indicators* **129**, 107999.

Makiola A, Compson ZG, Baird DJ, Barnes MA, Boerlijst SP (2020) Key questions for next-generation biomonitoring. *Frontiers in Environmental Science* **7**, 197.

Marchetto A, Agostinelli C, Alber R, Beghi A, Balsamo S, et al. (2013) Indice Per Valutazione Della Qualità Delle Acque Lacustri Italiane A Partire Dalle Diatomee Epifitiche Ed Epilitiche (Epi-L). In *Indici Per La Valutazione Della Qualità Ecologica Dei Laghi*. pp. 75–92. CNR-ISE, Italy.

Markert PDB, Breure A, Zechmeister H (2003) Bioindicators and biomonitors: Principles, concepts and applications. *Trace Metals and Other Contaminants in the Environment* **6**, 15–25.

Martiny AC, Treseder K, Pusch G (2013) Phylogenetic conservatism of functional traits in microorganisms. *The ISME Journal* **7**, 830–838.

Mesquita S, Noble RT (2013) Recent Developments in Monitoring of Microbiological Indicators of Water Quality Across a Range of Water Types. In *Water Resources Planning, Development and Management*. (Ed R Wurbs) pp. 29–51. InTechOpen, London.

Mitchell TM (1997) Does Machine Learning Really Work? *AI Magazine* **18**, 11.

Mori AS, Fujii S, Kitagawa R, Koide D (2015) Null model approaches to evaluating the relative role of different assembly processes in shaping ecological communities. *Oecologia* **178**, 261–273.

Mori AS, Isbell F, Seidl R (2018) β-Diversity, community assembly, and ecosystem functioning. *Trends in Ecology & Evolution* **33**, 549–564.

Namkung J (2020) Machine learning methods for microbiome studies. *Journal of Microbiology* **58**, 206–216.

Niu L, Li Y, Wang P, Zhang W, Wang C, et al. (2018) Development of a microbial community-based index of biotic integrity

(MC-IBI) for the assessment of ecological status of rivers in the Taihu Basin, China. *Ecological Indicators* **85**, 204–213.

Overmann J, Huang S, Nübel U, Hahnke RL, Tindall BJ (2019) Relevance of phenotypic information for the taxonomy of not-yet-cultured microorganisms. *Systematic and Applied Microbiology* **42**, 22–29.

Pawlowski J, Kelly-Quinn M, Altermatt F, Apothéloz-Perret-Gentil L, Beja P, *et al.* (2018) The future of biotic indices in the ecogenomic era: Integrating (e)DNA metabarcoding in biological assessment of aquatic ecosystems. *Science of The Total Environment* **637–638**, 1295–1310.

Pawlowski J, Bonin A, Boyer F, Cordier T, Taberlet P (2021) Environmental DNA for biomonitoring. *Molecular Ecology* **30**(13), 2931–2936. doi:10.1111/mec.16023

Pearman JK, Afandi F, Hong P, Carvalho S (2018) Plankton community assessment in anthropogenic-impacted oligotrophic coastal regions. *Environmental Science and Pollution Research International* **25**, 31017–31030.

Pearman JK, Wood SA, Vandergoes MJ, Atalah J, Waters S, *et al.* (2022) A bacterial index to estimate lake trophic level: National scale validation. *Science of The Total Environment* **812**, 152385. doi:10.1016/j.scitotenv.2021.15238

Pochon X, Wood SA, Keeley NB, Lejzerowicz F, Esling P, *et al.* (2015) Accurate assessment of the impact of salmon farming on benthic sediment enrichment using foraminiferal metabarcoding. *Marine Pollution Bulletin* **100**, 370–382.

Pochon X, Wood SA, Atalah J, Laroche O, Zaiko A, *et al.* (2020) A validated protocol for benthic monitoring of New Zealand's salmon farms using environmental DNA. Prepared for Seafood Innovation Ltd, New Zealand King Salmon Company Ltd, Ministry for Primary Industries and Marlborough District Council. Cawthron Report No. 3400.

Poikane S, Herrero FS, Kelly MG, Borja A, Birk S (2020) European aquatic ecological assessment methods: A critical review of their sensitivity to key pressures. *Science of The Total Environment* **740**, 140075.

Pörtner HO, Scholes RJ, Agard J, Archer E, Arneth A, *et al.* (2021) *Scientific Outcome of the Ipbes-Ipcc Co-Sponsored Workshop on Biodiversity and Climate Change*, IPBES Secretariat. Bonn, Germany. doi:10.5281/Zenodo.4659158

Reker J, Murray C, Gelabert ER, Abhold K, Korpinen S, *et al.* (2019) *Marine Messages II: Navigating the course towards clean, healthy and productive seas through implementation of an ecosystem-based approach*. European Environment Agency.

Rimet F, Aylagas E, Borja Á, Bouchez A, Canino A, *et al.* (2021) Metadata standards and practical guidelines for specimen and DNA curation when building barcode reference libraries for aquatic life. *Metabarcoding and Metagenomics* **5**(e58056), 17–33.

Rivera SF, Vasselon V, Jacquet S, Bouchez A, Ariztegui D, *et al.* (2018) Metabarcoding of lake benthic diatoms: from structure assemblages to ecological assessment. *Hydrobiologia* **807**, 37–51.

Sagova-Mareckova M, Boenigk J, Bouchez A, Cermakova K, Chonova T, *et al.* (2021) Expanding ecological assessment by integrating microorganisms into routine freshwater biomonitoring. *Water Research* **191**, 116767.

Samuel RM, Meyer R, Buttigieg PL, Davies N, Jeffery NW, *et al.* (2021) Toward a global public repository of community protocols to encourage best practices in biomolecular ocean observing and research. *Frontiers in Marine Science* **8**, 758694.

Sanford RA, Lloyd KG, Konstantinidis KT, Löffler FE (2021) Microbial taxonomy run Amok. *Trends in Microbiology* **29**, 394–404.

Seitz TJ, Schütte UME, Drown DM (2022) Unearthing shifts in microbial communities across a soil disturbance gradient. *Frontiers in Microbiology* **13**, 781051.

Sgro G, Poole J, Johansen J (2009) Diatom species composition and ecology of the Animas River Watershed. *Western North American Naturalist* **67**, 510–519.

Shah RM, Hillyer KE, Stephenson S, Crosswell J, Karpe AV, *et al.* (2021) Functional analysis of pristine estuarine marine sediments. *Science of The Total Environment* **781**, 146526.

Simonin M, Voss KA, Hassett BA, Rocca JD, Wang SY, *et al.* (2019) In search of microbial indicator taxa: shifts in stream bacterial communities along an urbanization gradient. *Environmental Microbiology* **21**, 3653–3668.

Smith MB, Rocha AM, Smillie CS, Olesen SW, Paradis C, *et al.* (2015) Natural bacterial communities serve as quantitative geochemical biosensors. *Mbio* **6**, e00326-15.

Socolar JB, Gilroy JJ, Kunin WE, Edwards DP (2016) How should beta-diversity inform biodiversity conservation? *Trends in Ecology & Evolution* **31**, 67–80.

Sogin ML, Morrison HG, Huber JA, Welch DM, Huse SM (2006) Microbial diversity in the deep sea and the underexplored 'rare biosphere'. *Proceedings Of The National Academy Of Sciences Of The United States Of America* **103**, 12115–12120.

Steveson J (2014) Ecological assessments with algae: a review and synthesis. *Journal of Phycology* **50**, 437–461.

Su X (2021) Elucidating the beta-diversity of the microbiome: from global alignment to local alignment. *mSystems* **6**, e00363–e00321.

Sun J, Chen X, Yu J, Chen Z, Liu L, *et al.* (2021) Deciphering historical water-quality changes recorded in sediments using eDNA. *Frontiers in Environmental Science* **9**, 184.

Tapolczai K, Keck, F, Bouchez A, Rimet F, Kahlert M, *et al.* (2019) Diatom DNA metabarcoding for biomonitoring: strategies to avoid major taxonomical and bioinformatical biases limiting molecular indices capacities. *Frontiers in Ecology and Evolution* **7**, 00409.

Tapolczai K, Vasselon V, Bouchez A, Stenger-Kovács C, Padisák J, *et al.* (2019) The impact of OTU sequence similarity threshold on diatom-based bioassessment: A case study of the rivers of Mayotte (France, Indian Ocean). *Ecology and Evolution* **9**, 166–179.

Tyson GW, Chapman J, Hugenholtz P, Allen EE, Ram RJ, *et al.* (2004) Community structure and metabolism through reconstruction of microbial genomes from the environment. *Nature* **428**, 37–43.

United Nations (2021) *The Second World Ocean Assessment*. New York.

Vasselon V, Rimet F, Tapolczai K, Bouchez A (2017) Assessing ecological status with diatoms DNA metabarcoding: Scaling-up on a WFD monitoring network. *Ecological Indicators* **82**, 1–12.

Venter JC, Remington K, Heidelberg JF, Halpern AL, Rusch D, *et al.* (2004) Environmental genome shotgun sequencing of the Sargasso Sea. *Science* **304**, 66–74.

Visco JA, Apothéloz-Perret-Gentil L, Cordonier A, Esling P, Pillet L, *et al.* (2015) Environmental monitoring: Inferring the diatom index from next-generation sequencing data. *Environmental Science & Technology* **49**, 7597–7605.

W.W.F. (2018) *Living Planet Report 2018: Aiming higher.* Edited by G.N.A. Rea. Gland.

Weigand H, Beermann AJ, Čiampor F, Costa FO, Csabai Z, *et al.* (2019) DNA barcode reference libraries for the monitoring of aquatic biota in Europe: Gap-analysis and recommendations for future work. *Science of The Total Environment* **678**, 499–524.

Wen X, Chen F, Lin Y, Zhu H, Yuan F, *et al.* (2020) Microbial indicators and their use for monitoring drinking water quality – a review. *Sustainability* **12**, 2249.

Wilhelm RC, Van Es HM, Buckley DH (2022) Predicting measures of soil health using the microbiome and supervised machine learning. *Soil Biology and Biochemistry* **164**, 108472.

Woodiwiss F (1964) The biological system of stream classification used by the Trent River Board. *Chemistry & Industry* **11**, 443–447.

Yan D, Gellie NJ, Mills JG, Connell G, Bissett A, *et al.* (2020) A soil archaeal community responds to a decade of ecological restoration. *Restoration Ecology* **28**, 63–72.

20 Perspective – The promise of ecotoxicogenomics for assessing aquatic health

Alvine C. Mehinto, Toxicology Department, Southern California Coastal Water Research

As the nature and toxic potency of stressors found in aquatic environments have evolved, so has the need to improve toxicity assessment to protect aquatic life. A few decades ago, the focus was on high usage pesticides and improper disposal of waste discharges that contaminated waterways and posed severe acute risks to aquatic organisms (Johnson and Finley 1980; Martyniuk *et al.* 2020). One such example is dichloro-diphenyl-trichloroethane (DDT), a persistent insecticide widely used in the 1950–1970s that accumulated in sediment and fatty tissues, leading to impaired development and reproduction, and increased mortality in fish and invertebrates. Nowadays, environmental water quality managers are faced with very different challenges, as the increasingly complex chemical mixtures found in the environment have more subtle chronic impacts on individual organisms and populations (Nilsen *et al.* 2019). Additionally, environmental institutions are now considering the adoption of proactive and precautionary rather than reactive monitoring strategies to reduce the likelihood of toxicological and ecological impacts.

Ecotoxicogenomic monitoring approaches that include RNA- and protein-based analyses are promising for the development and application of such precautionary strategies as they allow for the detection of early molecular bioindicators of toxicological responses, disease susceptibility, and population viability (Connon *et al.* 2012; Mehinto *et al.* 2012). Ecotoxicogenomics are currently used as research tools to investigate the relationships between chemical exposure (single or mixtures) and changes to organisms at the molecular level (Hutchinson *et al.* 2006; Martinović-Weigelt *et al.* 2014; Bahamonde *et al.* 2015). These studies have demonstrated that the nature and magnitude of molecular changes in organisms can be linked to water quality. They enable detection of sublethal effects of chemicals before severe organismal or population-level impacts are observed in the environment. Because specific molecular changes can be linked to classes of contaminants, such information could be valuable to environmental managers to target classes of contaminants requiring further monitoring or evaluate the efficacy of water treatment technologies in removing potentially harmful contaminants.

Over the last decade, environmental managers have embraced the use of genomics approaches such as eDNA technology to assess species diversity including endangered and invasive species (Akre *et al.* 2019; Basu *et al.* 2019; Ames *et al.* 2021). However, the use of ecotoxicogenomics tools for decision making has been hindered in part due to the complexity and reduced stability of RNA molecules compared to DNA (the main target of eDNA analyses). While molecular bioindicators provide insights into biological functions, our ability to extrapolate these changes to meaningful endpoints of regulatory concern remains limited, especially for ecologically significant species. This has made the development of standardised laboratory practice, data analyses and interpretation challenging. Thus, to date, the science focus remains on the development and validation of ecotoxicogenomics practices rather than its application. One noteworthy initiative is that of Canadian researchers working on the development and commercialisation of a chip, called EcoToxChip, which measures expression of key functional genes in indicator species used for Canadian risk assessment and environmental monitoring (e.g. African clawed frog, double-crested cormorant, rainbow trout). They also provide a bioinformatic tool for streamlined data interpretation (Basu *et al.* 2019). The project's objective is to facilitate the use of transcriptomics data for risk assessment and chemical prioritisation. This project sponsored by the Canadian government could be among the first ecotoxicogenomic analyses to be implemented by a government agency to improve toxicity assessment and protection of aquatic habitats.

While changing established practices is difficult, the potential of genomics tools for water quality and ecological assessment is undeniable. The increasing number of success stories with eDNA and the development of new ecotoxicogenomic initiatives focusing on technology transfer are bringing us closer to global adoption and to better environmental protection.

REFERENCES

Akre TS, Parker LD, Ruther E, Maldonado JE, Lemmon L, *et al.* (2019) Concurrent visual encounter sampling validates eDNA selectivity and sensitivity for the endangered wood turtle (*Glyptemys insculpta*). *PloS One* **14**(4), e0215586. doi:10.1371/journal.pone.0215586.

Ames CL, Ohdera AH, Colston SM, Collins AG, Fitt WK, *et al.* (2021) Fieldable environmental DNA sequencing to assess jellyfish biodiversity in nearshore waters of the Florida keys, United States. *Frontiers in Marine Science*. doi:10.3389/fmars.2021.640527.

Bahamonde PA, McMaster ME, Servos MR, Martyniuk CJ, Munkittrick KR (2015) Molecular pathways associated with the intersex condition in rainbow darter (*Etheostoma caeruleum*) following exposures to municipal wastewater in the Grand River basin, ON, Canada. Part B. *Aquatic Toxicology (Amsterdam, Netherlands)* **159**, 302–316. doi:10.1016/j.aquatox.2014.11.022.

Basu N, Crump D, Head J, Hickey G, Hogan N (2019) EcoToxChip: A next-generation toxicogenomics tool for chemical prioritization and environmental management. *Environmental Toxicology and Chemistry* **38**(2), 279–288. doi:10.1002/etc.4309.

Connon RE, Geist J, Werner I (2012) Effect-based tools for monitoring and predicting the ecotoxicological effects of chemicals in the aquatic environment. *Sensors (Basel, Switzerland)* **12**(9), 12741–12771. doi:10.3390/s120912741.

Hutchinson TH, Ankley GT, Segner H, Tyler CR (2006) Screening and testing for endocrine disruption in fish-biomarkers as 'signposts,' not 'traffic lights,' in risk assessment. *Environmental Health Perspectives* **114** (Suppl 1), 106–114. doi:10.1289/ehp.8062.

Johnson WW, Finley MT (1980) *Handbook of Acute Toxicity of Chemicals to Fish and Aquatic Invertebrates: Summaries of Toxicity Tests Conducted at Columbia National Fisheries Research Laboratory, 1965–78*. Vol. 137. US Department of the Interior, Fish and Wildlife Service, Washington, DC.

Martinović-Weigelt D, Mehinto AC, Ankley GT, Denslow ND, Barber LB, *et al.* (2014) Transcriptomic effects-based monitoring for endocrine active chemicals: Assessing relative contribution of treated wastewater to downstream pollution. *Environmental Science & Technology* **48**(4), 2385–2394. doi:10.1021/es404027n.

Martyniuk CJ, Mehinto AC, Denslow ND (2020) Organochlorine pesticides: Agrochemicals with potent endocrine-disrupting properties in fish. *Molecular and Cellular Endocrinology* **507**, 110764. doi:10.1016/j.mce.2020.110764.

Mehinto AC, Martyniuk CJ, Spade DJ, Denslow ND (2012) Applications for next-generation sequencing in fish ecotoxicogenomics. *Frontiers in Genetics* **3**, 62. doi:10.3389/fgene.2012.00062.

Nilsen E, Smalling KL, Ahrens L, Gros M, Miglioranza KS (2019) Critical review: Grand challenges in assessing the adverse effects of contaminants of emerging concern on aquatic food webs. *Environmental Toxicology and Chemistry* **38**(1), 46–60. doi:10.1002/etc.4290.

SPATIAL GENOMICS

21 Unravelling plant-pollinator interactions through pollen DNA analysis

Liz Milla and Francisco Encinas-Viso

ABSTRACT

Pollination, an essential ecosystem service that supports food security and maintenance of biodiversity, is highly threatened by global change. Understanding and monitoring of the plant-pollinator networks that underpin this service is crucial to preserving ecosystem function. However, traditional methods used to identify the interactions between plants and insect pollinators tend to be very laborious and time-consuming. Genomic techniques to infer species interactions have created new opportunities for researchers and land managers to study plant-pollinator networks in a cost-effective manner. DNA metabarcoding of pollen is a novel genomic approach that has been successfully used to quantify plant-pollinator interactions and the movement of pollen across space and time. In this chapter, we explain the benefits and limitations of pollen DNA metabarcoding and its usefulness for managers and practitioners to address questions regarding conservation of plant-pollinator communities and ecosystem management. Furthermore, we explore the potential of this approach for future applications in environmental monitoring, biosecurity and investigating the effects of climate change on plant-pollinator communities.

PLANT-POLLINATOR COMMUNITIES AND THEIR ROLE IN ECOSYSTEM MANAGEMENT

Pollination of plants by animals is one of the most valuable of ecosystem services (Kearns *et al.* 1998). Most flowering plants are animal-pollinated (Ollerton *et al.* 2011), largely by insects, with many plant species depending solely on pollinators for reproduction. Critically, up to 30% of food production from agricultural crops also depends on animal pollination (Klein *et al.* 2007), predominantly by European honey bees (*Apis mellifera*), with increasingly recognised contributions from alternative insect pollinators (Rader *et al.* 2016; Cook *et al.* 2020). Mounting pressure from factors such as climate change, habitat destruction, disease and pesticide use have impacted pollinator populations worldwide (Allen-Wardell *et al.* 1998; Potts *et al.* 2010; Burkle *et al.* 2013) and threaten the communities that depend on their services. For example, observed declines in bee pollinator diversity in Europe have been linked to parallel declines in the plants they pollinate (Biesmeijer *et al.* 2006).

Ecosystem disturbances, such as land fragmentation, local extinctions, and the arrival of invasive taxa can disrupt plant-pollinator communities and alter their structure and function. To effectively manage these communities, we need to understand their relationships and how they are shaped by the environment. Ecological communities are organised in non-random assemblages of interacting species, which can be thought of as networks with nodes representing species and connecting lines representing interactions (Fig. 21.2C). Plant-pollinator networks are usually constructed from information gathered through plant-centric field surveys, where observers watch plants along transects

Fig. 21.1. Genomic methods using metabarcoding of plant DNA allow us to 'read' the pollen record carried by insect pollinators such as this tiny Australian native *Lassioglossum* bee. This information can then be used to reconstruct the plant-pollinator networks without the need for field observations (Photo Liz Milla).

and record visitors as they land on open flowers. This approach can be costly and time-consuming, requiring observers to be trained in the field identification of both plant and pollinator species, with insects particularly difficult to identify due to their small size. A more recently developed approach is to reconstruct pollinator-centric or pollen-transport networks by identifying plant species from pollen loads carried by pollinators (Bosch *et al.* 2009), and using this information to infer interactions. Studies of pollen loads have shown that pollen can be used to detect a significant number of unobserved interactions across time and space, substantially changing the structure of a network based on observations alone (Bosch *et al.* 2009). However, pollen identification based on morphology via methods such as microscopy requires significant expertise and time, with results often attainable only to family or genus level (Rahl 2008; Sniderman *et al.* 2018).

Today we can apply highly sensitive DNA-based methods that can 'read' the genetic information present in pollen (Fig. 21.1) and trace it back to its parent species. These methods rely on discriminating species from differences in DNA sequences rather than relying on external morphological characters. In this chapter, we will discuss how DNA-based methods work with pollen and how they can be used to study plant-pollinator interactions, focusing on insect pollinators. We will also show through different demonstration cases how this methodology can be applied

to investigate multiple research questions about conservation and habitat restoration, and the impact of global changes in plant-pollinator communities.

DNA-BASED METHODS FOR RECONSTRUCTING POLLINATOR INTERACTION NETWORKS

All animals and plants carry DNA, which they shed into the environment throughout their lives. These environmental DNA fragments contain genetic information that can be used to identify species (Shokralla *et al.* 2012). DNA metabarcoding is a technique used to simultaneously amplify short gene fragments from mixed DNA samples to identify the various species present (Taberlet *et al.* 2012). It is a widely applicable method that has been used to infer species interactions in food webs (Rytkönen *et al.* 2019; Zamora-Terol *et al.* 2020; Chapter 4), between hosts and parasites (Doña *et al.* 2019), plants and herbivores (Pitteloud *et al.* 2021) and plants and animals (González-Varo *et al.* 2014). More recently, metabarcoding has been used to study networks of pollen transport by insects (Pornon *et al.* 2016; Arstingstall *et al.* 2021; Encinas-Viso *et al.* 2022). Many insects forage on plants for food, particularly pollen and nectar. While foraging on flowers, pollen grains become attached to parts of the insect's body, and they are carried along as it visits other plants. Early studies demonstrated that these pollen grains contain DNA suitable for plant identification through metabarcoding (Galimberti *et al.* 2014; Hawkins *et al.* 2015; Richardson *et al.* 2015). Metabarcoding uses highly conserved genomic markers to detect a comprehensive range of species (see Box 21.1) and employs widely available laboratory methods and technologies such as PCR and high-throughput sequencing platforms that allow many samples to be processed concurrently. We identify species present in pollen samples by matching the amplified sequences to DNA reference databases derived from expertly identified plant vouchers. This approach provides a reliable and effective way to identify multiple plant species within a pollen sample without specialist palynological knowledge. DNA metabarcoding has been shown to identify plant species from pollen with greater efficiency, sensitivity and repeatability of results than microscopy (Richardson *et al.* 2015; Bell *et al.* 2017). Aside from pollen, there are alternatives sources of genomic information that can be used to study plant-pollinator interactions. For example, insects leave traces of DNA on the flowers they visit, and this has been explored through metabarcoding of insect DNA from the stigmas of wildflowers (Thomsen and Sigsgaard 2019). However, pollen gathered by insects is often more abundant, visible, and straight-forward to collect; thus in this chapter we will focus on using pollen carried by insects to study plant-pollinator communities.

Box 21.1: Commonly used plant metabarcoding markers

There are three important factors to consider when choosing genetic markers for metabarcoding studies: 1) the DNA amplification success of a particular marker, 2) the availability of reference sequences for species of interest and 3) the inter-specific discrimination power of the marker. Currently, there is no single marker that outperforms all others in the three areas above (Hollingsworth 2011), so a combination of markers is often used. The amplified product length is also important, as commonly used short read sequencing platforms are limited in the maximum sequence length they can accurately read (often around 600 bp). Longer products may require newer technologies (e.g. PacBio, MinIon) that can yield longer reads. Here we describe the most common markers used in pollen metabarcoding studies:

1. **ITS2.** Non-coding nuclear ribosomal internal transcribed spacer 2. Barcode length ranges between 100 and 700 bp using primers described in White *et al.* (1990) and Chen *et al.* (2010), and has relatively high discrimination success in plants as well as animals (Yao *et al.* 2010). ITS2 DB (Ankenbrand *et al.* 2015) is one the largest curated databases publicly available for metabarcoding.
2. **matK.** Coding chloroplast marker, different primer sets available for region around 1500 bp in length (Yu *et al.* 2011). First of two CBOL markers designated as official plant identification loci (CBOL Plant Working Group 2009). Amplification success is relatively low but good discriminating power at species level (Lahaye *et al.* 2008).
3. **rbcLa.** Coding chloroplast marker, part of the rbcL gene. Regions range in length around 500–1000 bp depending on primer sets used (Bell *et al.* 2017). Second of two CBOL markers designated as official plant identification loci (CBOL Plant Working Group 2009). Good recovery success and sequence quality, but low discriminating power at species level (Hollingsworth 2011).
4. **trnH-psbA.** Non-coding chloroplast spacer marker, length mostly around 296–500 bp, with some species yielding over 1000 bp (CBOL Plant Working Group 2009). High amplification success in flowering plants (93%) and good differentiation to genus level (Kress and Erickson 2007).
5. **trnL.** Non-coding region chloroplast marker. The most commonly used section is the short P6-loop region, which ranges in length between 10–143 bp. High amplification success but very low species level discrimination (Taberlet *et al.* 2006). Suitable for highly degraded DNA, particularly associated with eDNA.

Experimental design for pollen-based networks

One of the first considerations when building a plant pollinator network is to select the type of pollinators to survey. This will determine the subset of the plant-pollinator community being studied and the geographical area it occupies. Insect pollinators can vary widely in their foraging range and pollen-carrying capacity. For example, European honey bees have foraging ranges of up to 10 km (Beekman and Ratnieks 2000), although they often forage closer to their hive depending on the availability of resources (Danner *et al.* 2018). Australian native bees tend to visit a wider variety of native plants than honey bees (Elliott *et al.* 2021) but are often much smaller in size, and therefore their foraging range is likely to be smaller. On the other hand, some migratory insects such as bogong moths (*Agrotis infusa*) may have travelled large distances and fed on plants located hundreds of kilometres away (Warrant *et al.* 2016). Flies are abundant pollinators (Orford, Vaughan and Memmott 2015), particularly in alpine areas (Inouye and Pyke 1988), but smaller species may carry only few pollen grains thereby yielding little plant DNA. Additionally, knowledge about plant phenology and the ecology of pollinators (e.g. nocturnal vs. day foraging) is crucial to designing a pollinator network study and interpreting the subsequent results.

Pollen sources and pollen DNA extraction

Pollen for DNA extraction can be taken directly from the individual pollinator's body (Pornon *et al.* 2016; Lucas *et al.* 2018), or it can be collected with pollen traps (Cornman *et al.* 2015; Tremblay *et al.* 2019), extracted from honey (Hawkins *et al.* 2015; Milla *et al.* 2022) or taken from brood cells found in nests (Keller *et al.* 2015; McFrederick and Rehan 2019). Most pollinators are solitary and their nests can be difficult to find; therefore collecting individual adults and washing pollen off their bodies is the most widely applicable method for

reconstructing pollen-transport networks. Fig. 21.2 shows a basic overview of the steps involved in pollen metabarcoding. Pollen-carrying insects should be collected using a sterile net or tube to avoid potential cross-contamination, and preferably kept cool to minimise DNA degradation. For processing individual insects, the most common method is to remove pollen by washing the whole insect or external parts of its body in a liquid buffer or detergent (Pornon *et al.* 2016; Macgregor *et al.* 2019; Suchan *et al.* 2019), then extract DNA from the supernatant liquid (Fig. 21.2B) using one of several available kits suited to pollen (Bell *et al.* 2016). Some level of rupturing the outer pollen coat by milling with beads has been recommended as a preliminary step for DNA extraction from pollen (Parducci *et al.* 2005; Leontidou *et al.* 2018); however, the effects are variable across species (Swenson and Gemeinholzer 2021) and some studies have found little difference in DNA yield (Pornon *et al.* 2016; Gous *et al.* 2018).

Alternative methods to pollen recovery from pollinators include washing residual pollen after insects have

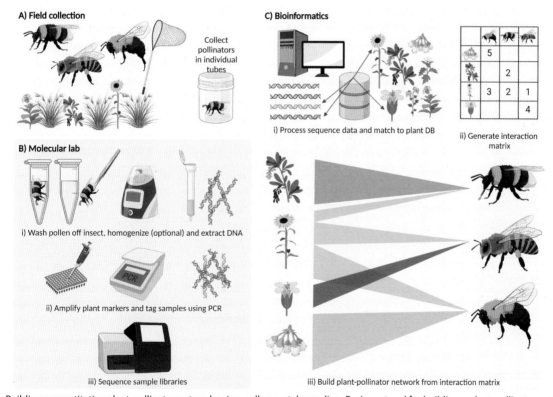

Fig. 21.2. Building a quantitative plant-pollinator network using pollen metabarcoding. Basic protocol for building a plant-pollinator network from pollen metabarcoding reads. A) Field collection involves collecting pollinators within a designated study area. Each individual is stored in a separate sterile tube. Molecular lab protocols involve: B-i) washing pollen off each insect using a detergent or buffer, optionally homogenising the sample, and extracting DNA from the supernatant. B-ii) Each DNA extraction is then amplified using plant metabarcoding markers and library tags are added using PCR. B-iii) Tagged libraries are sequenced in a high-throughput sequencing platform, such as Illumina MiSeq. Bioinformatics process involves C-i) Trimming, cleaning and clustering reads to find OTUs or ASVs and matching them to a plant reference database, C-ii) generating an interaction matrix from the identified plants and pollinator samples, C-iii) building a network using a package such as bipartite in R. Figure created with BioRender.com.

been allowed to walk through a sterile tube (Potter *et al.* 2019). This non-destructive method requires further refinement as the amount of residual pollen in tubes can be substantially lower than that obtained from the whole insect (Potter *et al.* 2019). Most pollen involved in pollination will be carried on the exterior of the body; however, if pollen or nectar consumption is of interest, the body of the insect can be homogenised for DNA extraction (Mayr *et al.* 2021).

Pollen DNA sequence amplification and analysis

After DNA extraction, the next step is to amplify plant genes using highly conserved primers to recover as many species as possible. There are several genetic markers suitable for plant metabarcoding, each presenting their own advantages and disadvantages, with the most common being ITS2, rbcL, matK, trnH-psbA and trnL-P6 loop (Box 21.1). More recent pollen metabarcoding studies have employed a combination of markers (two or more) to identify a wider range of species (Prosser and Hebert 2017; Richardson *et al.* 2019; Milla *et al.* 2021). Public databases, particularly NCBI's GenBank, are widely used sources of information for reference sequence matching. However, there are also a few databases of curated sequences available for common plant markers, for example, ITS2 DB (Ankenbrand *et al.* 2015), rbcL (Bell *et al.* 2017) and PlantAligDB (Santos *et al.* 2019). PCR products resulting from the amplification of the chosen markers are tagged with individual sample identifiers, also called library tags, through a PCR process either during target DNA amplification or in a subsequent step. These tagged libraries are then pooled and sequenced on a next-gen platform, such as the Illumina MiSeq. During the amplification process, it is highly recommended to use multiple PCR replicates to mitigate for DNA amplification bias (Ficetola *et al.* 2015; Mata *et al.* 2019) and to include negative controls for identifying and removing potential contamination in downstream analyses (De Barba *et al.* 2014). See Chapter 1 for further design considerations.

To generate identifiable sequences from sequencing reads, reads can be 'denoised' (sequencing errors corrected), merged if paired, and clustered into molecular operational taxonomic units based on similarity thresholds (e.g. 95% similarity, referred to as MOTUs or OTUs) or into unique sequences (referred to as amplicon sequence variants or ASVs). The representative sequences for each OTU or ASV are then matched to a reference using local alignment programs or sequence classifiers, such as the algorithms implemented by the programs BLAST (Altschul *et al.* 1990), USEARCH (Edgar 2010) or DADA2 (Callahan *et al.* 2016). Plant taxa are identified to the lowest possible level within a given confidence range; however, where sequences at species level are shared amongst taxa, the next highest taxonomic level is assigned by default.

One of the most common questions regarding pollen metabarcoding is whether quantification of pollen grains is possible from metabarcoding reads. Reports on quantification with metabarcoding are mixed, with a number of studies finding a positive correlation between pollen grains counts and sequencing reads (Baksay *et al.* 2020; Bänsch *et al.* 2020; Richardson *et al.* 2021), while some have found results are not consistent (Bell *et al.* 2017, 2018). There are several reasons why pollen loads on individual insects are difficult to translate to plant abundance or other quantification measures. For example, species can vary in the amount of pollen produced and the DNA yield from the pollen grains (Pornon *et al.* 2016). When using metabarcoding, there are additional factors that can complicate pollen quantification, such as variation in gene copy number, differences in the DNA extraction process and PCR primer biases (Brooks *et al.* 2015; Bell *et al.* 2016; Moorhouse-Gann *et al.* 2018). However, pollen load composition is useful for cross-sample comparisons. For example, pollen reads can be converted to percentages or relative read abundances (Deagle *et al.* 2019) to account for variability in lab protocols or sequencing depth (Box 4.3 in Chapter 4).

Plant-pollinator interactions and network analysis

Once we have identified the species present in mixed pollen samples, we can use this information to infer interactions and reconstruct pollen transport networks. Network analysis is a relatively new approach in the study of ecological communities that can help us identify key species and their level of specialisation (i.e. generalist vs. specialist) and to predict community-wide responses to changes or disturbance (see Box 21.2 for an introductory explanation of ecological network analysis and Bascompte and Jordano (2007) for an extended overview). The first step in network analysis is to build a matrix of interactions, also called the adjacency matrix (Bascompte and Jordano 2007). An example of an adjacency matrix is placing plants detected along rows and insect species across columns and the frequency of interaction (i.e. number of specimens per insect species where each plant was detected) at the intersection (Fig. 21.2C). The adjacency matrix can also be converted to binary data to represent presence (1) or absence (0) of interaction. This matrix can then be used as input to an analysis package to generate a basic interaction network (Fig. 21.2D).

In an early example of applying pollen metabarcoding to build quantitative plant-pollinator networks, Bell *et al.* (2017) used pollen from bees collected from managed forestry sites in Florida. They converted metabarcoding reads from one marker (ITS2) and pooled the interactions for each bee species to generate a quantitative plant-bee network. Their proof-of-concept network connected 51 distinct plant taxa to 37 bee species and found clear advantages in efficiency and resolution over microscopic identification for the construction of pollinator networks.

Box 21.2: Ecological network analysis

Basic ecological network analysis consists of two steps: 1) topological analysis depicting/characterising/mapping the overall plant-pollinator network structure, and 2) species-level network analysis determining the relative role of each species in the network. This analysis of bipartite networks can be done using the 'bipartite' R package (Dormann *et al.* 2008). These steps are briefly described below:

1. *Topological analysis*: basic network metrics (e.g. **connectance, nestedness**) can be quantified from any ecological network to reveal topological properties related to network robustness (Revilla *et al.* 2015), specialisation (Blüthgen *et al.* 2006) and compartmentalisation (Olesen *et al.* 2007). The main metrics are:
   a. Network robustness: quantifies the vulnerability of ecological communities to species loss. This is calculated by simulating species extinction scenarios, for example, related to the effects of anthropogenic disturbances or climate change (Revilla *et al.* 2015). Insights from robustness analysis are commonly used to improve conservation and restoration outcomes (Devoto *et al.* 2012).
   b. Network-level specialisation (H'): provides a measure of the proportion of specialist species (i.e. taxa with a relatively low number of interacting partners) present in a network (Dormann 2011). Ranges between 0 (no specialisation) and 1 (complete specialisation).
2. Compartmentalisation or **modularity**: quantifies the number of modules or groups of species that interact more closely among them than with other species in the network (Olesen *et al.* 2007). Reflects the structural heterogeneity of ecological networks, which can be the result of habitat heterogeneity, coevolutionary forces, functional trait or spatio-temporal variability (Olesen *et al.* 2007; Dalsgaard *et al.* 2013; Andreazzi *et al.* 2017).
3. Species-level analysis: investigates in depth the role of each species in the network. The role refers to the structural importance of a species in terms of connectivity and centrality, that is, how important is a species connecting directly or indirectly other species in the network (Gómez and Perfectti 2012; Arceo-Gómez *et al.* 2020). For example, some species (e.g. honey bees) are considered 'hubs' by connecting multiple modules or compartments in the network (Olesen *et al.* 2007). Similarly, we can quantify the level of specialisation (e.g. d' index) and weighted number of interactions of each species (e.g. linkage density; Blüthgen *et al.* 2006). These metrics are relevant, for example, to identify keystone species and evaluate dependency or diet breadth of threatened taxa (Traveset *et al.* 2017).

The statistical significance of the above network metrics is evaluated using null models, which quantifies how far observed values are from random expectations (Dormann *et al.* 2009). This allows confidence and certainty in the estimated values using statistically robust methods. The tests compare observed values (values obtained from a sampled network) against expected values from randomly assembled webs (null model networks). Thus, statistical analysis can be used to test whether a species is significantly more specialised than other species in the network or whether a network is more compartmentalised than others than expected by chance. There are multiple null models implemented in the 'bipartite' package which vary on their constraints about network dimensions or marginal totals (see Dormann *et al.* 2017, for a detailed review). Additionally, network sampling completeness is also conducted to evaluate the effects of sampling effort in network structure (for more information see Rivera-Hutinel *et al.* 2012).

APPLICATIONS OF POLLEN DNA METABARCODING IN ECOSYSTEM MANAGEMENT
Revealing rare or unseen plant-pollinator interactions

One of the major advantages of using genomic methods to study plant-pollinator communities is the ability to detect interactions that are not easily observable in the field. For example, Pornon *et al.* (2016) compared the number of interactions detected by pollen metabarcoding to those detected through field observations of sub-alpine communities in the French Pyrenees. Their metabarcoding network had two and half times more interactions than the network based on field observations alone. Some of these interactions were with species outside the target community and were likely derived from pollen collected over multiple hours or even days. This increase in the spatial and temporal windows of interaction can have a significant impact on the perceived structure of the network (Bosch *et al.* 2009).

Networks of nocturnal pollinators are some of the most challenging to reconstruct, as observations are difficult to carry out at night. Nocturnal pollination can also be disrupted by artificial light (MacGregor *et al.* 2015); therefore, collecting pollinators and identifying pollen through metabarcoding is a particularly suitable approach for this type of community. Macgregor *et al.* (2019) showed in their study of moth pollinators within farmland that metabarcoding was able to detect the interactions between plants and different families of nocturnal moths with higher sensitivity than pollen microscopy. Another challenging network to reconstruct through observations alone is one involving long-distance migratory insects. Suchan *et al.* (2019) investigated the diet of the migratory butterfly *Vanessa cardui* from samples collected in Spain. Through pollen metabarcoding, they detected traces of DNA from African species absent from Europe, including some plants endemic to the Canary Islands, providing new insights into the flight path of this migratory butterfly and the timing of its seasonal arrival into Europe.

Rare plant species are often difficult to detect in the field, particularly in sensitive and fragile environments where access is restricted. Metabarcoding of the pollen carried by their pollinators has shown some potential to detect species present in low abundances. Using constructed pollen mixtures, Pornon *et al.* (2016) found that as few as five pollen grains were able to detect a 'rare' species; although amplification success was inconsistent. Gresty *et al.* (2018) analysed the brood cell contents of cavity-nesting bees and detected several plant species present in low abundances even when other abundant resources were available near their nests. Pornon *et al.* (2019) found that some insects can become more specialised on a floral resource as its density in the community decreases, suggesting rare plant species are not necessarily ignored by pollinators. However, one of the challenges of pollen metabarcoding is balancing detection of rare pollens with removing potential false-positives by excluding taxa with few sequencing reads (Bell *et al.* 2017), as results can be confounded by field or procedural contamination (Gresty *et al.* 2018).

Studying pollinator foraging preferences within communities

As pollinator communities around the world decline, determining and preserving the quality of pollination services has become a concern. Pollen metabarcoding is a powerful technique that can be used to obtain detailed information on insect foraging preferences. We have shown that honey bees, for example, tend to forage on a different set of floral resources from a larger geographical area than those typically found by ground vegetation surveys (Milla *et al.* 2022). In a study of pollination by honey bees and bumble bees (*Bombus terrestris*), Bänsch *et al.* (2020) analysed over 150 pollen samples to quantify strawberry pollen collection by different sized colonies in the presence of increasing densities of a parallel mass-flowering crop (oilseed rape). The study found that increasing strawberry cover was the main factor influencing the amount of strawberry pollen collected, while the increasing availability of oilseed rape crop led to a decrease in strawberry pollen collection. They used both metabarcoding and microscopy to identify pollen types carried by bees. With pollen metabarcoding, they were able to detect that bumble bees were collecting nearly five times more plant genera than honey bees, while microscopy failed to detect some rare pollen taxa. Although pollen grain counts of the main pollen types using microscopy were positively correlated with metabarcoding reads, they found quantification with metabarcoding to be less reliable. Overall, the study showed that, even in the presence of dominant crops, bees continue to seek out a diversity of plants to supplement their diet, and therefore maintaining floral diversity around agricultural landscapes can help support pollinator populations.

In another study, Richardson *et al.* (2021) examined honey bee foraging across an urban-agricultural gradient in Columbus, Ohio, USA. During spring and fall/autumn for 2 consecutive years, they gathered pollen samples weekly from eight beehives located at four different sites using pollen traps, collecting a total of 109 samples. They verified the metabarcoding results by analysing a small subset of pollen samples under a microscope. As predicted, they found lower species diversity in pollen and decreased turnover of resources over time from bees foraging within agricultural sites compared to urban and suburban sites. Because of the suitability of pollen metabarcoding for automation and high-throughput sample processing, experiments such as this could be readily expanded to provide a highly detailed insights into pollinator foraging over time and space.

Investigating ecosystem role of species within communities

Plant-pollinator networks tend to be highly heterogenous, with a few highly interacting species (generalists), and the

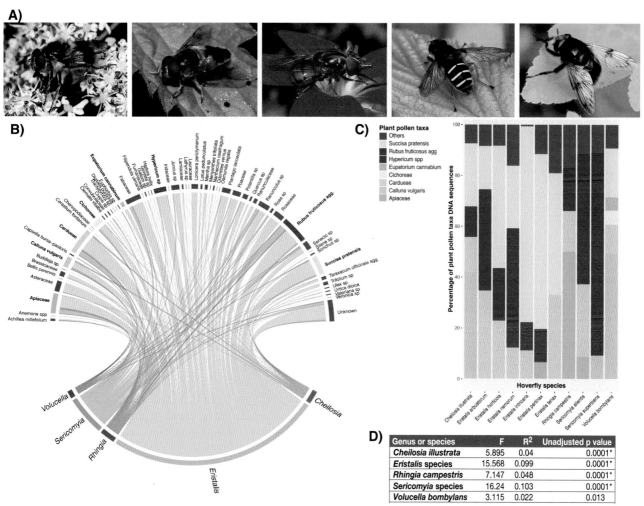

Fig. 21.3. Case study. Using pollen metabarcoding to investigate floral resource partitioning by hoverflies within grasslands. Hoverflies (Syrphidae) are often treated as a single functional group. Lucas *et al.* (2018) collected specimens from five genera of hoverflies and sequenced *rbcL* from pollen. Genera studied from L-R: A) *Cheilosia, Eristalis, Rhingia, Sericomyia* and *Volucella*. B) The resulting network of all hoverfly genera from all sites. Network specialisation metric *d'* (Box 21.2) suggested networks were similarly generalised, with no significant difference between three sampled sites and few exclusive plant/hoverfly species interactions recorded. However, analysis of pollen loads. C) indicated that there was a significant difference in the composition of pollen collected by different hoverfly genera. D) suggesting resource partitioning that would have likely gone undetected based on observations alone. (Sources: A (L-R): Hectonichus CC-BY-SA-3.0, Sandy Rae CC-BY-SA-3.0, Sanja565658 CC-BY-SA-3.0, Frank Vassen CC-BY-SA-2.0, Martin Andresson CC-BY-SA-3.0; B, C, and D: modified from Lucas *et al.* 2018 under CC-BY-SA-4.0)

bulk of species having few connections to others (specialists; Bascompte and Jordano 2007). Network analysis is a useful tool to investigate the role of species in ecological communities. It can provide valuable information about the robustness of communities and species' vulnerabilities against environmental changes and identify key species for ecosystem services and functioning. This approach therefore is particularly useful for practitioners involved in conservation and management of threatened ecosystems. For example, Olesen *et al.* (2007) examined 51 plant-pollinator networks and estimated that around 15% of the species in

each network were underpinning its structural stability. The loss of these key species was more likely to lead to extinction cascades, suggesting conservation efforts could be more effective when targeted towards those species.

Currently, there are very few examples combining network analysis and pollen metabarcoding to determine ecosystem roles. Lucas *et al.* (2018) compared the floral resource usage of five different genera of hoverflies (Syrphidae) at three grassland sites of conservation significance. They constructed individual networks for each site and found that all networks were similarly generalised with few exclusive interactions between hoverflies and plants. However, there was a significant difference in the composition of the pollen each hoverfly genus collected. The results suggested an ecological niche role was being filled by each pollinator group. For more details about this study, see Fig. 21.3.

Conservation and restoration of past and present communities

Conservation and restoration programs can target communities not just individual species. For example, the provision of suitable resources to support pollinators has become an important issue given the reported worldwide pollinator decline. Gresty *et al.* (2018) used pollen metabarcoding to investigate resource use by solitary cavity nesting bees. They compared the pollen resources the bees stored in their brood cells to plants sold in wildflower mixes. Their results showed that solitary bees did not forage on plants sown from the mixes even if they were flowering near their nests. They recommended additional planting of *Rosa canina*, which was detected in 95% of all brood cells, to better support these solitary bee species. Potter *et al.* (2019) similarly investigated foraging plants for bees and other pollinators within commercial seed mixes sold for restoration. They found that pollinators tended to visit only a few species sown from the commercial mix and visited many other plants outside the planted flower strips. As pollen metabarcoding can capture interactions outside an observation plot, this result may not have been possible to obtain if only observations of the flowering strip were conducted. Another interesting aspect of this study was their use of a non-destructive pollen sampling method, which can further contribute to the conservation of pollinators.

The reconstruction of historical plant-pollinator interactions is another area where pollen metabarcoding has great potential, particularly to study the impact of global changes. Pollen grains have tough outer walls that can help preserve DNA for long periods. For example, DNA from ancient pollen grains found in lake sediments has been extracted and used to infer the population history of tree species and their paleoecology (Parducci *et al.* 2005; Magyari *et al.* 2011). Pinned specimens in insect collections are often associated with a single plant observation but often retain pollen from different plants on their bodies. Pollen samples taken from insect specimens not only contain potential information about pollinator dietary shifts, but they could also provide information about past distributions of plant taxa, with implications for community restoration. Gous *et al.* (2018) used pollen metabarcoding to identify 25 plant taxa from 22 pinned specimens of the South African native bee *Megachile venusta*, dating back from 1914 to 2007. Metabarcoding was successful in amplifying taxa regardless of the age of the specimen. In this experiment, all the plant taxa they detected had records from the area where the bee was collected.

FUTURE DIRECTIONS AND OUTSTANDING QUESTIONS

One of the most exciting areas for future applications of pollen DNA metagenomics is in the field of environmental monitoring. Pollen DNA metabarcoding is a promising tool to monitor changes in terrestrial ecosystems due to anthropogenic disturbances and climate change. For example, we recently showed that analysing honey and pollen collected by European honeybees (*Apis mellifera*) using DNA metabarcoding revealed a much larger diversity of flowering plants compared to traditional vegetation surveys based on human observation (Milla *et al.* 2022). These findings also have important implications not only for the way we monitor terrestrial ecosystems but for the development of novel surveillance methods for biosecurity. Early detection of weeds could be possible using foraged pollen by bccs or sampling airborne pollen and other eDNA for detection of wind-pollinated weeds (e.g. invasive grasses) (Johnson *et al.* 2021). Analysing pollen DNA in honey has also been used to detect historical changes in plant communities and the effects of agricultural intensification (Jones *et al.* 2021) as well as revealing bee foraging behaviour and plant diversity at a continental scale (Milla *et al.* 2021).

Pollen sampled using air samplers has applications for public health and environmental monitoring. For example, recent studies have used DNA metabarcoding to monitor for airborne pollen allergens (Campbell *et al.* 2020; Rowney *et al.* 2021) and plant community composition (Leontidou *et al.* 2021). The increase in taxonomic resolution compared to light-microscopy methods provides accurate and cost-effective monitoring across multiple environments (e.g. urban, natural) and ecosystems.

Finally, pollen can be a vehicle for multiple microorganisms, including bacteria, fungi, and viruses (Manirajan *et al.* 2018; Keller *et al.* 2021). There is evidence of a strong overlap between microbiomes of flowers and bees suggesting that flowers are important hubs of microbial transmission (Keller *et al.* 2021). Meta-omics, including the analysis of eRNA in pollen, can also be used to detect plant viruses and other potential plant and pollinator pathogens

(Roberts *et al.* 2018). All of these are potential applications for future biosecurity research incorporating pollen DNA.

DISCUSSION TOPICS

1. Can flower visitation be used to infer pollination efficiency? What information would you need to determine whether an insect is an efficient pollinator?
2. How can insects collect pollen other than by visiting flowers directly?
3. What can we learn about climate change impacts on biodiversity by reconstructing historical pollination networks?

REFERENCES

Allen-Wardell G, Bernhardt P, Bitner R, Burquez A, Buchmann S, et al. (1998) The potential consequences of pollinator declines on the conservation of biodiversity and stability of food crop yields. *Conservation Biology* 12(1), 8–17. doi:10.1046/j.1523-1739.1998.97154.x

Altschul SF, Gish W, Miller W, Myers EW, Lipman DJ (1990) Basic local alignment search tool. *Journal of Molecular Biology* 215, 403–410. doi:10.1016/S0022-2836(05)80360-2

Andreazzi CS, Thompson JN, Guimarães PR (2017) Network structure and selection asymmetry drive coevolution in species-rich antagonistic interactions. *The American Naturalist* 190(1), 99–115. doi:10.1086/692110

Ankenbrand MJ, Keller A, Wolf M, Schultz J, Förster F (2015) ITS2 database V: Twice as much. *Molecular Biology and Evolution* 32(11), 3030–3032. doi:10.1093/molbev/msv174

Arceo-Gómez G, Barker D, Stanley A, Watson T, Daniels J (2020) Plant-pollinator network structural properties differentially affect pollen transfer dynamics and pollination success. *Oecologia* 192(4), 1037–1045.

Arstingstall KA, DeBano SJ, Li X, Wooster DE, Rowland MM, et al. (2021) Capabilities and limitations of using DNA metabarcoding to study plant-pollinator interactions. *Molecular Ecology* 30(20), 5266–5297. doi:10.1111/mec.16112

Baksay S, Pornon A, Burrus M, Mariette J, Andalo C, et al. (2020) Experimental quantification of pollen with DNA metabarcoding using ITS1 and trnL. *Scientific Reports* 10(1), 4202. doi:10.1038/s41598-020-61198-6

Bänsch S, Tscharntke T, Wünschiers R, Netter L, Brenig B, et al. (2020) Using ITS2 metabarcoding and microscopy to analyse shifts in pollen diets of honey bees and bumble bees along a mass-flowering crop gradient. *Molecular Ecology* 29(24), 5003–5018. doi:10.1111/mec.15675

De Barba M, Miquel C, Boyer F, Mercier C, Rioux D, et al. (2014) DNA metabarcoding multiplexing and validation of data accuracy for diet assessment: Application to omnivorous diet. *Molecular Ecology Resources* 14(2), 306–323. doi:10.1111/1755-0998.12188

Bascompte J, Jordano P (2007) Plant-animal mutualistic networks: the architecture of biodiversity. *Annual Review of Ecology, Evolution, and Systematics* 38, 567–593.

Beekman M, Ratnieks FLW (2000) Long-range foraging by the honey-bee, *Apis mellifera L. Functional Ecology* 14(4), 490–496. doi:10.1046/J.1365-2435.2000.00443.X

Bell KL, De Vere N, Keller A, Richardson RT, Gous A, et al. (2016) Pollen DNA barcoding: current applications and future prospects. *Genome* 59(9), 629–640. doi:10.1139/gen-2015-0200

Bell KL, Fowler J, Burgess KS, Dobbs EK, Gruenewald D, et al. (2017) Applying pollen DNA metabarcoding to the study of plant-pollinator interactions. *Applications in Plant Sciences* 5(6), 160024. doi:10.3732/apps.1600124

Bell KL, Burgess KS, Botsch JC, Dobbs EK, Read TD, et al. (2018) Quantitative and qualitative assessment of pollen DNA metabarcoding using constructed species mixtures. *Molecular Ecology* 28(2), 431–455. doi:10.1111/mec.14840

Bell L, Loeffler VM, Brosi BJ (2017) An rbcL reference library to aid in the identification of plant species mixtures by DNA metabarcoding. *Applications in Plant Sciences* 5(3), 1600110.

Biesmeijer JC Roberts SP, Reemer M, Ohlemuller R, Edwards M, et al. (2006) Parallel declines in pollinators and insect-pollinated plants in Britain and the Netherlands. *Science* 313(5785), 351–354. doi:10.1126/science.1127863

Blüthgen NN, Menzel F, Blüthgen NN (2006) Measuring specialization in species interaction networks. *BMC Ecology* 6(1), 1–12. doi:10.1186/1472-6785-6-9

Bosch J, Martín González AM, Rodrigo A, Navarro D (2009) Plant-pollinator networks: adding the pollinator's perspective. *Ecology Letters* 12(5), 409–419.

Brooks JP, Edwards DJ, Harwich MD, Rivera MC, Fettweis JM, et al. (2015) The truth about metagenomics: Quantifying and counteracting bias in 16S rRNA studies. *BMC Microbiology* 15(1), 66. doi:10.1186/s12866-015-0351-6

Burkle A, Marlin JC, Knight TM (2013) Plant-pollinator interactions over 120 years: Loss of species, co-occurrence, and function. *Science* 339(6127), 1611–1615. doi:10.1126/science.1232728

Callahan BJ, McMurdie PJ, Rosen MJ, Han AW, Johnson AJ, et al. (2016) DADA2: High-resolution sample inference from Illumina amplicon data. *Nature Methods* 13(7), 581–583.

Campbell BC, Al Kouba J, Timbrell V, Noor MJ, Massel K, et al. (2020) Tracking seasonal changes in diversity of pollen allergen exposure: targeted metabarcoding of a subtropical aerobiome. *Science of the Total Environment* 747, 14118.

CBOL Plant Working Group (2009) A DNA barcode for land plants. *Proceedings of the National Academy of Sciences of the United States of America* 106(31), 12794–12797.

Chen S, Yao H, Han J, Liu C, Song J, et al. (2010) Validation of the ITS2 region as a novel DNA barcode for identifying medicinal plant species. *PLoS One* 5(1), e8613.

Cook DF, Voss SC, Finch JT, Rader RC, Cook JM, et al. (2020) The role of flies as pollinators of horticultural crops: An Australian case study with worldwide relevance. *Insects* 11(6), 341.

Cornman RS, Otto CR, Iwanowicz D, Pettis JS (2015) Taxonomic characterization of honey bee (*Apis mellifera*) pollen foraging based on non-overlapping paired-end sequencing of nuclear ribosomal loci. *PLoS One* 10(12). doi:10.1371/journal.pone.0145365

Dalsgaard B, Trøjelsgaard K, Martín González AM, Nogués-Bravo D, Ollerton J, et al. (2013) Historical climate-change influences modularity and nestedness of pollination networks. *Ecography* **36**(12), 1331–1340.

Danner N, Keller A, Härtel S, Steffan-Dewenter I (2018) Honey bee foraging ecology: Season but not landscape diversity shapes the amount and diversity of collected pollen. *PLoS One* **12**(8), e0183716. doi:10.1371/journal.pone.0183716

Deagle BE, Thomas AC, McInnes JC, Clarke LJ, Vesterinen EJ, *et al.* (2019) Counting with DNA in metabarcoding studies: How should we convert sequence reads to dietary data?. *Molecular Ecology* **28**(2), 391–406. doi:10.1111/mec.14734

Devoto M, Bailey S, Craze P, Memmott J (2012) Understanding and planning ecological restoration of plant-pollinator networks. *Ecology Letters* **15**(4), 319–328. doi:10.1111/j.1461-0248. 2012.01740.x

Doña J, Serrano D, Mironov S, Montesinos-Navarro A, Jovani R (2019) Unexpected bird–feather mite associations revealed by DNA metabarcoding uncovers a dynamic ecoevolutionary scenario. *Molecular Ecology* **28**(2), 379–390. doi:10.1111/mec.14968

Dormann CF (2011) How to be a specialist? Quantifying specialisation in pollination networks. *Network Biology* **1**(1), 1–20.

Dormann CF, Fründ J, Schaefer HM (2017) Identifying causes of patterns in ecological networks: opportunities and limitations. *Annual Review of Ecology, Evolution, and Systematics* **48**, 559–584.

Dormann F, Fründ J, Blüthgen N, Gruber B (2009) Indices, graphs and null models: analyzing bipartite ecological networks. *The Open Ecology Journal* **2**, 1.

Dormann F, Gruber B, Fründ J (2008) Introducing the bipartite package: analysing ecological networks. *interaction* **1**, 0.2413793.

Edgar RC (2010) Search and clustering orders of magnitude faster than BLAST. *Bioinformatics* **26**(19), 2460–2461. doi:10.1093/bioinformatics/btq461

Elliott B, Wilson R, Shapcott A, Keller A, Newis R, *et al.* (2021) Pollen diets and niche overlap of honey bees and native bees in protected areas. *Basic and Applied Ecology* **50**, 169–180.

Encinas-Viso F, Bovill J, Albrecht DE, Florez-Fernandez J, Lessard B, *et al.* (2022) Pollen DNA metabarcoding reveals cryptic diversity and high spatial turnover in alpine plant–pollinator networks. *Molecular Ecology* **00**, 1–17. doi:10.1111/mec.16682

Ficetola GF, Pansu J, Bonin A, Coissac E, Giguet-Covex C, *et al.* (2015) Replication levels, false presences and the estimation of the presence/absence from eDNA metabarcoding data. *Molecular Ecology Resources* **15**(3), 543–556. doi:10.1111/1755-0998. 12338

Galimberti A, De Mattia F, Bruni I, Scaccabarozzi D, Sandionigi A, *et al.* (2014) A DNA barcoding approach to characterize pollen collected by honeybees. *PLoS One* **9**(10), e109363.

Gómez JM, Perfectti F (2012) Fitness consequences of centrality in mutualistic individual-based networks. *Proceedings of the Royal Society B: Biological Sciences* **279**(1734), 1754–1760.

González-Varo JP, Arroyo JM, Jordano P (2014) Who dispersed the seeds? The use of DNA barcoding in frugivory and seed dispersal studies. *Methods in Ecology and Evolution* **5**(8), 806–814. doi:10.1111/2041-210X.12212

Gous A, Swanevelder DZ, Eardley CD, Willows-Munro S (2018) Plant-pollinator interactions over time: Pollen metabarcoding

from bees in a historic collection. *Evolutionary Applications* **12**(2), 187–197.

Gresty CEA, Clare E, Devey DS, Cowan RS, Csiba L, *et al.* (2018) Flower preferences and pollen transport networks for cavity-nesting solitary bees: Implications for the design of agri-environment schemes. *Ecology and Evolution* **8**(15), 7574–7587. doi:10.1002/ece3.4234

Hawkins J, De Vere N, Griffith A, Ford CR, Allainguillaume J, *et al.* (2015) Using DNA metabarcoding to identify the floral composition of honey: A new tool for investigating honey bee foraging preferences. *PLoS One* **10**(8), e0134735.

Hollingsworth PM (2011) Refining the DNA barcode for land plants. *Proceedings of the National Academy of Sciences* **108**(49), 19451–19452.

Inouye DW, Pyke GH (1988) Pollination biology in the Snowy Mountains of Australia: Comparisons with montane Colorado, USA. *Australian Journal of Ecology* **13**(2), 191–205.

Johnson MD Fokar M, Cox RD, Barnes MA (2021) Airborne environmental DNA metabarcoding detects more diversity, with less sampling effort, than a traditional plant community survey. *BMC Ecology and Evolution* **21**(1), 1–15.

Jones L, Brennan GL, Lowe A, Creer S, Ford CR, *et al.* (2021) Shifts in honeybee foraging reveal historical changes in floral resources. *Communications Biology* **4**(1), 37. doi:10.1038/s42003-020-01562-4

Kearns CA, Inouye DW, Waser NM (1998) Endangered mutualisms: The conservation of plant-pollinator interactions. *Annual Review of Ecology and Systematics* 83–112. doi:10.1146/annurev.ecolsys.29.1.83

Keller A, Danner N, Grimmer G, Ankenbrand MV, Von Der Ohe K, *et al.* (2015) Evaluating multiplexed next-generation sequencing as a method in palynology for mixed pollen samples. *Plant Biology* **17**(2), 558–566.

Keller A, McFrederick QS, Dharampal P, Steffan S, Danforth BN, *et al.* (2021) (More than) Hitchhikers through the network: The shared microbiome of bees and flowers. *Current Opinion in Insect Science* **44**, 8–15.

Klein A-M Vaissière BE, Cane JH, Steffan-Dewenter I, Cunningham SA, *et al.* (2007) Importance of pollinators in changing landscapes for world crops. *Proceedings of the Royal Society B: Biological Sciences* **274**(1608), 303–313. doi:10.1098/rspb.2006.3721

Kress WJ, Erickson DL (2007) A two-locus global DNA barcode for land plants: The coding rbcL gene complements the non-coding trnH-psbA spacer region. *PLoS One* **2**(6), e508.

Lahaye R, Van der Bank M, Bogarin D, Warner J, Pupulin F, *et al.* (2008) DNA barcoding the floras of biodiversity hotspots. *Proceedings of the National Academy of Sciences* **105**(8), 2923–2928. doi:10.1073/pnas.0709936105

Leontidou K, Vokou D, Sandionigi A, Bruno A, Lazarina M, *et al.* (2018) DNA metabarcoding of airborne pollen: New protocols for improved taxonomic identification of environmental samples. *Aerobiologia* **34**(1), 63–74. doi:10.1007/s10453-017-9497-z

Leontidou K, Vokou D, Sandionigi A, Bruno A, Lazarina M, *et al.* (2021) Plant biodiversity assessment through pollen DNA metabarcoding in Natura 2000 habitats (Italian Alps). *Scientific Reports* **11**(1), 18226. doi:10.1038/s41598-021-97619-3

Lucas A, Bodger O, Brosi BJ, Ford CR, Forman DW, *et al.* (2018) Generalisation and specialisation in hoverfly (Syrphidae) grassland pollen transport networks revealed by DNA metabarcoding. *Journal of Animal Ecology* **87**(4), 1008–1021.

MacGregor C, Pocock MJ, Fox R, Evans DM (2015) Pollination by nocturnal Lepidoptera, and the effects of light pollution: a review. *Ecological Entomology* **40**(3), 187–198.

Macgregor CJ, Kitson JJ, Fox R, Hahn C, Lunt DH, *et al.* (2019) Construction, validation, and application of nocturnal pollen transport networks in an agro-ecosystem: A comparison using light microscopy and DNA metabarcoding. *Ecological Entomology* **44**(1), 17–29. doi:10.1111/een.12674

Magyari EK, Major Á, Bálint M, Nédli J, Braun M, *et al.* (2011) Population dynamics and genetic changes of *Picea abies* in the South Carpathians revealed by pollen and ancient DNA analyses. *BMC Evolutionary Biology* **11**(1), 1–16.

Manirajan BA, Maisinger C, Ratering S, Rusch V, Schwiertz A, *et al.* (2018) Diversity, specificity, co-occurrence and hub taxa of the bacterial-fungal pollen microbiome. *FEMS Microbiology Ecology* **94**(8), fiy112.

Mata VA, Rebelo H, Amorim F, McCracken GF, Jarman S, *et al.* (2019) How much is enough? Effects of technical and biological replication on metabarcoding dietary analysis. *Molecular Ecology* **28**(2), 165–175. doi:10.1111/mec.14779

Mayr A V, Keller A, Peters MK, Grimmer G, Krischke B, *et al.* (2021) Cryptic species and hidden ecological interactions of halictine bees along an elevational gradient. *Ecology and Evolution* **11**(12), 7700–7712.

McFrederick S, Rehan SM (2019) Wild bee pollen usage and microbial communities co-vary across landscapes. *Microbial Ecology* **77**(2), 513–522. doi:10.1007/s00248-018-1232-y

Milla L, Sniderman K, Lines R, Mousavi-Derazmahalleh M, Encinas-Viso F (2021) Pollen DNA metabarcoding identifies regional provenance and high plant diversity in Australian honey. *Ecology and Evolution* **11**(13), 8683–8698.

Milla L, Schmidt-Lebuhn A, Bovill J, Encinas-Viso F (2022) Monitoring of honey bee floral resources with pollen DNA metabarcoding as a complementary tool to vegetation surveys. *Ecological Solutions and Evidence* **3**(1), e12120.

Moorhouse-Gann RJ, Dunn JC, De Vere N, Goder M, Cole N, *et al.* (2018) New universal ITS2 primers for high-resolution herbivory analyses using DNA metabarcoding in both tropical and temperate zones. *Scientific Reports* **8**(1), 1–15.

Olesen JM, Bascompte J, Dupont YL, Jordano P (2007) The modularity of pollination networks. *Proceedings of the National Academy of Sciences* **104**(50), 19891–19896. doi:10.1073/pnas.0706375104

Ollerton J, Winfree R, Tarrant S (2011) How many flowering plants are pollinated by animals? *Oikos* **120**(3), 321–326. doi:10.1111/j.1600-0706.2010.18644.x

Orford KA, Vaughan IP, Memmott J (2015) The forgotten flies: the importance of non-syrphid Diptera as pollinators. *Proceedings of the Royal Society B: Biological Sciences* **282**(1805), 20142934.

Parducci L, Suyama Y, Lascoux M, Bennett KD (2005) Ancient DNA from pollen: a genetic record of population history in Scots pine. *Molecular Ecology* **14**(9), 2873–2882. doi:10.1111/j.1365-294X.2005.02644.x

Pitteloud C, Walser JC, Descombes P, Novaes de Santana C, Rasmann S, *et al.* (2021) The structure of plant-herbivore interaction networks varies along elevational gradients in the European Alps. *Journal of Biogeography* **48**(2), 465–476.

Pornon A, Escaravage N, Burrus M, Holota H, Khimoun A, *et al.* (2016) Using metabarcoding to reveal and quantify plant-pollinator interactions. *Scientific Reports* **6**, 27282.

Pornon A, Baksay S, Escaravage N, Burrus M, Andalo C (2019) Pollinator specialization increases with a decrease in a mass-flowering plant in networks inferred from DNA metabarcoding. *Ecology and Evolution* **9**(24), 13650–13662. doi:10.1002/ece3.5531

Potter C, De Vere N, Jones LE, Ford CR, Hegarty MJ (2019) Pollen metabarcoding reveals broad and species-specific resource use by urban bees. *PeerJ* **7**, e5999. doi:10.7717/peerj.5999

Potts SG, Biesmeijer JC, Kremen C, Neumann P, Schweiger O, *et al.* (2010) Global pollinator declines: trends, impacts and drivers. *Trends in Ecology & Evolution* **25**(6), 345–353.

Prosser SWJ, Hebert PDN (2017) Rapid identification of the botanical and entomological sources of honey using DNA metabarcoding. *Food Chemistry* **214**, 183–191. doi:10.1016/j.foodchem.2016.07.077

Rader R, Bartomeus I, Garibaldi LA, Garratt MP, Howlett BG (2016) Non-bee insects are important contributors to global crop pollination. *Proceedings of the National Academy of Sciences* **113**(1), 146–151.

Rahl M (2008) Microscopic identification and purity determination of pollen grains. In: *Allergy Methods and Protocols.* Methods in Molecular Medicine, Vol. 138. Humana Press, Totowa, NJ, USA. doi:10.1007/978-1-59745-366-0_22

Revilla TA, Encinas-Viso F, Loreau M (2015) Robustness of mutualistic networks under phenological change and habitat destruction. *Oikos* **124**(1), 22–32. doi:10.1111/oik.01532

Richardson R, Eaton TD, Lin CH, Cherry G, Johnson RM, *et al.* (2021) Application of plant metabarcoding to identify diverse honeybee pollen forage along an urban-agricultural gradient. *Molecular Ecology* **30**(1), 310–323. doi:10.1111/mec.15704

Richardson RT, Lin CH, Sponsler DB, Quijia JO, Goodell K, *et al.* (2015) Application of ITS2 metabarcoding to determine the provenance of pollen collected by honey bees in an agroecosystem. *Applications in Plant Sciences* **3**(1), 1400066.

Richardson RT, Curtis HR, Matcham EG, Lin CH, Suresh S, *et al.* (2019) Quantitative multi-locus metabarcoding and waggle dance interpretation reveal honey bee spring foraging patterns in Midwest agroecosystems. *Molecular Ecology* **28**(3), 686–697.

Rivera-Hutinel A, Bustamante RO, Marín VH, Medel R, *et al.* (2012) Effects of sampling completeness on the structure of plant-pollinator networks. *Ecology* **93**(7), 1593–1603.

Roberts JM, Ireland KB, Tay WT, Paini D (2018) Honey bee-assisted surveillance for early plant virus detection. *Annals of Applied Biology* **173**(3), 285–293.

Rowney FM, Brennan GL, Skjøth CA, Griffith GW, McInnes RN (2021) Environmental DNA reveals links between abundance and composition of airborne grass pollen and respiratory health. *Current Biology* **31**(9), 1995–2003.

Rytkönen S, Brennan GL, Skjøth CA, Griffith GW, McInnes RN, *et al.* (2019) From feces to data: A metabarcoding method for analyzing consumed and available prey in a bird-insect food web. *Ecology and Evolution* **9**(1), 631–639.

Santos C, Carneiro J, Pereiram F (2019) A web-based platform of nucleotide sequence alignments of plants. *bioRxiv* 617035.

Shokralla S, Spall JL, Gibson JF, Hajibabaei M (2012) Next-generation sequencing technologies for environmental DNA research. *Molecular Ecology* 1794–1805. doi:10.1111/j.1365-294X.2012.05538.x

Sniderman JK, Matley KA, Haberle SG, Cantrill DJ (2018) Pollen analysis of Australian honey. *PLoS One* 13, 5.

Suchan T, Talavera G, Sáez L, Ronikier M, Vila R (2019) Pollen metabarcoding as a tool for tracking long-distance insect migrations. *Molecular Ecology Resources* 19(1), 149–162.

Swenson SJ, Gemeinholzer B (2021) Testing the effect of pollen exine rupture on metabarcoding with Illumina sequencing. *PloS one* 16(2), e0245611. doi:10.1371/journal.pone.0245611

Taberlet P, Coissac E, Pompanon F, Gielly L, Miquel C, *et al.* (2006) Power and limitations of the chloroplast trn L (UAA) intron for plant DNA barcoding. *Nucleic Acids Research* 35(3), e14–e14. doi:10.1093/nar/gkl938

Taberlet P, Coissac E, Pompanon F, Brochmann C, Willerslev E (2012) Towards next-generation biodiversity assessment using DNA metabarcoding. *Molecular Ecology* 21(8), 2045–2050.

Thomsen PF, Sigsgaard EE (2019) Environmental DNA metabarcoding of wild flowers reveals diverse communities of terrestrial arthropods. *Ecology and Evolution* 9(4), 1665–1679.

Traveset A, Tur C, Eguíluz VM (2017) Plant survival and keystone pollinator species in stochastic coextinction models: Role of intrinsic dependence on animal-pollination. *Scientific Reports* 7(1), 1–10.

Tremblay ÉD, Duceppe MO, Thurston GB, Gagnon MC, Côté MJ (2019) High-resolution biomonitoring of plant pathogens and plant species using metabarcoding of pollen pellet contents collected from a honey bee hive. *Environmental DNA* 1(2), 155–175. doi:10.1002/edn3.17

Warrant E, Frost B, Green K, Mouritsen H, Dreyer D (2016) The Australian Bogong moth *Agrotis infusa*: A long-distance nocturnal navigator. *Frontiers in Behavioral Neuroscience* 10, 77.

White TJ (1990) *PCR Protocols*. (Ed J Bartlett, D Stirling) Humana Press, Totowa, NJ, USA. doi:10.1016/b978-0-12-372180-8.50042-1

Yao H, Song J, Liu C, Luo K, Han J, *et al.* (2010) Use of ITS2 region as the universal DNA barcode for plants and animals. *PLoS One* 5(10), 10. doi:10.1371/journal.pone.0013102

Yu J, Xue JH, Zhou SL (2011) New universal matK primers for DNA barcoding angiosperms. *Journal of Systematics and Evolution* 49(3), 176–181.

Zamora-Terol S, Novotny A, Winder M (2020) Reconstructing marine plankton food web interactions using DNA metabarcoding. *Molecular Ecology* 29(17), 3380–3395.

22 Genomic approaches to study dispersal in wild animal populations: implications for wildlife management

Hugo Cayuela, Jérôme G. Prunier and Quentin Rougemont

ABSTRACT

Dispersal is a central eco-evolutionary process determining the demographic and genetic dynamics of wild populations. Therefore, wildlife managers are often interested in quantifying frequency and distances of dispersal within spatially structured populations, by considering dispersal (i.e. movements followed or not by a successful reproduction event) and gene flow (i.e. movements followed by a successful reproduction event). Yet, dispersal is a difficult process to measure through direct observation. Genomic approaches to studying dispersal capitalise on the rich genealogical information obtainable from DNA sequences and its distribution within the landscape. The continued reduction in costs of DNA sequencing, and the development and diversification of analytical techniques, means that DNA-based measurement of dispersal is now a mainstream activity applied to such diverse applications as conservation, wild harvest, and pest control. Here, we provide a synthetic snapshot of existing genomic methods to assess dispersal and gene flow in wild animal populations. We identify the strengths and weaknesses of each method, provide recommendations about their use, and illustrate these with case studies.

DISPERSAL AND CONSERVATION ISSUES IN THE ERA OF GENOMICS

What is dispersal?

Dispersal designates the movement of an individual from its birth patch to its breeding patch (i.e. natal dispersal), or between successive breeding patches (i.e. breeding dispersal; Clobert *et al.* 2009; Matthysen 2012). Dispersal is usually modelled as a three-stage process including emigration (i.e. departure), transience (i.e. movement into the landscape), and immigration (i.e. arrival). The evolution of dispersal is determined by the balance between the costs incurred during the three stages and fitness benefits associated with settlement in another patch (Bonte *et al.* 2012). Dispersing individuals often differ from resident individuals phenotypically (i.e. *condition-dependent dispersal*, Clobert *et al.* 2004), leading to complex dispersal syndromes (Ronce and Clobert 2012; Cote *et al.* 2017). Moreover, dispersal is a highly plastic behaviour where individuals adjust their emigration and immigration decisions according to social (e.g. public information; Boulinier *et al.* 2008) and environmental cues (i.e. *context-dependent dispersal*) reflecting fitness prospects at a given site (Clobert *et al.* 2009; Matthysen 2012). In addition, individual movements during the transience step are constrained by landscape composition and configuration and the presence of physical barriers that determine connectivity between patches (Baguette and Van Dyck 2007; Baguette *et al.* 2013).

Individual behavioural processes at the three dispersal steps have tremendous effects on the dynamics of spatially structured populations (SSP, *sensu* Thomas and Kunin 1999), which are populations composed of subpopulations occupying discrete habitat patches linked together by dispersal. Dispersal rate, distance, and direction determine the level of demographic interdependency of subpopulations, local colonisation–extinction dynamics, as well as the whole SSP persistence (Hansson 1991; Hanski and Gaggiotti 2004). Dispersal is therefore central to the *metapopulation* paradigm used by ecologists and evolutionary biologists for decades to understand the links between landscape structure, demography, and evolution (Hanski 1998).

When it is followed by successful reproduction, dispersal becomes a central evolutionary force (called *gene flow, migration, or effective dispersal* in the literature; Hanski and Gaggiotti 2004; Ronce 2007; Broquet and Petit 2009; Cayuela *et al.* 2018). In combination with genetic drift, selection, and mutation, gene flow shapes population genetic structure, producing various patterns of genetic clustering and clines at different spatial scales (Bohonak 1999; Slatkin 2017). Gene flow strongly influences adaptive processes, by either eroding local adaptation via the swamping of locally beneficial alleles (Lenormand 2002; Tigano and Friesen 2016), or strengthening adaptation via matching habitat choice (*directed gene flow*; Edelaar *et al.* 2008; Jacob *et al.* 2017). In addition, gene flow mitigates the negative effect of genetic drift on genetic diversity and reduces inbreeding depression in small populations through the introduction of foreign genotypes and the masking of deleterious recessive alleles (Whitlock *et al.* 2000; Keller and Waller 2002). Ultimately, gene flow influences speciation by modulating the level of reproductive isolation among populations and lineages (Mayr 1963; Coyne and Orr 2004).

Methods for measuring dispersal in environmental management

Because of its effects on the dynamics and genetics of SSPs, dispersal is an important parameter to consider when wildlife managers develop conservation strategies for threatened species, when practitioners design harvesting plans for exploited species (e.g. seafood), or when national agencies determine plans for pest and disease control. Demographic studies on dispersal usually aim to quantifying annual or seasonal dispersal rates and distances, as well as the degree of demographic interdependency (i.e. *demographic connectivity, sensu* Lowe and Allendorf 2010) among the subpopulations of an SSP. These studies also evaluate functional connectivity (i.e. landscape influence on movement during transience, *sensu* Taylor *et al.* 1993) and examine the influence of patch quality on emigration and immigration (Baguette *et al.* 2013; Cayuela *et al.* 2018). These demographic approaches may help

environmental managers to quantify the degree of population isolation and identify potential habitat corridors, assess the effect of management operations (e.g. habitat restoration) on connectivity, define the limits of protected areas, and evaluate the risks associated with spread of invasive species and pests.

Studying dispersal is usually achieved through two types of approaches: direct observation methods (i.e. individual monitoring using capture-mark-recapture or telemetry approaches) and indirect observation methods (i.e. genetic approaches). Direct observation methods are based on longitudinal individual data with spatial information that allow quantifying dispersal rates and distances at different time scales, and examining finely the influence of phenotype, environmental variation, and their interactions on the three dispersal steps (reviewed in Cayuela *et al.* 2018). These methods are usually costly in terms of logistic and human resources and are not applicable to organisms of very small body size, having very large population sizes (e.g. most invertebrates) or living in environments that cannot be sampled easily (e.g. most marine species). Furthermore, although genetics may be useful for individual identification in some capture-recapture studies (e.g. Cayuela *et al.* 2021; see Chapters 10 and 11), genotype-based recognition can be costly, especially when it is used in long-term population monitoring.

In the cases where direct observation methods cannot be used due to technical or financial constraints, genetic methods provide interesting methodological solutions to study dispersal (Broquet and Petit 2009; Cayuela *et al.* 2018). Genetic studies of dispersal aim at estimating ancient or contemporary migration rates, assessing gene flow distance, and studying population genetic structure (neutral or adaptive; Broquet and Petit 2009; Cayuela *et al.* 2018). They also examine genetic connectivity, namely the influence of landscape and especially anthropogenic physical barriers on among-patches genetic differentiation (Schwartz *et al.* 2010; Manel and Holderegger 2013). Like demographic approaches, these genetic studies are particularly useful for managers to assess the level of population fragmentation, define the spatial limits of protected areas and fishing stocks, and reconstruct the history of colonisation of invasive species.

Dispersal studies and high-throughput sequencing technologies

The use of genetic markers to study population differentiation and demographic processes dates to the 1940s, when Theodosius Dobzhansky began to compare changes in the frequency of chromosomal rearrangements in natural

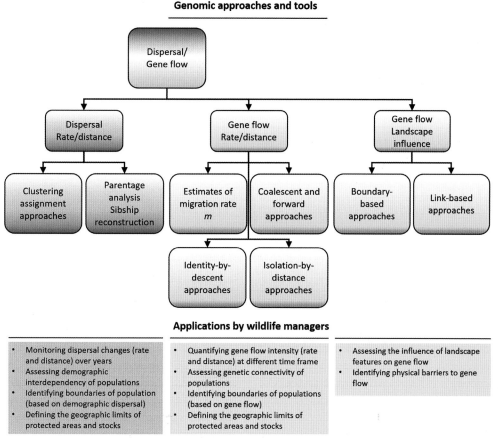

Fig. 22.1. Genomic approaches used to investigate dispersal (in blue) and gene flow (in yellow) and applications by wildlife managers.

populations of *Drosophila pseudoobscura* (Dobzhansky 1943). During the 1990s and 2000s, the use of AFLP (amplified fragment length polymorphism) and microsatellite DNA markers has played a major role in basic and applied studies on dispersal (Sunde *et al.* 2020), allowing the development of completely novel research fields such as *landscape genetics* (Manel *et al.* 2003). During the last two decades, the continuous development of Next Generation Sequencing (NGS) technologies opened up new opportunities for generating more precise estimates of dispersal and gene flow. The use of thousands of genomic markers (i.e. *single nucleotide polymorphisms*, SNP) increases the accuracy of sibship reconstruction, and the robustness of parentage and kinship analyses, used to estimate dispersal (see section 'Parentage and kinship analyses'). In addition, it provides higher statistical power to detect small genetic variation among populations (Waples 1998; Gagnaire *et al.* 2015; Galla *et al.* 2022) and allows increased precision in measures of genetic differentiation used to assess gene flow. Furthermore, NGS approaches facilitate the discovery of markers under selection and hitchhiker markers that usually allow a more efficient delineation of management units

(Flanagan *et al.* 2018; see Chapter 14). Finally, in most methods described below, dense SNP data considerably reduce the needs to sample a large number of individuals in a single sampling locality (e.g. Willing *et al.* 2012). Another benefit of such strong marker density is a better sampling of the whole genome, and a decreased in sampling variance among loci (Morin *et al.* 2004). Here, we review the genomic methods usually considered to investigate dispersal and gene flow (Fig. 22.1). We discuss the strength and limitations of each method and provide a general reflection on the use of NGS methods in the framework of dispersal studies.

ESTIMATING DISPERSAL RATES AND DISTANCES USING NEXT GENERATION SEQUENCING
Clustering and assignment approaches

Clustering analyses allow the assignment of sampled individuals to discrete genetic clusters of origin (Pritchard *et al.* 2000; Corander *et al.* 2003), based on their individual genotype and sometimes including spatial information (Guillot *et al.* 2012; Caye *et al.* 2018). These approaches investigate the spatial subdivision of populations and may thus help identify potential physical barriers to gene flow. The use of these approaches, which are sensitive to a non-exhaustive sample of populations (Puechmaille 2016), is appropriate when populations are effectively fragmented and spatially structured (Lawson *et al.* 2018; Pritchard *et al.* 2000). In such conditions, it is possible to estimate dispersal rates by dividing the number of first-generation dispersers (or F_0, that is, individuals assigned to a cluster different from the ones they were sampled in) by the sample size (Broquet and Petit 2009). Examples of clustering analyses adapted to NGS data are implemented in the program ADMXITURE (Alexander 2009) and the R-package LEA (Frichot and François 2015), among others. Clustering analyses based on SNP data has been used by many studies on a broad range of organisms including molluscs (Kess *et al.* 2018), insects (Yadav *et al.* 2021), crustaceans (Vu *et al.* 2021), amphibians (Wei *et al.* 2020), reptiles (van der Zee *et al.* 2021), fishes (Moore *et al.* 2014; Rougemont *et al.* 2019, 2022), birds (Söderquist *et al.* 2017) and mammals (Wultsch *et al.* 2016).

Clustering analyses can nevertheless come with technical limitations, which can be circumvented by some promising new methods. For instance, isolation-by-distance (IBD) patterns may lead to an inflation of the signals of population structure since most clustering methods assign individuals to discrete genetic clusters by assuming that allelic frequencies are constant within each cluster and do not consider spatial autocorrelation in allelic frequencies (Frantz *et al.* 2009; Meirmans 2012; but see Galpern *et al.* 2014, Bradburd *et al.* 2018). The R-package *conStruct* (Bradburd *et al.* 2018) provides a statistical framework for the simultaneous inference of continuous and discrete patterns of population structure based on SNP data. This method explicitly addresses the *clines-versus-clusters* problem in modelling population genetic variation. Clustering methods may also show low efficiency when population differentiation is low ($F_{ST} < 0.05$), and/or when the number of genome-wide markers is limited (Paetkau *et al.* 2004; Faubet *et al.* 2007; Meirmans 2014). The R-package *Assigner*, which implements the *gsi_sim* method of Anderson *et al.* (2008), allows assignment analysis to be conducted when inferences are robust even when population differentiation is low ($F_{ST} < 0.05$).

Parentage and kinship analyses

Parentage analyses (i.e. parentage assignment and sibship reconstruction) use the genotypes of individuals – possibly assessed using SNP data (Snyder-Mackler *et al.* 2016; Grashei *et al.* 2018; Dodds *et al.* 2019; Jasper *et al.* 2019) – to assess parent–offspring relationships and kin relationships

from which dispersal rates and distances can be then quantified (Broquet and Petit 2009; Cayuela *et al.* 2018; see also Chapter 11). Accurate parentage assignments and sibship reconstruction can be obtained from a small number of SNP makers (50–100 SNPs; see Huisman 2017). However, to be efficient, these approaches classically require an extensive individual sampling of both the parents and their progeny (Broquet and Petit 2009) and are therefore generally best suited to small, isolated, and spatially structured populations. Provided that false-positives are properly dealt with (Städele and Vigilant 2016), kinship analyses allow assessing familial relationships in the absence of parentage data using various relatedness estimators (Blouin 2003), which can be further used to infer relatedness structure and IBD within spatially structured populations (e.g. amphibians: Unglaub *et al.* 2021; lek-breeding birds: Cayuela *et al.* 2019). For instance, Prunier *et al.* (2021) used kinship reconstruction in the freshwater fish ectoparasite *Tracheliastes polycolpus* to assess the distribution of full-sibs within and among fish hosts and to estimate individual dispersal distances at various spatial scales. At local scales, they showed that *T. polycolpus* sibs tend to be aggregated within fish shoals but not within host individuals, a dispersal strategy that may limit the risk of inbreeding depression. At the river scale, they detected a strong IBD pattern, resulting from a combination of passive upstream-to-downstream dispersal events (passive drift with current) and some active host-driven downstream-to-upstream dispersal events. Parentage and kinship analyses performed to infer dispersal were traditionally based on microsatellite DNA markers (e.g. Telfer *et al.* 2003; Lepais *et al.* 2010; Woltmann *et al.* 2012; Almany *et al.* 2017; Unglaub *et al.* 2021) whereas the use of SNP markers is still relatively rare (e.g. birds: Aguillon *et al.* 2017; butterflies: Fountain *et al.* 2018; fishes: Feutry *et al.* 2017; Beacham *et al.* 2022).

ESTIMATING GENE FLOW INTENSITY AND DISTANCE USING NEXT GENERATION SEQUENCING

NGS approaches to quantify gene flow

Genetic tools have been historically designed to infer gene flow (Wright 1943; Slatkin 1981). Many of the currently available methods have been originally designed for microsatellite DNA data and were then adapted to be used with SNP data. Some of these approaches allow quantification of gene flow patterns at historical timescales (e.g. coalescent and forward approaches) whereas other enable estimating more contemporary gene flow (e.g. identity-by-descent approaches). Landscape genetic/genomic methods provide a framework to evaluate the influence of landscape features on gene flow and to identify physical barriers shaping population genetic structure.

Isolation-by-distance

Both movement capacity and behaviour of propagules (or of their dispersal vectors) generally make gene flow a spatially limited process, leading to spatial autocorrelation in the distribution of allelic frequencies (Wright 1943). Inter-individual or inter-population genetic measures of relatedness tend to decrease with distance, a process known as isolation-by-distance (IBD; Wright 1943). IBD is usually assessed through the regression of pairwise genetic distances (e.g. F_{ST}) against geographic distances, which allows estimating absolute or relative average long-term dispersal distances, provided that populations are at migration-drift equilibrium (see Glossary) and that both population sizes and gene flow are spatially homogeneous. Assuming that local densities were properly estimated, the slope of the regression of $F_{ST}/(1-F_{ST})$ values against geographic distances may for instance allow inferring the absolute mean axial parent–offspring dispersal distance (Rousset 1997; Rousset and Billiard 2000). Alternatively, the distance thresholds at which pairwise correlations become null in spatial correlograms (Sokal and Oden 1978) may be compared across distinct genetic datasets and hence under certain conditions interpreted as estimates of the relative – rather than absolute – spatial extents of gene flow (Vekemans and Hardy 2004). Studying IBD is an excellent alternative to direct approaches in systems where capture-mark-recapture or telemetry is not an option. For instance, Filipović et al. (2020) successfully determined the mean dispersal distance of the mosquito *Aedes aegypti*, a major arboviral vector, as 45 m, with a 10% probability of dispersal greater than 100 m. Other examples can be found for instance in fishes (Puebla et al. 2009, De Keyzer et al. 2019) and reptiles (Wen et al. 2021).

Migration rate, *m*

An early genetic approach to estimating migration rate (*m* in the population genetic literature) relies on the use of Wright's F-statistics to measure correlation of allele frequencies within and among populations. These statistics were developed under the *island model*, a theoretical model in which each population is made of the same effective number of individuals N_e (or **effective population size**) and receives and provides the same number of immigrants at a rate *m* per generation (symmetric migration). Under this migration-drift equilibrium scenario, there is no selection or mutation and $F_{ST} \approx 1/(4N_e m+1)$ (Wright 1943). This relationship can be used to estimate $N_e m = 1/4(1/F_{ST}-1)$ the product of the migration rate and the effective population size. This approach has been fundamental to study the movement of lineages with geographic distances under the coalescent theory (section 'Coalescent and forward approaches') and to understand patterns of IBD (section 'Isolation-by-distance'). Nevertheless, the number of assumptions in the above equation makes its interpretation far from straightforward (Whitlock and McCauley 1999; Marko and Hart 2011). Moreover, low F_{ST} can result from either large *Ne* or small *m* (Waples and Gaggiotti 2006) making it necessary to distinguish effective population size from migration. From an applied perspective and given the body of research related to the above-mentioned limits, we caution against a literal interpretation of F_{ST} in terms of dispersal and against its use for making a direct link with any dispersal process. Fortunately, improved methods have been developed for simultaneously estimating both *Ne* and *m* as presented below.

Coalescent and forward approaches

Coalescent theory describes the movement of lineages as one moves backward in time. Development of the coalescent theory by Kingman (1982) has enabled the emergence of methods to infer population genetic parameters including the migration rate, *m*. When applied to a small number of loci, the coalescent theory, as well as F_{ST}-based methods, provide information about gene genealogy in the deep past. It is therefore informative about patterns of historical migration on long evolutionary time scales (in the order of N_e generations). This approach has been developed initially under the isolation with migration framework (IM) (Wakeley 1996). Recent improvement now allows inferring historical migration under more realistic demographic histories (reviewed in Cayuela et al. 2018). Furthermore, developments in approximate bayesian computation (ABC) combined with the flexibility of coalescent simulations enable the implementation of models estimating migration rates among multiple populations connected by gene flow (Beaumont 2019). For instance, recent anthropogenic hybridisation between domesticated and wild cats could be inferred with ABC with a surprising precision with ABC applied on RAD-sequencing data (Howard-McCombe et al. 2021). However, it is worth mentioning that ABC approaches generally rely on the use of summary statistics (e.g. F_{ST}, π, θ) and therefore remain limited to characterising historical gene flow events. Machine learning methods exploit the raw genotype data, bypassing the compressing step incurred by the use of summary statistics. For instance, Battey *et al.* (2020) developed a neural network to infer the location of individuals based on unphased diploid genotypes and applied their methods to *Plasmodium* parasites, *Anopheles* mosquitoes, and *Homo sapiens*. Their work takes advantage of the correlation between the genealogy and geography to infer the location of 'spatial pedigrees', which has been described in great detail by Bradburd and Ralph (2019; see Box 22.1). Similarly, Osmond and Coop (2021) developed a method to infer recent dispersal and locate genetic ancestors. Applying their method to the plant *Arabidopsis thaliana*, they were able to infer recent long-distance dispersal. This important progress is made possible by the availability of whole genome sequence data and progress in forward simulation of whole genomes across geographic landscapes (Haller and Messer 2019). They make it possible to move beyond characterising dispersal between discrete populations connected by discrete migration events to continuously distributed samples of individuals characterised by a distribution of dispersal distances across recent times. Combining IBD theory and coalescent simulation, Aguillon *et al.* (2017) were able to infer a signal of IBD with dispersal distances ranging from 500 m to 10 km in Florida scrub-jays. While appealing, the use of these methods remained relatively limited due to ongoing progress in methodological development and scarce sequencing data available outside of a few well studied systems. Therefore, while these methods may be practically useful in the future, they are not yet fully relevant for managers with limited budget and sequencing data.

Box 22.1: Illustration of the concept of spatial pedigree by Bradburd and Ralph (2019) and its potential use for wildlife management

The spatial pedigree can be used to track the spatial distribution of genetic ancestors across the geographic landscape at different time points (Bradburd and Ralph 2019). In theory, and with dense enough sampling and whole genome data, it should be possible to infer whether the position of a genetic ancestor has greatly changed in recent time. This information could then be used to draw correlations with human alterations of the connectivity landscape or infer change in the distribution of natural barriers to dispersal. The spatial pedigree has recently been used to infer long range dispersal in *Arabidopsis thaliana* (Osmond and Coop 2021) or to identify ancestors and infer dispersal in three different species (Battey *et al.* 2020).

Figures were taken from Bradburd and Ralph (2019) based on simulation of a spatial pedigree. Figure (a) provides an example of a pedigree with one modern day sample with its ancestors (maternal in red hues and paternal in blue hues, dashed line = mating; solid line = parentage). Figure (b) shows the geographic distribution of individuals and the spatial pedigree. The plane in the spatial pedigree corresponds to a sampled region in non-overlapping generations. Each dot displays the birth location of each individual. The pedigree of the focal individual is highlighted back through time and across space. If there is a strong change in connectivity (for instance due to landscape artificialisation) associated with an alteration of the population demography, variation in pedigree through space and time is expected.

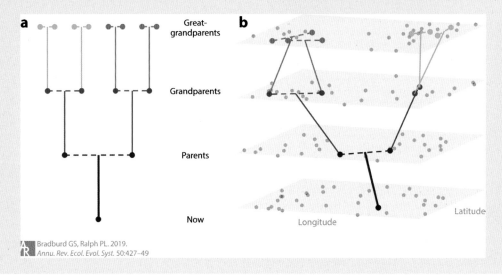

Bradburd GS, Ralph PL. 2019. *Annu. Rev. Ecol. Evol. Syst.* 50:427–49

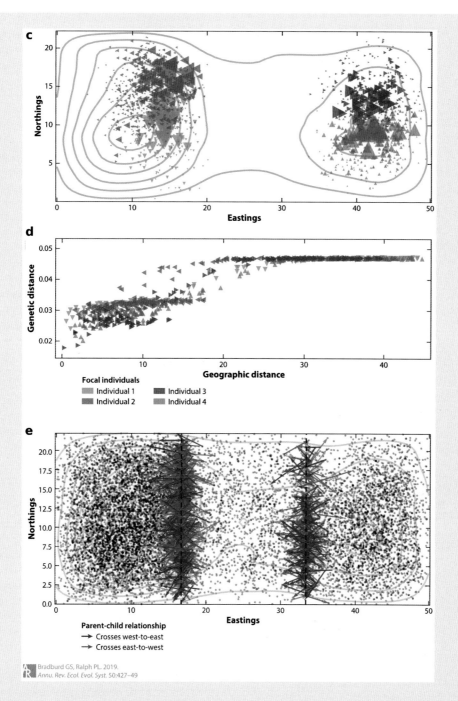

Bradburd GS, Ralph PL. 2019.
Annu. Rev. Ecol. Evol. Syst. 50:427–49

Figure (c) shows a map of four focal individuals along with their close genealogical relatives, each represented by a different colour with their geographical location. The triangle size is proportional to the expected proportion of genome shared. Figure (d) displays the positive relationship between genetic distance and geographic distance for the four focal individuals and 100 other individuals corresponding to panel a). Figure (e) shows the dispersal flow (i.e. dispersal events at each generation) across the two valleys separated by a given boundary on the same continuous map; all individuals from Figure (a) are shown as small dots at approximately eight generations and every parent–child relationship crossing a dotted line is represented by red arrow for west-to-east crosses and blue arrow for east-to-west crosses.

Spatial pedigrees is an area of active research and a promising approach to study the influence of landscape modifications (e.g. habitat fragmentation and loss) and conservation management (restoration of ecological corridors) on fine-scale dispersal movement across multiple generations.

Identity-by-descent blocks

The decreasing cost of whole genome sequencing enables the analysis of long continuous tracks of the genome known as haplotype blocks (reviewed in Browning and Browning 2012; Leitwein *et al.* 2020). These tracks, when unbroken by recombination, form large blocks whose size is gradually reduced at each generation of reproduction (Leitwein *et al.* 2020). Therefore, it is possible to study the distribution of track length between hybridising populations to evaluate the timescale and intensity of recent gene flow (Pool and Nielsen 2009; Gravel 2012). Similarly, blocks that are identical-by-descent (i.e. haplotypes inherited t generations ago from a common ancestor by a pair of individuals) can be used to infer migration rates (m) on recent time scales (Browning and Browning 2012; Palamara *et al.* 2012). The length of a segment decreases approximately at a rate $1/t$ and can therefore provide information on dispersal from a few tens of generations ago. A potentially useful method was developed recently to infer recent dispersal distance using these identity-by-descent blocks (Ringbauer *et al.* 2017). Similarly, Al-Asadi *et al.* (2019) developed maps of population effective size and migration rate at different time periods. The accuracy of the inference from these methods is still coarse and will be affected by the population demographic history, suggesting that substantial methodological improvement could be made in the future. While promising, to the best of our knowledge, the methods of Ringbauer *et al.* (2017) and Al-Asadi *et al.* (2019) have not been deployed beyond humans, due to the lack of genomic resources in managed species or species with conservation issues. Nonetheless, an interesting approach based on admixture tracts has been developed and used in an exploited species, the Atlantic and Mediterranean sea bass, as exemplified in Box 22.2. Overall, approaches based on identity-by-descent blocks could be used to measure contemporary dispersal and recent changes in genetic connectivity (for instance due with anthropogenic factors) among populations without suffering the limitations associated with F_{st}-based measures. These methods could therefore be of high relevance to best manage populations and improve opportunity for gene flow between isolated patches having undergone strong human-driven fragmentation.

INVESTIGATING THE INFLUENCE OF ENVIRONMENT ON TRANSIENCE AND SUBSEQUENT GENE FLOW USING NGS APPROACHES

The transience phase of dispersal may be affected by various between-patch processes such as habitat fragmentation or predation (e.g. Fahrig 2007; Bonnot *et al.* 2013), in turn influencing gene flow and spatial genetic structures. Two main kinds of tools may be considered to indirectly investigate these processes, namely boundary-based and link-based methods (Wagner and Fortin 2013). Because of their genome-wide distribution, SNPs may provide a better spatiotemporal resolution than markers with lower genome coverage (e.g. microsatellites) in the detection of weak and/or recent landscape-driven changes in dispersal patterns (McCartney-Melstad *et al.* 2018; Maigret *et al.* 2020), provided only neutral markers are considered (Storfer *et al.* 2018; but see Landguth and Balkenhol 2012).

Boundary-based approaches

Boundary-based methods are primarily used to spatially delineate populations through the detection of significant edges between genetic entities (Jacquez *et al.* 2000) or through the identification of homogeneous genetic clusters, with and without assumptions about underlying population genetic models (i.e. markers are at both Hardy-Weinberg and linkage equilibrium, see Glossary; Jombart *et al.* 2008, 2009; François and Durand 2010). Once mapped, inferred genetic boundaries can be visually or statistically examined with respect to landscape features so as to identify potential barriers to gene flow (Balkenhol *et al.* 2009). For instance, LaCava *et al.* (2021) used both principal component analysis (PCA) and Bayesian clustering to spatially delineate three admixed genetic groups in the mule deer *Odocoileus hemionus*. They then used a link-based approach to assess landscape functional connectivity both within each group and across groups. They revealed important regional variations in functional connectivity in that species, with gene flow in some groups being only limited by IBD, whereas gene flow in other groups were constrained by elevation, vegetation cover and/or anthropogenic infrastructures such as highways.

Link-based approaches

Link-based methods are used to assess the influence of landscape heterogeneity on genetic differentiation between habitat patches, here considered a proxy for extent of gene flow. Link-based methods generally rely on the statistical comparison of pairwise matrices and are designed to explicitly take the inherent non-independence of pairwise data into consideration. The primary frameworks are the Mantel test (Mantel 1967) and its various extensions and refinements (e.g. Smouse *et al.* 1986; Ferrier *et al.* 2007; Crabot *et al.* 2019), the maximum-likelihood population-effects model (MLPE; Clarke *et al.* 2002; Selkoe *et al.* 2010; Van Strien *et al.* 2012), non-linear Bayesian or machine learning algorithms (e.g. Bradburd *et al.* 2013; Peterman 2018; Box 22.3) and causal models (Fourtune *et al.* 2018). Pairwise genetic distances (response matrix) may be computed at the individual or at the population level from a stratified random sampling design (Anderson 2010; Storfer *et al.* 2018). When the sampling units are populations, a limitation of link-based methods is that they are only valid under the strict assumption of equal effective population sizes, or once the spatial heterogeneity in drift has been taken into account (e.g. Murphy *et al.* 2010; Prunier *et al.* 2017). The use of genome-wide SNPs may allow increasing the number of sampling locations and thus optimising the spatial sampling design (Prunier *et al.* 2013) since reliable allelic frequencies may be obtained from a reduced number of samples from each deme (Willing *et al.* 2012). Landscape distances (predictor matrices) represent the probability of transience between sampling locations under the hypotheses of IBD (e.g. Euclidean distances) and/or isolation-by-resistance (IBR; e.g. distances based on least-cost-paths or circuit theory; McRae and Beier 2007). In the latter case, different

approaches may be considered to assign resistance values to landscape features (Spear *et al.* 2010; Peterman *et al.* 2019) and to take spatial autocorrelation into account (e.g. Dray *et al.* 2006; Arjona *et al.* 2020). Linked-based methods using SNP markers have been deployed to assess the influence of landscape configuration on patterns of gene flow in a diversity of organisms, such as mammals (Kozakiewicz *et al.* 2019; LaCava *et al.* 2021), insects (Trense *et al.* 2021; Dudaniec *et al.* 2022), amphibians (Ferreira *et al.* 2020), and reptiles (Maigret *et al.* 2020) (see also Box 22.3). For instance, Creel *et al.* (2019) used RAD sequencing data and Mantel tests to compare the impact of anthropogenic activities as measured from a spatial Human Footprint Index on functional connectivity in two interacting large African carnivores, the lion (*Panthera leo*), a dominant competitor, and the African wild dog (*Lycaon pictus*), a subordinate competitor. They found a much stronger impact of anthropogenic activities on patterns of gene flow in lions than in African wild dogs, in line with the hypothesis that subordinate species are able (and adapted) to cross unfavourable landscape areas to reduce competition with dominant species.

Box 22.2: Using admixture tracts to infer dispersal distance: case study of Duranton *et al.* (2019)

Duranton *et al.* (2019) used the distribution of admixture tracts to infer dispersal distance in the European sea bass (*Dicentrarchus labrax*) within the Mediterranean Sea (the figure below, panel (a)). The authors considered individuals from the eastern Mediterranean Sea (orange circle, in panel (a)) and from the western Mediterranean Sea (red circle). Admixture between Atlantic (red chromosomes in panel (b)) and Mediterranean (yellow in panel (b)) sea bass lineages resulted in the introgression of Atlantic tracts in the Mediterranean Sea (panel (b), red arrows display the diffusion process). As shown in

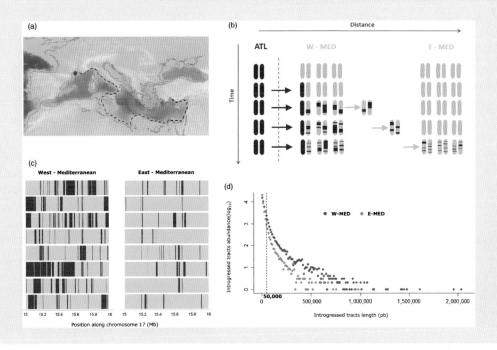

panel (b), the blocks of foreign ancestry are shortened by recombination during the diffusion process of the Atlantic block from the west to the east (yellow arrow) of the Mediterranean Sea, enabling the estimation of effective dispersal. One individual (two chromosomes) is represented in the Atlantic and three-individuals (six chromosomes) are represented in western and eastern populations. As expected, due to recombination (see panel (c)), the distribution of **ancestry tracts** from Atlantic population (red) to the Mediterranean (yellow) populations along chromosome 17 differs between the western Mediterranean (W-MED) and eastern Mediterranean (E-MED) populations. The abundance of tracts was negatively correlated with their length (panel (d)) in both the W-MED and E-MED populations, with shorter tracts expected to provide information on a longer time-scale. To estimate recent dispersal, Duranton *et al.* limited their analyses to tracks longer than 50kb (vertical dotted line in panel (d)). From an applied point of view, this study emphasises that the refined knowledge of dispersal and connectivity provided by the analysis of admixture tracts may help delineate Marine Protected Areas in a fish with high commercial value.

INVESTIGATING THE INFLUENCE OF ENVIRONMENT ON EMIGRATION–IMMIGRATION AND SUBSEQUENT GENE FLOW

Methods used to study the transience phase of dispersal usually rely on the assumption of random gene flow, all individuals being considered equally likely to disperse (Edelaar and Bolnick 2012). However, individuals may make informed choices, deciding to leave a patch (emigration) and/or to settle in a new one (immigration) depending on both their internal state and their perception of local environment (e.g. local carrying capacity or patch quality; Edelaar *et al.* 2008; Clobert *et al.* 2009). Furthermore, settlement may fail because of local environment or sexual selection acting upon some immigrants (Nosil *et al.* 2005). Understanding the whole dispersal process thus implies disentangling the influence of these at-site mechanisms on the spatial distribution of genome-wide allelic frequencies from the influence of among-site landscape processes impacting the transience phase. The isolation-by-environment (IBE) framework states that neutral pairwise genetic distances should increase with environmental differences between patches because of the non-randomness of immigration, whatever the processes operating during transience (Wang *et al.* 2013; Wang and Bradburd 2014). That is, organisms are most likely to move between similar environments (habitat matching choice; Edelaar *et al.* 2008) or may fail to settle in environments that differ from their original one (local adaptation). IBE can be assessed using linked-based statistical analyses, by measuring the effect of pairwise IBE metrics on pairwise genetic distances, in addition to classical IBD and/or IBR pairwise metrics (e.g. Sexton *et al.* 2014; Murray *et al.* 2019). For instance, Fenker *et al.* (2021) used SNP markers to explore whether dispersal was limited by geographic distance (IBD), geographic barriers (IBR) and/ or environmental heterogeneity (IBE) in several co-distributed lizard taxa from the topographically and climatically complex monsoonal tropics of Australia. They found that IBE was the strongest predictor of genetic divergence in all taxa, with both temperature and precipitation acting as factors limiting dispersal, suggesting patterns of local adaptation. By considering both at-site (nodes) and among-site (edges) processes within a network-based analysis, gravity models (Fotheringham and O'Kelly 1989) allow identifying the respective drivers of emigration (e.g. patch productivity) and immigration (e.g. predation) and disentangling their influence and that of transience on spatial patterns of genetic differentiation (Murphy *et al.* 2010; Parsley *et al.* 2020). Gravity models might also be used to rule out the influence of spatial heterogeneity in effective population sizes, a prerequisite for the proper interpretation of genetic differentiation in terms of gene flow.

FUTURE DIRECTIONS

We have provided a synthetic snapshot of the most recently developed analytical methods to quantify dispersal, with a specific emphasis on wildlife management issues. Among the approaches that are currently under active development, long identical-by-descent blocks and migrant tracts appear highly promising as they can potentially provide information on gene flow (and population size) on recent timescales both within spatially structured populations and among diverging populations (reviewed in Leitwein *et al.* 2020). Recent timescales are likely the most relevant for conservation geneticists who may want to investigate how environmental factors constraint gene flow and effective sizes, identify population boundaries, and define management areas (see the examples in Boxes 22.2 and 22.3). These approaches stand in contrast to methods relying on the site frequency spectrum (Gutenkunst *et al.* 2009), which provides information on long evolutionary timescales (in the order of N_e generations).

One of the main limitations of identity-by-descent methods is the need for large amount of genetic data, namely dense SNP data from whole genome sequencing or SNP arrays, and eventually a linkage map (e.g. Ringbauer *et al.* 2017). However, these methods can be used with a small number of spatially geolocalised individuals in the study area, which can be useful in the context of conservation programs on rare/elusive species. Successful application of identity-by-descent methods will certainly necessitate extensive collaboration between practitioners and research laboratories. To the best of our knowledge, the

study of Duranton *et al.* (2019) is the only case study using **identity-by-descent tracts** to infer dispersal and connectivity in a context of wildlife management (stock management of the Atlantic sea bass in the Mediterranean basin), as detailed in Box 22.2. However, with decreasing cost of sequencing technologies, this approach could be applied in the near future to many species of conservation concerns. Indeed, recent technological progress currently makes long read sequencing available for conservation genomics studies at relatively low cost (Browning and Browning 2011; Meier *et al.* 2021).

Box 22.3: Using linked-based methods to quantify and predict population connectivity of an outbreaking forest insect pest: case study of Larroque *et al.* (2022)

The eastern spruce budworm (*Choristoneura fumiferana*) is a lepidopteran that periodically outbreaks (~ every 35 years) and defoliates millions of hectares of forests in North America, with severe socio-economic consequences. In Quebec, the last outbreak started in 2006. Larroque *et al.* (2022) investigated the spatial environmental determinants of dispersal in this species using 3562 SNP loci from 447 larvae covering most of the outbreak area. They optimised landscape resistance surfaces given pairwise measures of genetic differentiation using the machine learning algorithm ResistanceGA (Peterman 2018), and found that landscape connectivity decreased drastically when mean daily July precipitation was less than 50mm (figure below, panel (a)), suggesting that water stress may hinder both dispersal and the probability of success of settlement through survival. Mapping the most likely paths of the spread of the outbreak given present environmental conditions, they identified one large high connectivity area surrounded by two low-connectivity areas to the East and West (panel (b)), suggesting that the western part of Quebec could potentially act as a barrier with Ontario. Similarly, mapping the most likely dispersal paths given expected environmental conditions in the next outbreak (~2040), they predicted an increase in connectivity in the western part of Quebec (panel (c)), paving the way for targeted pest control policies in well-connected but not yet attacked areas, through pre-emptive treatments such as spraying or harvest.

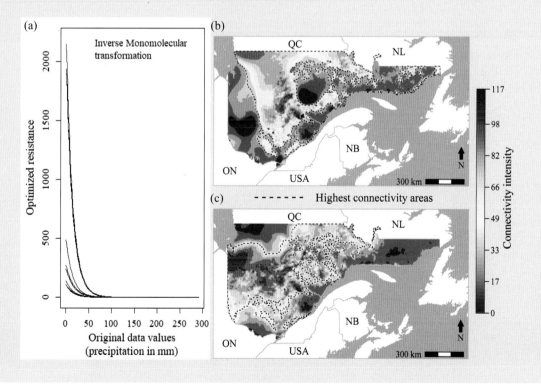

Lastly, we emphasise the critical importance of genomic marker choice to investigate dispersal and gene flow. The vast majority of the methods described above rely on population genetic concepts that hold true under neutrality. However, the neutrality hypothesis is often neglected by genomic studies that quantify gene flow or assess landscape connectivity from a mix of neutral and adaptive markers. We argue that gene flow estimates (rate and distance) should preferentially be performed using markers that are virtually non-affected by selection to meet the neutrality assumption of population genetic theory. This step of marker selection is especially important in study systems (e.g. many marine organisms) with high gene flow and/or large effective population size since adaptive markers may have a strong contribution to population genetic structure in these systems (Xuereb *et al.* 2021). When a reference genome is available in the studied species, the filtering of non-neutral markers can be achieved by removing the SNPs that are located within the sequence of protein-coding genes and regulatory regions, and considering the extent of linkage disequilibrium around these genomic regions and keeping SNPs in the most highly recombining regions (Pouyet *et al.* 2018; see also Chapter 14). When no reference genome is available, putatively adaptive SNPs associated with environmental variables can be identified using standard genome scan approaches (e.g. F_{ST}-based analysis) such as BayPass (Gautier 2015) or mixed models (implemented in LFMM2, Caye *et al.* 2019). We recommend employing conservative thresholds when delimiting putatively neutral and adaptive markers since processes such as linked selection and biased gene conversion may affect neutrality along large stretches of the genome (Pouyet *et al.* 2018; see also Johri *et al.* 2022 for a review and recommendations).

CONCLUSION

Dispersal plays a central role in population dynamics and viability and is therefore of critical importance for wildlife management. In many organisms, quantifying dispersal using direct observations is a complicated task and genetic approaches have proven particularly useful for studying gene flow resulting from dispersal. For a long time, studies on gene flow suffered from a lack of power to assess the genetic structure of populations due to a limited number of markers. Twenty years ago, the advent of NGS approaches – generating thousands of SNP markers – revolutionised our ability to study dispersal and gene flow, especially in the context of conservation operations, natural resource management, and pest control programs. The ongoing decrease in sequencing costs allows assembling reference genomes and producing large amounts of genomic data that are particularly useful to analyse dispersal and its genetic consequences at different spatial and temporal scales. NGS approaches provide wildlife managers with robust tools that may improve the delimitation of conservation and harvesting areas, notably in species showing seemingly weak genetic structure. In addition, these methods allow estimating accurate dispersal parameters even when the number of available samples (i.e. individuals) is small, which is very often the case in rare, endangered species.

DISCUSSION TOPICS

1. A new road is proposed to be built through a wild landscape. The developers will install wildlife bridges that they think will enable animals to safely cross the road. Suggest an experimental design for a genomics investigation (including sampling and methods of analysis) to determine if: a) the road reduces animal movements; b) the road reduces gene flow; c) the bridges are used by wildlife to cross the road.

REFERENCES

Aguillon SM, Fitzpatrick JW, Bowman R, Schoech SJ, Clark AG, *et al.* (2017) Deconstructing isolation-by-distance: The genomic consequences of limited dispersal. *PLoS Genetics* **13**, e1006911.

Al-Asadi H, Petkova D, Stephens M, Novembre J (2019) Estimating recent migration and population-size surfaces. *PLOS Genetics* **15**, e1007908.

Alexander DH, NovembreJ, Lange K (2009) Fast model-based estimation of ancestry in unrelated individuals. *Genome Research* **19**, 1655–1664.

Almany GR, Planes S, Thorrold SR, Berumen ML, Bode M, *et al.* (2017) Larval fish dispersal in a coral-reef seascape. *Nature Ecology & Evolution* **1**, 1–7.

Anderson CD (2010) Effects of movement and mating patterns on gene flow among overwintering hibernacula of the Timber Rattlesnake (*Crotalus horridus*). *Copeia* **1**, 54–61.

Anderson EC, Waples RS, Kalinowski ST (2008) An improved method for predicting the accuracy of genetic stock identification. *Canadian Journal of Fisheries and Aquatic Sciences* **65**, 1475–1486.

Arjona Y, Fernández-López J, Navascués M, Alvarez N, Nogales M, *et al.* (2020) Linking seascape with landscape genetics: Oceanic currents favour colonization across the Galápagos Islands by a coastal plant. *Journal of Biogeography* **47**, 2622–2633.

Baguette M, Van Dyck H (2007) Landscape connectivity and animal behavior: Functional grain as a key determinant for dispersal. *Landscape Ecology* **22**, 1117–1129.

Baguette M, Blanchet S, Legrand D, Stevens VM, Turlure C (2013) Individual dispersal, landscape connectivity and ecological networks. *Biological Reviews* **88**, 310–326.

Balkenhol N, Waits LP, Dezzani RJ (2009) Statistical approaches in landscape genetics: An evaluation of methods for linking landscape and genetic data. *Ecography* **32**, 818–830.

Battey CJ, Ralph PL, Kern AD (2020) Predicting geographic location from genetic variation with deep neural networks. *ELife* **9**, e54507.

Beacham TD, Jonsen K, Sutherland BJG, Lynch C, Rondeau EB (2022) Assessment of mixed-stock fisheries and hatchery broodstocks for coho salmon in British Columbia, Canada via parentage-based tagging and genetic stock identification. *Fisheries Research* **245**, 106136.

Beaumont MA (2019) Approximate bayesian computation. *Annual Review of Statistics and Its Application* **6**, 379–403.

Blouin MS (2003) DNA-based methods for pedigree reconstruction and kinship analysis in natural populations. *Trends in Ecology & Evolution* **18**, 503–511.

Bohonak AJ (1999) Dispersal, gene flow, and population structure. *The Quarterly Review of Biology* **74**, 21–45.

Bonnot N, Morellet N, Verheyden H, Cargnelutti B, Lourtet B, *et al.* (2013) Habitat use under predation risk: Hunting, roads and human dwellings influence the spatial behaviour of roe deer. *European Journal of Wildlife Research* **59**, 185–193.

Bonte D, Van Dyck H, Bullock JM, Coulon A, Delgado M, *et al.* (2012) Costs of dispersal. *Biological Reviews* **87**, 290–312.

Boulinier T, McCoy KD, Yoccoz NG, Gasparini J, Tveraa T (2008) Public information affects breeding dispersal in a colonial bird: kittiwakes cue on neighbours. *Biology Letters* **4**, 538–540.

Bradburd GS, Ralph PL, Coop GM (2013) Disentangling the effects of geographic and ecological isolation on genetic differentiation: Isolation by geographic and ecological distance. *Evolution* **67**, 3258–3273.

Bradburd GS, Coop GM, Ralph PL (2018) Inferring continuous and discrete population genetic structure across space. *Genetics* **210**, 33–52.

Bradburd GS, Ralph PL (2019) Spatial population genetics: It's about time. *Annual Review of Ecology, Evolution, and Systematics* **50**, 427–449.

Broquet T, Petit EJ (2009) Molecular estimation of dispersal for ecology and population genetics. *Annual Review of Ecology, Evolution, and Systematics* **40**, 193–216.

Browning BL, Browning SR (2011) A fast, powerful method for detecting identity by descent. *The American Journal of Human Genetics* **88**, 173–182.

Browning SR, Browning BL (2012) Identity by descent between distant relatives: detection and applications. *Annual Review of Genetics* **46**, 617–633.

Caye K, Jay F, Michel O, François O (2018) Fast inference of individual admixture coefficients using geographic data. *The Annals of Applied Statistics* **12**, 586–608.

Caye K, Jumentier B, Lepeule J, François O (2019) LFMM 2: Fast and accurate inference of gene-environment associations in genome-wide studies. *Molecular Biology and Evolution* **36**, 852–860.

Cayuela H, Rougemont Q, Prunier JG, Moore JS, Clobert J, *et al.* (2018) Demographic and genetic approaches to study dispersal in wild animal populations: A methodological review. *Molecular Ecology* **27**, 3976–4010.

Cayuela H, Boualit L, Laporte M, Prunier JG, Preiss F, *et al.* (2019) Kin-dependent dispersal influences relatedness and genetic structuring in a lek system. *Oecologia* **191**, 97–112.

Cayuela H, Prunier JG, Laporte M, Gippet JM, Boualit L, *et al.* (2021) Demography, genetics, and decline of a spatially structured population of lekking bird. *Oecologia* **195**, 117–129.

Clarke RT, Rothery P, Raybould AF (2002) Confidence limits for regression relationships between distance matrices: Estimating gene flow with distance. *Journal of Agricultural, Biological, and Environmental Statistics* **7**, 361–372.

Clobert J, Ims RA, Rousset F (2004) Causes, mechanisms and consequences of dispersal. In *Ecology, Genetics and Evolution of Metapopulations*. (Eds I Hansk, OE Gaggiotti) pp. 307–335. Academic Press.

Clobert J, Le Galliard J-F, Cote J, Meylan S, Massot M (2009) Informed dispersal, heterogeneity in animal dispersal syndromes and the dynamics of spatially structured populations. *Ecology Letters* **12**, 197–209.

Corander J, Waldmann P, Sillanpää MJ (2003) Bayesian analysis of genetic differentiation between populations. *Genetics* **163**, 367–374.

Cote J, Bestion E, Jacob S, Travis J, Legrand D, *et al.* (2017) Evolution of dispersal strategies and dispersal syndromes in fragmented landscapes. *Ecography* **40**, 56–73.

Coyne JA, Orr HA (2004) *Speciation*. Sinauer & Associates, Sunderland, MA, USA.

Crabot J, Clappe S, Dray S, Datry T (2019) Testing the Mantel statistic with a spatially-constrained permutation procedure. *Methods in Ecology and Evolution* **10**, 532–540.

Creel S, Spong G, Becker M, Simukonda C, Norman A, *et al.* (2019) Carnivores, competition and genetic connectivity in the Anthropocene. *Scientific Reports* **9**, 16339.

De Keyzer ELR, De Corte Z, Van Steenberge M, Raeymaekers JAM, Calboli FCF, *et al.* (2019) First genomic study on Lake Tanganyika sprat *Stolothrissa tanganicae*: A lack of population structure calls for integrated management of this important fisheries target species. *BMC Evolutionary Biology* **19**, 6.

Dobzhansky T (1943) Genetics of natural populations IX. Temporal changes in the composition of populations of Drosophila pseudoobscura. *Genetics* **28**, 162.

Dodds KG, McEwan JC, Brauning R, van Stijn TC, Rowe SJ, *et al.* (2019) Exclusion and genomic relatedness methods for assignment of parentage using genotyping-by-sequencing data. *G3: Genes, Genomes, Genetics* **9**, 3239–3247.

Dray S, Legendre P, Peres-Neto PR (2006) Spatial modelling: A comprehensive framework for principal coordinate analysis of neighbour matrices (PCNM). *Ecological Modelling* **196**, 483–493.

Dudaniec RY, Carey AR, Svensson EI, Hansson B, Yong CJ, *et al.* (2022) Latitudinal clines in sexual selection, sexual size dimorphism and sex-specific genetic dispersal during a poleward range expansion. *Journal of Animal Ecology* **91**, 1104–1118.

Duranton M, Bonhomme F, Gagnaire PA (2019) The spatial scale of dispersal revealed by admixture tracts. *Evolutionary Applications* **12**, 1743–1756.

Edelaar P, Siepielski AM, Clobert J (2008) Matching habitat choice causes directed gene flow: A neglected dimension in evolution and ecology. *Evolution* **62**, 2462–2472.

Edelaar P, Bolnick DI (2012) Non-random gene flow: An under-appreciated force in evolution and ecology. *Trends in Ecology & Evolution* **27**, 659–665.

Fahrig L (2007) Non-optimal animal movement in human-altered landscapes. *Functional Ecology* **21**, 1003–1015.

Faubet P, Waples RS, Gaggiotti OE (2007) Evaluating the performance of a multilocus Bayesian method for the estimation of migration rates. *Molecular Ecology* **16**, 1149–1166.

Fenker J, Tedeschi LG, Melville J, Moritz C (2021) Predictors of phylogeographic structure among codistributed taxa across the complex Australian monsoonal tropics. *Molecular Ecology* **30**, 4276–4291.

Ferreira AS, Lima AP, Jehle R, Ferrão M, Stow A (2020) The influence of environmental variation on the genetic structure of a poison frog distributed across continuous Amazonian rainforest. *Journal of Heredity* **111**, 457–470.

Ferrier S, Manion G, Elith J, Richardson K (2007) Using generalized dissimilarity modelling to analyse and predict patterns of beta diversity in regional biodiversity assessment. *Diversity and Distributions* **13**, 252–264.

Feutry P, Berry O, Kyne PM, Pillans RD, Hillary RM, *et al.* (2017) Inferring contemporary and historical genetic connectivity from juveniles. *Molecular Ecology* **26**, 444–456.

Filipović I, Hapuarachchi HC, Tien W-P, Razak MABA, Lee C, *et al.* (2020) Using spatial genetics to quantify mosquito dispersal for control programs. *BMC Biology* **18**, 104.

Flanagan SP, Forester BR, Latch EK, Aitken SN, Hoban S (2018) Guidelines for planning genomic assessment and monitoring of locally adaptive variation to inform species conservation. *Evolutionary Applications* **11**, 1035–1052.

Fotheringham AS, O'Kelly ME (1989) *Spatial Interaction Models: Formulations and Applications.* Kluwer Academic Publishers, Dordrecht, Netherlands.

Fountain T, Husby A, Nonaka E, DiLeo MF, Korhonen JH, *et al.* (2018) Inferring dispersal across a fragmented landscape using reconstructed families in the Glanville fritillary butterfly. *Evolutionary Applications* **11**, 287–297.

Fourtune L, Prunier JG, Paz-Vinas I, Loot G, Veyssière C, *et al.* (2018) Inferring causalities in landscape genetics: An extension of Wright's causal modeling to distance matrices. *The American Naturalist* **191**, 491–508.

François O, Durand E (2010) Spatially explicit Bayesian clustering models in population genetics. *Molecular Ecology Resources* **10**, 773–784.

Frantz AC, Cellina S, Krier A, Schley L, Burke T (2009) Using spatial Bayesian methods to determine the genetic structure of a continuously distributed population: Clusters or isolation by distance? *Journal of Applied Ecology* **46**, 493–505.

Frichot E, François O (2015) LEA: An R package for landscape and ecological association studies. *Methods in Ecology and Evolution* **6**, 925–929.

Gagnaire PA, Broquet T, Aurelle D, Viard F, Souissi A, *et al.* (2015) Using neutral, selected, and hitchhiker loci to assess connectivity of marine populations in the genomic era. *Evolutionary Applications* **8**, 769–786.

Galla SJ, Brown L, Couch-Lewis Y, Cubrinovska I, Eason D, *et al.* (2022) The relevance of pedigrees in the conservation genomics era. *Molecular Ecology* **31**, 41–54.

Galpern P, Peres-Neto PR, Polfus J, Manseau M (2014) MEMGENE: Spatial pattern detection in genetic distance data. *Methods in Ecology and Evolution* **5**, 1116–1120.

Gautier M (2015) Genome-wide scan for adaptive divergence and association with population-specific covariates. *Genetics* **201**, 1555–1579.

Grashei KE, Ødegård J, Meuwissen TH (2018) Using genomic relationship likelihood for parentage assignment. *Genetics Selection Evolution* **50**, 1–11.

Gravel S (2012) Population genetics models of local ancestry. *Genetics* **191**, 607–619.

Guillot G, Renaud S, Ledevin R, Michaux J, Claude J (2012) A unifying model for the analysis of phenotypic, genetic, and geographic data. *Systematic Biology* **61**, 897–911.

Gutenkunst RN, Hernandez RD, Williamson SH, Bustamante CD (2009) Inferring the joint demographic history of multiple populations from multidimensional SNP frequency data. *PLoS Genetics* **5**, e1000695.

Haller BC, Messer PW (2019) SLiM 3: Forward genetic simulations beyond the Wright–Fisher model. *Molecular Biology and Evolution* **36**, 632–637.

Hanski I (1998) Metapopulation dynamics. *Nature* **396**, 41–49.

Hanski IA, Gaggiotti OE (2004) *Ecology, Genetics and Evolution of Metapopulations.* Academic Press.

Hansson L (1991) Dispersal and connectivity in metapopulations. *Biological Journal of the Linnean Society* **42**, 89–103.

Howard-McCombe J, Ward D, Kitchener AC, Lawson D, Senn HV, *et al.* (2021) On the use of genome-wide data to model and date the time of anthropogenic hybridisation: An example from the Scottish wildcat. *Molecular Ecology* **30**, 3688–3702.

Huisman J (2017) Pedigree reconstruction from SNP data: Parentage assignment, sibship clustering and beyond. *Molecular Ecology Resources* **17**, 1009–1024.

Jacob S, Legrand D, Chaine AS, Bonte D, Schtickzelle N, *et al.* (2017) Gene flow favours local adaptation under habitat choice in ciliate microcosms. *Nature Ecology & Evolution* **1**, 1407–1410.

Jacquez GM, Maruca S, Fortin MJ (2000) From fields to objects: A review of geographic boundary analysis. *Journal of Geographical Systems* **2**, 221–241.

Jasper M, Schmidt TL, Ahmad NW, Sinkins SP, Hoffmann AA (2019) A genomic approach to inferring kinship reveals limited intergenerational dispersal in the yellow fever mosquito. *Molecular Ecology Resources* **19**, 1254–1264.

Johri P, Aquadro CF, Beaumont M, Charlesworth B, Excoffier L, *et al.* (2022) Recommendations for improving statistical inference in population genomics. *PLoS Biology* **20**, e3001669.

Jombart T, Devillard S, Dufour AB, Pontier D (2008) Revealing cryptic spatial patterns in genetic variability by a new multivariate method. *Heredity* **101**, 92–103.

Jombart T, Dray S, Dufour A-B (2009) Finding essential scales of spatial variation in ecological data: A multivariate approach. *Ecography* **32**, 161–168.

Keller LF, Waller DM (2002) Inbreeding effects in wild populations. *Trends in Ecology & Evolution* **17**, 230–241.

Kess T, Galindo J, Boulding EG (2018) Genomic divergence between Spanish *Littorina saxatilis* ecotypes unravels limited admixture and extensive parallelism associated with population history. *Ecology and Evolution* **8**, 8311–8327.

Kingman JFC (1982) The coalescent. *Stochastic Processes and their Applications* **13**, 235–248.

Kozakiewicz CP, Burridge CP, Funk WC, Salerno PE, Trumbo DR, et al. (2019) Urbanization reduces genetic connectivity in bobcats (*Lynx rufus*) at both intra– and interpopulation spatial scales. *Molecular Ecology* **28**, 5068–5085.

LaCava MEF, Gagne RB, Gustafson KD, Oyler-McCance S, Monteith KL, et al. (2021) Functional connectivity in a continuously distributed, migratory species as revealed by landscape genomics. *Ecography* **44**, 987–999.

Landguth EL, Balkenhol N (2012) Relative sensitivity of neutral versus adaptive genetic data for assessing population differentiation. *Conservation Genetics* **13**, 1421–1426.

Larroque J, Wittische J, James PMA (2022) Quantifying and predicting population connectivity of an outbreaking forest insect pest. *Landscape Ecology* **37**, 763–778.

Lawson DJ, Van Dorp L, Falush D (2018) A tutorial on how not to over-interpret STRUCTURE and ADMIXTURE bar plots. *Nature Communications* **9**, 1–11.

Leitwein M, Duranton M, Rougemont Q, Gagnaire PA, Bernatchez L (2020) Using haplotype information for conservation genomics. *Trends in Ecology & Evolution* **35**, 245–258.

Lenormand T (2002) Gene flow and the limits to natural selection. *Trends in Ecology & Evolution* **17**, 183–189.

Lepais O, Darvill BEN, O'connor S, Osborne JL, Sanderson RA, et al. (2010) Estimation of bumblebee queen dispersal distances using sibship reconstruction method. *Molecular Ecology* **19**, 819–831.

Lowe WH, Allendorf FW (2010) What can genetics tell us about population connectivity? *Molecular Ecology* **19**, 3038–3051.

Maigret TA, Cox JJ, Weisrock DW (2020) A spatial genomic approach identifies time lags and historical barriers to gene flow in a rapidly fragmenting Appalachian landscape. *Molecular Ecology* **29**, 673–685.

Manel S, Schwartz MK, Luikart G, Taberlet P (2003) Landscape genetics: combining landscape ecology and population genetics. *Trends in Ecology & Evolution* **18**, 189–197.

Manel S, Holderegger R (2013) Ten years of landscape genetics. *Trends in Ecology & Evolution* **28**(10), 614–621.

Mantel N (1967) The detection of disease clustering and a generalized regression approach. *Cancer Research* **27**, 209–220.

Marko PB, Hart MW (2011) The complex analytical landscape of gene flow inference. *Trends in Ecology & Evolution* **26**, 448–456.

Matthysen E (2012) Multicausality of dispersal: A review. In *Dispersal Ecology and Evolution*. (Eds J Clobert, M Baguette, TG Benton, JM Bullock) pp. 3–18. Oxford University Press.

Mayr E (1963) *Animal Species and Evolution*. Harvard University Press.

McCartney-Melstad E, Vu JK, Shaffer HB (2018) Genomic data recover previously undetectable fragmentation effects in an endangered amphibian. *Molecular Ecology* **27**, 4430–4443.

McRae BH, Beier P (2007) Circuit theory predicts gene flow in plant and animal populations. *Proceedings of the National Academy of Sciences* **104**, 19885–19890.

Meier JI, Salazar PA, Kučka M, Davies RW, Dréau A, et al. (2021) Haplotype tagging reveals parallel formation of hybrid races in two butterfly species. *Proceedings of the National Academy of Sciences* **118**, e2015005118.

Meirmans PG (2012) The trouble with isolation by distance. *Molecular Ecology* **21**, 2839–2846.

Meirmans PG (2014) Nonconvergence in Bayesian estimation of migration rates. *Molecular Ecology Resources* **14**, 726–733.

Morin PA, Luikart G, Wayne RK (2004) SNPs in ecology, evolution and conservation. *Trends in Ecology & Evolution* **19**, 208–216.

Moore J-S, Bourret V, Dionne M, Bradbury I, O'Reilly P, et al. (2014) Conservation genomics of anadromous Atlantic salmon across its North American range: outlier loci identify the same patterns of population structure as neutral loci. *Molecular Ecology* **23**, 5680–5697.

Murphy MA, Dezzani R, Pilliod DS, Storfer A (2010) Landscape genetics of high mountain frog metapopulations. *Molecular Ecology* **19**, 3634–3649.

Murray KD, Janes JK, Jones A, Bothwell HM, Andrew RL, et al. (2019) Landscape drivers of genomic diversity and divergence in woodland Eucalyptus. *Molecular Ecology* **28**, 5232–5247.

Nosil P, Vines TH, Funk DJ (2005) Reproductive isolation caused by natural selection against immigration from divergent habitats. *Evolution* **59**, 705–719.

Osmond MM, Coop G (2021) Estimating dispersal rates and locating genetic ancestors with genome-wide genealogies. *BioRxiv* 2021.07.13.452277; doi: 10.1101/2021.07.13.452277

Paetkau D, Slade R, Burden M, Estoup A (2004) Genetic assignment methods for the direct, real-time estimation of migration rate: a simulation-based exploration of accuracy and power. *Molecular Ecology* **13**, 55–65.

Palamara PF, Lencz T, Darvasi A, Pe'er I (2012) Length distributions of identity by descent reveal fine-scale demographic history. *The American Journal of Human Genetics* **91**, 809–822.

Parsley MB, Torres ML, Banerjee SM, Tobias ZJC, Goldberg CS, et al. (2020) Multiple lines of genetic inquiry reveal effects of local and landscape factors on an amphibian metapopulation. *Landscape Ecology* **35**, 319–335.

Peterman WE (2018) ResistanceGA: An R package for the optimization of resistance surfaces using genetic algorithms. *Methods in Ecology and Evolution* **9**, 1638–1647.

Peterman WE, Winiarski KJ, Moore CE, Carvalho CdaS, Gilbert AL, et al. (2019) A comparison of popular approaches to optimize landscape resistance surfaces. *Landscape Ecology* **34**, 2197–2208.

Pool JE, Nielsen R (2009) Inference of historical changes in migration rate from the lengths of migrant tracts. *Genetics* **181**, 711–719.

Pouyet F, Aeschbacher S, Thiéry A, Excoffier L (2018) Background selection and biased gene conversion affect more than 95% of the human genome and bias demographic inferences. *eLife* **7**, e36317.

Pritchard JK, Stephens M, Donnelly P (2000) Inference of population structure using multilocus genotype data. *Genetics* **155**, 945–959.

Prunier JG, Kaufmann B, Fenet S, Picard D, Pompanon F, et al. (2013) Optimizing the trade-off between spatial and genetic sampling efforts in patchy populations: Towards a better assessment of functional connectivity using an individual-based sampling scheme. *Molecular Ecology* **22**, 5516–5530.

Prunier JG, Dubut V, Chikhi L, Blanchet S (2017) Contribution of spatial heterogeneity in effective population sizes to the variance in pairwise measures of genetic differentiation. *Methods in Ecology and Evolution* **8**, 1866–1877.

Prunier JG, Saint-Pé K, Blanchet S, Loot G, Rey O (2021) Molecular approaches reveal weak sibship aggregation and a high dispersal propensity in a non-native fish parasite. *Ecology and Evolution* **11**, 6080–6090.

Puebla O, Bermingham E, Guichard F (2009) Estimating dispersal from genetic isolation by distance in a coral reef fish (*Hypoplectrus puella*). *Ecology* **90**, 3087–3098.

Puechmaille SJ (2016) The program structure does not reliably recover the correct population structure when sampling is uneven: subsampling and new estimators alleviate the problem. *Molecular Ecology Resources* **16**, 608–627.

Ringbauer H, Coop G, Barton NH (2017) Inferring recent demography from isolation by distance of long shared sequence blocks. *Genetics* **205**, 1335–1351.

Ronce O (2007) How does it feel to be like a rolling stone? Ten questions about dispersal evolution. *Annual Review of Ecology, Evolution, and Systematics* **38**, 231–253.

Ronce O, Clobert J (2012) In *Dispersal Syndromes. Dispersal Ecology and Evolution*. (Eds J Clobert, M Baguette, TG Benton, JM Bullock) pp. 119–138. Oxford University Press.

Rougemont Q, Carrier A, Le Luyer J, Ferchaud AL, Farrell JM, *et al.* (2019) Combining population genomics and forward simulations to investigate stocking impacts: A case study of Muskellunge (*Esox masquinongy*) from the St. Lawrence River basin. *Evolutionary Applications* **12**, 902–922.

Rougemont Q, Perrier C, Besnard AL, Lebel I, Abdallah Y, *et al.* (2022) Population genetics reveals divergent lineages and ongoing hybridization in a declining migratory fish species complex. *Heredity* **129**, 137–151.

Rousset F (1997) Genetic differentiation and estimation of gene flow from F-statistics under isolation by distance. *Genetics* **145**, 1219–1228.

Rousset F, Billiard S (2000) A theoretical basis for measures of kin selection in subdivided populations: Finite populations and localized dispersal. *Journal of Evolutionary Biology* **13**, 814–825.

Schwartz MK, McKelvey KS, Cushman SA, Luikart G (2010) Landscape genomics: a brief perspective. In *Spatial Complexity, Informatics, and Wildlife Conservation*. pp. 165–174. Springer, Tokyo.

Selkoe KA, Watson JR, White C, Horin TB, Iacchei M, *et al.* (2010) Taking the chaos out of genetic patchiness: Seascape genetics reveals ecological and oceanographic drivers of genetic patterns in three temperate reef species. *Molecular Ecology* **19**, 3708–3726.

Sexton JP, Hangartner SB, Hoffmann AA (2014) Genetic isolation by environment or distance: Which pattern of gene flow is most common? *Evolution* **68**, 1–15.

Slatkin M (1981) Estimating levels of gene flow in natural populations. *Genetics* **99**, 323–335.

Slatkin M (2017) 1. Gene Flow and Population Structure. In: *Ecological Genetics*. (Ed L Real) pp. 1–17. Princeton University Press, Princeton, NJ, USA.

Smouse PE, Long JC, Sokal RR (1986) Multiple-regression and correlation extensions of the mantel test of matrix correspondence. *Systematic Zoology* **35**, 627–632.

Snyder-Mackler N, Majoros WH, Yuan ML, Shaver AO, Gordon JB, *et al.* (2016) Efficient genome-wide sequencing and low-coverage pedigree analysis from noninvasively collected samples. *Genetics* **203**, 699–714.

Söderquist P, Elmberg J, Gunnarsson G, Thulin CG, Champagnon J, *et al.* (2017) Admixture between released and wild game birds: a changing genetic landscape in European mallards (*Anas platyrhynchos*). *European Journal of Wildlife Research* **63**(6), 1–13.

Sokal RR, Oden NL (1978) Spatial autocorrelation in Biology. 1. Methodology. *Biological Journal of the Linnean Society* **10**, 199–228.

Spear SF, Balkenhol N, Fortin M-J, Mcrae BH, Scribner K (2010) Use of resistance surfaces for landscape genetic studies: Considerations for parameterization and analysis. *Molecular Ecology* **19**, 3576–3591.

Städele V, Vigilant L (2016) Strategies for determining kinship in wild populations using genetic data. *Ecology and Evolution* **6**, 6107–6120.

Storfer A, Patton A, Fraik AK (2018) Navigating the interface between landscape genetics and landscape genomics. *Frontiers in Genetics* **9**, 68.

Sunde J, Yıldırım Y, Tibblin P, Forsman A (2020) Comparing the performance of microsatellites and RADseq in population genetic studies: Analysis of data for pike (*Esox lucius*) and a synthesis of previous studies. *Frontiers in Genetics* **11**, 218.

Taylor PD, Fahrig L, Henein K, Merriam G (1993) *Connectivity Is a Vital Element of Landscape Structure*. Oikos, 571–573.

Telfer S, Piertney SB, Dallas JF, Stewart WA, Marshall F, *et al.* (2003) Parentage assignment detects frequent and large-scale dispersal in water voles. *Molecular Ecology* **12**, 1939–1949.

Thomas CD, Kunin WE (1999) The spatial structure of populations. *Journal of Animal Ecology* **68**, 647–657.

Tigano A, Friesen VL (2016) Genomics of local adaptation with gene flow. *Molecular Ecology* **25**, 2144–2164.

Trense D, Schmidt TL, Yang Q, Chung J, Hoffmann AA, *et al.* (2021) Anthropogenic and natural barriers affect genetic connectivity in an Alpine butterfly. *Molecular Ecology* **30**, 114–130.

Unglaub B, Cayuela H, Schmidt BR, Preißler K, Glos J, *et al.* (2021) Context-dependent dispersal determines relatedness and genetic structure in a patchy amphibian population. *Molecular Ecology* **30**, 5009–5028.

van der Zee JP, Christianen MJ, Bérubé M, Nava M, Schut K, *et al.* (2021) The population genomic structure of green turtles (*Chelonia mydas*) suggests a warm-water corridor for tropical marine fauna between the Atlantic and Indian oceans during the last interglacial. *Heredity* **127**, 510–521.

Van Strien MJ, Keller D, Holderegger R (2012) A new analytical approach to landscape genetic modelling: Least-cost transect analysis and linear mixed models. *Molecular Ecology* **21**, 4010–4023.

Vekemans X, Hardy OJ (2004) New insights from fine-scale spatial genetic structure analyses in plant populations. *Molecular Ecology* **13**, 921–935.

Vu NT, Zenger KR, Silva CN, Guppy JL, Jerry DR (2021) Population structure, genetic connectivity, and signatures of local adaptation of the Giant Black tiger shrimp (*Penaeus monodon*) throughout the Indo-Pacific region. *Genome Biology and Evolution* **13**, evab214.

Wagner HH, Fortin M-J (2013) A conceptual framework for the spatial analysis of landscape genetic data. *Conservation Genetics* **14**, 253–261.

Wakeley J (1996) Distinguishing migration from isolation using the variance of pairwise differences. *Theoretical Population Biology* **49**, 369–386.

Wang IJ, Glor RE, Losos JB (2013) Quantifying the roles of ecology and geography in spatial genetic divergence. *Ecology Letters* **16**, 175–182.

Wang IJ, Bradburd GS (2014) Isolation by environment. *Molecular Ecology* **23**, 5649–5662.

Waples RS (1998) Separating the wheat from the chaff: Patterns of genetic differentiation in high gene flow species. *Journal of Heredity* **89**, 438–450.

WaplesRS, Gaggiotti O (2006) INVITED REVIEW: What is a population? An empirical evaluation of some genetic methods for identifying the number of gene pools and their degree of connectivity. *Molecular Ecology* **15**, 1419–1439.

Wei S, Li Z, Momigliano P, Fu C, Wu H, *et al.* (2020) The roles of climate, geography and natural selection as drivers of genetic and phenotypic differentiation in a widespread amphibian *Hyla annectans* (Anura: Hylidae). *Molecular Ecology* **29**, 3667–3683.

Wen G, Jin L, Wu Y, Wang X, Fu J, *et al.* (2021) Low diversity, little genetic structure but no inbreeding in a high-density island endemic pit-viper *Gloydius shedaoensis*. *Current Zoology* **68**, 526–534.

Whitlock MC, McCauley DE (1999) Indirect measures of gene flow and migration: FST not equal to 1/(4Nm + 1). *Heredity* **82**, 117–125.

Whitlock MC, Ingvarsson PK, Hatfield T (2000) Local drift load and the heterosis of interconnected populations. *Heredity* **84**, 452–457.

Willing E-M, Dreyer C, van Oosterhout C (2012) Estimates of genetic differentiation measured by FST do not necessarily require large sample sizes when using many SNP markers. *PLoS ONE* **7**, e42649.

Woltmann S, Sherry TW, Kreiser BR (2012) A genetic approach to estimating natal dispersal distances and self-recruitment in resident rainforest birds. *Journal of Avian Biology* **43**, 33–42.

Wultsch C, Waits LP, Kelly MJ (2016) A comparative analysis of genetic diversity and structure in jaguars (*Panthera onca*), pumas (*Puma concolor*), and ocelots (*Leopardus pardalis*) in fragmented landscapes of a critical Mesoamerican linkage zone. *PLoS one* **11**, e0151043.

Wright S (1943) Isolation by distance. *Genetics* **28**, 114.

Xuereb A, D'Aloia CC, Andrello M, Bernatchez L, Fortin MJ (2021) Incorporating putatively neutral and adaptive genomic data into marine conservation planning. *Conservation Biology* **35**, 909–920.

Yadav S, J Stow A, Dudaniec RY (2021) Microgeographical adaptation corresponds to elevational distributions of congeneric montane grasshoppers. *Molecular Ecology* **30**, 481–498.

23 Conservation prioritisation based on evolutionary distinctiveness of communities

Renee A. Catullo, Christiana McDonald-Spicer and Craig C. Moritz

ABSTRACT

The limited resources available for conservation mean that prioritising areas and resource allocation is crucial. Historically, species richness and **endemism** have been used for conservation prioritisation. However, metrics measuring evolutionary distinctiveness, such as phylogenetic diversity and **phylogenetic endemism**, add value to traditional methods. These metrics use phylogenies to calculate the unique evolutionary diversity present in an area, and phylogenetic endemism also prioritises spatially restricted evolutionary diversity. Using phylogenetic metrics allows conservation planning to depend less on accuracy of current taxonomy, to capture evolutionary potential, and in some cases to better protect ecosystem function. For these reasons, measures of evolutionary diversity are increasingly used in the spatial prioritisation of landscapes, including through identifying diversity hotspots, identifying areas with important species, and systematic gap analyses of conservation reserve systems. Phylogenetic measures are used to understand the impacts of anthropogenic change on diversity, and modelling diversity through time. Future directions in this field include understanding better the relationship between evolutionary diversity metrics and **functional diversity**, and the evolutionary processes that lead to areas of high phylogenetic endemism. Additionally, increasing survey data through tools such as eDNA, combined with larger datasets at a phylogeographic scale, will enable a larger uptake of these measures by conservation managers.

INTRODUCTION

Conservation of biodiversity is underpinned by the goal of maintaining ecosystem functioning over time (Convention on Biological Diversity 2010). It often relies on maintaining a functionally diverse set of organisms that play a wide variety of roles in an ecosystem and that can utilise a wide set of resources (Tilman *et al.* 1997; Tilman 1999). Historically, choosing areas to prioritise for conservation based on functional diversity has been a difficult problem, as the functional role of individual species is generally poorly understood and therefore difficult to model. This is important because the lands and resources available for conservation are generally limited (McCarthy *et al.* 2012; Waldron *et al.* 2013), making prioritising resource allocation essential (Margules and Pressey 2000; Bottrill *et al.* 2008; Tallis *et al.* 2021; Zurell *et al.* 2021).

Species richness has often been used as a proxy for ecosystem function because more species diversity should be equivalent to more functionally distinct taxa (Tilman 2001), and high species diversity can show clear positive effects for ecosystem services (Tilman *et al.* 1996; Gamfeldt *et al.* 2013; Huang *et al.* 2018). However, species richness is not always strongly correlated with functional diversity (Hector *et al.* 1999; Petchey *et al.* 2004; Halpern and Floeter 2008). This lack of correlation can be caused by a number of factors, particularly the functional redundancy of species within ecosystems, where co-distributed species are ecologically similar, and therefore the addition or subtraction of a species does not change functional diversity by an identical amount (Cadotte *et al.* 2011; Reich *et al.* 2012). It is also true that closely related species tend to have similar ecological functions – phylogenetic niche conservatism (Wiens and Graham 2005). Therefore, areas with many phylogenetically distinct taxa can be expected to have greater functional diversity, although there can be exceptions (see Mazel *et al.* 2018). It follows that metrics that capture this evolutionary aspect of diversity should add value in conservation assessments.

Phylogeny-based measures of diversity

Phylogenetic diversity (PD) (Faith 1992) is a metric that represents the evolutionary distinctiveness of organisms. It is calculated as the union of all branch lengths in the

phylogenetic tree for the tips represented in an area (Box 23.1). It is comparable to species richness, but each tree terminal is scaled by the phylogenetic branch lengths, which represents the uniqueness of the taxa present. It therefore represents the amount of evolutionary diversity represented by any set of taxa in an area.

A significant advantage of phylogeny-based methods of assessing diversity is that they do not depend on an updated and complete taxonomy (i.e. naming of species), but can instead use intraspecific lineage-level phylogenetic data in their calculation (Rosauer *et al.* 2016, 2018; Fenker *et al.* 2020). In such analyses, distributions of genetically divergent lineages are modelled as a subset of the distribution of a large species complex, linking unique evolutionary diversity to an explicit

---

Box 23.1: Phylogenetic diversity and evolutionary distinctiveness

Phylogenetic diversity (PD) combines phylogenetic and distribution data to measure the amount of the tree of life that is represented within a defined region. PD is calculated by summing the lengths of the phylogenetic branches connecting all the taxa represented in the region, through to the root of the phylogenetic tree (Faith 1992):

$$PD = \sum_{j}^{T} L$$

where for a set of species in an area there is a corresponding set of *T* branch segments. Each segment (*j*) has a length (*L*). PD for an area is the sum of all branch segments represented in that area (Nipperess 2016).

For example, using Fig. 23.1, a location with the species B, D and E is calculated by summing the branch lengths represented by species. Species B represents branches 2, 4, 5 and 7, and the sum of those branch lengths equals 200. The next species in the area, species D, adds branch 3 to those in the area, equalling 143. Because the evolutionary history represented by branch 2 is already represented by species B, including species D does not add that as new evolutionary diversity. Finally, species E is very distinct and adds all of branch 1, equal to 200. In total, the phylogenetic diversity of this area is 543 (57+67+52+24+143+200). As this number is only in units of branch lengths, its practical meaning may vary depending on whether it is calculated using a **phylogram** or a **chronogram**.

Using the same approach, an area with species A and C would have a value of 276 (57 + 67 + 76 + 52 + 24). An area with species A and D would have a value of 343 (57 + 67 + 76 + 143). Species D and E alone have a score of 400 (57 + 143 + 200). This illustrates that the highest PD comes from having representation from each major lineage. In lieu of protecting all lineages, representatives of the most evolutionarily distinct lineages will generate the highest PD.

A similar approach can be used to estimate the **evolutionary distinctiveness** (ED) of individual taxa on a phylogeny. ED is a method for measuring species' relative contributions to PD (Isaac *et al.* 2007). It is calculated by dividing the length of each branch by the number of species descending from it, and summing these values for all branches leading from the root to the species' tip (Table 23.1). High ED values indicate a species has few close relatives.

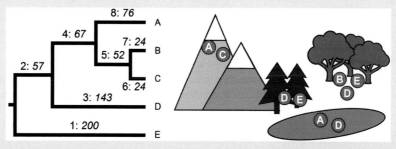

Fig. 23.1. Example phylogeny for calculation of phylogenetic diversity and evolutionary distinctiveness, showing species A through E. Values on branches indicate branch number and branch length (italics). Habitats represent different areas, occupied by different species.

Table 23.1.   Evolutionary distinctiveness (ED) calculations for each species in the phylogeny in Fig. 23.1.

In the calculation column, the branch number of the phylogeny is shown in parentheses, followed by the branch length divided by the number of species the length is shared across.

Species	Calculation	ED
A	(2) 57/4 + (4) 67/3 + (8) 76/1	112.6
B	(2) 57/4 + (4) 67/3 + (5) 52/2 + (7) 24/1	86.6
C	(2) 57/4 + (4) 67/3 + (5) 52/2 + (7) 24/1	86.6
D	(2) 57/4 + (3) 143/1	157.3
E	(1) 200/1	200

distribution, independent of taxonomic naming. This improves conservation planning outcomes in a number of ways. Taxonomic groups often differ in the resolution and completeness of taxonomy, and there is a bias towards completion in vertebrates and vascular plants. For groups where taxonomy is largely incomplete, such as invertebrates, we can overcome a lack of nomenclature by using **reciprocally monophyletic** lineages in place of named taxa. Using these lineages, or evolutionary significant units (Moritz 1994), can better represent the true distribution of diversity across groups of organisms than species richness.

Phylogenetic trees may be chronograms or phylograms, and the choice between them can have a large impact on estimation of PD (Elliott *et al.* 2018). Phylograms provide a measure of the number of genetic character changes that have occurred along a given branch. When using phylograms to calculate PD, taxa that have accelerated rates of molecular evolution, which may correlate with evolutionary distinctiveness, are emphasised. However, rates of molecular evolution are impacted by a wide array of factors such as generation time (Bromham 2009; Thomas *et al.* 2010). This means that when comparing phylogram-based PD in taxa with substantially different life histories (e.g. annual species vs. species that live for decades), it must be done thoughtfully to avoid biasing results towards the taxa with a higher rate of molecular evolution.

Chronograms are time-calibrated phylogenetic trees, where branch lengths explicitly represent the amount of time that something has been divergent. PD calculated using a chronogram emphasises combinations of taxa that have been distinct for a long period of time. Chronograms allow age-calibrated phylogenetic diversity to be calculated, such that branch length in the trees are equivalent to time across taxonomic groups, enabling the same PD value to be equivalent across different taxonomic groups. The choice between a phylogram or chronogram requires careful consideration whether the goal is conservation of distinct genetic features, or the breadth of the tree of life (Elliott *et al.* 2018).

In the context of ecosystem function, preservation of phylogenetically diverse sets of organisms has been associated with ecosystem productivity and stability (Petchey and Gaston 2002; Flynn *et al.* 2011; Cadotte *et al.* 2012; Craven *et al.* 2018). Therefore, PD can represent a proxy for preserving ecosystem function. However, optimising PD as a proxy for functional diversity is poorly supported in a number of situations (Mayfield and Levine 2010; Swenson 2013; Tucker *et al.* 2018). When a clade has recently rapidly diversified (both in the rate of speciation and in trait diversity), a phylogenetic approach will prioritise conservation of few species in the clade due to the short branch lengths, resulting in a loss of functional trait diversity. Alternatively, when species diversified long ago but have changed little in their functional traits, phylogeny-based methods will prioritise conserving more lineages due to their long branch lengths, but this adds little to the overall functional diversity. Overall, PD can improve conservation of different aspects of ecosystem function but requires clear goals and understanding of the evolutionary dynamics of the group in question. Beyond preserving functional diversity, protection of evolutionary diversity *per se* is another goal of conservation because of an intrinsic obligation to protect the diversity of life (Vucetich *et al.* 2015). When approaching conservation for the purposes of protection of the breadth of diversity, few metrics are as suitable as phylogenetic diversity.

Another priority for conservation is areas of endemism – regions with a concentration of spatially restricted species (Box 23.3). Areas of endemism are important to conservation as they have high numbers of narrow-range species, which are intrinsically more at risk of extinction (Purvis *et al.* 2000; Cardillo *et al.* 2005; Cooper *et al.* 2008; Bohm *et al.* 2016; Newsome *et al.* 2020). For systematic conservation planning (Margules and Pressey 2000) such areas are highly irreplaceable. Of particular interest are areas with a concentration of both endemism and PD. Rosauer *et al.* (2009) proposed such a method: *Phylogenetic endemism* (PE, Box 23.2). PE combines PD with weighted endemism. Weighted endemism is

Box 23.2: Phylogenetic endemism

Phylogenetic endemism (PE) combines weighted endemism with PD to measure the amount of geographically restricted evolutionary diversity in a region. To calculate the weighted endemism a species contributes to an area, each species is assigned a value that is the inverse of its range (Crisp *et al.* 2001). A species that only occupies one cell out of 100 will have a weight of 1, a species occurring in five cells will have a weight of 0.2, and a species occurring in all 100 cells will have a weight of 0.01. Combining weighted endemism with PD allows endemism to be evaluated in a way that is consistent across scale changes such as populations, species and genera.

PE is calculated by summing the length of branches connecting all the taxa represented in the region, as with PD, but with each branch length multiplied by the proportion of a clade's range that occurs in that region, similar to weighted endemism. This includes all the internal phylogenetic branches represented at the location (Rosauer *et al.* 2009):

$$PE = \sum_{j}^{T} L / R$$

where for a set of species in an area there is a corresponding set of *T* branch segments. Each segment (*j*) has a length (*L*) and a range (*R*). PE for an area is the sum of all branch segments represented in that area, weighted by their range (Rosauer *et al.* 2009).

For example, using Fig. 23.1 (Box 23.1), a location with the species A and C is calculated by summing the branch lengths represented by species, multiplied by the proportion of the branch's total range present at the location. Species A represents branches 2, 4 and 8. Branch 2 has length 57 and its descending taxa occur in four regions, giving the branch a value of $57 \times \frac{1}{4}$ or 14.25. Similarly, branch 4 has a value of 22.33 $(67 \times \frac{1}{3})$ and branch 8 has a value of 38 $(76 \times \frac{1}{2})$, giving species A a value of 74.58. Species C adds branches 5 and 6 to those in the area, equalling 50. In total, the phylogenetic diversity of this area is 124.58 (74.58 + 50).

Using the same approach, an area with species B, D and E would have a PE value of 234.25. An area with species A and D would have a value of 122.25, and an area with species D and E have a score of 161.92.

The impact of including range size in spatial prioritisation can be seen when comparing the location with species A and D to that with species A and C. While the first location had a higher PD score than the second (see Box 23.1), the large range size of species D means that the second location contained more *spatially restricted* PD, and thus higher PE.

Box 23.3: Case study – Conservation planning in the Kimberley

The Kimberley is a region in northern Western Australia, covering approximately 421 000 km^2. It is a major centre of species diversity and endemism for a large range of taxonomic groups, with a rapid rate of species discovery and high levels of as-yet taxonomically unrecognised lineage diversity (e.g. Gibson and McKenzie 2012; Kohler and Criscione 2013; Shelley *et al.* 2019). The limited impact of intensive land uses in the region, such as mining, intensive agriculture and urbanisation, provides flexibility for effective conservation planning prior to development.

Rosauer *et al.* (2018) focused on skinks and geckos in the Kimberley, which had undergone extensive fieldwork and sampling in previous years and represented the most complete sampling for any taxon. Using this uniquely complete dataset from a highly under-sampled region, the authors identified the areas that would provide the greatest additional protection of phylogenetic diversity if the size of the existing reserve system was increased by five percent.

Calculation of PD requires a phylogeny, with the distribution of each tip clearly defined. Each genus had a separate phylogenetic tree generated from the same genes, for comparable rates of molecular evolution. To provide consistency in the delineation of intraspecific diversity across genera, ecologically significant units were defined as clades with a six percent pairwise mitochondrial sequence divergence. The distribution of each **evolutionarily significant unit** was then estimated using species distribution modelling relying on the sequenced samples of each ESU. An alternative method to using lineage-level distribution models, particularly when too few genetic samples exist, is to create a model at the species level using historical distribution records. This wider distribution can be split into lineages following the methods of Rosauer *et al.* (2015). Marxan (Watts *et al.* 2009) was then used to prioritise regions based on how much additional PD they contributed to the existing network of protected areas. Compared to a prioritisation aiming to represent all described species in the region, the prioritisation using PD identified different areas to be conserved. The prioritisation using species missed large areas in the

Fig. 23.2. Prioritising areas for conservation in the Kimberley region (A) of Australia using phylogenetic diversity. A phylogenetic tree (B) was generated for evolutionarily significant units within 11 genera of lizards, and species distribution models were generated for each unit. These were combined to calculate genus-level PD (C). Marxan used to identify the most important regions to add to the conservation network considering PD in all 11 genera. In (D), the existing reserve system is shown in grey, and areas selected for addition to the reserve system due to high PD are shaded by how often they were selected by Marxan (green is always selected, red is sometimes). Lizard genera used in the analysis included (E) *Eremiascincus,* (F) *Gehyra,* and (G) *Carlia.* Spatial maps are from Rosauer *et al.* (2018). Photos by Damien Esquerré.

West Kimberley and far northeast Kimberley that were highly important in the prioritisation using PD. In addition, the prioritisation using species added far less PD to the conservation network than when PD was directly targeted.

Using PD in conservation prioritisation allowed this study to capture the as-yet unnamed diversity that would otherwise be ignored in structured conservation planning approaches (Fig. 23.2). The resulting prioritisation is also robust to the inevitable description of new species. This is particularly valuable in biodiversity-rich regions where taxonomy lags behind our current understanding of evolutionary diversity.

the proportion of the range of a species that is within the defined area (Crisp *et al.* 2001). PE is calculated the same as PD, but with each tree branch divided by the range of the clade it belongs to (Rosauer *et al.* 2009), where the highest values represent regions with phylogenetically distinct species that are also found only within a narrow area. One challenge with PE is that it can be difficult to distinguish between mid-range areas, as those with high PD and low endemism appear the same as areas with low PD and high endemism (Rosauer *et al.* 2017). However, the identification of areas with high PE is a significantly useful conservation tool.

Phylogenetic measures such as PD and PE can have several advantages in conservation planning over traditional methods. Phylogenetic measures allow for conservation across the tree of life and for the conservation of evolutionary potential by protecting the breadth of diversity, which leads to diversification and lineage persistence (Davis *et al.* 2008; Vandergast *et al.* 2008; Sgro *et al.* 2011). However, it must be acknowledged that in some circumstances of systematic conservation planning, simpler metrics such as

species diversity can be equally efficient (Rodrigues and Gaston 2002; Rapacciuolo *et al.* 2019). When extinction risk is phylogenetically random, little may be gained from a phylogenetic approach when the target is a threatened species (Thuiller *et al.* 2011; Pio *et al.* 2014). Even in these circumstances, marginal improvements in conservation of biodiversity can be found from including phylogenetic information (Rodrigues and Gaston 2002). Incomplete taxon sampling for community-level phylogenies can bias estimations of PD and reduce its effectiveness as a conservation planning tool (Park *et al.* 2018). However, when carefully applied, phylogenetic-based prioritisation methods can help in the preservation of diverse sets of species, and highly distinct and highly endemic lineages.

SPATIAL PRIORITISATION OF LANDSCAPES

Spatial prioritisation of landscapes can be used to identify the most irreplaceable areas to target for conservation, and to help prioritise management actions including habitat restoration, managing invasive species, and restoring habitat connectivity (Margules and Pressey 2000). Increasing availability of phylogenetic data has allowed the direct integration of phylogenetic measures into conservation planning. Studies on spatial prioritisation using phylogenetic measures generally take one or a combination of these three approaches: identifying important species, mapping biodiversity hotspots, or undertaking systematic gap analyses.

Identifying important species

Highly evolutionarily distinct species are often a priority for conservation because they represent unique and irreplaceable diversity. To assess this, a unique measure of phylogenetic distinctiveness can be assigned to individual species (Isaac *et al.* 2007). Evolutionary distinctiveness (ED) is calculated by dividing the phylogenetic diversity of a clade between all species (Box 23.1). Areas can then be prioritised for conservation by calculating the mean ED value across all species occurring there (Safi *et al.* 2013; Yessoufou *et al.* 2017).

One example of identifying important species is the Evolutionarily Distinct and Globally Endangered (EDGE) species list by the Zoological Society of London (Isaac *et al.* 2007; Safi *et al.* 2013). EDGE species are ranked by combining their evolutionary distinctiveness with their IUCN threat status, prioritising species with high ED that are threatened with extinction. These rankings are then used to prioritise individual species for conservation investment. When applied to spatial conservation planning, areas with a high mean EDGE value are of higher priority to protect, as these contain more species that are both evolutionarily distinct and threatened with extinction (Safi *et al.* 2013; Yessoufou *et al.* 2017).

Mapping biodiversity hotspots

Identifying biodiversity hotspots involves mapping phylogenetic measures such as PD or PE across the landscape, prioritising areas with particularly high values (often the top 5 or 10% of locations). This approach is frequently used to assess how well protected areas conserve regions of high PD and PE; high-value areas not currently protected are identified as priorities for improving overall conservation of evolutionary diversity (Rosauer *et al.* 2016; Yessoufou *et al.* 2017; Daru *et al.* 2019; Dagallier *et al.* 2020; Fenker *et al.* 2020; Kougioumoutzis *et al.* 2021). Combining PE with a human pressure index produces Human Impacted PE – a measure of the range-restricted evolutionary diversity that is most threatened by human actions (Gumbs, Gray, *et al.* 2020; Gumbs, Williams, *et al.* 2020). Regions identified as priority areas for future conservation using this approach include South Malawi (Dagallier *et al.* 2020), Brazil's Cerrado (Oliveira *et al.*

2017; Fenker *et al.* 2020) and Australia's Darwin-Litchfield region (Rosauer *et al.* 2016).

Systematic gap analysis

The third commonly used approach to spatial prioritisation of landscapes is systematic conservation planning and gap analysis. Systematic conservation planning aims to maximise the amount of diversity conserved, while taking into account existing conservation land as well as the limited additional land available for conservation (Margules and Pressey 2000). It is often conducted with tools such as Zonation (Moilanen 2007), Marxan (Watts *et al.* 2009), or Prioritizr (Hanson *et al.* 2021), which allow the user to explicitly define conservation objectives. The total amount of land available for conservation can also be set to reflect limited resources and competing land uses. It can include levels of protection rather than binary measures (Kling *et al.* 2019). Sites are selected using complementarity – based on what they add to the overall conservation network rather than what they contain in isolation (Margules and Pressey 2000). For example, a site that has low PD but in which lineages are not well-represented in the network will have higher complementarity than a site with high PD but containing lineages that are already represented within the reserve system. Sites selected using phylogenetic measures do not always align with those selected using species measures such as richness (Rosauer *et al.* 2017; Xu *et al.* 2019). Phylogenetic measures, however, generally result in more conservation targets being met, and the same amount of area conserved protects a greater amount of diversity (Rosauer *et al.* 2017). This same approach can be used to identify sets of areas that most efficiently represent phylogeographic diversity within species complexes, again providing assessments that are robust to taxonomic uncertainty or change (Carvalho *et al.* 2017; Rosauer *et al.* 2018).

Assessing impacts of change

Effective conservation management must plan for the future distribution of biodiversity as well as protecting biodiversity distributed on the landscape today. To do this, it is important to understand the impacts that change will have on patterns of diversity. This enables us to prioritise protection of areas and species predicted to be the most at risk (Kougioumoutzis *et al.* 2021). Previously, prioritisation metrics assessed changes in patterns of species richness or rarity, but phylogenetic measures are being increasingly used as they add to understanding of evolutionary diversity (Petchey and Gaston 2002; Flynn *et al.* 2011; Cadotte *et al.* 2012; Craven *et al.* 2018).

Ideally, changes in PD and PE would be measured using repeated surveys to directly observe change over time (D. Li *et al.* 2020); however, the temporal scale of the data required has resulted in such studies being uncommon. Instead, assessments of the impacts of change on PD and PE generally take one of two approaches – using space-for-time substitution or modelling change through time. Space-for-time substitutions look at how spatial patterns in diversity are correlated with the environmental variation at one point in time to identify likely impacts as those environmental features change over time. The most common use of this method is to understand the impacts of intensifying land-use on diversity. This approach compares diversity patterns across land-use types to identify the impacts of increasing human impacts on those land types over time. Overall, anthropogenic land-use causes declines in PD and PE (Dopheide *et al.* 2020; D. Li *et al.* 2020).

Modelling change through time first identifies how individual species distributions are likely to be impacted by habitat loss and climate change. Using aggregated individual species' models allows the assessment of changes in PD and PE through time and space. This approach generally uses species distribution models – correlative models that use species occurrence records and environmental data to predict species ranges (Elith and Leathwick 2009). These models can be projected forwards or backwards through time, and, when combined with species' phylogenies, phylogenetic measures calculated for distributions in the present day and the projected time period. Comparing diversity patterns between pre-Columbian forests and present-day ranges using this method identified that deforestation has drastically altered the distribution of PD and PE in the Atlantic Forest of Brazil; however, despite an over 90% loss of forest, substantial PD still exists (Brown *et al.* 2020). This approach has also been used to model the impacts of anthropogenic climate change by identifying areas that will see the most loss of evolutionary diversity (Gonzalez-Orozco *et al.* 2016; Veron *et al.* 2019), as well as refugial areas that will protect diversity from extinction (Gonzalez-Orozco *et al.* 2016). Identifying and conserving areas predicted to have high PE under future change protects large amounts of rare diversity as the component species become more range-restricted (Gonzalez-Orozco *et al.* 2016).

Another dimension of assessing evolutionary dimensions of change is to discriminate between regions of diversification or **refugia**. Further refinements of PD and PE methods allow this. Categorical analysis of neo- and paleo-endemism (CANAPE) (Mishler *et al.* 2014) is a metric that categorises areas of high PE as one of three categories. Centres of neo-endemism are areas with shorter branches than expected, suggesting high rates of diversification, and are important for protection of evolutionary potential (Davis *et al.* 2008; Vandergast *et al.* 2008; Sgro *et al.* 2011). Areas with high paleo-endemism are

regions with more long branches than expected, and may have acted as refugial areas through time, particularly for taxa that have gone extinct elsewhere (Mishler *et al.* 2014). Of greatest value to conservation is the identification of areas of mixed endemism: centres of both persistence and diversification that are both cradles of diversification and refugia. Identifying areas in these categories can add value to future conservation efforts. Areas predicted to be centres of paleo-endemism in the future are important to protect as these may act as refugia (Gonzalez-Orozco *et al.* 2016). Mixed endemism sites may be particularly cost-effective to protect because they provide an overlap between refugia and centres of diversification (Kougioumoutzis *et al.* 2021). It is important to note that CANAPE is impacted by the completeness of the phylogenetic tree. For example, taxa that have recently migrated to a region will appear to be phylogenetically isolated and contribute a long branch length to the analysis, even if the clade is not range restricted or particularly old. For this reason it may be best to use complete clades in clearly defined regions, or to acknowledge the limitations of the method when conducting analyses. However, when used appropriately, CANAPE can be useful in identifying and prioritising regions of diversity.

FUTURE DIRECTIONS AND OUTSTANDING QUESTIONS

Despite the potential for phylogenetic metrics to improve conservation decision making, managers and policy makers have in general persisted with species-based measures. In part, this is because there is still uncertainty about the near-term benefits in taking on this additional layer of information. In the following, we suggest some areas of future research that could demonstrate this value.

Future work is needed to understand when and where PD acts as a proxy for functional diversity and ecosystem resilience as current evidence is mixed. A critical part of this will be to evaluate and understand how this relationship varies across taxonomic groups. For example, while studies using vertebrate phylogenies often suggest that including phylogenetic measures yields only incremental improvements in preserving functional diversity (Rodrigues and Gaston 2002; Rapacciuolo *et al.* 2019), studies on plants indicate PD can be a useful proxy (Flynn *et al.* 2011; Cadotte *et al.* 2012; Craven *et al.* 2018). There is also a need to extend such analyses to invertebrates and across different trophic levels.

Increasing the availability of survey data across time will allow us to map ongoing human impacts on evolutionary diversity, and ground-truth models of the impact of anthropogenic change. Of particular interest to this goal is the increased sequencing of DNA from environmental samples, known as environmental DNA (eDNA). eDNA sampling allows sequencing of all organisms sampled at a location and is inherently phylogenetic in approach. Linking these data with PD and functional diversity has great potential for assessing changes in ecosystem function across spatial and temporal scales. Improved technology, lowered costs and greater uptake of these measures make it possible to conduct genomic surveys of entire ecosystems (Thomsen and Willerslev 2015; Stat *et al.* 2017; Djurhuus *et al.* 2020), allowing for regular monitoring of PD and PE. Indeed, eDNA studies using PD approaches have been able to identify shifts in oceanic bacterial diversity associated with human impact (Garlapati *et al.* 2021), and reductions in PD with human disturbance in rivers (F. Li *et al.* 2020).

Phylogenetic metrics can also be applied within species to reveal spatial patterns of genetic diversity, i.e. phylogeography. Using a phylogeny that represents genetically divergent units, rather than species-level phylogeny, will make measures of evolutionary diversity more robust to taxonomic change. Species-level phylogenies, while more robust than species diversity measures such as richness, are still impacted by taxonomic changes such as splitting or combining species. Phylogenies built at a finer scale, including populations and species complexes, are more robust to these changes (Rosauer *et al.* 2016), particularly for groups and regions where taxonomy lags behind the scientific understanding of diversity. Such approaches could help us move forward with effective conservation of hyperdiverse invertebrate taxa where, at a given location, perhaps only a few have been named. These datasets would also help capture genetic diversity, allowing detection of loss of major components of genetic diversity through high population extinction rates and thus species range contractions. An overarching question for future study is how to split species consistently across taxa, to make them comparable when taxonomy is ignored.

A better understanding of how spatial patterns of speciation, range shifting, and extinction give rise to high PE, that is, areas of spatially restricted PD, will help inform appropriate management actions. Species on long branches and which have narrow ranges can arise in two ways: they can be either a poorly diversifying lineage which has persisted for a long time, or a more rapidly diversifying clade that has had many extinctions (Mishler *et al.* 2014). Species with low diversification rates may well have relatively high tolerances to changing habitats or have been able to persist in refugia over long periods of time. Relictual species in clades that have suffered high extinction rates may be sensitive to environmental change. In both circumstances, the species can contribute the same amount of PE despite widely differing evolutionary histories. Further research is needed on how the patterns of speciation and extinction in a clade should affect our interpretation of the conservation needs of species in areas of high PE.

The measure of success for phylogeny-based metrics will be their increasing use by conservation agencies in management planning and monitoring. This requires research testing for strong correlations between these metrics and conservation goals and identifying the circumstances where they may be either more or less suitable, as discussed above. Uptake of these methods will also be determined by the success in making these methods accessible and useful for a broad array of specific questions – and in particular making phylogenetic trees widely available in usable formats. However, phylogeny-based metrics have significant potential to improve conservation planning and management actions, supporting the preservation of the diversity of life and the functioning of ecosystems.

CONSIDERATIONS FOR NEW RESEARCHERS OR PRACTITIONERS

As we hope is clear from the above, incorporating phylogenetic measures into conservation assessments is conceptually elegant and can be of practical benefit. A key question is when this approach will add value, given that resources are already overstretched. Or, to put it another way, how might the results of a PD, PE or EDGE analysis lead to a substantial impact on conservation action in the real world? At the core is whether our social goal should be to protect the legacy of past evolution, and ongoing evolutionary potential, rather than just a list of named species (Frankel 1974). If the former, then the approaches outlined here are essential. Even if, as most legislation dictates, maintaining named taxa is the intent, then these approaches still have considerable value in providing assessments robust to taxonomic uncertainty and in providing a more nuanced approach (Rosauer *et al.* 2018). In the face of accelerating environmental change, and associated impacts on biodiversity, there is an ever-increasing need to focus conservation effort. The good news is that the extent and quality of information on the relationships and distributions of species is improving rapidly. Likewise methods for analysing and visualising this information continue to improve. Yet, there is always a need for increased dialogue between researchers and practitioners, so that the former can focus on problems that matter and the latter understand how best to apply new biodiversity knowledge in their work.

From a practical perspective, it's important to remember that a phylogenetic tree is a hypothesis that is always somewhat wrong – some phylogenetic trees are just less wrong than others. When applying methods such as these, very minor differences between phylogenetic trees are not likely to significantly impact the analyses, so it's not usually necessary to spend years generating the 'perfect' phylogenetic tree. However, the spatial scale (the amount of area included in the analyses) and resolution (size of the individual spatial units used) will impact the results, and what questions can be answered. To have the maximum conservation impact, ensure that the questions are discussed with conservation organisations prior to the study, so decisions about scale and resolution ensure useful answers are generated.

DISCUSSION TOPICS

1. Phylogenetic trees can be either phylograms (where branch lengths represent the number of character changes in the data used to build the tree) or chronograms (where branch lengths are proportional to time since divergence). How does each impact the interpretation of phylogenetic diversity, and what conservation management objectives are suitable to each tree type?
Starting literature: Elliott *et al.* (2018)

2. How would using a phylogeny that only consists of species distributed in your areas of interest (i.e. not including relatives that are outside the area) affect values of PD and PE? What about CANAPE? What conservation goals would make using such a phylogeny appropriate?
Starting literature: Mishler *et al.* (2014)

3. What are the circumstances when prioritising the most evolutionarily distinct species may not result in the best conservation outcomes?
Starting literature: Morelli *et al.* (2018)

4. What are the positives and negatives of calculating PD and PE with a lineage-level phylogeny (i.e. evolutionarily significant units, not species)?
Starting literature: Rosauer *et al.* (2018)

REFERENCES

Bohm M, Williams R, Bramhall HR, McMillan KM, Davidson AD, *et al.* (2016) Correlates of extinction risk in squamate reptiles: The relative importance of biology, geography, threat and range size. *Global Ecology and Biogeography* 25, 391–405. doi:10.1111/geb.12419

Bottrill MC, Joseph LN, Carwardine J, Bode M, Cook C, *et al.* (2008) Is conservation triage just smart decision making? *Trends in Ecology & Evolution* 23, 649–654. doi:10.1016/j.tree.2008.07.007

Bromham L (2009) Why do species vary in their rate of molecular evolution? *Biology Letters* 5, 401–404. doi:10.1098/rsbl.2009.0136

Brown JL, Paz A, Reginato M, Renata CA, Assis C, *et al.* (2020) Seeing the forest through many trees: Multi-taxon patterns of phylogenetic diversity in the Atlantic Forest hotspot. *Diversity and Distributions* 26, 1160–1176. doi:10.1111/ddi.13116

Cadotte MW, Carscadden K, Mirotchnick N (2011) Beyond species: Functional diversity and the maintenance of ecological processes and services. *Journal of Applied Ecology* 48, 1079–1087. doi:10.1111/j.1365-2664.2011.02048.x

Cadotte MW, Dinnage R, Tilman D (2012) Phylogenetic diversity promotes ecosystem stability. *Ecology* 93, S223–S233. doi:10.1890/11-0426.1

Cardillo M, Mace GM, Jones KE, Bielby J, Bininda-Emonds OR, *et al.* (2005) Multiple causes of high extinction risk in large mammal species. *Science* 309, 1239–1241. doi:10.1126/science.1116030

Carvalho SB, Velo-Anton G, Tarroso P, Portela AP, Barata M, *et al.* (2017) Spatial conservation prioritization of biodiversity spanning the evolutionary continuum. *Nature Ecology & Evolution* 1, 1–8. doi:10.1038/s41559-017-0151

Convention on Biological Diversity (2010) *Aichi Target 11—Technical Rationale Extended (COP/10/INF/12/Rev.1.).* Available at: <https://www.cbd.int/sp/targets/rationale/target-11/>

Cooper N, Bielby J, Thomas GH, Purvis A (2008) Macroecology and extinction risk correlates of frogs. *Global Ecology and Biogeography* 17, 211–221. doi:10.1111/j.1466-8238.2007.00355.x

Craven D, Eisenhauer N, Pearse WD, Hautier Y, Isbell F, *et al.* (2018) Multiple facets of biodiversity drive the diversity-stability relationship. *Nature Ecology & Evolution* 2(10), 1579–1587. doi:10.1038/s41559-018-0647-7

Crisp MD, Laffan S, Linder HP, Monro AN (2001) Endemism in the Australian flora. *Journal of Biogeography* 28(2), 183–198. doi:10.1046/j.1365-2699.2001.00524.x

Dagallier L-PMJ, Janssens SB, Dauby G, Blach-Overgaard A, Mackinder BA, *et al.* (2020) Cradles and museums of generic plant diversity across tropical Africa. *New Phytologist* 225(5), 2196–2213. doi:10.1111/nph.16293

Daru BH, le Roux PC, Gopalraj J, Park DS, Holt BG, *et al.* (2019) Spatial overlaps between the global protected areas network and terrestrial hotspots of evolutionary diversity. *Global Ecology and Biogeography* 28(6), 757–766. doi:10.1111/geb.12888

Davis EB, Koo MS, Conroy C, Patton JL, Moritz C (2008) The California Hotspots Project: Identifying regions of rapid diversification of mammals. *Molecular Ecology* 17(1), 120–138. doi:10.1111/j.1365-294X.2007.03469.x

Djurhuus A, Closek CJ, Kelly RP, Pitz KJ, Michisaki RP, *et al.* (2020) Environmental DNA reveals seasonal shifts and potential interactions in a marine community. *Nature Communications* 11(1), 254. doi:10.1038/s41467-019-14105-1

Dopheide A, Makiola A, Orwin KH, Holdaway RJ, Wood JR, *et al.* (2020) Rarity is a more reliable indicator of land-use impacts on soil invertebrate communities than other diversity metrics. *ELife* 9, e52787. doi:10.7554/eLife.52787

Elith J, Leathwick JR (2009) Species distribution models: Ecological explanation and prediction across space and time. *Annual*

Review of Ecology, Evolution, and Systematics **40**(1), 677–697. doi:10.1146/annurev.ecolsys.110308.120159

Elliott MJ, Knerr NJ, Schmidt-Lebuhn AN (2018) Choice between phylogram and chronogram can have a dramatic impact on the location of phylogenetic diversity hotspots. *Journal of Biogeography* **45**(9), 2190–2201. doi:10.1111/jbi.13399

Faith DP (1992) Conservation evaluation and phylogenetic diversity. *Biological Conservation* **61**(1), 1–10. doi:10.1016/0006-3207(92)91201-3

Fenker J, Domingos FM, Tedeschi LG, Rosauer DF, Werneck FP, *et al.* (2020) Evolutionary history of Neotropical savannas geographically concentrates species, phylogenetic and functional diversity of lizards. *Journal of Biogeography* **47**(5), 1130–1142. doi:10.1111/jbi.13800

Flynn DFB, Mirotchnick N, Jain M, Palmer MI, Naeem S (2011) Functional and phylogenetic diversity as predictors of biodiversity-ecosystem-function relationships. *Ecology* **92**(8), 1573–1581. doi:10.1890/10-1245.1

Frankel OH (1974) Genetic conservation: our evolutionary responsibility. *Genetics* **78**(1), 53–65. doi:10.1093/genetics/78.1.53

Gamfeldt L, Snäll T, Bagchi R, Jonsson M, Gustafsson L, *et al.* (2013) Higher levels of multiple ecosystem services are found in forests with more tree species. *Nature Communications* **4**(1), 1340. doi:10.1038/ncomms2328

Garlapati D, Kumar BC, Muthukumar C, Madeswaran P, Ramu K, *et al.* (2021) Assessing the *in situ* bacterial diversity and composition at anthropogenically active sites using the environmental DNA (eDNA). *Marine Pollution Bulletin* **170**(11259), 3. doi:10.1016/j.marpolbul.2021.112593

Gibson LA, McKenzie NL (2012) Identification of biodiversity assets on selected Kimberley islands: Background and implementation. In *Records of the Western Australian Museum Supplement 81*. (Eds CJY Gibson, P Doughty) pp. 1–14. Western Australian Museum, Perth.

Gonzalez-Orozco CE, Pollock LJ, Thornhill AH, Mishler BD, Knerr N, *et al.* (2016) Phylogenetic approaches reveal biodiversity threats under climate change. *Nature Climate Change* **6**(12), 12. doi:10.1038/nclimate3126

Gumbs R, Gray CL, Böhm M, Hoffmann M, Grenyer R, *et al.* (2020) Global priorities for conservation of reptilian phylogenetic diversity in the face of human impacts. *Nature Communications* **11**(1), 2616. doi:10.1038/s41467-020-16410-6

Gumbs R, Williams RC, Lowney AM, Smith D (2020) Spatial and species-level metrics reveal global patterns of irreplaceable and imperiled gecko phylogenetic diversity. *Israel Journal of Ecology and Evolution* **66**(4), 239–252. doi:10.1163/22244662-bja10020

Halpern BS, Floeter SR (2008) Functional diversity responses to changing species richness in reef fish communities. *Marine Ecology Progress Series* **364**, 147–156. doi:10.3354/meps07553

Hanson JO, Schuster R, Morrell N, Strimas-Mackey M, Edwards BPM, *et al.* (2021) prioritizr: Systematic Conservation Prioritization in R. https://cran.r-project.org/package=prioritizr

Hector A, Schmid B, Beierkuhnlein C, Caldeira MC, Diemer M, *et al.* (1999) Plant diversity and productivity experiments in European grasslands. *Science* **286**(5442), 1123–1127. doi:10.1126/science.286.5442.1123

Huang Y, Chen Y, Castro-Izaguirre N, Baruffol M, Brezzi M, *et al.* (2018) Impacts of species richness on productivity in a large-scale subtropical forest experiment. *Science* **362**(6410), 80–83. doi:10.1126/science.aat6405

Isaac NJB, Turvey ST, Collen B, Waterman C, Baillie JE (2007) Mammals on the EDGE: Conservation priorities based on threat and phylogeny. *PLoS One* **2**(3), e296. doi:10.1371/journal.pone.0000296

Kling MM, Mishler BD, Thornhill AH, Baldwin BG, Ackerly DD (2019) Facets of phylodiversity: Evolutionary diversification, divergence and survival as conservation targets. *Philosophical Transactions of the Royal Society B: Biological Sciences* **374**(1763), 20170397. doi:10.1098/rstb.2017.0397

Kohler F, Criscione F (2013) Small snails in a big place: A radiation in the semi-arid rangelands in northern Australia (Eupulmonata, Camaenidae, *Nanotrachia* gen. nov.). *Zoological Journal of the Linnean Society* **169**(1), 103–123. doi:10.1111/zoj.12051

Kougioumoutzis K, Kokkoris IP, Panitsa M, Kallimanis A, Strid A, *et al.* (2021) Plant endemism centres and biodiversity hotspots in Greece. *Biology* **10**(2), 72. doi:10.3390/biology10020072

Li D, Olden JD, Lockwood JL, Record S, McKinney ML, *et al.* (2020) Changes in taxonomic and phylogenetic diversity in the Anthropocene. *Proceedings of the Royal Society B: Biological Sciences* **287**(1929), 20200777. doi:10.1098/rspb.2020.0777

Li F, Altermatt F, Yang J, An S, Li A, *et al.* (2020) Human activities' fingerprint on multitrophic biodiversity and ecosystem functions across a major river catchment in China. *Global Change Biology* **26**(12), 6867–6879. doi:10.1111/gcb.15357

Margules CR, Pressey RL (2000) Systematic conservation planning. *Nature* **405**(6783), 243–253. doi:10.1038/35012251

Mayfield MM, Levine JM (2010) Opposing effects of competitive exclusion on the phylogenetic structure of communities. *Ecology Letters* **13**(9), 1085–1093. doi:10.1111/j.1461-0248.2010.01509.x

Mazel F, Pennell MW, Cadotte MW, Diaz S, Dalla Riva GV, *et al.* (2018) Prioritizing phylogenetic diversity captures functional diversity unreliably. *Nature Communications* **9**(1), 2888. doi:10.1038/s41467-018-05126-3

McCarthy DP, Donald PF, Scharlemann JP, Buchanan GM, Balmford A, *et al.* (2012) Financial costs of meeting global biodiversity conservation targets: Current spending and unmet needs. *Science* **338**(6109), 946–949. doi:10.1126/science.1229803

Mishler BD, Knerr N, González-Orozco CE, Thornhill AH, Laffan SW, *et al.* (2014) Phylogenetic measures of biodiversity and neo- and paleo-endemism in Australian Acacia. *Nature Communications* **5**(1), 4473. doi:10.1038/ncomms5473

Moilanen A (2007) Landscape Zonation, benefit functions and target-based planning: Unifying reserve selection strategies. *Biological Conservation* **134**(4), 571–579. doi:10.1016/j.biocon.2006.09.008

Morelli F, Benedetti Y, Perna P, Santolini R (2018) Associations among taxonomic diversity, functional diversity and evolutionary distinctiveness vary among environments. *Ecological Indicators* **88**(8), 16. doi:10.1016/j.ecolind.2018.01.022

Moritz C (1994) Defining 'Evolutionarily Significant Units' for conservation. *Trends in Ecology & Evolution* **9**(10), 373–375. doi:10.1016/0169-5347(94)90057-4

Newsome TM, Wolf C, Nimmo DG, Kopf RK, Ritchie EG, *et al.* (2020) Constraints on vertebrate range size predict extinction risk. *Global Ecology and Biogeography* **29**(1), 76–86. doi:10.1111/geb.13009

Nipperess DA (2016) The rarefaction of phylogenetic diversity: Formulation, extension and application. In *Biodiversity Conservation and Phylogenetic Systematics: Preserving Our Evolutionary Heritage in an Extinction Crisis.* (Eds R Pellens, P Grandcolas) pp. 197–217. Springer, Heidelberg, Germany. doi:10.1007/978-3-319-22461-9_10

Oliveira U, Soares-Filho BS, Paglia AP, Brescovit AD, De Carvalho CJ, Silva DP, *et al.* (2017) Biodiversity conservation gaps in the Brazilian protected areas. *Scientific Reports* **7**(1), 9141. doi:10.1038/s41598-017-08707-2

Park DS, Worthington S, Xi Z (2018) Taxon sampling effects on the quantification and comparison of community phylogenetic diversity. *Molecular Ecology* **27**(5), 1296–1308. doi:10.1111/mec.14520

Petchey OL, Gaston KJ (2002) Functional diversity (FD), species richness and community composition. *Ecology Letters* **5**(3), 402–411. doi:10.1046/j.1461-0248.2002.00339.x

Petchey OL, Hector A, Gaston KJ (2004) How do different measures of functional diversity perform? *Ecology* **85**(3), 847–857. doi:10.1890/03-0226

Pio DV, Engler R, Linder HP, Monadjem A, Cotterill FP, *et al.* (2014) Climate change effects on animal and plant phylogenetic diversity in southern Africa. *Global Change Biology* **20**(5), 1538–1549. doi:10.1111/gcb.12524.

Purvis A, Gittleman JL, Cowlishaw G, Mace GM (2000) Predicting extinction risk in declining species. *Proceedings of the Royal Society of London Series B: Biological Sciences* **267**(1456), 1947–1952. doi:10.1098/rspb.2000.1234

Rapacciuolo G, Graham CH, Marin J, Behm JE, Costa GC, *et al.* (2019) Species diversity as a surrogate for conservation of phylogenetic and functional diversity in terrestrial vertebrates across the Americas. *Nature Ecology & Evolution* **3**(1), 53–61. doi:10.1038/s41559-018-0744-7

Reich PB, Tilman D, Isbell F, Mueller K, Hobbie SE, *et al.* (2012) Impacts of biodiversity loss escalate through time as redundancy fades. *Science* **336**(6081), 589–592. doi:10.1126/science.1217909

Rodrigues ASL, Gaston KJ (2002) Maximising phylogenetic diversity in the selection of networks of conservation areas. *Biological Conservation* **105**(1), 103–111. doi:10.1016/S0006-3207(01)00208-7

Rosauer DF, Laffan SW, Crisp MD, Donnellan SC, Cook LG (2009) Phylogenetic endemism: A new approach for identifying geographical concentrations of evolutionary history. *Molecular Ecology* **18**(19), 4061–4072. doi:10.1111/j.1365-294X.2009.04311.x

Rosauer DF, Catullo RA, VanDerWal J, Moussalli A, Moritz C (2015) Lineage range estimation method reveals fine-scale endemism linked to Pleistocene stability in Australian rainforest herpetofauna. *PLOS ONE* **10**(5), e0126274. doi:10.1371/journal.pone.0126274

Rosauer DF, Blom MP, Bourke G, Catalano S, Donnellan S, *et al.* (2016) Phylogeography, hotspots and conservation priorities: An example from the Top End of Australia. *Biological Conservation* **204**, 83–93. doi:10.1016/j.biocon.2016.05.002

Rosauer DF, Pollock LJ, Linke S, Jetz W (2017) Phylogenetically informed spatial planning is required to conserve the mammalian tree of life. *Proceedings of the Royal Society B: Biological Sciences* **284**(1865), 20170627. doi:10.1098/rspb.2017.0627

Rosauer DF, Byrne M, Blom MP, Coates DJ, Donnellan S, *et al.* (2018) Real-world conservation planning for evolutionary diversity in the Kimberley, Australia, sidesteps uncertain taxonomy. *Conservation Letters* **11**(4), e12438. doi:10.1111/conl.12438

Safi K, Armour-Marshall K, Baillie JE, Isaac NJ (2013) Global patterns of evolutionary distinct and globally endangered amphibians and mammals. *PLoS One* **8**(5), e63582. doi:10.1371/journal.pone.0063582

Sgro CM, Lowe AJ, Hoffmann AA (2011) Building evolutionary resilience for conserving biodiversity under climate change. *Evolutionary Applications* **4**(2), 326–337. doi:10.1111/j.1752-4571.2010.00157.x

Shelley JJ, Dempster T, Le Feuvre MC, Unmack PJ, Laffan SW, *et al.* (2019) A revision of the bioregionalisation of freshwater fish communities in the Australian Monsoonal Tropics. *Ecology and Evolution* **9**(8), 4568–4588. doi:10.1002/ece3.5059

Stat M, Huggett MJ, Bernasconi R, DiBattista JD, Berry TE, *et al.* (2017) Ecosystem biomonitoring with eDNA: Metabarcoding across the tree of life in a tropical marine environment. *Scientific Reports* **7**(1), 12240. doi:10.1038/s41598-017-12501-5

Swenson NG (2013) The assembly of tropical tree communities – the advances and shortcomings of phylogenetic and functional trait analyses. *Ecography* **36**(3), 264–276. doi:10.1111/j.1600-0587.2012.00121.x

Tallis H, Fargione J, Game E, McDonald R, Baumgarten L, *et al.* (2021) Prioritizing actions: Spatial action maps for conservation. *Annals of the New York Academy of Sciences* **1505**(1), 118–141. doi:10.1111/nyas.14651

Thomas JA, Welch JJ, Lanfear R, Bromham L (2010) A generation time effect on the rate of molecular evolution in invertebrates. *Molecular Biology and Evolution* **27**(5), 1173–1180. doi:10.1093/molbev/msq009

Thomsen P, Willerslev E (2015) Environmental DNA – An emerging tool in conservation for monitoring past and present biodiversity. *Biological Conservation* **183**, 4–18. doi:10.1016/j.biocon.2014.11.019

Thuiller W, Lavergne S, Roquet C, Boulangeat I, Lafourcade B, *et al.* (2011) Consequences of climate change on the tree of life in Europe. *Nature* **470**(7335), 531–534. doi:10.1038/nature09705

Tilman D, Knops J, Wedin D, Reich P, Ritchie M, *et al.* (1997) The influence of functional diversity and composition on ecosystem processes. *Science* **277**(5330), 1300–1302. doi:10.1126/science.277.5330.1300

Tilman D (1999) The ecological consequences of changes in biodiversity: A search for general principles. *Ecology* **80**(5), 1455–1474. doi:10.1890/0012-9658(1999)080[1455:TECOCI]2.0.CO;2

Tilman D (2001) Functional diversity. In *Encyclopedia of Biodiversity.* (Ed. S Asher Levin) pp. 109–120. Academic Press, Cambridge, MA, USA.

Tilman D, Wedin D, Knops J (1996) Productivity and sustainability influenced by biodiversity in grassland ecosystems. *Nature* **379**(6567), 718–720. doi:10.1038/379718a0

Tucker CM, Davies TJ, Cadotte MW, Pearse WD (2018) On the relationship between phylogenetic diversity and trait diversity. *Ecology* **99**(6), 1473–1479. doi:10.1002/ecy.2349

Vandergast AG, Bohonak AJ, Hathaway SA, Boys J, Fisher RN (2008) Are hotspots of evolutionary potential adequately protected in southern California? *Biological Conservation* **141**(6), 1648–1664. doi:10.1016/j.biocon.2008.04.009

Veron S, Mouchet M, Govaerts R, Haevermans T, Pellens R (2019) Vulnerability to climate change of islands worldwide and its impact on the tree of life. *Scientific Reports* **9**(1), 14471. doi:10.1038/s41598-019-51107-x

Vucetich JA, Bruskotter JT, Nelson MP (2015) Evaluating whether nature's intrinsic value is an axiom of or anathema to conservation. *Conservation Biology* **29**(2), 321–332. doi:10.1111/cobi.12464

Waldron A, Mooers AO, Miller DC, Nibbelink N, Redding D, *et al.* (2013) Targeting global conservation funding to limit immediate biodiversity declines. *Proceedings of the National Academy of Sciences* **110**(29), 12144–12148. doi:10.1073/pnas.1221370110

Watts ME, Ball IR, Stewart RS, Klein CJ, Wilson K, *et al.* (2009) Marxan with Zones: Software for optimal conservation based land- and sea-use zoning. *Environmental Modelling & Software* **24**(12), 1513–1521. doi:10.1016/j.envsoft.2009.06.005

Wiens JJ, Graham CH (2005) Niche conservatism: Integrating evolution, ecology, and conservation biology. *Annual Review of Ecology, Evolution, and Systematics* **36**(1), 519–539. doi:10.1146/annurev.ecolsys.36.102803.095431

Xu Y, Huang J, Lu X, Ding Y, Zang R (2019) Priorities and conservation gaps across three biodiversity dimensions of rare and endangered plant species in China. *Biological Conservation* **229**, 30–37. doi:10.1016/j.biocon.2018.11.010

Yessoufou K, Daru BH, Tafirei R, Elansary HO, Rampedi I (2017) Integrating biogeography, threat and evolutionary data to explore extinction crisis in the taxonomic group of cycads. *Ecology and Evolution* **7**(8), 2735–2746. doi:10.1002/ece3.2660

Zurell D, König C, Malchow AK, Kapitza S, Bocedi G, *et al.* (2021) Spatially explicit models for decision-making in animal conservation and restoration. *Ecography* **4**. doi:10.1111/ecog.05787

BIOSECURITY AND DISEASE MONITORING

24 Invasive species detection and management using genomic methods

*Katarina C. Stuart, Andrew P. Woolnough and
Lee A. Rollins*

ABSTRACT

Invasive alien species (IAS) cause significant economic and environmental damage worldwide. For decades, genetic approaches have been used to detect IAS, clarify their taxonomy, determine pathways of introduction, estimate levels of gene flow (between populations and between invasive and native species), and measure the success of eradication efforts. More recently, we have benefitted from technologies that enable detection from environmentally derived samples, even at low IAS densities. Further, the development of in-field testing devices and PCR-free detection technologies are now extending capabilities to manage IAS. Next-generation sequencing is now commonly employed to characterise populations of IAS. While whole genome resequencing remains the gold standard, reduced-representation sequencing approaches can often provide sufficient genome-wide data without the need for expensive whole genome sequencing. Using such data, it is possible to carefully monitor changes in invasive populations, including whether adaptation is occurring, which may signify whether populations are approaching the exponential expansion phase often seen in well-established invasions. Coupled with these advances in sequencing technology and computing capabilities, modelling and data analyses are extending our ability to understand how evolutionary processes affect invasive populations, enabling the design of more effective approaches in their management. Here we present current and developing technologies of use in the genetic management of IAS. We also discuss how these data can be translated to useful management advice.

INTRODUCTION

Invasive alien species (IAS) are an ever-increasing risk to global biodiversity (Blackburn *et al.* 2014; Bellard *et al.* 2016; Schmeller and Bridgewater 2016). The increased negative impact of IAS are a direct result of growing human modification of the environment, alongside increased globalised travel and trade (Hulme 2009). IAS have cumulatively cost the world's economy in excess of US$1.2 trillion, with annual mean costs climbing steeply (Diagne *et al.* 2021). Much of these estimated costs are primarily attributed to lost agricultural revenue because ecological loss is hard to financially quantify (Hoffmann and Broadhurst 2016); nevertheless IAS are one of the leading threats to biodiversity (Pereira *et al.* 2012; Blackburn *et al.* 2014; Bellard *et al.* 2016). Managing IAS, and the ecological impact they have, requires collaboration across a diverse range of biological disciplines, including taxonomy, population modelling, and evolutionary biology, in which genetic analyses play a key role. Incorporating information derived from heritable materials such as DNA (i.e. genetics) in analytical frameworks may assist at all invasion stages (Box 24.1), from identification of unknown organisms, to mitigating overabundance and irreversible impacts. Given the potentially detrimental outcomes of mismanaged

Box 24.1: Invasion stages and management techniques

Management techniques may be categorised into prevention, eradication, containment, and asset-based protection stages (Department of Industries 2010). These categories are well-aligned with invasion stages (transport, colonisation, establishment, spread (Kolar and Lodge 2001); and cast against increasing invader numbers and control costs, form the invasion curve (Fig. 24.1; Harris *et al.* 2018). Genetic approaches can assist management at each stage, and from the management perspective, the ultimate aims at each of these stages may be similar but subtly different. For early detection, techniques ideally should be easy to operate by a non-specialist; deliver rapid results; be cheap to operate (including the equipment); be autonomous (i.e. should not require ongoing operational and analytical support from a research institution); and be accurate, reliable, and precise (few false-positives). Some of these technical requirements shift during later stages of the invasion curve, but the cost, accuracy and precision are fundamental for informing management decisions. For asset-based protection, other more complex genetic technologies may be considered (see Chapter 26 for gene drive as an example). At this final stage of the invasion curve, the focus should be on whether the technology is safe (for both ecology and humans), ethical (just because something *can* be done does not mean it *should* be done), humane, cheap to execute across an often-large geographic area, and effective (see Discussion Topics). Additionally, as the invasion curve progresses, it is vital for IAS managers to consider broad consequences in the ecological community, not just focus on single-species issues. IAS can have complex ecological interactions with both native and other invasive species, and targeting efforts may have unintended cascade effects (Baker *et al.* 2020; Bergstrom *et al.* 2009). Prevention and eradication yield greater returns on investment than managing the impacts of widely established IAS. Nonetheless, public investment tends to gravitate towards the 'squeaky wheel' of widespread species that are widely known and persecuted (e.g. European foxes in Australia) rather than preventing and/or responding to incursions of what may be perceived to be harmless species but just as ecologically damaging (e.g. reptiles; García-Díaz *et al.* 2017).

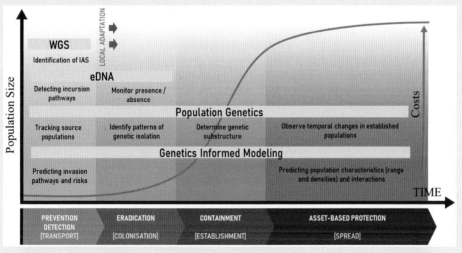

Fig. 24.1. The invasion curve, and a brief overview comparison of genetic strategies that may be employed at each invasion stage. Terms: eDNA = environmental DNA, WGS = whole genome sequencing.

invasive populations, it is then vital that the genetic technologies used are validated and repeatable, simple, and economically feasible to implement, and accessible by a range of users and institutions. Application of genetic technologies is becoming a critical part of an integrated approach to managing IAS. Here we summarise current technologies in use, as well as forthcoming developments, and discuss important risks and dilemmas that may face those working on IAS management using genetic approaches.

Prevention

Once a species has been determined to be a potential risk (e.g. either by examining invasion history or through modelling using climate matching, (Bomford *et al.* 2010), the most cost-effective route for management is to prevent new introductions. For this, knowing past or potential sources of an IAS species is critical for understanding invasion pathways and ensuring that they are blocked or managed (Bariche *et al.* 2017; García-Díaz *et al.* 2018). While we may be able to model pathways based on existing IAS distribution, known transportation routes, and introduction times, genetic evidence can provide definitive evidence as to the source of a pest identified by quarantine agencies (Brandenburger *et al.* 2019; Tsai *et al.* 2020). Further, genetic tools can be used for rapid detection of pests by quarantine officials to block entry; for example, the detection of known agricultural insect pests using loop-mediated isothermal amplification (**LAMP**) has been used on-site by Swiss authorities with minimal training and without the need for a sophisticated laboratory equipment, to provide informative results in less than one hour (Blaser *et al.* 2018).

Even if an IAS evades quarantine, identifying invasion pathways may be an essential tool for some management operations. For example, Australia's efforts to prevent introduction of rock snot (*Didymosphenia geminata*), a fast-growing diatomaceous alga native to the northern hemisphere, were assisted by the identification of source populations. Genetic analysis helped to identify that new outbreaks in New Zealand and Australia are likely the result of recent introductions of this species (Kilroy and Unwin 2011). This information has then informed biosecurity risk management, which carefully monitors the main incursion risk posed by angler tourism, where transported contaminated aquatic and fishing equipment could introduce the diatom widely to waterways.

DETECTION
Detecting species at low densities
Detection and identification of invasive organisms in a new environment remains critical for initiating early eradication procedures. However, here exists a dichotomy; control during early establishment is preferable to managing an invasion later in the invasion curve (Fig. 24.1) because damages are comparatively low; however, because negative impacts may not yet have occurred, the immediacy of this action may not be realised. Complexity of control at this stage may be exacerbated because the initial population size may be as small as two individuals (Kalinowski *et al.* 2010), making detection difficult and relatively costly due to the potential geographical range involved. Biosurveillance detection methods seek to track and respond to invasions in real time in the wild. Hence, they need to rely minimally on 'chance' encounters, provide results quickly, and additionally not be very costly or technical to encourage widespread usage. For some species, such as *D. geminata*, genetic tools are the most feasible way of detecting new incursions before its physical impacts are noticed (Jaramillo *et al.* 2015). Paradoxically, the goals of early invasive detection align quite closely with those of conservation biology, which necessitates tracking rare populations in the wild (e.g. Chapter 10), and these approaches have often been adopted for genetic management of IAS.

Emerging genomic technologies in detection of invaders
Of the detection technologies, environmental DNA (eDNA) is likely the most promising for widespread application (Díaz-Ferguson and Moyer 2014; Chapter 2). Organisms deposit cells into their environment as they move through and interact with it. Organic traces including faeces, shed coverings, and saliva serve as genetic samples that may be obtained through environmental sampling of waters, sediments, or plant matter (Thomsen and Willerslev 2015). This approach is particularly useful for cryptic introductions (discussed below), or in areas where remote surveillance is difficult. DNA may persist in an environment for long timeframes (Willerslev *et al.* 2003), making it useful for detection of dispersive species, but less ideal for tracking presence or absence changes over a short timescale, depending on the substrate sampled. Broadly, eDNA approaches fall into four categories. The two most common approaches are single species detection, achieved through quantification of specific DNA markers (for example, through polymerase chain reaction, 'PCR'), and DNA metabarcoding to target conserved DNA regions that contain distinct species-specific genomic sequences to enable multispecies detection (Thomsen and Willerslev 2015). Other methods for more targeted multispecies detection are enrichment capture (e.g. using magnetic beads to capture specific DNA sequences) or non-specific detection achieved through shotgun sequencing of random DNA in the sample (Zinger *et al.* 2020).

The success of eDNA applications is dependent on several factors, and so researchers must be clear about the limits of the techniques within their system, and eDNA's suitability to the question/s being addressed (see Chapter 1). Each step of eDNA sampling and processing introduces sources of error that may compound and lead to uncertain detection results, hence implantation within a new environment may require extensive troubleshooting (see Darling and Mahon 2011 for a summary of error sources). For example, taking samples in the field can lead to sampling errors despite having a successful laboratory assay. Sampling in the wrong place or at the wrong time could fail to detect an incursion. Similarly, sampling in an environment where DNA does not degrade easily (e.g. low UV, cold) might reveal a false-positive if the DNA-shedder is no longer at that location. And while improved technologies (for example, the use of faster degrading eRNA to provide a more spatio-temporally discreet means of environmental sampling; Cristescu 2019) may improve on these technical weakness, some element of stochasticity will always be inherent when analysing a sample representative of a large geographic area. Understanding the relationship between DNA and the environment from which it is sampled is critical for efficacy of the technique (Troth *et al.* 2021), and much site-specific validation is needed before eDNA methods may be implemented on the management level.

An extension of the concept of eDNA is that of invertebrate-derived DNA (iDNA) obtained via parasitic invertebrates such as mosquitos, ticks, and beetles. Isolating the ingested material in these invertebrates allows identification of host or scavenged organisms (Calvignac-Spencer *et al.* 2013; Cutajar and Rowley 2020). Further, the limited time that the target DNA persists in the digestive tract can then be used to infer recent presence of an invader. In principle, this approach would be most useful for target species known to have single-host parasites or have specific niches that overlap directly with an invertebrate pest (e.g. Doña *et al.* 2018), thus meaning tailored invertebrate traps may essentially be a direct proxy for genetic sampling of the invasive host. However, even if an IAS has co-evolved with a parasite, the latter may not be present within the invaded range; in such cases, iDNA sampling would need to be conducted using generalist parasites (e.g. Bettazzi *et al.* 2021). The use of iDNA is still in its early phases, but may prove to be invaluable for the detection of cryptic, rare, or non-dispersive IAS (Cutajar and Rowley 2020).

Across the barcode-based detection methods, there is a shift from first-generation (i.e. Sanger) sequencing methods to next-generation sequencing (NGS), with the latter having higher power to discriminate between sampled organisms (Choudhary *et al.* 2021; discussed further in the next section). Improvements in NGS approaches have been achieved through rapid low-coverage shotgun sequencing of genomic DNA, referred to as genome skimming (Dodsworth 2015). The utility of this has been demonstrated in plants, where only 1 GB of sequencing data obtained from a single lane of Illumina HiSeq 2500 was used to differentiate 48 plant species through coverage of common diagnostic genomic regions (plastid and nuclear ribosomal regions, Nevill *et al.* 2020). However, caution should be taken when interpreting the results of such approaches, particularly when amplifying genomic regions within organisms that may have undergone hybridisation or introgression, as this may confound results (McKinnon *et al.* 2001). Further, long read sequencing technology is

also being applied to IAS detection. Oxford Nanopore Technology (ONT) is a single-molecule sequencing platform with the ability to sequence long molecules of both DNA and RNA, including a small and portable single flow-cell device called the minION. ONT reads allow for rapid sequence identification through real time sequencing and analysis, and may produce useable results (from sequencing to classification) in as little as 1–2 hours (Chalupowicz *et al.* 2019). Sample preparation needs to also be portable and fast, and while such technologies are under development (e.g. Ubik by ONT), DNA preparation protocols will likely need to be specifically calibrated for the system in which sampling occurs for optimal results (Stebbins 2019).

For genetic detection approaches to be useful to managers, data processing needs to have low cost and short turnover time, which may be difficult when sampling occurs across large or remote regions. Several emerging technologies hold promise for integrated solutions to these challenges. Lab-on-a-chip technology using microfluidics is currently under development within ecological fields and may help bridge this analytical gap (Maw *et al.* 2018; Wimbles *et al.* 2021). The goal of such devices is to be designed to integrate all necessary steps or components of an analysis onto the same small, portable device and only require a small sample volume. There exist a few examples of lab-on-a-chip technologies being applied to species management that have the potential to be applied to IAS detection. One example of this is the Conservation X Lab's Nucleic Acid Barcode Identification Tool (NABIT), which was designed as a rapid, low-cost, field-based DNA testing for wildlife trafficking. The iSPEED is another such device, which uses PCR for on-site detection of forest pathogens, and is ideal for remote surveying because it is portable and chemical components are shelf stable for at least 12 months (Capron *et al.* 2020). Many other systems testing the feasibility of using real-time PCR in IAS detection (Lamarche *et al.* 2015; Rizzo *et al.* 2020) could be used to create portable in-field devices, but it should be noted that chip fabrication technology is still underway and many 'proof-of-concept' studies use technologies that are not suitable for large-scale, real-world, field-based assays. In addition to PCR based technologies, several options that do not require PCR are emerging. Rapid and portable DNA-amplification free technologies are also under development, such as electrochemiluminescence sensors that can be uniquely calibrated to emit signals when they come into contact with target DNA strands; for example, such devices can detect disease-associated microRNAs (e.g. miRNA-21) down to quantities of 500 attomoles

(Kerr *et al.* 2021). Also developed for human disease diagnostics, clustered regularly interspaced short palindromic repeats (CRISPR) based tools can be used to detect nucleic acids using isothermal amplification (Kaminski *et al.* 2021), and could be adapted for ecological applications. However, these approaches are primarily developed for model systems. Drawbacks include the need for extensive calibration for each study system, and sample preparation integration is often lacking. Hence, the utility of these techniques would be greatly benefited by unifying efforts and establishing standards for tool development, repeatability assessment, and genetic database maintenance across relevant departments and countries (Hamelin and Roe 2020; Martinez *et al.* 2020). Further, biosurveillance techniques should be optimised for biogeographic regions, taking into account differences within bioregions' ecological subcommunities, which may impact DNA sampling protocols based on species' life-history (Westfall *et al.* 2020).

Quantum sensing may offer a wholly different approach to species detection. Very simply, quantum sensing describes a device with the ability to response to exceedingly small stimulus by using quantum state disturbances and could be applied to processing low quantities of highly degradable organics such as DNA and RNA sampled in an environment (Di Ventra and Taniguchi 2016). It boasts superior capacity for detecting very small variations in the tested material properties, and may allow for real time continuous measurements of very small amounts of nucleic acids without need for invasive biological sampling, as has already been demonstrated by its use in bacterial growth sampling (Spedalieri *et al.* 2018). Emerging quantum sensing tools, such as quantum dots (Qiu and Hildebrandt 2015) when combined with other emerging technologies have the potential to enable rapid, portable, and longlasting detection measures that may be applied across a diverse variety of environments.

IDENTIFICATION OF INVADERS (AND THEIR GENES)

Detection techniques ultimately rely on the target IAS being previously identified in an environment, and/or genotyped previously, and their sequences being publicly available. For instance, DNA metabarcoding is entirely reliant on the existence of high-quality and validated reference libraries for marker generation, while even non-specific shotgun sequencing requires a sequence database that allows identification of the IAS genetic signature. For well-known and well-researched IAS, this may not be an issue because genetic resources (e.g. the species' genome, validated barcodes) may already be available. However, this is not always the case, especially for invertebrate and pathogenic invaders. Hence identification and characterisation of the invader must predate rapid genetic detection techniques. Novel species, or those with complex evolutionary histories (including but not limited to admixture and or hybridisation) will be more difficult to target (Percy *et al.* 2014). Further factors such as intraspecific and intragenomic variation must be considered, and is a major hurdle that must be addressed in major taxa lineages, for example fungal pathogen detection (Lücking *et al.* 2020).

Cryptic taxonomy

The occurrence of cryptic species (biological groups of organisms that are indistinguishable morphologically) is common, especially within invertebrate and fungal taxa (Godfray 2002). The occurrence of an invasive cryptic species means that initial identification of an introduction may be difficult, and even once the invader's presence is known, tracking population density and spread may be challenging. Genetic sequencing can confirm the identity and spread of a cryptic species.

Hybridisation

The occurrence of introgression or hybridisation is of interest to invasion biologists for many reasons and of particular interest to invasion biologists because of the increased opportunity for these events to occur following non-native introductions. Views on the appropriate management of such events might be context-specific, and may benefit from a genic view of introgression (Ottenburghs 2021). Genetic exchange between native and non-native species has, in some cases, resulted in adaptive introgression (e.g. Oziolor *et al.* 2019). However, hybridisation between the invasive and a native species, or hybridisation between two strains or populations of the invader, may play a significant evolutionary role in the establishment and long term success of the invader (Ellstrand and Schierenbeck 2000; Hovick and Whitney 2014). Other research indicates that it is possible that hybridisation may reduce invasive impacts and so may serve as targeted solutions for invasive management (Viard *et al.* 2020). Because the exact effect hybridisation has on a population will be taxa- or even population-specific, identifying the specific pattern of hybridisation and linking these to the specific invasion characteristics within an invasive population is of vital importance. Hybridisation occurs across many invasive taxa (Buhk and Thielsch 2015; Stephens *et al.* 2020) and may be difficult to identify and characterise across a population without the use of genetics. Previously, barcoding and microsatellites were used to characterise the level of genetic mixing between populations and species; however, often greater resolution of genetic information is needed to prevent widespread misclassification (McFarlane and Pemberton 2019). While older genetic technologies may be sufficient for some populations, reduced representation sequencing may be required to confidently identify hybrids and their backcrosses to ensure management is correctly informed of an individual's species classification (Fig. 24.3; Senn et al. 2019). Further, better information regarding lineage backcrosses may assist in the discovery of previously unidentified hybrids.

Emerging genomic technologies in identification of invaders

As described above, genetic sequencing may confirm or complement phenotype-based identification, so long as pre-existing genetic resources are available. In such cases, a unique barcode sequence may enable the identification of a foreign yet-unknown organism, or the barcoding may fail (Hickerson et al. 2006). In some cases, de novo whole genome sequencing (WGS) may be required (e.g. for identifying fungal pathogen strains, Cuomo 2017) which can be facilitated by short read Illumina sequencing or the previously discussed long read ONT MinION, that allows for WGS on a portable device (Fig. 24.3). Labour-intensive bioinformatic analyses (e.g. genome assembly) is not required for all species, but for some taxa where little comparative barcode information is available, it may assist in identification.

Once a novel genetic sequence is discovered, identification and classification of the organism are required. Phylogenetic data may be used alongside morphological data to confidently identify species (Scott et al. 2018). Genetic sequence data offers a rapid and accurate means of overcoming traditional taxonomic challenges (Kim et al. 2019); this is important because misidentification will cost time and money in an emergency IAS response. Even if little is known about the species itself, information about closely related species may help management predict the risk the IAS poses, as well as define other important factors such as its functional ranges. However, genetic proximity to related species alone cannot predict invasiveness, and should be employed as one of many risk-management tools in response to a new potential IAS incursion. For instance, two fruit fly species in Australia Bactrocera tryoni (wide range and pest status) and B. aquilonis (range limited) are nearly genetically indistinguishable and are thought to differ in invasiveness due to alternative mating strategies (Morrow et al. 2000). Even globally successful IAS, such as the starling (Sturnus vulgaris), have documented failed introductions (Feare 1984). Similarly, genetics alone cannot predict invasion risk, because a myriad of factors, including ecology, reproductive strategies, and stochastic factors may affect a species ability to establish and become invasive.

CONTAINMENT AND ERADICATION

Often, diagnosing an existing invasive population as a candidate for removal can be facilitated by population genetic assessment (Box 24.2). Population genomics encompasses a range of fundamental analytical tools for tracking organism movement into and throughout an invasive range. Population genomics analyses that include native range populations may identify sources of introductions and inform management decisions; for example, re-invading invasive rats across the Haida Gwaii archipelago were successfully identified as individuals from a known external source population rather than on-island survivors (Sjodin et al. 2020). Characterisation of gene flow is also vital for targeted management efforts within invasive ranges. Once the population substructure and dispersal patterns of an invasive population have been characterised, appropriate management goals may be set. For instance, microsatellite and mitochondrial sequence analyses were employed to identify a genetically isolated population of European starlings (Sturnus vulgaris) in Western Australia, thereby informing the feasibility of targeted eradication and ongoing monitoring efforts (Rollins et al. 2009, 2011; Fig. 24.2a, b). Similarly, characterisation of feral pig (Sus scrofa) populations in Western Australia resulted in the identification of discrete subpopulation boundaries, thereby enabling containment efforts by allowing each to be considered as separate management units (Spencer and Woolnough 2004; Fig. 24.2c, d). One should also not overlook the importance of understanding population structure prior to eradication work, because this information will be highly informative should subsequent introductions occur and will assist population monitoring.

As an IAS population becomes established, it often remains in the 'lag phase' (Fig. 24.1, 'colonisation'), where population size and geographic extent remains stable. In such cases, it may be useful to monitor allele frequencies to determine whether adaptation is occurring in these populations, because it is believed that such evolutionary changes may enable the 'expansion phase' (Fig. 24.1,

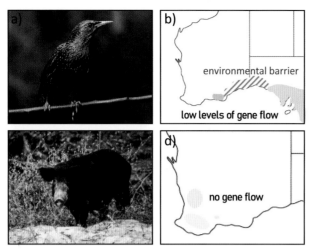

Fig. 24.2. Population genetic analyses being applied to IAS management to identify population substructure in two invasive species in Western Australia. Panel a) depicts a European starling, *Sturnus vulgaris*, and panel b) shows the starling population structure, with the blue indicating the western most range of the main starling population, the red indicating the expanding range edge, and the grey stripes indicating an environmental barrier (the Nullarbor Plain) that acts to severely restrict westward gene flow to the expanding range edge. Panel c) depicts a feral pig, *Sus scrofa*, and panel d) depicts the feral pig population structure, with minimal to no gene flow between distinct subpopulation clusters depicted in different colours.

'establishment'), when ranges and population size rapidly expand. For example, Pyrenean rocket (*Sisymbrium austriacum*) introduced to northern Europe remained in the lag phase for over a century and genetic analyses of herbarium specimens collected over this period revealed allele frequency changes in genes relating to flowering time; these genetic alterations seem likely to have contributed to the current rapid expansion of this species (Vandepitte *et al.* 2014). Selection analyses of contemporary populations may assist in prioritising which populations may be most likely to expand, though critical interpretation of adaptive patterns is essential as factors like allele surfing or historic introduction regime induced population structure may obscure results (Stuart *et al.* 2021).

Proof of eradication

Successful eradication schemes, such as the management of invasive European carp (*Cyprinus carpio*) across Australia (Haynes *et al.* 2009), or removal of multiple incursions of fire ants (*Solenopsis invicta*) from Queensland (Australia) (Wylie *et al.* 2016), have incorporated the use of population genetics to assist with operational area mapping and to provide a reference for potential future IAS reappearances. For example, ongoing fire ant eradication efforts use genotyping of the social ant form to predict how widespread the colony could be, and genotyping colonies to understand from where the IAS is introduced and how it spreads (Wylie *et al.* 2021). However, IAS removal efforts suffer from the law of diminishing returns (as do all control operations) because as population numbers decrease, it becomes increasingly more difficult to detect the invader's presence. Proof of successful eradication may then be extremely difficult, with techniques such as eDNA being employed to monitor over large spatial and temporal scales (Furlan *et al.* 2019). Advancements in IAS detection hence will also assist surveying efforts post eradication, which may be required to continue long after an eradication program appears to have been successfully executed.

Box 24.2: Population genetic approaches for invasion management

Population genetics is a fundamental tool for IAS management, particularly when tackling a new species, population, or ecosystem (Fig. 24.3). A diagnostic sample size may be achieved quite cost effectively, with a case study on the whitefly (*Bemisia tabaci*) revealing that as few as three individuals per population gave precise genetic differentiation (F_{ST}) measures (Qu *et al.* 2020), though larger sample sizes may be initially required because this information would not be known *a priori* (Nazareno *et al.* 2017). Ultimately, the sampling scheme will be informed by interindividual genetic variability and population structure. With a diverse range of reduced representation sequencing technologies available (e.g. RADseq, GBS, DArT-seq) that do not require in-house primer development (unlike microsatellite and mitochondrial markers), a well-informed population profile can be obtained easily without technical wet-lab expertise. Further, many sequencing companies can provide already processed SNP data, and while such data may require moderate analytical knowledge to interpret and analyse, expert advice or collaboration can greatly help to reduce technical difficulties during this process. At this point in time, WGS of large numbers of individuals is only practical for species with small genomes. In populations with high levels of homozygosity, where reduced representation sequencing would not provide the resolution to confidently determine subpopulation structure (e.g. asexual species), a WGS approach may be required (i.e. Dale *et al.* 2019). Once sequencing data is obtained, there is a range of analytically straightforward assessments that may be conducted to directly inform management whether eradication or containment are feasible options. This includes using population structure and gene

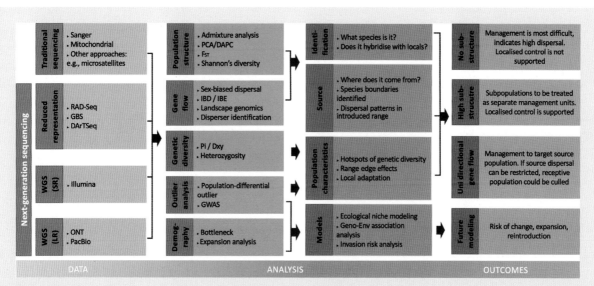

Fig. 24.3. A summary of common population genetic data and analytical approaches, along with the management questions and strategies that they can inform. (Abbreviations: RAD-Seq = Restriction site Associated DNA Sequencing, GBS = Genotyping-by-Sequencing, DArTSeq = Diversity Arrays Technology targeted genotyping, WGS = whole genome sequencing, SR = short read, LR = long read, ONT = Oxford Nanopore Technologies, IBD = isolation by distance, IBE = isolation by environment).

flow analysis to identify how interconnected IAS from different sampling sites may be and to identify population boundaries. Understanding patterns of genetic divergence and diversity, and selection analyses, can help identify the occurrence of local adaptation, range edge effects, and signatures of range expansion; these data may assist with long-term IAS population modelling and risk management. Pragmatically, obtaining genetic samples of individuals across a managed invasive population may be relatively inexpensive and adds great value in terms of fundamental discovery in applied research. A balanced research portfolio approach when dealing with IAS is highly beneficial, because IAS research is a source of fundamental discovery and any tissue samples collected may be used to their fullest extent to gain indispensable information about the organism and/or the ecosystem in which they reside.

ASSET-BASED PROTECTION

Emerging methods

Once a population is established across a wide enough geographic area, containment and removal may not been feasible from a practical or financial perspective. In such cases, asset-based protection may be required. There is a range of manipulative genomic approaches to IAS control, for instance using genetics to disrupt reproductive success (e.g. Teem *et al.* 2020). The details of such techniques are reviewed in Chapter 26. Genetics can also be used in concert with pathogen-based control methods, to track different strains of a pathogen throughout a population and monitor efficacy (for example, introduced rabbits within Australia and rabbit haemorrhagic disease; Capucci *et al.* 1996).

In addition to population reduction approaches, genetic tools provide information that may assist managers with asset-based protection during later stage IAS. These techniques focus on understanding and tracking the genetic characteristics of the focal IAS population, so that

long-term management strategies may be developed, financially forecast, and have meaningful impacts on the native organisms, ecosystems, and agriculture they seek to protect. Ongoing gene flow analysis of an IAS population can provide clarity and certainty around management decisions. For example, ongoing wild dog management in Australia has required careful identification of gene flow corridors (Stephens 2011), enabling management to focus on specific regions, such that culling efforts may produce a meaningful reduction of effective populations size. Similarly, genetic data can be used to parameterise population models used in cost-benefit analyses to inform management (e.g. Campbell *et al.* 2016).

Predicting change in an invasive population

Modelling future population density and range change is also fundamental to the long-term management of IAS. Understanding how an expanding population may interact with the new ecosystems they encounter (Doody *et al.* 2018),

Box 24.3: Translating genomic data into something useful for a manager

One of the ever-present barriers in invasion genomics is the divide between technical genetic approaches and the environmental managers who seek to implement decisions based on the outputs. Bridging this divide is essential for improving both research and management outcomes, and many research spheres are focusing specifically on this (e.g. BioSAFE, Hamelin and Roe 2020).

Genetic approaches can be bench ready and/or commercially available, or they can require research and development to address complex questions. In many cases, the manager's decision to use genetic approaches, and which techniques are most appropriate, will be based on cost, timeliness and a pre-existing understanding and trust in the tools. The manager does not necessarily need to know how the laboratory analyses work, but they do need to understand what questions genetic approaches will answer and then how the genetic data can inform the management action.

The technician needs to be expert in genetic approaches, data analysis and data presentation is a way that is meaningful for the manager. For a new incursion, this may mean that the data are delivered quickly but for a small number of samples. For a widespread IAS, time may be less of a factor, but the datasets and analyses could be more complicated. The key is translating the genomic data into an informative product that is simple, effective, and non-jargonistic.

At the heart of this cross-discipline relationship are trust and communication. Successful relationships work when there is a common objective identified at the outset, a mutual understanding of roles, responsibilities and drivers, and delivery of clearly defined outputs and outcomes (Fig. 24.4; Chapter 27).

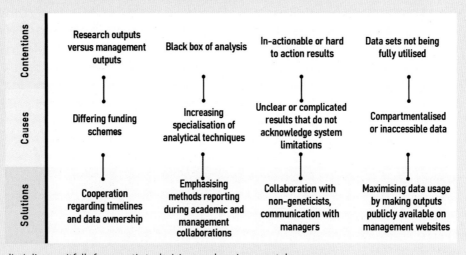

Fig. 24.4. Cross-disciplinary pitfalls for genetic technicians and environmental managers

or how climate change or land alteration may impact existing invasive populations (Walton *et al.* 2017) will help inform pre-emptive adjustments to management strategies, such as shifting monitoring borders, altering the native species being surveyed for impact, and managing culling efforts. Developing realistic models is difficult, but performance can be improved by increasing model specificity based on the focal invader's characteristics (Liu *et al.* 2020). Ecological niche modelling is often used to predict the spread of an invader, and to aid this various forms of genetic information may be used to better tailor models to a specific population, including specifying subpopulation lineage information (Banerjee *et al.* 2019), including adaptive genetic markers (Sillero *et al.* 2020), and population wide genetic variation data (Lyons *et al.* 2016). It seems likely that when epigenetic research on

wild populations is more commonly available, such data will also be incorporated into models to better capture the genotype × environmental interactions within the invasive range (Sarma *et al.* 2021). Such information will assist in improved prediction of region-specific interactions between the genetic diversity patterns across the IAS and the spatial and environmental patterns of the focal invaded range.

As analytical techniques become more sophisticated, big data and higher volumes of samples can be included in all manner of analyses. However, as the breath of genetic information available to such analyses increases, so do the models become more complicated. As models become more sophisticated, they are often harder to understand, and easier to misuse or misapply. Translating useful data into information that can be interpreted and applied by IAS managers across a range of levels is vital and remains a major hurdle (Korf 2011). Machine learning is already being used as a means to assess analytically complex predictive models that incorporate genetic data (Pless *et al.* 2021), but such analyses may be computer intensive. Here, quantum computing may play a role in the future (Asano *et al.* 2015). The shifts in quantum states of the computer device can deal with extraordinarily complex computation, making them ideal for conducting analyses with huge numbers of simultaneous possibilities (Sherwin 2018). This makes computing models easier, cheaper, and faster, thereby increasing the application of sophisticated analysis across many areas of ecological management.

CONCLUSION

Although integrating the highly technical nature of modern genetic analyses with practical and responsive management advice can be challenging, there are clearly many uses for these data that are demonstrated to have assisted invasive species management. In this chapter, we have highlighted how genetic information is most useful at each stage of species invasion (Box 24.1, Fig. 24.1: transport/prevention, colonisation/eradication, establishment/containment, spread/asset-based protection). We have described well-tested and emerging technologies in this field of research and how they are best applied. We also have outlined population genetic analyses that can improve invasive species management (Box 24.2, Fig. 24.2). Importantly, we have discussed the interface between the genetic technician and the invasive species manager (Box 24.3, Fig. 24.4), with the aim to maximise the utility of these collaborations. Genetic analyses have great potential to inform invasive species management and with careful consideration between the technician and manager, optimal and cost-effective strategies can be developed to hinder the progression of invasions across the planet.

DISCUSSION TOPICS

1. What ethical factors should be considered when controlling an IAS population?
2. In what circumstances are invasive species beneficial? How can IAS improve the population viability for native species or ecosystem services?

REFERENCES

Asano M, Khrennikov A, Ohya M, Tanaka Y, Yamato I (2015) *Quantum Adaptivity in Biology: From Genetics to Cognition.* Springer, Netherlands. doi:10.1007/978-94-017-9819-8

Baker CM, Plein M, R S, Bode M (2020) Simultaneous invasive alien predator eradication delivers the best outcomes for protected island species. *Biological Invasions* **22**, 1085–1095. doi:10.1007/s10530-019-02161-z

Banerjee AK, Mukherjee A, Guo W., WL N, Huang Y (2019) Combining ecological niche modeling with genetic lineage information to predict potential distribution of *Mikania micrantha* Kunth in South and Southeast Asia under predicted climate change. *Global Ecology and Conservation* **20**, e00800.

Bariche M, Kleitou P, Kalogirou S, Bernardi G (2017) Genetics reveal the identity and origin of the lionfish invasion in the Mediterranean Sea. *Scientific Reports* **7**, 6782. doi:10.1038/s41598-017-07326-1

Bellard C, P C, Blackburn TM (2016) Alien species as a driver of recent extinctions. *Biology Letters* **12**, 20150623. doi:10.1098/rsbl.2015.0623

Bergstrom DM, Lucieer A, Kiefer K, Wasley J, Belbin L, *et al.* (2009) Indirect effects of invasive species removal devastate World Heritage Island. *Journal of Applied Ecology* **46**, 73–81. doi:10.1111/j.1365-2664.2008.01601.x

Bettazzi F, Orlandini S, Zhang L, Laschi S, *et al.* (2021) A simple and selective electrochemical magneto-assay for sea lice eDNA detection developed with a quality by design approach. *Science of The Total Environment* **791**, 148111. doi:10.1016/j.scitotenv.2021.148111

Blackburn TM, Essl F, Evans T, Hulme PE, Jeschke JM, *et al.* (2014) A unified classification of alien species based on the magnitude of their environmental impacts. *PLOS Biology* **12**, e100185.

Blaser S, Diem H, Von FA, Gueuning M, Andreou M, *et al.* (2018) From laboratory to point of entry: development and implementation of a loop-mediated isothermal amplification (LAMP)-based genetic identification system to prevent introduction of quarantine insect species. *Pest Management Science* **74**, 1504–1512. doi:10.1002/ps.4866

Bomford M, SC B, Lawrence E (2010) Predicting establishment success for introduced freshwater fishes: a role for climate matching. *Biological Invasions* **12**, 2559–2571. doi:10.1007/s10530-009-9665-3

Brandenburger CR, Sherwin WB, Creer SM, Buitenwerf R, Poore AGB, *et al.* (2019) Rapid reshaping: The evolution of morphological changes in an introduced beach daisy. *Proceedings of the Royal Society B: Biological Sciences* **286**, 20181713. doi:10.1098/rspb.2018.1713

Buhk C, Thielsch A (2015) Hybridisation boosts the invasion of an alien species complex: Insights into future invasiveness. *Perspectives in Plant Ecology, Evolution and Systematics* **17**, 274–283. doi:10.1016/j.ppees.2015.05.001

Calvignac-Spencer S, Merkel K, Kutzner N, Kühl H, Boesch C, *et al.* (2013) Carrion fly-derived DNA as a tool for comprehensive and cost-effective assessment of mammalian biodiversity. *Molecular Ecology* **22**, 915–924. doi:10.1111/mec.12183

Campbell S, Roberts EJ, Craemer R, Pacioni C, L R, Woolnough AP (2016) Assessing the economic benefits of starling detection and control to Western Australia. *Australasian Journal of Environmental Management* **23**, 81–99. doi:10.1080/14486563.2015.1028486

Capron A, Stewart D, Hrywkiw K, Allen K, Feau N, *et al.* (2020) In Situ Processing and Efficient Environmental Detection (iSPEED) of tree pests and pathogens using point-of-use real-time PCR. *PLoS One* **15**, e022686.

Capucci L, Fusi P, Lavazza A, ML P, Rossi C (1996) Detection and preliminary characterization of a new rabbit calicivirus related to rabbit hemorrhagic disease virus but nonpathogenic. *Journal of Virology* **70**, 8614–8623. doi:10.1128/jvi.70.12.8614-8623.1996

Chalupowicz L, Dombrovsky A, Gaba V, Luria N, Reuven M, *et al.* (2019) Diagnosis of plant diseases using the Nanopore sequencing platform. *Plant Pathology* **68**, 229–238. doi:10.1111/ppa.12957

Choudhary P, Singh BN, H C, Saxena AK (2021) DNA barcoding of phytopathogens for disease diagnostics and bio-surveillance. *World Journal of Microbiology and Biotechnology* **37**, 54. doi:10.1007/s11274-021-03019-0

Cristescu ME (2019) Can environmental RNA revolutionize biodiversity science? *Trends in Ecology & Evolution* **34**, 694–697. doi:10.1016/j.tree.2019.05.003

Cuomo CA (2017) Harnessing whole genome sequencing in medical mycology. *Current Fungal Infection Reports* **11**, 52–59. doi:10.1007/s12281-017-0276-7

Cutajar T, Rowley J (2020) Surveying frogs from the bellies of their parasites: Invertebrate-derived DNA as a novel survey method for frogs. *Global Ecology and Conservation* **22**, e00978.

Dale AL, Feau N, Everhart SE, Dhillon B, Wong B, *et al.* (2019) Mitotic recombination and rapid genome evolution in the invasive forest pathogen *Phytophthora ramorum. MBio* **10**, 02452–18. doi:10.1128/mBio.02452-18

Darling J, Mahon A (2011) From molecules to management: Adopting DNA-based methods for monitoring biological invasions in aquatic environments. *Environmental Research* **11**, 978–988. doi:10.1016/j.envres.2011.02.001

Department of Primary Industries (2010) *Invasive Plants and Animals*. DPI Victoria, Melbourne.

Di Ventra M, Taniguchi M (2016) Decoding DNA, RNA and peptides with quantum tunnelling. *Nature Nanotechnology* **11**, 117–126. doi:10.1038/nnano.2015.320

Diagne C, Leroy B, Vaissière A-C, Gozlan RE, Roiz D, *et al.* (2021) High and rising economic costs of biological invasions worldwide. *Nature* **592**, 571–576. doi:10.1038/s41586-021-03405-6

Díaz-Ferguson E, Moyer G (2014) History, applications, methodological issues and perspectives for the use of environmental DNA (eDNA) in marine and freshwater environments. *Revista De Biologia Tropical* **62**, 1273–1284. doi:10.15517/rbt.v62i4.13231

Dodsworth S (2015) Genome skimming for next-generation biodiversity analysis. *Trends in Plant Science* **20**, 525–527. doi:10.1016/j.tplants.2015.06.012

Doña J, Proctor H, Mironov S, D S, Jovani R (2018) Host specificity, infrequent major host switching and the diversification of highly host-specific symbionts: The case of vane-dwelling feather mites. *Global Ecology and Biogeography* **27**, 188–198. doi:10.1111/geb.12680

Doody JS, McHenry C, Letnic M, Everitt C, Sawyer G, *et al.* (2018) Forecasting the spatiotemporal pattern of the cane toad invasion into north-western Australia. *Wildlife Research* **45**, 718–725. doi:10.1071/WR18091

Ellstrand N, Schierenbeck K (2000) Hybridization as a stimulus for the evolution of invasiveness in plants? *Proceedings of the National Academy of Sciences* **97**, 7043–7050. doi:10.1073/pnas.97.13.7043

Feare C (1984) *The Starling*. Shire Publications, UK.

Furlan EM, Gleeson D, Wisniewski C, J Y, Duncan RP (2019) eDNA surveys to detect species at very low densities: A case study of European carp eradication in Tasmania, Australia. *Journal of Applied Ecology* **56**, 2505–2517. doi:10.1111/1365-2664.13485

García-Díaz P, Kerezsy A, Unmack PJ, Lintermans M, Beatty SJ, *et al.* (2018) Transport pathways shape the biogeography of alien freshwater fishes in Australia. *Diversity and Distributions* **24**, 1405–1415. doi:10.1111/ddi.12777

García-Díaz P, Ramsey DSL, Woolnough AP, Franch M, Llorente GA, *et al.* (2017) Challenges in confirming eradication success of invasive red-eared sliders. *Biological Invasions* **19**, 2739–2750. doi:10.1007/s10530-017-1480-7

Godfray HCJ (2002) Challenges for taxonomy. *Nature* **417**, 17–19. doi:10.1038/417017a

Hamelin R, Roe A (2020) Genomic biosurveillance of forest invasive alien enemies: A story written in code. *Evolutionary Applications* **13**, 95–115. doi:10.1111/eva.12853

Harris S, Elliott C, A W, Barclay C (2018) A heuristic framework for invasive species research species research planning and measurement. Developing an invasive species research strategy in Tasmania. *Record of the Queen Victoria Museum and Art Gallery* **117**, 3–13.

Haynes GD, Gilligan DM, P G, Nicholas FW (2009) Population genetics and management units of invasive common carp *Cyprinus carpio* in the Murray–Darling Basin, Australia. *Journal of Fish Biology* **75**, 295–320. doi:10.1111/j.1095-8649.2009.02276.x

Hickerson MJ, CP M, Moritz C (2006) DNA barcoding will often fail to discover new animal species over broad parameter space. *Systematic Biology* **55**, 729–739. doi:10.1080/10635150600969898

Hoffmann B, Broadhurst L (2016) The economic cost of managing invasive species in Australia. *NeoBiota* **31**, 1–18. doi:10.3897/neobiota.31.6960

Hovick S, Whitney K (2014) Hybridisation is associated with increased fecundity and size in invasive taxa: meta-analytic support for the hybridisation-invasion hypothesis. *Ecology Letters* **17**, 1464–1477. doi:10.1111/ele.12355

Hulme PE (2009) Trade, transport and trouble: managing invasive species pathways in an era of globalization. *Journal of Applied Ecology* **46**, 10–18. doi:10.1111/j.1365-2664.2008.01600.x

Jaramillo A, Osman D, L C, Cardenas L (2015) Molecular evidence of a *Didymosphenia geminata* (Bacillariophyceae) invasion in Chilean freshwater systems. *Harmful Algae* **49**, 117–123. doi:10.1016/j.hal.2015.09.004

Kalinowski ST, Muhlfeld CC, CS G, Cox B (2010) Founding population size of an aquatic invasive species. *Conservation Genetics* **11**, 2049–2053. doi:10.1007/s10592-009-0041-8

Kaminski MM, Abudayyeh OO, Gootenberg JS, F Z, Collins JJ (2021) CRISPR-based diagnostics. *Nature Biomedical Engineering* **5**, 643–656. doi:10.1038/s41551-021-00760-7

Kerr E, Farr R, Doeven EH, Nai YH, Alexander R, *et al.* (2021) Amplification-free electrochemiluminescence molecular beacon-based microRNA sensing using a mobile phone for detection. *Sensors and Actuators B: Chemical* **330**, 129261. doi:10.1016/j.snb.2020.129261

Kilroy C, Unwin M (2011) The arrival and spread of the bloom-forming, freshwater diatom, *Didymosphenia geminata*, in New Zealand. *Aquatic Invasions* **6**, 349–362.

Kim K-H, Kim J-S, Cho H-J, Lee J-H, T-H J, *et al.* (2019) Identification of key genes for the precise classification between *Solenopsis invicta* and *S. geminata* Facilitating the Quarantine Process. *Genes* **10**, 812.

Kolar C, Lodge D (2001) Progress in invasion biology: Predicting invaders. *Trends in Ecology & Evolution* **16**, 199–204. doi:10.1016/S0169-5347(01)02101-2

Korf BR (2011) Genetics and genomics education: The next generation. *Genetics in Medicine* **13**, 201–202. doi:10.1097/GIM.0b013e31820986cd

Lamarche J, Potvin A, Pelletier G, Stewart D, Feau N, *et al.* (2015) Molecular detection of 10 of the most unwanted alien forest pathogens in Canada using real-time PCR. *PLoS One* **10**, e013426.

Liu C, Wolter C, W X, Jeschke JM (2020) Species distribution models have limited spatial transferability for invasive species. *Ecology Letters* **23**, 1682–1692. doi:10.1111/ele.13577

Lücking R, Aime MC, Robbertse B, Miller AN, Ariyawansa HA, *et al.* (2020) Unambiguous identification of fungi: where do we stand and how accurate and precise is fungal DNA barcoding? *IMA Fungus* **11**, 14. doi:10.1186/s43008-020-00033-z

Lyons MP, DB S, Kozak KH (2016) Determinants of range limits in montane woodland salamanders (Genus *Plethodon*). *Copeia* **104**, 101–110. doi:10.1643/OT-14-222

Martinez B, Reaser JK, Dehgan A, Zamft B, Baisch D, *et al.* (2020) Technology innovation: advancing capacities for the early detection of and rapid response to invasive species. *Biological Invasions* **22**, 75–100. doi:10.1007/s10530-019-02146-y

Maw MM, Pan X, Peng Z, Wang Y, Zhao L, *et al.* (2018) A changeable lab-on-a-chip detector for marine nonindigenous microorganisms in ship's ballast water. *Micromachines* **9**, 20.

McFarlane S, Pemberton J (2019) Detecting the true extent of introgression during anthropogenic hybridization. *Trends in Ecology & Evolution* **34**, 315–326. doi:10.1016/j.tree.2018.12.013

McKinnon GE, Vaillancourt RE, HD J, Potts BM (2001) Chloroplast sharing in the Tasmanian eucalypts. *Evolution* **55**, 703–711. doi:10.1111/j.0014-3820.2001.tb00806.x

Morrow J, Scott L, Congdon B, Yeates D, M F, *et al.* (2000) Close genetic similarity between two sympatric species of tephritid fruit fly reproductively isolated by mating time. *Evolution* **54**, 899–910.

Nazareno AG, Bemmels JB, CW D, Lohmann LG (2017) Minimum sample sizes for population genomics: An empirical study from an Amazonian plant species. *Molecular Ecology Resources* **17**, 1136–1147. doi:10.1111/1755-0998.12654

Nevill PG, Zhong X, Tonti-Filippini J, Byrne M, Hislop M, *et al.* (2020) Large scale genome skimming from herbarium material for accurate plant identification and phylogenomics. *Plant Methods* **16**(1), 1–8.

Ottenburghs J (2021) The genic view of hybridization in the Anthropocene. *Evolutionary Applications* **14**, 2342–2360. doi:10.1111/eva.13223

Oziolor EM, Reid NM, Yair S, Lee KM, VerPloeg SG, *et al.* (2019) Adaptive introgression enables evolutionary rescue from extreme environmental pollution. *Science* **364**, 455–457. doi:10.1126/science.aav4155

Percy DM, Argus GW, Cronk QC, Fazekas AJ, Kesanakurti PR, *et al.* (2014) Understanding the spectacular failure of DNA barcoding in willows (*Salix*): Does this result from a trans-specific selective sweep? *Molecular Ecology* **23**, 4737–4756. doi:10.1111/mec.12837

Pereira HM, LM N, Martins IS (2012) Global biodiversity change: The bad, the good, and the unknown. *Annual Review of Environment and Resources* **37**, 25–50. doi:10.1146/annurev-environ-042911-093511

Pless E, Saarman NP, Powell JR, C A, Amatulli G (2021) A machine-learning approach to map landscape connectivity in Aedes aegypti with genetic and environmental data. *Proceedings of the National Academy of Sciences* **118**, e2003201118. doi:10.1073/pnas.2003201118

Qiu X, Hildebrandt N (2015) Rapid and multiplexed microRNA diagnostic assay using quantum dot-based Förster resonance energy transfer. *ACS Nano* **9**, 8449–8457. doi:10.1021/acsnano.5b03364

Qu W-M, Liang N, Wu Z-K, Y-G Z, Chu D (2020) Minimum sample sizes for invasion genomics: Empirical investigation in an invasive whitefly. *Ecology and Evolution* **10**, 38–49. doi:10.1002/ece3.5677

Rizzo D, Lio DD, Bartolini L, Cappellini G, Bruscoli T, *et al.* (2020) A duplex real-time PCR with probe for simultaneous detection of *Geosmithia morbida* and its vector *Pityophthorus juglandis*. *PLoS One* **15**, e024110.

Rollins LA, Woolnough AP, Sinclair R, NJ M, Sherwin WB (2011) Mitochondrial DNA offers unique insights into invasion history of the common starling. *Molecular Ecology* **20**, 2307–2317. doi:10.1111/j.1365-294X.2011.05101.x

Rollins LA, Woolnough AP, Wilton AN, R S, Sherwin WB (2009) Invasive species can't cover their tracks: using microsatellites to assist management of starling (*Sturnus vulgaris*) populations in Western Australia. *Molecular Ecology* **18**, 1560–1573. doi:10.1111/j.1365-294X.2009.04132.x

Sarma RR, Crossland MR, Eyck HJF, DeVore JL, Edwards RJ, *et al.* (2021) Intergenerational effects of manipulating DNA methylation in the early life of an iconic invader. *Philosophical Transactions of the Royal Society B: Biological Sciences* **376**, 20200125. doi:10.1098/rstb.2020.0125

Schmeller D, Bridgewater P (2016) The Intergovernmental Platform on Biodiversity and Ecosystem Services (IPBES): Progress and next steps. *Biodiversity and Conservation* **25**, 801–805. doi:10.1007/s10531-016-1095-9

Scott R, Zhan A, Brown EA, Chain FJJ, Cristescu ME, *et al.* (2018) Optimization and performance testing of a sequence processing pipeline applied to detection of nonindigenous species. *Evolutionary Applications* **11**, 891–905. doi:10.1111/eva.12604

Senn HV, Ghazali M, Kaden J, Barclay D, Harrower B, *et al.* (2019) Distinguishing the victim from the threat: SNP-based methods reveal the extent of introgressive hybridization between wildcats and domestic cats in Scotland and inform future in situ and ex situ management options for species restoration. *Evolutionary Applications* **12**, 399–414. doi:10.1111/eva.12720

Sherwin WB (2018) Entropy, or information, unifies ecology and evolution and beyond. *Entropy* **20**, 727.

Sillero N, Huey RB, Gilchrist G, L R, Pascual M (2020) Distribution modelling of an introduced species: Do adaptive genetic markers affect potential range? *Proceedings of the Royal Society B: Biological Sciences* **287**, 20201791. doi:10.1098/rspb.2020.1791

Sjodin BMF, Irvine RL, Ford AT, GR H, Russello MA (2020) *Rattus* population genomics across the Haida Gwaii archipelago provides a framework for guiding invasive species management. *Evolutionary Applications* **13**, 889–904. doi:10.1111/eva.12907

Spedalieri G, S P, Braunstein SL (2018) Symmetric and asymmetric discrimination of bosonic loss: Toy applications to biological samples and photodegradable materials. *Physical Review A* **98**, 53836. doi:10.1103/PhysRevA.98.053836

Spencer P, Woolnough A (2004) Size should matter: Distribution and genetic considerations for pest animal management. *Ecological Management & Restoration* **5**, 231–234. doi:10.1111/j.1442-8903.2004.209-9.x

Stebbins B (2019) *A Novel Infield Metagenomic Approach to Evaluating Surface Water Quality in Lake Warner.* University of Massachusetts Amherst, MA, USA.

Stephens D (2011) *The Molecular Ecology of Australian Wild Dogs: Hybridisation, Gene Flow and Genetic Structure at Multiple Geographic Scales.* The University of Western Australia, Perth.

Stephens K, Measey J, C R, Le Roux JJ (2020) Occurrence and extent of hybridisation between the invasive Mallard Duck and native Yellow-billed Duck in South Africa. *Biological Invasions* **22**, 693–707. doi:10.1007/s10530-019-02122-6

Stuart KC, Cardilini APA, Cassey P, Richardson MF, Sherwin WB, *et al.* (2021) Signatures of selection in a recent invasion reveal adaptive divergence in a highly vagile invasive species. *Molecular Ecology* **30**, 1419–1434. doi:10.1111/mec.15601

Teem JL, Alphey L, Descamps S, Edgington MP, Edwards O, *et al.* (2020) Genetic biocontrol for invasive species. *Frontiers in Bioengineering and Biotechnology* **8**, 452.

Thomsen P, Willerslev E (2015) Environmental DNA – An emerging tool in conservation for monitoring past and present biodiversity. *Biological Conservation* **183**, 4–18. doi:10.1016/j.biocon.2014.11.019

Troth CR, Sweet MJ, J N, Burian A (2021) Seasonality, DNA degradation and spatial heterogeneity as drivers of eDNA detection dynamics. *Science of The Total Environment* **768**, 144466. doi:10.1016/j.scitotenv.2020.144466

Tsai C-L, Lee H-C, Cho G, Liao Y-C, M-M Y, *et al.* (2020) Invasive and quarantine risks of *Cacopsylla chinensis* (Hemiptera: Psyllidae) in East Asia: Hybridization or gene flow between differentiated lineages. *Journal of Economic Entomology* **113**, 2890–2899. doi:10.1093/jee/toaa189

Vandepitte K, De MT, Helsen K, Van AK, Roldán-Ruiz I, *et al.* (2014) Rapid genetic adaptation precedes the spread of an exotic plant species. *Molecular Ecology* **23**, 2157–2164. doi:10.1111/mec.12683

Viard F, C R, Bierne N (2020) Anthropogenic hybridization at sea: three evolutionary questions relevant to invasive species management. *Philosophical Transactions of the Royal Society B: Biological Sciences* **375**, 20190547. doi:10.1098/rstb.2019.0547

Walton Z, Samelius G, M O, Willebrand T (2017) Variation in home range size of red foxes *Vulpes vulpes* along a gradient of productivity and human landscape alteration. *PLOS ONE* **12**, e017529.

Westfall KM, TW T, Abbott CL (2020) A new approach to molecular biosurveillance of invasive species using DNA metabarcoding. *Global Change Biology* **26**, 1012–1022. doi:10.1111/gcb.14886

Willerslev E, Hansen AJ, Binladen J, Brand TB, Gilbert MTP, *et al.* (2003) Diverse plant and animal genetic records from Holocene and Pleistocene sediments. *Science* **300**, 791–795. doi:10.1126/science.1084114

Wimbles R, Melling LM, Cain B, Davies N, Doherty J, *et al.* (2021) On-site genetic analysis for species identification using lab-on-a-chip. *Ecology and Evolution* **11**, 1535–1543. doi:10.1002/ece3.7053

Wylie R, J O, Williams ER (2021) Alleles and algorithms: The role of genetic analyses and remote sensing technology in an ant eradication program. *NeoBiota* **66**, 55–73. doi:10.3897/neobiota.66.64523

Wylie R, Jennings C, McNaught MK, J O, Harris EJ (2016) Eradication of two incursions of the Red Imported Fire Ant in Queensland, Australia. *Ecological Management & Restoration* **17**, 22–32. doi:10.1111/emr.12197

Zinger L, Donald J, Brosse S, Gonzalez MA, Iribar A, *et al.* (2020) Advances and prospects of environmental DNA in neotropical rainforests. In *Advances in Ecological Research*. 62nd edn. (Eds A Dumbrell, E Turner, T Fayle) (pp. 331–373). Academic Press, Cambridge, MA, USA.

25 Genomic identification and surveillance of infectious diseases in natural systems

Jocelyn P. Colella, Stephen E. Greiman, Susan Kutz, Holly L. Lutz and Joseph A. Cook

ABSTRACT

Parasites are of fundamental concern for the biosphere, human health, and food security. In the last decade, genomic, and specifically metagenomic, sequencing has catalysed the discovery and classification of parasitic organisms, including viruses, bacteria, fungi, protozoa, and helminth worms. We review practical applications of genomics to emerging pathogen research in natural systems, including 1) identifying and characterising pathogens; 2) tracing pathogen transmission routes; 3) forecasting, simulating, and modelling emergence, distributions, and risk; and 4) pathogen surveillance through biological collections. Sequence-based taxonomy has proven a practical first step in pathogen discovery and detection, but robust characterisation of new pathogens requires that sequence data are anchored to a physical **voucher specimen**, of both the pathogen and its host, permanently archived in a biological collection. Such collections allow for pathogen–host associations to be critically examined from ecological and evolutionary perspectives across space, time, and taxonomic diversity. Paired with genomic methods, biodiversity sampling can be leveraged to identify the geographic range of suitable hosts and environments, characterise transmission routes, and fuel epidemiological modelling. Genomic, ecological, and environmental data, which are collectively served through interoperable biocollection databases, can now be powerfully exploited by machine learning and **artificial intelligence** technologies to predict host-pathogen compatibility, environmental suitability, adaptive potential, and high-risk geographic interfaces for targeted surveillance. Connecting community-based monitoring efforts directly to biological collections will increase genomic surveillance capacities internationally and foster a proactive approach to emerging disease.

INTRODUCTION

A diverse array of parasitic macro and microorganisms, including viruses, bacteria, fungi, protozoa, and helminth worms, have the capacity to infect and cause disease in a range of wild and domestic host species, as well as people (Brooks *et al.* 2014; Brooks *et al.* 2019; Fisher *et al.* 2020), and are collectively termed 'pathogens'. Parasitism has long been characterised as a close, co-evolving relationship between a host and associated pathogen; however, molecular data and expanded taxonomic sampling demonstrate much greater evolutionary complexity across host-parasite or host-pathogen systems. It is not uncommon, given the opportunity, for pathogens to invade and spread throughout novel host populations and become endemic, a phenomenon known as 'host switching' (Hoberg and Brooks 2008; Araujo *et al.* 2015). Host switches can have disastrous consequences for biodiversity, food security, human health, and global economies (World Bank 2012; Hoberg and Brooks 2013; Araujo *et al.* 2015; Cutler and Summers 2020; Dobson *et al.* 2020; Giggacher 2020; Brooks *et al.* 2021). As an agent reaches endemic equilibrium in a new host, pathogenicity can reduce through a combination of host immunity and evolutionary pressure to increase transmission through reduced mortality. Recent events have framed emerging zoonotic diseases, those capable of moving between wildlife and people, as one of the greatest public health challenges of the 21st Century (Grubaugh *et al.* 2019; World Health Organization (WHO) 2020). In recent decades, viruses such as Ebola, Nipah, Middle East respiratory syndrome coronavirus (MERS), Zika, influenza A (H5N1, H1N1), and most recently severe acute respiratory syndrome coronavirus-2 (SARS-CoV-2), the causative agent of COVID-19, have jumped to humans from animal hosts. We are only now beginning to appreciate the role of wild mammals as zoonotic reservoirs of many other pathogens (e.g. fungi, Hamm *et al.* 2020). On average, three or four new pathogens are detected in humans each year, most are zoonotic, and spillover is increasing in both frequency and severity (Woolhouse *et al.* 2012; Alexander *et al.* 2018). Furthermore, climate change and anthropogenic activity, including but not limited to habitat modification, urbanisation, and global trade (Sabin *et al.* 2020), exacerbate the spread of zoonotic pathogens by driving host range shifts, which may precipitate contact with new, previously isolated communities (Morales-Castilla *et al.* 2021), as is the case for rodent-borne Lassa fever virus in sub-Saharan Africa (Klitting *et al.* 2021). Taken together, these examples highlight the potential burden that zoonotic diseases place on human well-being and public health systems worldwide (Fauci 2001; Coker *et al.* 2011; World Bank 2012).

Beyond affecting human health, global consequences of agricultural diseases, those that afflict crops or livestock, are well illustrated by the recent re-emergence and rapid transmission of African swine fever virus (ASFV) in China. Direct economic losses from ASFV totaled over US$ 110 billion within 16 months of the initial outbreak (Wang *et al.* 2018; You *et al.* 2021). China, the world's largest pork producer and consumer, was further forced to cull 40% of their swine population (Chen *et al.* 2020) and public mistrust of food safety slowed recovery of the pork industry (Woonwong *et al.* 2020; Brooks *et al.* 2021). Many agricultural diseases are capable of 'spilling over' (the first stage of a host switch) into wild plants and animals, suggesting that opportunity, not suitability, is the primary bottleneck to transmission (Araujo *et al.* 2015; Brooks *et al.* 2021; Gryseels *et al.* 2021). ASFV, for instance, regularly moves between domestic pigs and wild boar, which has made the disease especially difficult to control in areas with native suids (Dixon *et al.* 2020). Similarly, as a consequence of

international trade and unrecognised cryptic species diversity, other agricultural diseases, like tomato yellow leaf curl disease (*Begomovirus*) which first emerged in the Middle East, have spread globally and now infect several wild species (Jones 2020).

Pathogens also contribute to the looming biodiversity crisis. The fungus, *Pseudogymnoascus destructans* (*Pd*), the causative agent of white-nose syndrome, for example, has killed 5–6 million North American bats since it was unintentionally introduced to the eastern U.S. from Europe in the early 2000s (Leopardi *et al.* 2015; Lorch *et al.* 2016) and subsequently spread to the West Coast. White-nose syndrome disproportionately affects colonial roosting, non-migratory bat species that play key ecological roles in the reduction of agricultural pests and disease vectors (Boyles *et al.* 2011; Wilder *et al.* 2011). Chytrid fungus (*Batrachochytrium*) causes chytridiomycosis in amphibians, is linked to recent extinctions and global declines (Fisher and Garner 2020), and is regarded as the most devastating wildlife disease on record (Skerratt *et al.* 2007). Changes in community structure driven by biodiversity losses can have far-reaching impacts (Keuler *et al.* 2020), creating conditions ripe for cross-species transmission (Fischhoff *et al.* 2020) or increased risk of spillover to humans (Ostfeld 2009). Thus, human pathogen dynamics are inextricable from those of natural systems.

Estimates suggest that millions of pathogens, and associated host relationships, remain undetected and undescribed (Brooks 2000; Gómez and Nichols 2013; Carroll *et al.* 2018). High-throughput genomic sequencing methods, however, have accelerated detection of microorganisms, with practical applications for 1) novel pathogen identification and description, 2) characterising transmission routes, 3) predicting pathogen emergence and risk, and 4) surveillance, which are reviewed in this chapter. We emphasise a central role for biological collections in transitioning from a reactive response to pathogens, as witnessed during the COVID-19 pandemic, towards proactive research and response strategies based on understanding, surveillance, and mitigation. Best practices require coincident sampling and permanent archiving of both host and pathogen voucher specimens in natural history biorepositories that are tied to global informatics resources. This practice ensures that material is taxonomically verified and preserved for future extended scientific applications (Colella *et al.* 2020; Thompson *et al.* 2021). Physical vouchers anchor each pathogen record to a specific host or environmental sample in space and time, thereby connecting both the pathogen and its host(s) to a suite of ecological and environmental features that are essential for robust detection, monitoring, forecasting, and mitigation of emerging infectious diseases worldwide (Dunnum *et al.* 2017; Colella *et al.* 2021). Inconsistent vouchering practices in pathobiology and other disciplines that sample microorganisms has resulted in major knowledge gaps related to pathogen evolution, responses to changing climate and shifting host distributions (Dobson and Carper 1992; Patz *et al.* 2008; Cohen *et al.* 2020).

PRACTICAL APPLICATION 1: GENOMIC DETECTION AND IDENTIFICATION OF PATHOGENS

The global catalog of known and putative pathogens has ballooned over the last decade (viruses, Simmonds *et al.* 2017; Edgar *et al.* 2022; bacteria, Parker *et al.* 2019; plants, fungi, Turland *et al.* 2018), aided in large part by the availability of affordable, high-throughput sequencing technology. Determining whether a microorganism is pathogenic historically required physical isolation of the putative pathogen from a diseased host, followed by culturing, inoculation, recapitulation of disease in a naive host, and, finally, re-isolation of the microorganism (Henle-Koch postulates; cited in Evans 1976; Antonelli and Cutler 2016). Beyond this etiological paradigm, pathogen species definitions have generally been descriptive, based on intensive studies of host species, geographic distributions, morphology, epidemiology, or transmission routes (Simmonds 2018; Parker *et al.* 2019). Such approaches to pathogen discovery and description are critically important, but also time and resource intensive, and require a depth of taxonomic and methodological expertise that is not always available (Kutz *et al.* 2001).

High-throughput molecular sequencing, and especially metagenomic and metatranscriptomic sequencing methods, offer a powerful and cost effective method of rapid pathogen detection (Bibby 2013; Schlaberg *et al.* 2017; Susi *et al.* 2019) that does not require the traditional approaches of culturing, experimental infection, or even *priori* knowledge that a pathogen may be present in a given host or sample (Bibby 2013; Miller *et al.* 2013). Indeed, many potential pathogens are now being described based solely on genomic sequence data, which has allowed pathogen discovery to quickly outpace our capacities for thorough downstream description and characterisation (Simmonds 2018; Lücking *et al.* 2021; Edgar *et al.* 2022). Shotgun metagenomic sequencing, now among the most widely used techniques for surveying microbial community diversity, provides a taxonomically unbiased sample of all

genetic material in a given host or in a particular environment. Host genetic material is computationally removed after sequencing and quality filtered reads are queried against one or more reference database of known microorganisms (or pathogens) to classify sequences into species or, often, coarser taxonomic units (genus or family) and determine their relative abundances (Bibby 2013; Miller *et al.* 2013). Genomic and transcriptomic sequencing are pragmatic for rapid detection and classification of microorganisms, as well as for distinguishing cryptic diversity, where distinctive evolutionary groups may share similar morphologies.

Sequencing approaches are not without challenges, however, and several important factors must be considered when utilising genomic methods for identification of microorganisms (pathogens or otherwise). First, regardless of the sequence fragment(s) used for initial description, gold-standard characterisation of a microorganism requires additional targeted sequencing and open sharing of 'barcode' regions (Zimmermann *et al.* 2014). Core genes, shared across sections of the Tree of Life, including ribosomal RNAs (*12S, 16S, 18S*), mitochondrial genes (*COI, cytb*), and nuclear internal transcribed spacers (*ITS*) are used as taxonomic 'barcodes' to classify sequences by microbial species (Morand 2018). Most abundance estimation programs classify sequences by matching reads to databases of barcode regions (Table 25.1). Because barcode databases contain only a small fraction of each microbial species' total genome, they can be searched rapidly, but also only classify a small percentage of sequences output from a typical metagenomic sample. Even advanced classification schemes (e.g. k-mer or substring based methods) are limited by the number of described taxa included in a database (e.g. 8500 taxa in the Kraken database, Wood and Salzberg 2014; >10 500 genomes × 381 genes in the Web of Life database, Zhu *et al.* 2019). The power of metagenomic methods, therefore, hinges on the quality and completeness of available reference databases (Pignatelli *et al.* 2008; Gómez-Rodríguez *et al.* 2015). Taxonomic expansion of these databases will allow for reanalysis of previous work and improved resolution in future investigations. Barcode regions can also be PCR-amplified and multiplexed for high-throughput amplicon sequencing, which offers a more affordable, targeted sequencing option (Davidson and Epperson 2018).

The second critical factor is that sequence data for a new pathogen species must be anchored to a physical voucher specimen of both the pathogen and its host (Dunnum *et al.* 2017; Thompson *et al.* 2021) or, in the case of eDNA, a physical environmental sample. If the entire original specimen

Table 25.1.   Microbial sequence reference databases.

Database	Acronym	Contents	Taxa
American Type Culture Collection*	ATCC	Microbial reference strains	Human microbiome samples (bacterial, protists, viruses, fungi); U.S. National Park Service cultures, eumycetozoan strains (bacterial, protists, viruses, fungi)
Avian Malaria Database	MalAvi	Cytochrome b	Avian malaria parasites *Plasmodium* and related haemosporidians
High Quality Ribosomal RNA Database	SILVA	rRNA small subunit (*16S, 18S, SSU*), large subunit (*23S, 28S, LSU*)	Bacteria, Archaea, Eukarya
Ribosomal Database Project	RDP	*16S, 28S* rRNA	Bacteria, Archaea, Fungi
Genomes OnLine Database	GOLD	Genome projects and metadata	All
National Center for Biotechnology Information Reference Sequence Database	RefSeq	Genomic, transcript, and protein sequences	All
Virus Metadata Resource	VMR (by ITVC)	Genomic reference sequences	Viruses
Barcode of Life DataSystems*	BOLD	Barcode Index Numbers (BINs)	Animals, Plantae, Fungi, Protista
WormBase ParaSite	–	Genomes, transcriptomes	Helminths, flatworms
ITS One Database	ITSoneDB	Internal Transcribed Spacer 1 (ITS)	Eukarya
U.S. Food and Drug Administration	FDA-ARGOS	Infectious disease next generation sequencing (ID-NGS)	All
GreenGenes	–	*16S* rRNA	Archaea, Bacteria
Web of Life ToolKit App	WOLTKA	Genomes, rRNA (*5S, 16S, 23S*)	All
Virus Pathogen Resource	ViPR	Genomes, annotations, proteins, strains	Viruses
Influenza Research Database	IRD	Genomic, proteomic, epitome data	Influenza
Global Mammal Parasite Database	–	Taxonomy, transmission modes	Viruses, Bacteria, Protozoa, Helminths, Arthropoda, Fungi

*indicates databases that routinely anchor genetic sequence data to physical voucher specimens

(holotype) is consumed during nucleic acid extraction, additional specimens, ideally from the same sampled host or environment, may be designated as paratypes. Historically, the critical step of preserving permanent, archived samples has been a major methodological gap in training the next generation of practitioners, particularly in biomedical and veterinary sciences. This gap creates a peculiar reality, where a pathology is well understood in humans, but the ecology of the pathogen, wild reservoirs, and factors leading to spillover remain unknown. The PREDICT and STOP Spillover projects, for example, surveyed pathogens from >75 000 mammals globally, but largely failed to archive voucher specimens (Grange *et al.* 2021). Many hosts were only identified to the genus level and without vouchers, their species status cannot be confirmed and taxonomy cannot be updated, so the potential for validation or extension of that work is severely limited (Grange *et al.* 2021). Computational probing of publicly available sequence repositories recently discovered 10^5 new virus species, increasing known diversity by an order of magnitude; yet, 88% of the newly recognised viruses could not be traced to a known host or geographic location (Edgar *et al.* 2022). By digitally connecting microbial sequence data

or other evidence of pathogen presence/absence (i.e. serological information, screening method[s], taxa detected) to a physical voucher, of both the host and pathogen, we immediately gain critical layers of information regarding potential zoonotic sources, including ecology, geography, and phylogenetic affinities, while enabling future scientific replication via sequence regeneration from original source material (Colella *et al.* 2020; Thompson *et al.* 2021). Archiving reference material with a publicly accessible biological collection also aligns with increasing legal and ethical requirements for benefits sharing (Colella *et al.* in press; Adler Miserendino *et al.* 2022). Additional records of a pathogen in the same or different host(s) are critical to refining geographic limits, phylogenomic history, and phylogenetic associations and interactions of pathogens.

It is important that pathobiologists and microbiologists communicate preferred preservation standards and techniques to the biorepository community so that, together, these groups can collaboratively fund and grow the biodiversity infrastructure required for emerging pathogen research and response (Phillips *et al.* 2019; Colella *et al.* 2020, 2021; Thompson *et al.* 2021). In addition to preserving traditional voucher specimens (skin and skeletal material), modern biorepositories subsample and archive multiple tissue types. Freezing tissue in liquid nitrogen is considered a high-quality preservation method (Phillips *et al.* 2019), but may not well preserve fragile RNA molecules, including a large portion of viral diversity. Maximising the value of each sampling event through holistic collecting (Box 25.1) can help diversify preservation methods (i.e. DNA/RNA shield, dimethyl sulfoxide [DMSO], ethanol, RNAlater, etc.) and variety of tissues (i.e. lymphatic tissue or gut and faecal samples) preserved for diverse molecular applications. Expression profiling, for example, uses RNA biomarkers or gene expression signatures to diagnose various disease classes using real-time PCR (Wong and Medrano 2005). Historically, these 'grind-and-bind' techniques destroyed input tissues, making it impossible to preserve a voucher specimen or to map observed signals onto individual cells, but development of *in situ* hybridisation (ISH) methods for DNA and RNA now preserve tissue morphology while enabling chromosomal gene mapping, characterisation of genetic abnormalities associated with disease, and detection of viral genomes (Jin and Lloyd 1997). Some of these methods (RNAscope, Wang *et al.* 2012) are compatible with formalin-fixed, paraffin-embedded tissues, thus unlocking additional historical resources in biological collections. DNA extraction methods are increasingly prioritising the preservation of voucher specimens, which is now possible for larger parasitic fauna like helminths and arthropods (Santos *et al.* 2018; Reier, Sattmann and Haring 2020).

In addition to building more comprehensive specimen archives for pathogen discovery, voucher-backed, publicly accessible, and curated taxonomic reference databases of microbial sequences will be key to the success of future genomic investigations of pathogens. Aggregating and expanding existing databases to include more complete genomic content and structure will facilitate finer resolution investigations (e.g. WOLTKA, Zhu *et al.* 2022), as well as the development of targeted tiled-amplicon sequencing approaches for genomic epidemiology (Quick *et al.* 2017). Database expansion will also improve the ability of computational techniques, like subtractive or iterative mapping, which can be used to detect co-infections or fill in incomplete regions of novel pathogen genomes (Sarver *et al.* 2017). Detection and identification of novel pathogens has become an active area of research, with increased urgency due to growing global awareness of the many complex interfaces between humans and biodiversity.

Box 25.1: Holistic collecting and extended specimens

Holistic collecting is the process of maximising the amount of information gleaned from each field-based sampling event to fuel diverse scientific applications (Fig. 25.1). This method of collecting intentionally looks beyond the goals of a single research project, question, or grant cycle (Schindel and Cook 2018) to build capacity in biodiversity research and enable both scientific replication and extension through the preservation of multiple tissue types (often in multiple media types – frozen, ethanol, RNAlater, etc.), traditional voucher material (skin and skeleton), internal and external parasites, and field notes and other ecological data (Galbreath *et al.* 2019). Once collected, physical specimen resources and associated data can then be 'extended' to address additional questions, outside of the scope of the original investigation, using updated technologies and methods.

The degree to which a specimen can be 'extended' (Webster 2017), or utilised in other fields, directly depends on how it was collected. For example, a novel strain of the pathogenic bacterium, *Erysipelothrix rhusiopathiae*, was recently detected in the Arctic Archipelago (Kutz *et al.* 2015), associated with large-scale mortality events in muskoxen (*Ovibos moschatus*), as well as mortality in caribou, foxes, and seals (Wang *et al.* 2010; Forde *et al.* 2016; Spraker and White 2017). Genomically, the strain, or 'Arctic clone', is highly conserved, across hundreds of thousands of square kilometres and differs from those on mainland North America (Forde *et al.* 2016). The question remains: is this Arctic clone new or was it simply undetected until now? Decades of serological research indicate historical exposure to *Erysipelothrix* in muskox populations, but serology, unlike genomics, cannot distinguish between genotypes. Voucher specimens, which would allow scientists to retroactively address this question with genomic methods, were not archived (Mavrot *et al.* 2020). In contrast to that story, hantavirus emergence in the American West (1993) kick-started intensive, holistic rodent surveys by regional natural history biorepositories (Museum of Southwestern Biology) in collaboration with the U.S. Centers for Disease Control (Yates *et al.* 2002). Thousands of holistically collected and permanently archived specimens and their associated data were immediately used to identify the viral reservoir (*Peromyscus maniculatus*) and facilitate rapid mitigation responses and medical treatment. The same holistically collected specimens and data were then extended to understand the role of El Niño climate cycling in mediating hantavirus transmission and risk (Glass 2006). Later, other specimens completely revised our comprehension of this viral family by identifying new hantaviruses from a much wider range of hosts (shrews, bats, moles, and rodents; Yanagihara *et al.* 2015) and providing a new perspective on viral ecology and genomic evolution (Liphardt *et al.* 2020).

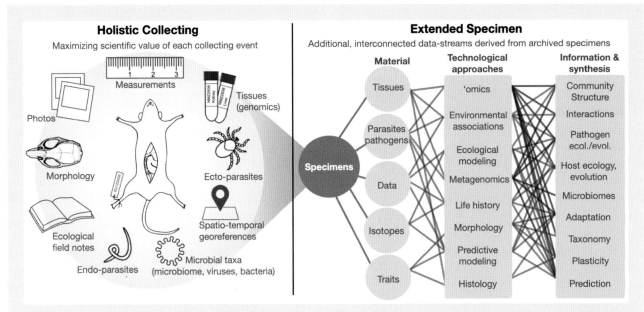

Fig. 25.1. Conceptual difference between *holistic collecting*, which occurs in the field, and *extended specimen* applications, which are limited by available specimens, preservation types, access, and technology. Red connections highlight the network of genome-enabled specimen information.

PRACTICAL APPLICATION 2: CHARACTERISING PATHOGEN ORIGINS AND TRANSMISSION ROUTES

Identification of a pathogen is the first step towards defining its spatial extent, which is always greater than the distribution of the disease itself (Audy 1958). Many pathogens are capable of infecting multiple hosts (e.g. Liphardt *et al.* 2020) and a subset of hosts may act as reservoirs, carrying and perhaps even transmitting the pathogen but experiencing less obvious pathogenesis. Transmission of a pathogen between individuals of the same or a different species depends on both opportunity and compatibility (Plowright *et al.* 2017). Zoonotic transmission refers to the movement of pathogens from non-human animals into people, and is dictated by the continuum of contacts between humans, animals, and their environments and products (e.g. the human–animal interface; also see e.g. Rahman *et al.* 2020). Transmission can occur directly, through contact with infected tissues, fluids, or aerosols (e.g. Ebola, SIV/HIV, coronaviruses, Lassa and other arenaviruses), indirectly via contact with contaminated surfaces or objects (e.g. influenza, cholera), through arthropod vectors, such as mosquitos, fleas, or ticks (e.g. Lyme disease, malaria, West Nile virus), or through non-arthropod vectors, mostly gastropods like mollusks (e.g. schistosomiasis and other trematodiases), or even through parasitic helminths themselves

(e.g. endosymbiotic *Wolbachia* and *Neorickettsia* bacteria; Box 25.2). Disrupting transmission between hosts or geographic areas is key to controlling or preventing pathogen emergence and spread (Blanchong *et al.* 2016). For humans, transmission control is further challenged by urbanisation and globalisation (Harper and Armelagos 2010).

For transmission to occur a host must first be susceptible. Determining susceptibility or receptor-binding site compatibility is an active area of research now aided by computational tools that model physiochemical interactions between hosts and pathogens from molecular sequence data (see *Practical Application #3*). Molecular detection or physical observation of a pathogen in a host or environment, however, provides more concrete empirical evidence of presence and, therefore, compatibility. Second, for transmission to occur there must be opportunity for a pathogen to move between hosts or individuals. Opportunity is largely mediated by the circumstances of pathogen origin; that is, where in geographic, host, molecular, and environmental space the pathogen emerged (Brooks *et al.* 2014; Stephens *et al.* 2016; Brooks *et al.* 2019). Emergence of a pathogen with zoonotic potential in a host that does not contact humans is of little concern to public health, whereas the reverse case can trigger a global pandemic. To establish transmission routes it is, therefore, essential that genomic data for pathogens be linked to information on host, geography, and environment

(Colella *et al.* 2021). Understanding these variables and their relationships across space and time provides a foundation for the design of effective and proactive intervention (Blanchong *et al.* 2016) and both fuels and improves informatic-based inquiry and prediction (see '*Practical Application*').

Phylogenetic methods are the most common means of identifying pathogen origins. Paired with a molecular clock, those methods can provide clues to potential host-switching events over the course of evolution in pathogen lineages. For example, sequence data was used to trace the wildlife origin of *Plasmodium falciparum*, the protozoa that causes malaria in people, to western gorillas, after eliminating chimps, bonobos, and eastern gorillas as potential sources based on sequence differences (Liu *et al.* 2010). Molecular similarity and demographic analysis of genomic data also successfully traced the origin of SARS-CoV-2 taxonomically to rhinolophid bats (Pekar *et al.* 2022; Worobey *et al.* 2022) and geographically to the Huanan Seafood Wholesale market in Wuhan, China (Worobey *et al.* 2022). Notably, however, a lack of publicly available archived specimens slowed SARS-CoV-2 reservoir identification. When combined with phylogenomic screening of the vast spatial, temporal, and taxonomic sampling available in biological collections, the origin of pathogens and breadth of transmission routes can be efficiently characterised and, importantly, placed within an evolutionary context (Yates *et al.* 2002; Yanagihara *et al.* 2015).

Ecological niche modelling is a powerful, albeit non-molecular, tool for identifying geographic origins, points of contact, high-risk interfaces, and environmentally suitable areas (Peterson 2003; Cobos and Peterson 2022). Combining niche modelling with genomic data is a nascent area of research (Cruzan and Hendrickson 2020; Stunz *et al.* 2022), challenged by the complexity of both dispersal and inheritance (i.e. many genes and regulatory regions may contribute to a single complex phenotype) making it difficult to associate phenotypes and genomic regions with specific environments, niches, or conditions (Zuk *et al.* 2012; F. Han *et al.* 2020; DeRaad *et al.* 2021) although some systems are more tractable for these types of integrated approaches than others. For example, bacterial strains that exhibit high levels of niche partitioning are useful models for identifying genes associated with niche evolution (Kelleher *et al.* 2017; Palomo *et al.* 2018). From a molecular perspective, gene-environment interaction studies are perhaps the most common way to identify the role of environmental factors, like temperature and precipitation, in disease risk by measuring responses of different genotypes to distinctive environments (Falconer 1996; Aschard *et al.* 2012). Such studies can be difficult to perform for non-human animals or outside of laboratory conditions, as they require large sample sizes and carefully controlled exposure and environments (Hunter 2005; Aschard *et al.* 2012). Nonetheless, climatic variation has been shown to influence host specificity in avian malaria parasites (Fecchio *et al.* 2019). Genomic-scale data now allow for analysis of more complex, and potentially non-linear relationships, and the tools available to analyse these data remain an active area of development (Albecker *et al.* 2022).

There are many other molecular approaches that address transmission dynamics directly or indirectly. Population and comparative genomic methods can be used to identify the genetic basis of adaptive phenotypes in pathogens or hosts (Novembre and Han 2012; Stukenbrock and Bataillon 2012; Storz 2021). Colonisation of a new host, for instance, may introduce a strong bottleneck on the effective population size of the host-switched pathogen, which may reduce genetic variability of the pathogen and lead to potential loss of advantageous alleles. Increased divergence as a consequence of a host-switch may constrain adaptive potential (Funk *et al.* 2001). Comparing genomes of pathogenic taxa to those of related, non-pathogenic taxa can identify genes associated with pathogenicity (Soanes *et al.* 2007). Uninformed scans for selection, quantitative trait locus mapping (QTL), and genome-wide association studies (GWAS) are useful for identifying candidate loci that control heritable phenotypic variation in hosts or pathogens (Plissonneau *et al.* 2017; Allen *et al.* 2021); however, the mechanism through which candidate loci contribute to an associated phenotype often remains unknown in these investigations. As an example, genome-wide association studies on the *P. falciparum* genome revealed many genomic regions associated with adaptive resistance to the human immune response and anti-malarial treatment (Mu *et al.* 2007; Van Tyne *et al.* 2011).

Investigations of evolutionary history, population structure, and demography can provide a foundation for interpreting linked evolutionary responses in both pathogens and hosts. For example, low- and high-elevation populations of native Hawaiian honeycreepers (amakihi, *Hemignathus virens*) experienced differential survival to the introduction of avian malaria (*Plasmodium relictum*; Foster *et al.* 2007; Eggert *et al.* 2008). Strong genetic structure across an elevational gradient and a high frequency of unique haplotypes in amakihi suggests that contemporary diversity arose from multiple remnant populations or a single historically large, diverse population. High genetic variation in high-elevation amakihi populations facilitated evolution of malaria resistance *in situ*, whereas other native species with less genetic structure and lower diversity (smaller population sizes) were unable to evolve resistance (apapane [*Himatione sanguinea*] and iiwi [*Vestiaria coccinea*]; Foster *et al.* 2007). As a counter example, lack of genetic structure in *Fusarium graminearum*, the causal agent of *Fusarium* head blight in wheat, barley, and maize, across proximal agricultural fields, suggests high regional gene flow and, therefore, high dispersal capabilities, which places neighboring fields at elevated risk (Talas and McDonald 2015). Genomic-scale analyses, including F-statistics and **ABBA-BABA** (Green *et al.* 2010; Martin *et al.* 2015), are sensitive to both contemporary and historical gene flow (Prasanna *et al.* 2010). Higher levels of dispersal and gene flow can identify higher-risk pathogens with a greater breadth of opportunity for 1) host switching to occur, 2) reassortment at contact zones, or 3) inter-pathogen recombination (Talas and McDonald 2015; Liphardt *et al.* 2020). Species specific mutation rates, inferred from

---

Box 25.2: Inter-kingdom interactions

Identifying transmission routes for pathogens with simple life cycles (i.e. single host associations) is relatively straightforward. The task is much more difficult for the many pathogens with complex life cycles, where discrete hosts are infected at various life stages (Choisy *et al.* 2003; Gandon 2004). Each host acts as a different environment, with different selective pressures. For example, *Staphylococcus aureus*, a bacterium infecting a range of mammalian hosts, exhibits evidence of positive selection on molecular pathways associated with amino acid metabolism and iron acquisition, but only in certain hosts (Richardson *et al.* 2018). Many protozoans, including *Leishmania*, malaria, and *Trypanosoma*, utilise arthropod vectors for growth and reproduction, and *Toxoplasma* and *Neospora* use predator–prey interactions for transmission. Parasitic platyhelminths, such as digeneans, have complex multi-host life cycles that may involve three or more host species (Fig. 25.2). The first intermediate host of a digenean is always a mollusk, the second intermediate host (if present) can be an invertebrate or vertebrate, and the definitive host is almost always a vertebrate (i.e. blood flukes, lung flukes, intestinal flukes, liver flukes, etc.). Adding complexity to these pathogen life cycles, is the fact that digeneans themselves can be vectors for bacterial endosymbiont pathogens (*Neorickettsia*; Vaughan *et al.* 2012). These bacterial pathogens are maintained through the complete life cycle of the digenean, and can be passed to vertebrate definitive hosts where *Neorickettsia* can cause potentially fatal diseases In wildlife (e.g. brown bears), domestic animals (dogs and horses), and people (sennetsu fever in Southeast Asia; Vaughan *et al.* 2012; Greiman and Tkach 2016). Metagenomic sequencing of liver flukes, *Fasciola hepatica*, in humans recently detected a novel *Neorickettsial* species – of which the impact on human health remains to be determined (McNulty *et al.* 2017).

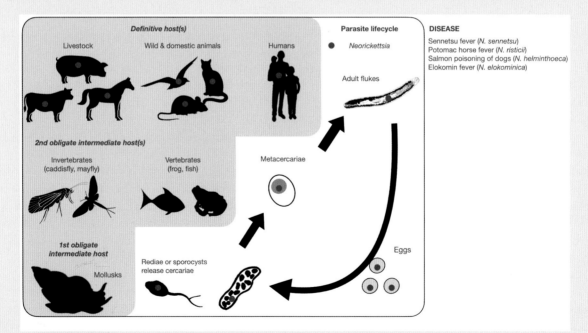

Fig. 25.2. Complex parasite lifecycle and tracking endosymbiont (*Neorickettsia*) through a web of obligate intermediate and definitive hosts. Adapted from Greiman *et al.* (2013).

genomic data of hosts or pathogens, and generation times can be used as molecular clocks to infer the timing of host-switching or population expansion or contraction (Li and Durbin 2011; Torres-Pérez *et al.* 2011; Bell *et al.* 2021), to temporally link emergence with historical demographic or environmental events. When tied to voucher specimens, within and between-host population genomic analyses can provide important spatio-temporal resolution of pathogen dynamics and dispersal across space and time (Hanke *et al.* 2016).

PRACTICAL APPLICATION 3: GENOME-INFORMED FORECASTING, SIMULATION, AND MODELLING

Massive volumes of machine-readable sequence data have ushered in a new research economy based on data mining, molecular modelling, and artificial intelligence. Those methods frequently leverage publicly available sequence data or integrate genomic data with additional ecological and environmental features to forecast pathogen emergence, host compatibility (Box 25.3), transmission, and disease risk under various environmental, ecological, or evolutionary scenarios (Newlands 2018; Wiens and Shenoy 2018; Al-Amin, Karim and Bushra 2019).

Data mining involves extraction and summation of information from a large pool of data to uncover subtle patterns and associations (Mukhopadhyay *et al.* 2010; Nourani, Khunjush and Durmuş 2015; Han *et al.* 2020). This technique capitalises on the growing mass of publicly available sequence data, but also ecological, environmental, and natural history data streams. Illustrating the power of these techniques for pathogen research, bioinformatic mining of RNA-dependent RNA polymerase sequences (RdRP, the only conserved gene among RNA viruses) from NCBI's GenBank sequence repository recently expanded known viral diversity by an order of magnitude, discovering 10^5 new viruses (Edgar *et al.* 2022). Data mining is also the initial data aggregation step for most modelling or artificial intelligence methods, which then apply data and inferred patterns to decision making. Advances in artificial intelligence (AI), including machine learning and **deep learning** methods, allow for rapid, parallel processing of large, complex data streams to identify patterns, infer solutions, and make forward-looking decisions (Fig. 25.3; Nourani *et al.* 2015; Agany *et al.* 2020; Perrakis and Sixma 2021).

Predicting host-pathogen suitability (also, compatibility or susceptibility) is an active area of research that leverages genomic sequence data to model the three-dimensional structure of proteins and protein-protein interactions to infer compatibility, often using machine learning algorithms (Baek *et al.* 2021; Jumper *et al.* 2021). Development of the neural network algorithm *AlphaFold* by Google's DeepMind in 2021 finally enabled near experimentally accurate prediction of protein structure, even in cases where no homologous structures were available through the Protein Data Bank (wwPDB Consortium 2019; Jumper *et al.* 2021). *AlphaFold*, and a similar approach, *RoseTTAfold* (Baek *et al.* 2021), integrates physical and biological knowledge of protein structures and genomic sequence alignments directly into its deep learning algorithm (Jumper *et al.* 2021). These methods are a step forward for understanding protein-protein interactions and are already being employed in drug and vaccine development (Jubb *et al.* 2012). Structural molecular modelling has proved useful in predicting host suitability through host–pathogen receptor-site compatibility modelling (Brierley and Fowler 2021; Yan *et al.* 2021). However, that framework generally assumes a strict co-evolutionary model, which is unlikely for many pathogens and may constrain insights, especially for pathogens with complex life histories that involve multiple hosts (Box 25.3). Once an effective drug or compatible host has been identified, field-based sampling and *in vivo* experimentation is required to validate model results.

Machine learning approaches use known features, genomic and otherwise, from one group (hosts or pathogens) to make a decision about the other (Box 25.3; Damas *et al.* 2020; Fischhoff *et al.* 2020; Carlson *et al.* 2021; Mollentze *et al.* 2021); do we expect a virus to be able to infect humans (i.e. is it zoonotic or not?), given the structure of its genome? To frame such a decision, input data, in this case genomes from many viruses, are classified into known groups: zoonotic vs. non-zoonotic. Input genomes are divided into training, validation, and testing datasets. Training data are used to build the model, validation data are used to tune hyperparameters, and testing data are used to evaluate model accuracy. Once the model is tuned, a series of machine learning algorithms (see Tantithamthavorn *et al.* 2020) are used to classify unknown viral genomes. Extending these binary (yes-or-no), linked prediction models to infer associations within networks of hosts and viruses will better represent biological complexity (Wardeh *et al.* 2020; Albery and Becker 2021; Farrell *et al.* 2022). Highly dimensional network analyses will be increasingly useful for unraveling the structure and function of microbial, and therefore pathogen, communities moving forward (Connor *et al.* 2017). Phylogenetic and phylodynamic modelling are also useful computational tools to quantify or predict susceptibility. Host phylogeny, for example, was found to explain variation in haemosporidian parasite infection status of avian hosts, indicating that in some cases susceptibility may be phylogenetically conserved (Barrow *et al.* 2019). If specimens and data are responsibly archived with biological collections, such models should increase in accuracy over time as cumulative, taxonomically verified data resources grow.

Influential features, identified through AI, can be manipulated as part of forward-time simulations to anticipate the development of high-risk interfaces based on changing conditions (Box 25.3). Forward-time simulation of environmental and geographic suitability for pathogens

and hosts under various climatic scenarios is frequently accomplished and visualised through ecological niche modelling (Peterson 2006; Escobar and Craft 2016). Warmer, wetter conditions experienced under El Niño-Southern Oscillation events, for instance, are connected to increased emergence and spread of numerous vector-borne diseases, including chagas, malaria, dengue, Rift Valley fever, African horse sickness, hantavirus, and plague (Harvell *et al.* 2002; Glass 2006). This information allows public health officials to proactively anticipate conditions leading to emergence of pathogens. Thermal tolerances of the avian malaria parasite (*P. relictum*) and its

---

Box 25.3: Forecasting beyond molecular compatibility

Receptor-site compatibility modelling is a rapid, low-cost 'first-pass' at identifying the range of potential susceptible hosts and reservoirs of a pathogen to enable evidence-driven surveillance and focus downstream investigations (Mollentze *et al.* 2021). Modelling of the SARS-CoV-2 spike protein and ACE2 (angiotensin I converting enzyme 2) receptor in vertebrates, for example, readily identified many mammal species as high risk (Damas *et al.* 2020; Huang *et al.* 2020; Rodrigues *et al.* 2020). While some of those predictions were confirmed *in vivo*, others do not match real-world outcomes (Deng *et al.* 2020; Gryseels *et al.* 2021). Pathogen distributions are more often the result of opportunity, rather than strict compatibility.

ACE2 receptor sequences are only available for <10% of mammal species. The receptor is relatively well conserved across mammals, which suggests it evolved in parallel with other traits for which additional data may be available. Supplementing molecular inputs to machine learning algorithms with other biological data (e.g. ecological, evolutionary, traits, etc.), available through biological collections databases (e.g. *Arctos, Specify*) and cross-collection aggregators (e.g. iDigBio, VertNet, Global Biodiversity Information Facility [GBIF], PANtheria, FuTRES, etc.), can help refine model and prediction accuracy (Fig. 25.3; Fountain-Jones *et al.* 2019; Han *et al.* 2020; Fischhoff *et al.* 2020; Carlson *et al.* 2021). Predictions from integrative models may also be more immediately relevant to public health policy. This is especially true for lower-income, biodiverse countries where pathogen emergence is most likely to occur but where biorepositories, sequencing, and computational resources are scarce and other phenotypes may be more useful for managing human-animal interfaces. For instance, Fischhoff *et al.* (2020) used integrated machine learning models to identify zoonotic capacity and proximity to humans as features associated with elevated transmission risk for several common mammals and further defined priority areas of geographic overlap between these taxa (Fischhoff *et al.* 2020).

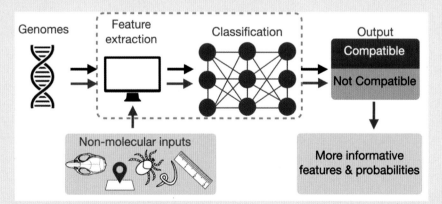

Fig. 25.3. Black arrows indicate a typical machine learning workflow that uses genomic data to infer host-pathogen molecular compatibility. Red arrows indicate a more integrative approach that combines molecular and non-molecular data sources, to address the same questions, but with a broader definition of compatibility. The latter approach yields greater accuracy and more informative output features and probabilities. The dashed line indicates the two steps of the pipeline that are combined in deep learning workflows.

vector (the southern house mosquito, *Culex quinquefasciatus*), for example, proved useful for understanding how temporal and site-specific differences in temperature shape transmission (Fortini *et al.* 2020). In addition to environmental simulation, demographic and evolutionary simulations using genomic data can reveal the population dynamics of pathogens associated with spillover, host switches, or outbreaks, essentially functioning as early warning signs that may present varying levels of risk to different communities. While no models are perfect, some may reveal circumstances under which new pathogens are likely to emerge, effectively acting as a guide for allocation of research and monitoring efforts (Stephens *et al.* 2016). Collectively, these methods represent a major step forward for proactive public health, food security, biodiversity conservation, and emerging disease forecasting and mitigation (Wardeh *et al.* 2020; Carlson *et al.* 2021; Mollentze *et al.* 2021).

PRACTICAL APPLICATION 4: MOLECULAR PATHOGEN SURVEILLANCE

Once a pathogen, its associated host(s), and transmission routes are identified, coordinated surveillance is the next step toward proactive outbreak detection, mitigation, and monitoring of change through time (Box 25.4). Computational methods that integrate environmental, socio-cultural, and biological variables are poised to guide strategic surveillance. In addition to targeted sampling of high-risk hosts and interfaces, broad taxonomic and spatial sampling of wildlife, that includes voucher-backed resurveys of historically sampled sites, will also be required to detect new instances of host-switching, range expansion, or otherwise shifting baselines due to environmental change (Schindel and Cook 2018; Colunga-Salas *et al.* 2020; Colella *et al.* 2021). Accumulation and sequencing of genomic resources for a breadth of pathogens and multiple individuals of each taxon will contribute to the development of pangenomes for each pathogen group. A pangenome is represented by three parts: (1) the core genome, which includes genes common across the group; (2) the accessory genome, which contains genes present between two and *n*-1 taxa; and (3) ancillary or remaining genes that are unique to only a single strain or taxon (Rouli *et al.* 2015; Golicz *et al.* 2020; Kim *et al.* 2020). Expanded availability of genomic resources for a breadth of pathogens will also foster development and application of more affordable reduced-representation sequencing methods useful for scaling surveillance globally and adapting sequencing techniques

to at-risk or threatened taxa that may be less represented in biocollections. Historically, reciprocity and integration between pathogen surveillance efforts and biorepositories has been a missing link in emerging disease response and surveillance efforts (e.g. WildHealthNet, PREDICT), but there are exceptions (e.g. Yates *et al.* 2002; Dunnum *et al.* 2017). Ultimately, all wildlife surveillance, motivated by public health or otherwise, should contribute to the growth of foundational biodiversity infrastructure (i.e. permanent biorepositories and associated informatics resources).

Research collections allow pathobiologists to 'go back in time' to see if a recent or newly detected pathogen was historically present in a given species or ecosystem (or not) and at what densities, to gauge change through time. Further assessment of ecological and environmental variables through time, possible through interoperable, georeferenced natural history databases, can help identify shifts in the pathogen itself, its host(s), or the environment that may have precipitated changes in distribution or pathology (Colunga-Salas *et al.* 2020). Recurrent sampling, archiving, and sequencing over time can serve to empirically calibrate mutation rates for wild taxa and associated pathogens. Robust mutation rates are fundamental for dating demographic, divergence, and emergence events. Mutation rates vary widely within and between species and understanding what drives rate variation is essential to understanding pathogen evolution and transmission dynamics (Murray *et al.* 2021). Due to the low fidelity of RNA polymerases, mutation rates of RNA viruses are very high, resulting in 1–2 mutations per replication, which facilitate evasion of the host immune system and allow for accelerated evolution of new strains (Peck and Lauring 2018).

High mutation rates challenge vaccine and drug development. For example, to accommodate rapid molecular evolution, influenza vaccines are reformulated each flu season to ensure effectiveness (Harding and Heaton 2018). High mutation rates combined with immunological selective pressures result in antigenic drift or the fixation of distinct variants that are unaffected by prior vaccination or infection (Harding and Heaton 2018). Different strains are often only distinguishable through molecular screening, either PCR amplification or shotgun metagenomic sequencing. Regularly sequencing metagenomes from a subset of samples flowing into biorepositories would provide gross regional metrics of pathogen diversity, density, and population dynamics. In addition to guiding vaccine development, such data collected across taxonomically diverse pathogens and hosts will significantly enrich training datasets for machine learning and AI-guided risk assessment tools, which serve

Box 25.4: Pathogen surveillance: bridging the divide between pathogens, genomics, and biological collections

Pathogen emergence is a global problem that requires decentralised, coordinated solutions (Watsa 2020; Colella *et al.* 2021). Collaborative networks have proven instrumental in coordinating public health responses to Ebola (Brownstein *et al.* 2009; Mawudeku *et al.* 2013), tuberculosis (Peter *et al.* 2021), and, more recently, SARS CoV-2 (Hunt *et al.* 2021), internationally. Building on those resources, Project ECHO's *Museums and Emerging Pathogens in the Americas* (MEPA) network aims to better integrate museum biorepositories with ongoing One Health and pathogen surveillance initiatives with the goal of building in-country biodiversity infrastructure that can act as a frontline of defense in pandemic preparedness particularly in biodiverse corners of the globe (Colella *et al.* 2021). Biodiversity infrastructure, in the form of temporally deep, spatial broad, and taxonomically diverse natural history biorepositories, staffed with full-time trained personnel in biodiverse countries, will facilitate the rapid collection, preservation, and sequencing of high-quality genomic sample that are at or near outbreak sites. The scale of sampling achieved through cumulative contribution far exceeds what is feasible for a single lab or institution. Such infrastructure also stimulates capacity building in genomics, biodiversity sciences, and public health and circumvents problems resulting from the dissociation of pathogen surveillance from permanent biodiversity sampling and associated metadata (Fig. 25.4).

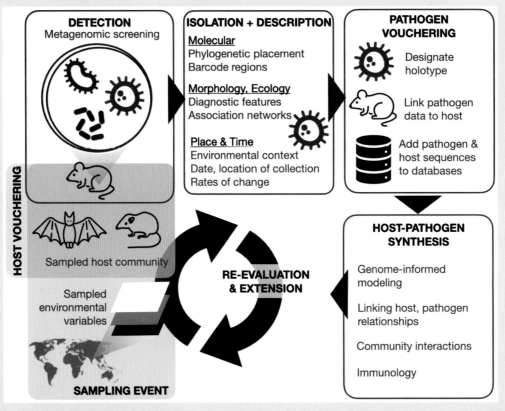

Fig. 25.4. An updated One Health paradigm that integrates biological research collections into regular pathogen surveillance efforts. Sampling occurs at a particular place and time, the details of which can be captured through holistic vouchering and archiving with natural history biorepositories. Metagenomic and other screening methods are useful for detecting known (grey) and novel (red) pathogens in a sampled host. The pathogen must then be isolated and described at molecular, morphological, and ecological levels, which is possible if material is available through biorepositories. Vouchering pathogens by establishing a holotype (or paratypes, as feasible) and linking results of pathogen screening (i.e. species detected, screening method[s] used) back to host vouchers in museum databases is critical for re-evaluation and extension of previous work, as well as synthetic inquiry into host-pathogen and pathogen-pathogen interactions. These linkages, as well as uploading barcode sequence data for novel microbial species to online sequence repositories, fuel genome-informed predictive modelling (i.e. machine learning, AI) of host compatibility, interactions, and immunology. Access to additional samples – different host species or the same species from different localities – through museums then provides opportunities for extension and re-evaluation of previous work and community level analyses.

as an early warning system to detect deviations from baseline conditions that elevate risk profiles. Risk for pathogenic avian influenza in Australia, for example, has been shown to be largely driven by mutation of wild-bird influenza strains in commercial poultry, rather than direct transfer from wildlife (Scott *et al.* 2020). Mutational modelling could identify high risk strains and biorepositories could be leveraged for monitoring (Barnes *et al.* 2019; Scott *et al.* 2020).

People now also play a major role in creating novel opportunities for disease transmission, as exemplified by records of SARS-CoV-2 transmission between humans and other mammals (and subsequent back transmission). Spillover from humans led to massive mink (*Neogale vision*) culling across Europe in an attempt to quell reverse zoonotic transmission (Rabalski *et al.* 2021; Enserink and Kupferschmidt 2022). Further, less than two years into the COVID-19 pandemic, 40% of wild white-tailed deer (*Odocoileus hemionus*) sampled in the mid-west and mid-Atlantic regions of the United States tested positive for SARS-CoV-2 (Chandler *et al.* 2021). With many other wild mammals identified as potentially susceptible (Damas *et al.* 2020; Fischhoff *et al.* 2020; Gryseels *et al.* 2021), broad surveillance will be the most powerful means of measuring changing SARS-CoV-2 prevalence in wild populations. In addition to threatening human health and food security (Brooks *et al.* 2021), wildlife diseases are accelerating the global biodiversity crisis. Chytrid fungus in amphibians (Stuart *et al.* 2004), white-nose syndrome in bats (Hoyt *et al.* 2021), and chronic wasting disease in ungulates (Schwabenlander *et al.* 2022) are each responsible for massive wildlife mortality. Wildlife surveillance for human health should complement surveillance motivated by biodiversity conservation and management (and vice versa) through collective contribution to and use of publicly accessible biorepositories (Box 25.4).

FUTURE DIRECTIONS AND OUTSTANDING QUESTIONS

Affordable, high-throughput genomic sequencing technology, when combined with the biodiverse sampling infrastructure and associated metadata, served by the global network of biological collections, is poised to transform our approach to pathogen research and response from reactive to proactive (Brooks *et al.* 2019; Colella *et al.* 2021). To meet this potential, there are three outstanding challenges that must be addressed. First is a cultural shift that democratises access to primary data and ensures a more robust approach to pathogen research through the deposition of permanent vouchers with publicly accessible biological collections, regardless of the original collection purpose or research question(s) (Colella *et al.* 2020; Thompson *et al.* 2021). Second, pipelines must be built between biological collections and sequencing cores that efficiently screen samples and leverage computational pipelines to form an early warning system for pathogen emergence. Third, biological collections must engage more directly in pathogen research by expanding the types of samples collected and their informatic capacities, by tying directly into genomic-data repositories (e.g. GenBank, SRA, DDBJ) and other large specimen-based data streams (e.g. IsoBank, Morpho-Bank, GoogleEarth). Building these interoperable data networks will accommodate and help synthesise the large volume and complexity of biodiversity data available through the specimen nexus and will enhance our ability to document and investigate networks of relationships among pathogens and hosts. Specimens, their genomes, and associated environmental and ecological data can then be powerfully leveraged by computational methods to predict pathogen distribution, compatibility, and emergence.

DISCUSSION TOPICS

1. What should strategic global pathogen surveillance look like from geographic, taxonomic, and temporal perspectives? See Afolayan *et al.* (2021) and Colella *et al.* (2021).
2. How can the research community better ensure that biological samples, regardless of original collection purpose, are archived in publicly accessible biological collections for future use? See Colella *et al.* (2020) and Thompson *et al.* (2021).
3. What preservation and molecular methods are most effective at recovering pathogen sequences from a diversity of hosts? See Tsangaras and Greenwood (2012) and Zacho *et al.* (2021).
4. What partnerships should be built between biological collections, sequencing cores, wildlife agencies, and the medical community to streamline pathogen research and response? See Cook *et al.* (2016), Schindel and Cook (2018), and Colella *et al.* (2021).

ACKNOWLEDGEMENTS

This chapter is dedicated to Karl M. Johnson, whose boundless energy, leadership, and perspicacity made him a key player in the identification of Machupo, hanta, and Ebola viruses. Formerly Chief of the US Centers for Disease Control and Prevention Special Pathogens Branch, he holds an

Emeritus Professorship at the University of New Mexico where he has enthusiastically encouraged junior scientists and promoted the theme of cross-disciplinary integration in pathobiology outlined in this chapter. We thank Schuyler Liphardt for editorial comments, and the many other colleagues cited in this chapter for contributing key ideas towards developing a greater appreciation of the critical role of biorepository in genomic approaches to biodiversity studies. US National Science Foundation grants no. 1901920 (JAC), 2026377 (JAC), 2100955 (JPC), and 2155222 (JPC, JAC) supported aspects of this work.

REFERENCES

Adler Miserendino RA, Meyer RS, Zimkus BM, Bates J, Silvestri L, et al. (2022) The case for community self-governance on access and benefit sharing of digital sequence information. *Bioscience* biac019.

Afolayan AO, Bernal JF, Gayeta JM, Masim ML, Shamanna V, et al. (2021) Overcoming data bottlenecks in genomic pathogen surveillance. *Clinical Infectious Diseases* 73(Issue Supplement 4), S267–S274.

Agany DDM, Pietri JE, Gnimpieba EZ (2020) Assessment of vector-host-pathogen relationships using data mining and machine learning. *Computational and Structural Biotechnology Journal* 18, 1704–1721.

Al-Amin M, Karim DZ, Bushra TA (2019) Prediction of Rice Disease from Leaves using Deep Convolution Neural Network towards a Digital Agricultural System. In: *2019 22nd International Conference on Computer and Information Technology (ICCIT)*, pp. 1–5.

Albecker MA, Trussell GC, Lotterhos KE (2022) A novel analytical framework to quantify co-gradient and countergradient variation. *Ecology Letters* 25, 1521–1533.

Albery GF, Becker DJ (2021) Fast-lived hosts and zoonotic risk. *Trends in Parasitology* 37(2), 117–129.

Alexander KA, Carlson CJ, Lewis BL, Getz WM, Marathe MV, et al. (2018) The ecology of pathogen spillover and disease emergence at the human-wildlife-environment interface. In *The Connections Between Ecology and Infectious Disease. Advances in Environmental Microbiology*, Vol. 5. (Ed CJ Hurst) pp. 267–298. Springer, Switzerland.

Allen JP, Snitkin E, Pincus NB, Hauser AR (2021) Forest and trees: Exploring bacterial virulence with genome-wide association studies and machine learning. *Trends in Microbiology* 29(7), 621–633.

Antonelli G, Cutler S (2016) Evolution of the Koch postulates: towards a 21st-century understanding of microbial infection. *Clinical Microbiology and Infection* 22(7), 583–584.

Araujo SBL, Braga MP, Brooks DR, Agosta SJ, Hoberg EP, et al. (2015) Understanding host-switching by ecological fitting. *PLoS One* 10(10), e0139225.

Aschard H, Lutz S, Maus B, Duell EJ, Fingerlin TE, et al. (2012) Challenges and opportunities in genome-wide environmental interaction (GWEI) studies. *Human Genetics* 131(10), 1591–1613.

Audy JR (1958) The localization of disease with special reference to the zoonoses. *Transcations of the Royal Society of Tropical Medicine and Hygiene* 52(4), 308–334.

Baek M, DiMaio F, Anishchenko I, Dauparas J, Ovchinnikov S, et al. (2021) Accurate prediction of protein structures and interactions using a three-track neural network. *Science* 373(6557), 871–876.

Barnes B, Scott A, Hernandez-Jover M, Toribio JA, Moloney B, et al. (2019) Modelling high pathogenic avian influenza outbreaks in the commercial poultry industry. *Theoretical Population Biology* 126, 59–71.

Barrow LN, McNew SM, Mitchell N, Galen SC, Lutz HL, et al. (2019) Deeply conserved susceptibility in a multi-host, multi-parasite system. *Ecology Letters* 22(6), 987–998.

Bell KC, Allen JM, Johnson KP, Demboski JR, Cook JA, et al. (2021) Disentangling lousy relationships: Comparative phylogenomics of two sucking louse lineages parasitizing chipmunks. *Molecular Phylogenetics and Evolution* 155, 106998.

Bibby K (2013) Metagenomic identification of viral pathogens. *Trends in Biotechnology* 31(5), 275–279.

Blanchong JA, Robinson SJ, Samuel MD, Foster JT (2016) Application of genetics and genomics to wildlife epidemiology. *Journal of Wildlife Management* 80(4), 593–608.

Boyles JG, Cryan PM, McCracken GF, Kunz TH (2011) Conservation. Economic importance of bats in agriculture. *Science* 332(6025), 41–42.

Brierley L, Fowler A (2021) Predicting the animal hosts of coronaviruses from compositional biases of spike protein and whole genome sequences through machine learning. *PLOS Pathogens* 17(4), e1009149.

Brooks DR (2000) Parasite systematics in the 21st century: opportunities and obstacles. *Memórias do Instituto Oswaldo Cruz* 95, 99–107.

Brooks DR, Hoberg EP, Boeger WA, Gardner SL, Galbreath KE, et al. (2014) Finding them before they find us: informatics, parasites, and environments in accelerating climate change. *Comparative Parasitology* 81(2), 155–164.

Brooks DR, Hoberg EP, Boeger WA, Trivellone V (2021) Emerging infectious disease: an underappreciated area of strategic concern for food security. *Transboundary and Emerging Diseases* 69, 254–267.

Brooks DR, Hoberg EP, Boeger WA (2019) *The Stockholm Paradigm: Climate Change and Emerging Disease*. University of Chicago Press, Chicago, IL, USA.

Brownstein JS, Freifeld CC, Madoff LC (2009) Digital disease detection–harnessing the Web for public health surveillance. *The New England Journal of Medicine* 360(21), 2153–2155,2157.

Carlson CJ, Farrell MJ, Grange Z, Han BA, Mollentze N, et al. (2021) The future of zoonotic risk prediction. *Philosophical Transactions of the Royal Society B* 376(1837), 20200358.

Carroll D, Daszak P, Wolfe ND, Gao GF, Morel CM, et al. (2018) The global virome project. *Science* 359(6378), 872–874.

Chandler JC, Bevins SN, Ellis JW, Linder TJ, Tell RM, et al. (2021) SARS-CoV-2 exposure in wild white-tailed deer (*Odocoileus virginianus*). *Proceedings of the National Academy of Sciences of the United States of America* 118(47), e2114828118.

Chen W, Zhao D, He X, Liu R, Wang Z, Zhang X, *et al.* (2020) A seven-gene-deleted African swine fever virus is safe and effective as a live attenuated vaccine in pigs. *Science China Life Sciences* **63**, 623–634.

Choisy M, Brown SP, Lafferty KD, Thomas F, *et al.* (2003) Evolution of trophic transmission in parasites: why add intermediate hosts? *The American Naturalist* **162**(2), 172–181.

Cobos ME, Peterson AT (2022) Detecting signals of species' ecological niches in results of studies with defined sampling protocols: Example application to pathogen niches. *Biodiversity Informatics* **17**, 50–58.

Cohen JM, Sauer EL, Santiago O, Spencer S, Rohr JR, *et al.* (2020) Divergent impacts of warming weather on wildlife disease risk across climates. *Science* **370**(6519), eabb1702.

Coker R, Rushton J, Mounier-Jack S, Karimuribo E, Lutumba P, *et al.* (2011) Towards a conceptual framework to support one-health research for policy on emerging zoonoses. *The Lancet Infectious Diseases* **11**(4), 326–331.

Colella JP, Stephens RB, Campbell ML, Kohli BA, Parsons DJ, *et al.* (2020) The Open-specimen movement. *Bioscience* **71**(4), 405–414.

Colella JP, Bates J, Burneo SF, Camacho MA, Carrion Bonilla C, *et al.* (2021) Leveraging natural history collections as a global, decentralized pathogen surveillance network. *PLoS Pathogens* **17**(6), e1009583.

Colella JP, Silvestri L, Suzán G, Weksler M, Cook JA, *et al.* (in press) Engaging with the Nagoya Protocol on access and benefit-sharing: Recommendations for non-commercial biodiversity researchers. *Journal of Mammalogy*.

Colunga-Salas P, Sánchez-Montes S, Grostieta E, Verde-Arregoitia LD, Cabrera-Garrido MY, *et al.* (2020) What do studies in wild mammals tell us about human emerging viral diseases in Mexico? *Transboundary and Emerging Diseases* **67**(1), 33–45.

Connor N, Barberán A, Clauset A (2017) Using null models to infer microbial co-occurrence networks. *PLoS One* **12**(5), e0176751.

Cook JA, Greiman SE, Agosta SJ, Anderson RP, Arbogast BS, *et al.* (2016) Transformational principles for NEON sampling of mammalian parasites and pathogens: A response to Springer and colleagues. *Bioscience* **66**(11), 917–919.

Cruzan MB, Hendrickson EC (2020) Landscape genetics of plants: Challenges and opportunities. *Plant Commun* **1**(6), 100100.

Cutler DM, Summers LH (2020) The COVID-19 pandemic and the $16 trillion virus. *JAMA* **324**(15), 1495–1496. doi:10.1001/jama.2020.19759

Damas J, Hughes GM, Keough KC, Painter CA, Persky NS, *et al.* (2020) Broad host range of SARS-CoV-2 predicted by comparative and structural analysis of ACE2 in vertebrates. *Proceedings of the National Academy of Sciences of the United States of America* **117**(36), 22311–22322.

Davidson RM, Epperson LE (2018) Microbiome sequencing methods for studying human diseases. In *Disease Gene Identification: Methods and Protocols*. (Ed JK DiStefano) pp. 77–90. Springer, New York, USA.

Deng W, Bao L, Gao H, Xiang Z, Qu Y, *et al.* (2020) Ocular conjunctival inoculation of SARS-CoV-2 can cause mild COVID-19 in rhesus macaques. *Nature Communications* **11**(1), 4400.

DeRaad DA, Cobos ME, Alkishe A, Ashraf U, Ahadji-Dabla KM, *et al.* (2021) Genome-environment association methods comparison supports omnigenic adaptation to ecological niche in malaria vector mosquitoes. *Molecular Ecology* **30**(23), 6468–6485.

Dixon LK, Stahl K, Jori F, Vial L, Pfeiffer DU, *et al.* (2020) African swine fever epidemiology and control. *Annual Review of Animal Biosciences* **8**, 221–246.

Dobson AP, Pimm SL, Hannah L, Kaufman L, Ahumada JA, *et al.* (2020) Ecology and economics for pandemic prevention. *Science* **369**(6502), 379–381.

Dobson AP, Carper R (1992) Global warming and potential changes in host-parasite and disease-vector relationships. In *Global Warming and Biological Diversity*. (Ed RL Peters). pp. 201–217. Yale University Press, New Haven, CT.

Dunnum JL, Yanagihara R, Johnson KM, Armien B, Batsaikhan N, Morgan L, *et al.* (2017) Biospecimen repositories and integrated databases as critical infrastructure for pathogen discovery and pathobiology research. *PLOS Neglected Tropical Diseases* **11**(1), 1–6.

Edgar RC, Taylor J, Lin V, Altman T, Barbera P, *et al.* (2022) Petabase-scale sequence alignment catalyses viral discovery. *Nature* **602**, 142–147.

Eggert LS, Terwilliger LA, Woodworth BL, Hart PJ, Palmer D, *et al.* (2008) Genetic structure along an elevational gradient in Hawaiian honeycreepers reveals contrasting evolutionary responses to avian malaria. *BMC Evolutionary Biology* **8**, 315.

Enserink M, Kupferschmidt K (2022) With COVID-19, modeling takes on life and death importance. *Science* **367**(6485), 1414–1415.

Escobar LE, Craft ME (2016) Advances and limitations of disease biogeography using ecological niche modeling. *Frontiers in Microbiology* **7**, 1174.

Evans AS (1976) Causation and disease: The Henle-Koch postulates revisited. *Yale Journal of Biology and Medicine* **49**(2), 175–195.

Falconer DS (1996) *Introduction to Quantitative Genetics*. Pearson Education India.

Farrell MJ, Elmasri M, Stephens DA, Davies TJ (2022) Predicting missing links in global host-parasite networks. *Journal of Animal Ecology* **91**(4), 715–726.

Fauci AS (2001) Infectious diseases: Considerations for the 21st century. *Clinical Infectious Diseases* **32**(5), 675–685.

Fecchio A, Wells K, Bell JA, Tkach VV, Lutz HL, *et al.* (2019) Climate variation influences host specificity in avian malaria parasites. *Ecology Letters* **22**(3), 547–557.

Fischhoff IR, Huang T, Hamilton SK, Han BA, LaDeau SL, *et al.* (2020) Parasite and pathogen effects on ecosystem processes: A quantitative review. *Ecosphere* **11**(5), e03057.

Fisher MC, Gurr SJ, Cuomo CA, Blehert DS, Jin H, *et al.* (2020) Threats posed by the fungal kingdom to humans, wildlife, and agriculture. *MBio* **11**, e00449–20.

Fisher MC, Garner TWJ (2020) Chytrid fungi and global amphibian declines. *Nature Reviews Microbiology* **18**(6), 332–343.

Forde T, Orsel K, Zadoks RN, Biek R, Adams LG, *et al.* (2016) Bacterial genomics reveal the complex epidemiology of an emerging pathogen in arctic and boreal ungulates. *Frontiers in Microbiology* **7**, 1759.

Fortini LB, Kaiser LR, LaPointe DA (2020) Fostering real-time climate adaptation: Analyzing past, current, and forecast temperature to understand the dynamic risk to Hawaiian honeycreepers from avian malaria. *Global Ecology and Conservation* **23**, e01069.

Foster JT, Woodworth BL, Eggert LE, Hart PJ, Palmer D, *et al.* (2007) Genetic structure and evolved malaria resistance in Hawaiian honeycreepers. *Molecular Ecology* **16**(22), 4738–4746.

Fountain-Jones NM, Machado G, Carver S, Packer C, Recamonde-Mendoza M, *et al.* (2019) How to make more from exposure data? An integrated machine learning pipeline to predict pathogen exposure. *Journal of Animal Ecology* **88**(10), 1447–1461.

Funk DJ, Wernegreen JJ, Moran NA (2001) Intraspecific variation in symbiont genomes: bottlenecks and the aphid-buchnera association. *Genetics* **157**(2), 477–489.

Galbreath KE, Hoberg EP, Cook JA, Armién B, Bell KC, *et al.* (2019) Building an integrated infrastructure for exploring biodiversity: Field collections and archives of mammals and parasites. *Journal of Mammalogy* **100**(2), 382–393.

Gandon S (2004) Evolution of multihost parasites. *Evolution* **58**(3), 455–469.

Giggacher J (2020) Pandemic will cause globe $US21 trillion in economic pain. Available at: <https://phys.org/news/2020-06-pandemic-globe-us21-trillion-economic.html>

Glass GE (2006) Hantavirus risk in 2006 for U.S. Southwest. *Occasional Papers of the Museum of Texas Tech University* **255**, 1–16.

Golicz AA, Bayer PE, Bhalla PL, Batley J, Edwards D, *et al.* (2020) Pangenomics comes of age: From bacteria to plant and animal applications. *Trends in Genetics* **36**(2), 132–145.

Gómez-Rodríguez C, Crampton-Platt A, Timmermans MJ, Baselga A, Vogler AP, *et al.* (2015) Validating the power of mitochondrial metagenomics for community ecology and phylogenetics of complex assemblages. *Methods in Ecology and Evolution* **6**(8), 883–894.

Gómez A, Nichols E (2013) Neglected wildlife: Parasitic biodiversity as a conservation target. *International Journal for Parasitology: Parasites and Wildlife* **2**, 222–227.

Grange ZL, Goldstein T, Johnson CK, Anthony S, Gilardi K, *et al.* (2021) Ranking the risk of animal-to-human spillover for newly discovered viruses. *Proceedings of the National Academy of Sciences of the United States of America* **118**(15), e2002324118.

Green RE, Krause J, Briggs AW, Maricic T, Stenzel U, *et al.* (2010) A draft sequence of the Neandertal genome. *Science* **328**, 710–722.

Greiman SE, Tkach VV (2016) The numbers game: Quantitative analysis of *Neorickettsia* sp. propagation through complex life cycle of its digenean host using real-time qPCR. *Parasitology Research* **115**(7), 2779–2788.

Greiman SE, Tkach VV, Vaughan JA (2013) Transmission rates of the bacterial endosymbiont, *Neorickettsia risticii*, during the asexual reproduction phase of its digenean host, *Plagiorchis elegans*, within naturally infected lymnaeid snails. *Parasites and Vectors* **6**(303), 1–7. doi:10.1186/1756-3305-6-303

Grubaugh ND, Ladner JT, Lemey P, Pybus OG, Rambaut A, *et al.* (2019) Tracking virus outbreaks in the twenty-first century. *Nature Microbiology* **4**, 10–19.

Gryseels S, De Bruyn L, Gyselings R, Calvignac-Spencer S, Leendertz FH, *et al.* (2021) Risk of human-to-wildlife transmission of SARS-CoV-2. *Mammal Review* **51**(2), 272–292.

Hamm PS, Taylor JW, Cook JA, Natvig DO, *et al.* (2020) Decades-old studies of fungi associated with mammalian lungs and modern DNA sequencing approaches help define the nature of the lung mycobiome. *PLOS Pathogens* **16**(7), e1008684.

Han B, O'Regan SM, Paul Schmidt J, Drake JM, *et al.* (2020) Integrating data mining and transmission theory in the ecology of infectious diseases. *Ecology Letters* **23**(8), 1178–1188.

Han F, Jamsandekar M, Pettersson ME, Su L, Fuentes-Pardo AP, *et al.* (2020) Ecological adaptation in Atlantic herring is associated with large shifts in allele frequencies at hundreds of loci. *elife* **9**, e61076.

Hanke D, Freuling CM, Fischer S, Hueffer K, Hundertmark K, *et al.* (2016) Spatio-temporal analysis of the genetic diversity of arctic rabies viruses and their reservoir hosts in Greenland. *PLOS Neglected Tropical Diseases* **10**(7), e0004779.

Harding AT, Heaton NS (2018) Efforts to improve the seasonal influenza vaccine. *Vaccines (Basel)* **6**(2), 19.

Harper K, Armelagos G (2010) The changing disease-scape in the third epidemiological transition. *International Journal of Environmental Research and Public Health* **7**(2), 675–697.

Harvell CD, Mitchell CE, Ward JR, Altizer S, Dobson AP, *et al.* (2002) Climate warming and disease risks for terrestrial and marine biota. *Science* **296**(5576), 2158–2162.

Hoberg EP, Brooks DR (2008) A macroevolutionary mosaic: episodic host-switching, geographical colonization and diversification in complex host-parasite systems. *Journal of Biogeography* **35**(9), 1533–1550.

Hoberg EP, Brooks DR (2013) Episodic processes, invasion, and faunal mosaics in evolutionary and ecological time. In *The Balance of Nature and Human Impact*. (Ed K Rohde) pp. 199–213. Cambridge University Press, Cambridge, UK.

Hoyt JR, Kilpatrick AM, Langwig KE (2021) Ecology and impacts of white-nose syndrome on bats. *Nature Reviews Microbiology* **19**(3), 196–210.

Huang X, Zhang C, Pearce R, Omenn GS, Zhang Y (2020) Identifying the zoonotic origin of SARS-CoV-2 by modeling the binding affinity between the spike receptor-binding domain and host ACE2. *Journal of Proteome Research* **19**(12), 4844–4856.

Hunt RC, Struminger BB, Redd JT, Herrmann J, Jolly BT, *et al.* (2021) Virtual peer-to-peer learning to enhance and accelerate the health system response to COVID-19: The HHS ASPR project ECHO COVID-19 clinical rounds initiative. *Annals of Emergency Medicine* **78**(2), 223–228.

Hunter DJ (2005) Gene-environment interactions in human diseases. *Nature Reviews Genetics* **6**(4), 287–298.

Jin L, Lloyd R V (1997) In situ hybridization: methods and applications. *Journal of Clinical Laboratory Analysis* **11**(1), 2–9.

Jones RAC (2020) Disease pandemics and major epidemics arising from new encounters between indigenous viruses and introduced crops. *Viruses* **12**(1388), 1–24.

Jubb H, Higueruelo AP, Winter A, Blundell TL, *et al.* (2012) Structural biology and drug discovery for protein-protein interactions. *Trends in Pharmacological Sciences* **33**(5), 241–248.

Jumper J, Evans R, Pritzel A, Green T, Figurnov M, *et al.* (2021) Highly accurate protein structure prediction with AlphaFold. *Nature* **596**(7873), 583–589.

Kelleher P, Bottacini F, Mahony J, Kilcawley KN, van Sinderen D, *et al.* (2017) Comparative and functional genomics of the *Lactococcus lactis* taxon; insights into evolution and niche adaptation. *BMC Genomics* **18**(1), 267.

Keuler KM, Bron GM, Griebel R, Richgels KL (2020) An invasive disease, sylvatic plague, increases fragmentation of black-tailed prairie dog (*Cynomys ludovicianus*) colonies. *PLoS One* **15**(7), e0235907.

Kim Y, Gu C, Kim HU, Lee SY, *et al.* (2020) Current status of pan-genome analysis for pathogenic bacteria. *Current Opinion in Biotechnology* **63**, 54–62.

Klitting R, Kafetzopoulou LE, Thiery W, Dudas G, Gryseels S, *et al.* (2021) Predicting the evolution of Lassa virus endemic area and populations at risk over the next decades. *Nature Communications* **13**, 5596. doi:10.1101/2021.09.22.461380

Kutz S, Bollinger T, Branigan M, Checkley S, Davison T, *et al.* (2015) *Erysipelothrix rhusiopathiae* associated with recent widespread muskox mortalities in the Canadian Arctic. *Canadian Veterinary Journal* **56**(6), 560–563.

Kutz SJ, Hoberg EP, Polley L (2001) A new lungworm in muskoxen: an exploration in Arctic parasitology. *Trends in Parasitology* **17**(6), 276–280.

Leopardi S, Blake D, Puechmaille SJ (2015) White-nose syndrome fungus introduced from Europe to North America. *Current Biology* **25**(6), R217–R219.

Li H, Durbin R (2011) Inference of human population history from whole genome sequence of a single individual. *Nature* **475**(7357), 493–496.

Liphardt SW, Kang HJ, Arai S, Gu SH, Cook JA, *et al.* (2020) Reassortment between divergent strains of Camp Ripley Virus (Hantaviridae) in the Northern Short-tailed shrew (*Blarina brevicauda*). *Frontiers in Cellular and Infection Microbiology* **10**(460), 1–10.

Liu W, Li Y, Learn GH, Rudicell RS, Robertson JD, *et al.* (2010) Origin of the human malaria parasite *Plasmodium falciparum* in gorillas. *Nature* **467**(7314), 420–425.

Lorch JM, Palmer JM, Lindner DL, Ballmann AE, George KG, *et al.* (2016) First detection of bat white-nose syndrome in western North America. *mSphere* **1**(4), e00148-16.

Lücking R, Aime MC, Robbertse B, Miller AN, Aoki T, *et al.* (2021) Fungal taxonomy and sequence-based nomenclature. *Nature Microbiology* **6**(5), 540–548.

Martin SH, Davey JW, Jiggins CD (2015) Evaluating the use of ABBA-BABA statistics to locate introgressed loci. *Molecular Biology and Evolution* **32**(1), 244–257.

Mavrot F, Orsel K, Hutchins W, Adams LG, Beckmen K, *et al.* (2020) Novel insights into serodiagnosis and epidemiology of *Erysipelothrix rhusiopathiae*, a newly recognized pathogen in muskoxen (*Ovibos moschatus*). *PLoS One* **15**(4), e0231724.

Mawudeku A, Blench M, Boily L, St. John R, Andraghetti R, *et al.* (2013) The global public health intelligence network. In: *Infectious Disease Surveillance*. pp. 457–469. John Wiley & Sons Ltd, Oxford, UK.

McNulty SN, Tort JF, Rinaldi G, Fischer K, Rosa BA, *et al.* (2017) Genomes of *Fasciola hepatica* from the Americas reveal colonization with *Neorickettsia* endobacteria related to the agents of Potomac horse and human Sennetsu fevers. *PLoS Genetics* **13**(1), e1006537.

Miller RR, Montoya V, Gardy JL, Patrick DM, Tang P, *et al.* (2013) Metagenomics for pathogen detection in public health. *Genome Medicine* **5**(9), 81.

Mollentze N, Babayan SA, Streicker DG (2021) Identifying and prioritizing potential human-infecting viruses from their genome sequences. *PLoS Biology* **19**(9), e3001390.

Morales-Castilla I, Pappalardo P, Farrell MJ, Aguirre AA, Huang S, *et al.* (2021) Forecasting parasite sharing under climate change. *Transactions of the Royal Society B* **376**(1837), 20200360.

Morand S (2018) Advances and challenges in barcoding of microbes, parasites, and their vectors and reservoirs. *Parasitology* **145**(5), 537–542.

Mu J, Awadalla P, Duan J, McGee KM, Keebler J, *et al.* (2007) Genome-wide variation and identification of vaccine targets in the *Plasmodium falciparum* genome. *Nature Genetics* **39**(1), 126–130.

Mukhopadhyay A, Maulik U, Bandyopadhyay S, Eils R, *et al.* (2010) Mining association rules from HIV-human protein interactions. In: *2010 International Conference on Systems in Medicine and Biology*, pp. 344–348.

Murray GGR, Balmer AJ, Herbert J, Hadjirin NF, Kemp CL, *et al.* (2021) Mutation rate dynamics reflect ecological change in an emerging zoonotic pathogen. *PLoS Genetics* **17**(11), e1009864.

Newlands NK (2018) Model-based forecasting of agricultural crop disease risk at the regional scale, integrating airborne inoculum, environmental, and satellite-based monitoring data. *Frontiers of Environmental Science and Engineering in China* **6**, 63.

Nourani E, Khunjush F, Durmuş S (2015) Computational approaches for prediction of pathogen-host protein-protein interactions. *Frontiers in Microbiology* **6**, 94.

Novembre J, Han E (2012) Human population structure and the adaptive response to pathogen-induced selection pressures. *Philosophical Transactions of the Royal Society B* **367**(1590), 878–886.

Ostfeld RS (2009) Biodiversity loss and the rise of zoonotic pathogens. *Clinical Microbiology and Infectious Diseases* **15**, 40–43.

Palomo A, Pedersen AG, Fowler SJ, Dechesne A, Sicheritz-Pontén T, *et al.* (2018) Comparative genomics sheds light on niche differentiation and the evolutionary history of comammox *Nitrospira*. *ISME Journal* **12**(7), 1779–1793.

Parker CT, Tindal BJ, Garrity GM (2019) International code of nomenclature of prokaryotes. *International Journal of Systematic and Evolutionary Microbiology* **69**(1A), S1–S111.

Patz JA, Olson SH, Uejio CK, Gibbs HK (2008) Disease emergence from global and land use change. *Medical Clinics of North America* **92**, 1473–1491.

Peck KM, Lauring AS (2018) Complexities of viral mutation rates. *Journal of Virology* **92**(14), e01031-17.

Pekar JE, Magee A, Parker E, Moshiri N, Izhikevich K, *et al.* (2022) The molecular epidemiology of multiple zoonotic origins of SARS-CoV-2. *Science* **377**, 960–966.

Perrakis A, Sixma TK (2021) AI revolutions in biology: The joys and perils of AlphaFold. *EMBO Reports* **22**(11), e54046.

Peter DD, Mziray SR, Lekule I, Kisonga R, Struminger BB (2021) Project Extension for Community Healthcare Outcomes (Project ECHO) Improves Care and Treatment for Multidrug-resistant Tuberculosis Patients in Tanzania. *AIJR Abstracts*, p. 52.

Peterson AT (2003) Predicting the geography of species' invasions via ecological niche modeling. *The Quarterly Review of Biology* **78**(4), 419–433.

Peterson AT (2006) Ecological niche modeling and spatial patterns of disease transmission. *Emerging Infectious Diseases* **12**(12), 1822–1826.

Phillips CD, Dunnum JL, Dowler RC, Bradley LC, Garner HJ, *et al.* (2019) Curatorial guidelines and standards of the American Society of Mammalogists for collections of genetic resources. *Journal of Mammalogy* **100**(5), 1690–1694.

Pignatelli M, Aparicio G, Blanquer I, Hernández V, Moya A, *et al.* (2008) Metagenomics reveals our incomplete knowledge of global diversity. *Bioinformatics* **24**(18), 2124–2125.

Plissonneau C, Benevenuto J, Mohd-Assaad N, Fouché S, Hartmann FE, *et al.* (2017) Using population and comparative genomics to understand the genetic basis of effector-driven fungal pathogen evolution. *Frontiers in Plant Science* **8**, 119.

Plowright RK, Parrish CR, McCallum H, Hudson PJ, Ko AI, *et al.* (2017) Pathways to zoonotic spillover. *Nature Reviews Microbiology* **15**, 502–510.

Prasanna HC, Sinha DP, Verma A, Singh M, Singh B, *et al.* (2010) The population genomics of begomoviruses: Global scale population structure and gene flow. *Virology Journal* **7**, 220.

Quick J, Grubaugh ND, Pullan ST, Claro IM, Smith AD, *et al.* (2017) Multiplex PCR method for MinION and Illumina sequencing of Zika and other virus genomes directly from clinical samples. *Nature Protocols* **12**(6), 1261–1276.

Rabalski L, Kosinski M, Smura T, Aaltonen K, Kant R, *et al.* (2021) Severe acute respiratory syndrome coronavirus 2 in farmed mink (*Neovison vison*), Poland. *Emerging Infectious Diseases* **27**(9), 2333–2339.

Rahman MT, Sobur MA, Islam MS, Ievy S, Hossain MJ, *et al.* (2020) Zoonotic diseases: Etiology, impact, and control. *Microorganisms* **8**(9), 1405.

Reier S, Sattmann H, Haring E (2020) Morphological imaging, DNA yield, specimen and DNA preservation. *Annalen des Naturhistorischen Museums in Wien. Serie B.* **122**, 175–182.

Richardson EJ, Bacigalupe R, Harrison EM, Weinert LA, Lycett S, *et al.* (2018) Gene exchange drives the ecological success of a multi-host bacterial pathogen. *Nature Ecology and Evolution* **2**(9), 1468–1478.

Rodrigues JPGLM, Barrera-Vilarmau S, Mc Teixeira J, Sorokina M, Seckel E, *et al.* (2020) Insights on cross-species transmission of SARS-CoV-2 from structural modeling. *PLOS Computational Biology* **16**(12), e1008449.

Rouli L, Merhej V, Fournier PE, Raoult D, *et al.* (2015) The bacterial pangenome as a new tool for analysing pathogenic bacteria. *New Microbes New Infect* **7**, 72–85.

Sabin NS, Calliope AS, Simpson SV, Arima H, Ito H, *et al.* (2020) Implications of human activities for (re)emerging infectious diseases, including COVID-19. *Journal of Physiological Anthropology* **39**(1), 1–12.

Santos D, Ribeiro GC, Cabral AD, Sperança MA, *et al.* (2018) A non-destructive enzymatic method to extract DNA from arthropod specimens: Implications for morphological and molecular studies. *PLoS One* **13**(2), e0192200.

Sarver BAJ, Keeble S, Cosart T, Tucker PK, Dean MD, *et al.* (2017) Phylogenomic insights into mouse evolution using a pseudoreference approach. *Genome Biology and Evolution* **9**(3), 726–739.

Schindel DE, Cook JA (2018) The next generation of natural history collections. *PLoS Biology* **16**(7), e2006125.

Schlaberg R, Chiu CY, Miller S, Procop GW, Weinstock G (2017) Validation of metagenomic next-generation sequencing tests for universal pathogen detection. *Archives of Pathology & Laboratory Medicine* **141**(6), 776–786.

Schwabenlander MD, Rowden GR, Li M, LaSharr K, Hildebrand EC, *et al.* (2022) Comparison of chronic wasting disease detection methods and procedures: implications for free-ranging white-tailed deer (*Odocoileus virginianus*) surveillance and management. *Journal of Wildlife Diseases* **58**(1), 50–62.

Scott A, Hernandez-Jover M, Groves P, Toribio JA, *et al.* (2020) An overview of avian influenza in the context of the Australian commercial poultry industry. *One Health* **10**, 100139.

Simmonds P, Adams MJ, Benkő M, Breitbart M, Rodney Brister J, *et al.* (2017) Consensus statement: Virus taxonomy in the age of metagenomics. *Nature Reviews Microbiology* **15**(3), 161–168.

Simmonds P (2018) A clash of ideas – the varying uses of the 'species' term in virology and their utility for classifying viruses in metagenomic datasets. *Journal of General Virology* **99**(3), 277–287.

Skerratt LF, Berger L, Speare R, Cashins S, McDonald KR, *et al.* (2007) The spread of chytridiomycosis has caused the rapid global decline and extinction of frogs. *Ecohealth* **4**, 125–134.

Soanes DM, Richards TA, Talbot NJ (2007) Insights from sequencing fungal and oomycete genomes: what can we learn about plant disease and the evolution of pathogenicity? *Plant Cell* **19**(11), 3318–3326.

Spraker TR, White PA (2017) Shaggy lame fox syndrome in Pribilof Island Arctic Foxes (*Alopex lagopus pribilofensis*), Alaska. *Veterinary Pathology* **54**(2), 258–268.

Stephens PR, Altizer S, Smith KF, Alonso Aguirre A, Brown JH, *et al.* (2016) The macroecology of infectious diseases: a new perspective on global-scale drivers of pathogen distributions and impacts. *Ecology Letters* **19**(9), 1159–1171.

Storz JF (2021) High-altitude adaptation: Mechanistic insights from integrated genomics and physiology. *Molecular Biology and Evolution* **38**(7), 2677–2691.

Stuart SN, Chanson JS, Cox NA, Young BE, Rodrigues AS, *et al.* (2004) Status and trends of amphibian declines and extinctions worldwide. *Science* **306**(5702), 1783–1786.

Stukenbrock EH, Bataillon T (2012) A population genomics perspective on the emergence and adaptation of new plant pathogens in agro-ecosystems. *PLOS Pathogens* **8**(9), e1002893.

Stunz E, Fetcher N, Lavretsky P, Mohl JE, Tang J, *et al.* (2022) Landscape genomics provides evidence of ecotypic adaptation and a barrier to gene flow at treeline for the Arctic foundation species *Eriophorum vaginatum*. *Frontiers in Plant Science* **13**, 860439.

Susi H, Filloux D, Frilander MJ, Roumagnac P, Laine AL, *et al.* (2019) Diverse and variable virus communities in wild plant populations revealed by metagenomic tools. *PeerJ* **7**, e6140.

Talas F, McDonald BA (2015) Genome-wide analysis of *Fusarium graminearum* field populations reveals hotspots of recombination. *BMC Genomics* **16**, 996.

Tantithamthavorn C, Hassan AE, Matsumoto K (2020) The impact of class rebalancing techniques on the performance and interpretation of defect prediction models. *IEEE Transactions on Software Engineering* **46**(11), 1200–1219.

Thompson C, Phelps KL, Allard MW, Cook JA, Dunnum JL, *et al.* (2021) Preserve a voucher specimen! The critical need for integrating natural history collections in infectious disease studies. *MBio* **12**(1), e02698–20.

Torres-Pérez F, Palma RE, Hjelle B, Holmes EC, Cook JA, *et al.* (2011) Spatial but not temporal co-divergence of a virus and its mammalian host. *Molecular Ecology* **20**(19), 4109–4122.

Tsangaras K, Greenwood AD (2012) Museum and disease: Using tissue archive and museum samples to study pathogens. *Annals of Anatomy* **194**(1), 58–73.

Turland NJ, Wiersema JH, Barrie FR, Greuter W, Hawksworth DL, *et al.* (2018) *International Code of Nomenclature for algae, fungi, and plants (Shenzhen Code) adopted by the Nineteenth International Botanical Congress Shenzhen, China, July 2017.* Koeltz Botanical Books.

Van Tyne D, Park DJ, Schaffner SF, Neafsey DE, Angelino E, *et al.* (2011) Identification and functional validation of the novel antimalarial resistance locus PF10_0355 in plasmodium falciparum. *PLoS Genetics* **7**(4), e1001383.

Vaughan JA, Tkach VV, Greiman SE (2012) Neorickettsial endosymbionts of the digenea: Diversity, transmission and distribution. In *Advances in Parasitology.* (Eds D Rollinson, SI Hay) pp. 253–297 Academic Press.

Wang F, Flanagan J, Su N, Wang LC, Bui S, *et al.* (2012) RNAscope: A novel in situ RNA analysis platform for formalin-fixed, paraffin-embedded tissues. *The Journal of Molecular Diagnostics: JMD* **14**(1), 22–29. doi:10.1016/j.jmoldx.2011.08.002

Wang Q, Chang BJ, Riley T V (2010) *Erysipelothrix rhusiopathiae.* *Veterinary Microbiology* **140**(3–4), 405–417.

Wang T, Sun Y, Qiu H (2018) African swine fever: An unprecedented disaster and challenge to China. *Infectious Diseases of Poverty* **7**(111), 66–70.

Wardeh M, Sharkey KJ, Baylis M (2020) Integration of shared-pathogen networks and machine learning reveals the key aspects of zoonoses and predicts mammalian reservoirs. *Proceedings of the Royal Society B* **287**(1920), 20192882.

Watsa M (2020) Rigorous wildlife disease surveillance. *Science* **369**(6500), 145–147.

Webster MS (2017) *The Extended Specimen: Emerging Frontiers in Collections-Based Ornithological Research.* CRC Press, Boca Raton, FL, USA.

Wiens J, Shenoy ES (2018) Machine learning for healthcare: On the verge of a major shift in healthcare epidemiology. *Clinical Infectious Diseases* **66**(1), 149–153.

Wilder AP, Frick WF, Langwig KE, Kunz TH (2011) Risk factors associated with mortality from white-nose syndrome among hibernating bat colonies. *Biology Letters* **7**(6), 950–953.

Wong ML, Medrano JF (2005) Real-time PCR for mRNA quantitation. *Biotechniques* **39**(1), 75–85.

Wood DE, Salzberg SL (2014) Kraken: Ultrafast metagenomic sequence classification using exact alignments. *Genome Biology* **15**(3), R46.

Woolhouse M, Scott F, Hudson Z, Howey R, Chase-Topping M (2012) Human viruses: Discovery and emergence. *Philosophical Transactions of the Royal Society B* **367**(1604), 2864–2871.

Woonwong Y, Do Tien D, Thanawongnuwech R (2020) The future of the pig industry after the introduction of African swine fever into Asia. *Animal Frontiers* **10**(4), 30–37.

World Bank (2012) People, pathogens and our planet: The economics of one health. *World Bank* **2**, 1–65.

World Health Organization (WHO) (2020) Urgent health challenges for the next decade. Available at: <https://www.who.int/news-room/photo-story/photo-story-detail/urgent-health-challenges-for-the-next-decade>

Worobey M, Levy JI, Serrano LM, Crits-Christoph A, Pekar JE, *et al.* (2022) The Huanan Seafood Wholesale Market in Wuhan was the early epicenter of the COVID-19 pandemic. *Science* **377**, 951–959.

wwPDB Consortium (2019) Protein Data Bank: The single global archive for 3D macromolecular structure data. *Nucleic Acids Res.* **47**(D1), D520–D528.

Yan H, Jiao H, Liu Q, Zhang Z, Xiong Q, *et al.* (2021) ACE2 receptor usage reveals variation in susceptibility to SARS-CoV and SARS-CoV-2 infection among bat species. *Nature Ecology and Evolution* **5**(5), 600–608.

Yanagihara R, Gu SH, Song J-W (2015) Expanded host diversity and global distribution of hantaviruses: implication for identifying and investigating previously unrecognized hantaviral diseases. In *Global virology: Identifying and investigating viral diseases.* (Ed P Shapshak) pp. 161–198. Springer-Verlag, New York.

Yates TL *et al.* (2002) The Ecology and Evolutionary History of an Emergent Disease: Hantavirus Pulmonary Syndrome: Evidence from two El Niño episodes in the American Southwest suggests that El Niño–driven precipitation, the initial catalyst of a trophic cascade that results in a delayed density-dependent rodent response, is sufficient to predict heightened risk for human contraction of hantavirus pulmonary syndrome. *Bioscience* **52**(11), 989–998.

You S, Liu T, Zhang M, Zhao X, Dong Y, *et al.* (2021) African swine fever outbreaks in China led to gross domestic product and economic losses. *Nature Food* **2**, 802–808.

Zacho CM, Bager MA, Margaryan A, Gravlund P, Galatius A, *et al.* (2021) Uncovering the genomic and metagenomic research potential in old ethanol-preserved snakes. *PLoS One* **16**(8), e0256353.

Zhu Q, Mai U, Pfeiffer W, Janssen S, Asnicar F, *et al.* (2019) Phylogenomics of 10,575 genomes reveals evolutionary proximity between domains Bacteria and Archaea. *Nature Communications* **10**(1), 5477.

Zhu Q, Huang S, Gonzalez A, McGrath I, McDonald D, *et al.* (2022) Phylogeny-aware analysis of metagenome community ecology based on matched reference genomes while bypassing taxonomy. *mSystems* **7**(2), e0016722.

Zimmermann J, Abarca N, Enk N, Skibbe O, Kusber WH, *et al.* (2014) Taxonomic reference libraries for environmental barcoding: A best practice example from diatom research. *PLoS One* **9**(9), e108793.

Zuk O, Hechter E, Sunyaev SR, Lander ES (2012) The mystery of missing heritability: Genetic interactions create phantom heritability. *Proceedings of the National Academy of Sciences of the United States of America* **109**(4), 1193–1198.

26 Management of vertebrate pests using genetic control techniques

Anna C. Clark, Alana Alexander, Jackson Champer, Rey Edison, Mandira Katuwal and Neil J. Gemmell

ABSTRACT

The proliferation of invasive species in new environments has significant impacts on food security, disease transmission, and conservation worldwide, particularly in insular island ecosystems where invasive species can have disproportionately large consequences. Traditional control techniques such as kill trapping, biocontrol, contraceptive, and poison control strategies have a long history of use for controlling problem species. However, concerns for animal welfare, off-target effects, and limitations to long-term efficiency have fuelled a search for novel, highly effective control techniques. Approaches that harness the power of genetics, such as species-specific toxins, the Trojan female technique and gene drives, show promise in addressing challenges associated with conventional management tools. Here, with a strong focus on vertebrate pests, we review concerns with existing invasive species management and then explore the current state of research and barriers to the development of genetic technology.

EMERGING CHALLENGES IN PEST MANAGEMENT

Invasive species, agricultural pests, and disease vectors are considered problematic globally due to their capacity to disrupt environmental systems, threaten food security, and impact human health (Pejchar and Mooney 2009). Conventional invasive species management strategies span direct culling, live and kill traps, toxins, biocontrol, and controlling reproductive capacity (Goldson *et al.* 2015). While many of these approaches have been utilised for centuries, there remain technical challenges associated with the large-scale and long-term use of these methods, and many are increasingly considered ethically unacceptable (van Eeden *et al.* 2017).

Direct culling and trapping

Hunting and the use of live capture or kill traps are effective for controlling vertebrate populations in areas with reasonable access (King and Edgar 1977; Cowan 1992; Alterio *et al.* 1999). However, their overall long-term effectiveness may be limited by cost and resource intensiveness, difficulties in large-scale system deployment and reduced performance at low densities (Campbell *et al.* 2015; Latham *et al.* 2015; Warburton and Gormley 2015; Anderson *et al.* 2016). A key issue with these direct control measures is behavioural resistance, whereby individuals avoid interactions with new objects due to either prior negative experiences or neophobia (the fear of anything new and unfamiliar) (Webster *et al.* 1994). In New Zealand (NZ), variations in trap avoidance behaviour have been observed for a variety of pest species including rats (Russell *et al.* 2008), possums (Adams *et al.* 2014), and stoats (Alterio *et al.* 1999; Anderson *et al.* 2016). Although self-resetting traps (Carter *et al.* 2016; Gronwald and Russell 2021) and more effective bait lures (e.g. audible cues) are being developed, refined, and implemented into many large-scale trapping systems, there are still substantial issues concerning maintenance cost, trap performance, and large-scale system deployment, particularly to remote areas (Campbell *et al.* 2015; Latham *et al.* 2015; Warburton and Gormley 2015; Anderson *et al.* 2016).

Vertebrate toxins

The use of poison has been important for controlling vertebrate species across large and remote areas (Eason *et al.* 2010). It has also been useful in urban areas where applications can be localised to infestation sites. Common poisons used to manage vertebrate species include the aerobic metabolism inhibitors cyanide and sodium monofluoroacetate (1080) (Eason *et al.* 2017) and anticoagulants such as brodifacoum and warfarin (Fisher *et al.* 2019). However, the mechanism of death associated with the use of some poisons, environmental persistence, contamination of soils and waterways, and the potential for mortality of non-target species (Box 26.1), presents ethical challenges. These are highlighted in the example of 1080, which is widely used in Australasia (Eason *et al.* 2011; Berry *et al.* 2012). The toxin has a broad toxicity profile, which makes it a valuable tool for coordinating the management of multiple invasive species at once (Warburton *et al.* 2021). However, this is also a drawback as both the bait and persisting toxin residue in carcasses presents a significant threat of secondary poisoning to non-target mammals, particularly to companion and working dogs (Meenken and Booth 1997). Upon ingestion, death is not immediate, and the prolonged suffering of animals subjected to 1080 toxicosis stimulates emotive discussions around its humaneness as a pest control tool (Eason *et al.* 2011). However, despite public concern and debate, there is clear evidence that native wildlife benefit from the use of such toxins to control invasive species (Green and Rohan 2012; Blackie *et al.* 2014; Russell and Broome 2016).

Modern toxins in development are more targeted to reduce impact on non-target species; however, this specificity also means that resistance is more evolutionarily accessible to the target population (Hawkins *et al.* 2019). Research efforts to combat vertebrate toxin resistance have therefore focused on improving the understanding of mechanisms that underpin the evolution of toxin resistance (reviewed in Hawkins *et al.* 2019), including functional variation with potential to confer toxin tolerance (Emami-Khoyi *et al.* 2020).

Global climate change also impacts pest management. Increasingly mild winters in NZ have led to an abundance of food, which makes poisoned baits less desirable (Latham *et al.* 2015). With abundant food, pest populations can remain large throughout the year, and reproduce more frequently with higher fecundity, requiring the application of more poison baits to achieve even modest levels of control (Tompkins *et al.* 2013). Although the application of poison has been used to eradicate vertebrate species on several offshore NZ islands, success on the mainland requires a significant reduction in resource requirements, and the development of population management strategies that are effective, despite seasonal and demographic variability (Eason *et al.* 1993; Russell and Broome 2016; Latham *et al.* 2017).

Biological control

Biological control is the use of natural enemies such as parasites, predators, and pathogens to control a target pest population. It is practised over 10% of the earth's total land surface (Tomasetto *et al.* 2017) and can provide a cost-effective and self-sustaining control measure when implemented with rigorous scientific and regulatory vetting (Van Lenteren *et al.* 1997; Bale *et al.* 2008; Cock *et al.* 2016). Among different approaches, classical biological control, which involves importing and establishing natural enemies to control invasive pests, has proven to be the most effective (Messing and Wright 2006; Barratt *et al.* 2018). Some noteworthy examples include control of invasive forage weevils (*Sitona obsoletus*, *S. discoideus*, and *Listronotus bonariensis*) with introduced parasitoid wasps (*Microctonus* spp.) in New Zealand (Barker and Addison 2006; Gerard *et al.* 2011); control of cottony cushion scale (*Icerya purchasi*) using the predatory coccinellid (*Rodolia cardinalis*) in California; the use of myxomatosis and rabbit haemorrhagic disease viruses to control European rabbits (*Oryctolagus cuniculus*) in Australia and New Zealand (Cooke 1983; Cooke and Fenner 2002); and control of the coconut moth (*Levuana iridescens*) using the tachinid fly (*Bessa remota*) in Fiji (Caltagirone 1981).

However, there are a multitude of challenges and risks associated with implementing successful classical biological control strategies (Barratt *et al.* 2018). These include lack of genetic, biological, and ecological data, off-target impacts on native biodiversity, and difficulty in assessing the stability of the control in the long term (Howarth 1991; Barratt *et al.* 2007; Hajek *et al.* 2016). Such limitations have contributed to the failure of multiple biological control programs in different parts of the world. For example, Asian lady beetles (*Harmonia axyridis*) were introduced into North America and several European countries as a biocontrol agent for a variety of arthropod pests. However, the ability of these new biocontrol agents to adapt rapidly to new

Box 26.1: Toxin specificity

The use of toxins in vertebrate management has been historically effective (Towns *et al.* 2012). However, non-target lethality in native species (Wright 2017) and important recreational and domestic species (Meenken and Booth 1997; Eason *et al.* 2013) heighten concerns related to their long-term use. Earlier searches for species-targeted toxins lead to the discovery of norbormide, a chemical compound that induces permanent peripheral vasoconstriction in rats but that is relatively harmless to other rodents and mammals (Roszkowski *et al.* 1965). Development of this toxin as an effective bait proved challenging as norbormide's acute toxicity produces immediate effects in the buccal cavity upon consumption, resulting in sublethal sampling of the bait, and the acquisition of bait aversion behaviour (Beveridge and Daniel 1966). Subsequent research has centred on identifying pro-toxicants and derivatives that are more palatable than the primary compound, while maintaining consistent narrow toxicity profiles (Rennison *et al.* 2013; Choi *et al.* 2016; Ma *et al.* 2019).

Another example is para-aminopropiophenone (PAPP), a compound that has high toxicity in carnivores when ingested. Used now in commercially available baits and being tested as a liquid toxin delivered by Canid Pest Ejectors (Allen 2019) to control wild dogs and foxes in Australia, PAPP is now being developed as a toxin for mustelid species and feral cats in New Zealand (Eason *et al.* 2014; Johnston *et al.* 2020). The primary biochemical mechanism of PAPP significantly increases oxygen-carrying haemoglobin conversion to non-oxygen carrying methaemoglobin, reducing the oxygen carrying capacity of the blood and ultimately producing hypoxia in vital organ tissue, resulting in death (Eason *et al.* 2014). PAPP at a sufficient dose is toxic to many species, but carnivores are particularly susceptible to its effects. Thus, the development of PAPP bait has focused on leveraging taxonomic behavioural differences, for example delivering PAPP in a meat or blood formulated medium that attracts carnivores while deterring non-target, herbivorous animals.

The identification and development of norbormide and PAPP has been expensive and time-consuming, involving adaptations and innovations in formulations or delivery to achieve a toxin that will be both efficient and specific. PAPP, for example, was first considered for use in vertebrate pest control in the 1980s, but was not approved for use in New Zealand on stoats and cats until 2011 (Eason *et al.* 2014). Such long timeframes from development to approved usage are not uncommon and present a significant barrier to the widescale usage of toxins as a solution to various problematic pest species. However, with the increasing power of artificial intelligence (AI) based predictive modelling and similar technologies in the pharmaceutical sector, improvements in the accuracy of toxicity profiling for novel pesticide agents (e.g. species-specific activity) may soon be on the horizon and may save years of research and development (Paul *et al.* 2021; Pérez Santín *et al.* 2021). As our understanding of genomics and biological processes progresses, leveraging *in silico* AI approaches will likely facilitate more economically efficient identification and biochemical profiling, as well as alleviating the ethical concerns associated with the extensive *in vivo* testing of toxic compounds (Hartung and Rovida 2009).

In addition to animal welfare concerns, and non-target species impact, toxin application may face decreased efficiency with the development of avoidance behaviour or bait-shyness (Ogilvie *et al.* 2010) or evolved resistance to toxins (e.g. 1080

Fig. 26.1. Norway rat interacting with norbormide bait in contained trials. Photo credit: Sam Brown (Manaaki Whenua – Landcare Research).

resistance in Australian rabbits; (Twigg *et al.* 2002); and warfarin resistance in several wild rodent populations; (Rost *et al.* 2009)) (Box 26.2). Lethal pesticides are strong selective agents so genomic variation that produces resistance to such compounds (i.e. reduction in the effective median lethal dose) would be significantly advantageous, likely to spread rapidly through target populations, and challenge the efficacy of management systems. Recent transcriptomic work on the NZ brushtail possum population revealed high levels of functional diversity in metabolic pathways relevant to the development of chemical tolerance reported in other marsupials (Emami-Khoyi *et al.* 2020). This study is a useful example of how genomic knowledge can be applied to help predict the likelihood of resistance emerging in a target pest population.

Box 26.2: Evolution of toxin resistance

Evolution of toxin resistance is a significant concern for pest management as it can decrease the effectiveness of control. Toxins designed for lethal pest control are powerful selective pressures for the evolution of resistance, providing an advantageous environment for genotypes that reduce an organisms or populations physiological and behavioural sensitivity to the toxic compound. Despite most instances of rapid evolution of resistance being documented in species with high fecundity and short generation times (Hemingway and Ranson 2003; Davies and Davies 2010), vertebrate species are not immune to the fundamental principles underlying the evolution of resistance (Twigg *et al.* 2002; Ishizuka *et al.* 2008). Resistance has been a major challenge to the development of effective and sustainable rodenticides, particularly anticoagulant based baits (McGee *et al.* 2020).

Mutations and polymorphisms from *de novo* and standing variation are the main sources of genomic toxin resistance in vertebrate species (Fig. 26.2) (Hawkins *et al.* 2019). In the context of pest control, *de novo* mutations refer to those that occur once the target population is exposed to the toxin (Messer and Petrov 2013). Variation arises at the background mutation rate, either once or through multiple independent events, and increases in frequency as toxin susceptible genotypes are removed from the gene pool. Resistance from standing variation refers to pre-existing mutations, either single or polygenic, that are rapidly advantageous in response to toxin exposure (Barrett and Schluter 2008). Standing variation may also interact with *de novo* mutations to influence the relative fitness of resistant individuals. Additional mechanisms for resistance in vertebrates are interspecific gene transfer (e.g. introgressive hybridisation in old world mice (Song *et al.* 2011)), behavioural resistance (e.g. predatory avoidance of introduced cane toads (Llewelyn *et al.* 2014)) and epigenetic changes (Ujvari *et al.* 2013; Allsop *et al.* 2017; Charlesworth *et al.* 2017).

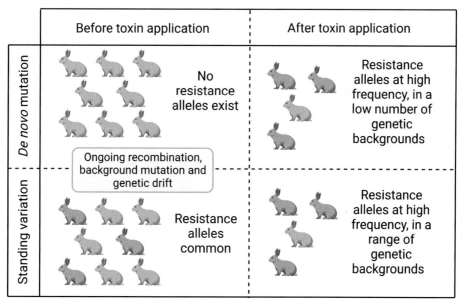

Fig. 26.2. Evolution of toxin resistance alleles (carried by blue individuals) via *de novo* mutation and selection from standing genetic variation. Created with BioRender.com.

environments (likely due to diverse polymorphism and morphology), resulted in the beetles themselves becoming an invasive species and threatening non-target insect populations (Soares *et al.* 2007). The deliberate introduction of cane toads (*Bufo marinus*) throughout the subtropics (Shanmuganathan *et al.* 2010), and mustelids (*Mustela spp.*) to control rabbits in New Zealand (Innes *et al.* 2010) have had similarly disastrous, but unintended, consequences.

Modern day biological control has adopted a much more rigorous framework of testing before deployment (Teem *et al.* 2020), but the spectre of past failures remains a grim reminder of what is at stake when this goes wrong. It is thus perhaps not surprising that new calls to develop genetically enhanced biocontrol are greeted with muted enthusiasm. While the application of genetic research in crop and livestock breeding is well established, attempts to improve biological control agents through genetic means have been scarce (Leung *et al.* 2020). However, the integration of genetic and biocontrol approaches (i.e. genetic biocontrol (Teem *et al.* 2020)) and next-generation biological control (Leung *et al.* 2020) has the potential to drive rapid enhancements in current biological control programs.

Controlling reproductive capacity

Targeting processes that precede embryonic development reduces welfare concerns associated with neuroanatomical and neurophysiological stress due to toxicosis from poison baits or physical trauma inflicted through trapping (Littin *et al.* 2004). Contraceptives and the sterile male technique (SMT) work by reducing the reproductive capacity of a population, and resolve several concerns with other management tools, including animal welfare and non-target impacts. Immunocontraception immunises an animal against proteins produced by its own gametes, ultimately producing an auto-immune response that results in infertility (Cowan 1996). Specificity has been achieved in research trials by targeting species-specific reproductive protein variants and administration of the vaccine in a species-specific manner (e.g. via an edible bait (Polkinghorne *et al.* 2005), subcutaneous injection to manage macropods in Australia (Wimpenny *et al.* 2021), or through drug dart delivery used to control white-tailed deer in America (Miller *et al.* 2000), wild horse populations on several islands including Assateague Island (Turner and Kirkpatrick 2002), and elephants in Africa (Jolly 1993; Duckworth *et al.* 1998; Fayrer-Hosken *et al.* 2000)). Subcutaneous hormonal levonorgestrel implants (ovulation inhibition) have also been developed to manage small, discrete populations of macropods (Wimpenny *et al.* 2021).

Despite promising results, immunogenetic resistance emerged as one of the major limitations of immunocontraceptives (Cooper and Larsen 2006). Ultimately, the system confers a substantial selective advantage to individuals that fail to elicit an immune response against their own gametes, which leads to both the rapid evolution of resistance and disease management challenges. Immunocompromised individuals have an increased susceptibility to transmit pathogens (e.g. tuberculosis), which could significantly reverse management outcomes (e.g. lead to a net increase in disease spread; Cooper and Larsen 2006). The ongoing maintenance costs associated with methods that require direct and sometimes repeated delivery of immunocontraceptive baits, vaccines, and drug darts stimulated research into alternative delivery mechanisms, such as the use of viral vectors (e.g. a herpes-type sexually transmitted disease (Barlow 1994; Tyndale-Biscoe 1994; Hardy *et al.* 2006)). However, concerns of disease immunity, transmission efficacy (i.e. where dispersing individuals are uninfected virgin juveniles), and spread to non-target populations challenges the long-term efficiency of this technique (Barlow 1994).

Proven successful for large-scale insect control, SMT uses large releases of sterile males to decrease female reproductive potential in wild populations (Alphey *et al.* 2010) and has successfully been used to control and eradicate insect species such as the parasitic screwworm fly in several countries (Scott *et al.* 2017). However, SMT has thus far been largely restricted to invertebrates due to the constraints of: (1) releasing large quantities of sterile males every year; (2) restricted mating behaviours in some vertebrates; (3) the physiological ability to tolerate sub-lethal doses of chemo-sterilant or irradiation; or (4) the financial cost, social license and legislative restrictions of genetically engineering sterility (see section 'Addressing additional barriers to research and development') (Franz and Robinson 2011; Magris *et al.* 2015; Scott *et al.* 2017). Even if these technical hurdles are overcome, theoretical modelling suggests that SMT would only be useful for relatively small populations of mammals (fewer than 100 individuals) (Gonçalves *et al.* 2010).

PEST MANAGEMENT USING GENETIC TECHNIQUES

Due to the reduced effectiveness of current pest control technology at low population densities, negative impacts on non-target species, toxin and behavioural resistance, and ethical issues, management of populations through fertility-based methods are generally preferred (Wilkinson and Fitzgerald 2006). Systems that deliver contraceptive-type control to target animals have been developed; however, their application remains limited to small populations of large vertebrates (Wimpenny *et al.* 2021). Strategies like species-specific toxins, the Trojan female technique, and gene drives are capable of manipulating pest populations at the molecular level to produce species-specific population suppression outcomes (Table 26.1). Here, we specifically discuss the key technical challenges associated with the development of these new technologies.

Species-specific toxins

Large-scale landscape application of poison is currently one of the most effective strategies for managing invasive species populations (Goldson *et al.* 2015). However, there is a significant risk of primary and secondary poisoning to economically, socially, and ecologically important non-target species (Meenken and Booth 1997). One of the most promising alternatives to address these concerns involves the characterisation of pest genomes to design species-specific toxins, through genome mining, comparative genomics, and functional experiments (Warburton *et al.* 2021). In the context of developing species-specific toxins, genome mining and comparative genomic approaches employ the use of high-quality annotated genomes to identify previously uncharacterised biological processes, products, and interactions (e.g. receptor gene families) that have evolved species-specific variation in target species and may therefore be suitable biochemical targets. For non-model species and species that are considered pests in very few areas, genomes are less likely to have been sequenced. In this case, using the genome of a closely related species may prove useful in identifying variants that are limited to a particular taxonomic group, and may minimise repercussions in non-target species. Functional experiments (i.e. gene knockouts) would subsequently be performed to rigorously characterise biological function of species-specific variants to inform the development of assays to test either chemical compounds or molecules (i.e. RNAi) that may disrupt biological function and produce lethal physiological changes in the organism.

Interfering RNA (RNAi) is a method of post-transcriptional gene silencing that has prospective application in targeting species-specific variants to produce lethal physiological effects (Horak 2020). In the RNAi process, a guide strand of RNA is combined with an enzyme complex, RNA-induced silencing complex (RISC), which degrades complementary mRNA produced by the cell to significantly disrupt the production of corresponding products (e.g. enzymes and other proteins). Where these products are necessary for normal biological processes, pathway disruption may produce lethal physiological effects, for instance, the accumulation of cytotoxic products. Such effects will stimulate similar ethical challenges to conventional chemical toxins (Eason *et al.* 2011). While RNAi techniques show application potential for population management (Heath *et al.* 2014), they face many of the same challenges as toxicants, including stability under diverse climatic and gastrointestinal environments (may be addressed through bioengineering techniques and nanoparticle delivery systems), cellular uptake, bait avoidance behaviour, complex social structures (i.e. ants; Allen 2021), sublethal bait sampling, and confirmation of species-specific effect (Horak 2020). Although the application of species-specific toxins is likely to be on par, if not more expensive than current toxin applications, they could be very valuable tools, but we need to develop rapid methods of determining if off-target effects are likely to occur. With the emergence of more genomic data and a larger understanding of biological processes, it may become possible to predict species-specific toxicity for a range of agents, including RNAi, using machine learning approaches (Paul *et al.* 2021; Pérez Santín *et al.* 2021).

Trojan female technique

The Trojan female technique (TFT) is a novel twist on the sterile male technique (SMT; see section 'Controlling reproductive capacity'), with the major advantage being TFT's self-sustaining, transgenerational mechanism to produce population suppression (Gemmell *et al.* 2013). Instead of large SMT releases every generation, population control using the TFT approach is achieved through the steady release of 'Trojan females' that carry naturally occurring, maternally inherited mitochondrial DNA (mtDNA) mutations that cause reductions to male, but not female fertility. Empirical experiments have demonstrated that mitochondrial variants that produce defective mitochondrial respiration impact sperm function, resulting in sperm that have significant motility issues and reduced fertilising capability, while effects on female survival and reproductive fitness in laboratory populations of mice (Nakada *et al.* 2006), and flies (Wolff *et al.* 2017) appear insignificant.

One of the key challenges is getting the TFT mutation to sufficiently high frequencies in a target population to achieve sustained management. To achieve population suppression below 1% within a decade, experimental modelling suggests that TFT release ratios are less than required for SMT (owing to the additive effect of releasing self-perpetuating mutations), with 22% and 65% annual releases respectively (Gemmell *et al.* 2013). However, if applied to NZ's 30 million brushtail possum population, such a release ratio is not ecologically feasible as population suppression would require the annual TFT release of 6.6 million females (2008/2009 estimate; Warburton *et al.* 2009). One method to circumvent this would be to use conventional tools (see section 'Emerging challenges in pest management') to initially reduce the target population size, and thus lower the required number of individuals, resource and reproductive competition for the Trojan females and minimise ecological impact of releasing these pests into the environment.

Understanding of this technique is currently limited to laboratory experiments using inbred lines of fruit flies (Wolff *et al.* 2017), raising concern about the application of TFT to different species, or even to fruit flies outside the laboratory. Empirical experiments using *Drosophila* carrying one proposed candidate TFT mutation located in the mitochondrial cytochrome b gene (*mit:Cyt-b*), demonstrate consistent reductions in male fertility across diverse temperature environments and nuclear genomic backgrounds (Wolff *et al.* 2016) and modest population suppression was achieved over 10 generations (Wolff *et al.* 2017). However, the fertility reductions were limited to 50% that of wild-type counterparts, suggesting that modifier alleles present in the nuclear genome may be compensating for the effect of the TFT mutation. Considering that male infertility is a strong selective agent, the evolution of compensatory nuclear loci is plausible, and pre-existing variation may already be widespread in large heterogeneous wild populations, which presents a challenge to TFT efficiency. Identification of TFT mutations that confer complete sterility regardless of variations in environmental or nuclear genomic contexts will be valuable for the continued development of this technique. Recent advances in mitochondrial genome editing (Mok *et al.* 2020) may enable the engineering of more effective mutations, alongside facilitating the production of more genetically diverse lines of carriers, and multiple TFT mutations per carrier. These characteristics have the potential to increase the effect of TFT on phenotype and reduce the probability of TFT phenotypic reversion back to wildtype (rapid detection and response to such evolutionary events may require intermittent population sampling and/or eDNA surveillance, see Chapter 24).

Gene drive techniques

Gene drives are genetic constructs that defy Mendel's law of equal segregation, allowing particular genetic material to be inherited at rates well beyond the 50:50 ratio we normally expect (Esvelt *et al.* 2014; Bier 2021) (Fig. 26.3A). Engineered gene drives typically are designed to either modify or suppress target populations (Price *et al.* 2020). The main principle underlying population modification gene drives is to replace wild-type alleles with drive alleles that confer desirable traits (e.g. a reduced capacity to transmit malaria or heightened susceptibility to toxins). When the drive inheritance rate is well above 50% in drive heterozygotes, major changes in gene frequencies in a population can happen within a few generations (McFarlane *et al.* 2018; Min *et al.* 2018). Another gene drive variation is the suppression gene drive to reduce or eliminate a population. Instead of just replacing wildtype alleles, the objective of a population suppression drive is to reduce or eliminate a population by biasing the sex ratio or disrupting haplosufficient genes (where one functional allele prevents any deleterious phenotype) that are essential for survival or reproduction. For example, targeted disruption to *doublesex*, an insect sex determination gene, has been successful in suppressing laboratory populations of *Anopheles gambiae* because females homozygous for the disrupted gene are sterile (Kyrou *et al.* 2018). Promising for vertebrates, the Y-shredder system is capable of eliminating the Y-chromosome in mouse embryonic stem cells with up to 90% efficiency, which could lead to population reduction when access to males becomes limiting (Prowse *et al.* 2019). However, the resulting female-biased population presents a risk of prolonged population stability and possibly even growth prior to demographic collapse (Boyle *et al.* 2014; Prowse *et al.* 2019).

One major technical challenge in the application of synthetic gene drives is the evolution of resistance, either molecular changes that directly affect the intrinsic drive mechanism or adaptations that change the behaviour or life history of drive carrying individuals in a way that impedes drive transmission (Price *et al.* 2020). Molecular resistance can be observed as pre-existing genetic variation found within the target genomic sites, a likely scenario in large wild populations that generally maintain high levels of genetic heterogeneity. Resistance may also arise through end-joining (EJ) repair following nuclease activity (Fig. 26.3B; Preston *et al.* 2006). Alleles that are capable of resisting drive conversion can have a strong selective advantage (for example, drive-carrying individuals in laboratory populations of *Anopheles* mosquitoes were reduced from approximately 77% to 20% over 21 generations due to

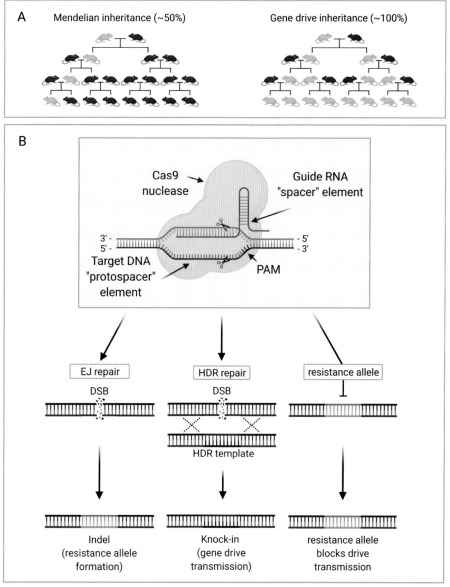

Fig. 26.3. (A) An example of the difference between average Mendelian and perfectly efficient homing gene drive inheritance over several generations after initially pairing a heterozygote (green marking individuals heterozygous for a transgenic allele) with a wildtype homozygote (grey). (B) Alternative molecular repair pathways following the nuclease activity of a CRISPR-Cas9 homing gene drive. Guide RNAs (gRNAs) direct the Cas9 endonuclease to a specific genomic locus, inducingCas9 to make a double-stranded break (DSB). One of two repair pathways are consequently activated – end-joining (EJ), which may introduce an insertion and/or deletion; or homology-directed repair (HDR) where a genomic template (i.e. gene drive construct) may be used to repair the cleaved site, copying its sequence. Alternatively, a resistance allele (pre-existing sequence variation at the target site or a sequence change formed earlier by end-joining repair after drive-induced cleavage) may prevent gRNA sequence recognition and nuclease induced cleavage altogether. Created with BioRender.com.

resistance alleles (Hammond *et al.* 2017)), unless the cost of resistance is similar to the drive (Unckless *et al.* 2017; Barrett *et al.* 2019; Holman 2019). Identifying evolutionarily conserved sites within functionally important regions (Kyrou *et al.* 2018), and characterisation of overall mutation or EJ rates in the target population is crucial to both predict and potentially help circumvent the evolution of resistance (Unckless *et al.* 2017).

Another tractable approach to prevent resistance alleles is to use a germline-specific promoter to restrict nuclease activity to a narrow temporal period in meiosis I (Champer, Oh *et al.* 2020). Adding this temporal component produces a substantial bias towards the homology-directed repair pathway instead of end-joining (HDR vs. EJ; Fig. 26.3B), increasing the probability of successful drive transmission. Further, the use of multiple gRNAs (multiplexing) has been shown to significantly increase conversion efficiency and reduce resistance rates of CRISPR **homing** gene drives in fruit flies (Champer *et al.* 2018) and yeast (Yan and Finnigan 2018). In addition, it provides a means of targeting independent genetic loci from the same distinct and/or parallel genetic pathways to establish a form of redundancy should resistance alleles arise. However, variations in gRNA activity levels, imperfect homology adjacent to target cleavage sites, and division of nuclease activity between many gRNAs have been found to limit increases in gene drive efficiency when employing multiplexing strategies (Champer, Oh *et al.* 2020). Initial estimates show that 2–4 independent gRNAs are optimal for maximising the drive conversion efficiency, after which there is a trade-off between reducing functional resistance alleles (resistance alleles that retain biological gene function at their loci, giving them a fitness advantage) and reducing drive efficiency (Champer, Oh *et al.* 2020).

Another major concern is the dispersal of gene drive organisms (GDO) across ecological and political boundaries beyond the targeted geographic location (for example, into the native range of species where they are not considered invasive (Moro *et al.* 2018)). This is of particular concern with highly efficient homing gene drives (including CRISPR-Cas gene drives (Fig. 26.3B) that convert wild-type alleles to drive alleles in the germline, often resulting in

rapid invasion dynamics (Hammond *et al.* 2021). Reversal drives, which work by 'overwriting' the original gene drive (Esvelt *et al.* 2014; DiCarlo *et al.* 2015; Wu *et al.* 2016; Xu *et al.* 2020), have been proposed to stop a drive system in unforeseen circumstances. Other containment measures involve engineering modified versions of drive systems that are self-limiting, naturally confined through dispersal thresholds, or only capable of targeting a specific population with 'private alleles' (Boxes 26.3 and 26.4). Self-limiting systems can consist of components that reduce the inherent invasiveness of gene drives (usually by placing a critical drive component at an unlinked genomic site where it cannot increase in frequency), which may be useful in management scenarios where complete population modification or suppression is not desired. The primary mechanism underlying threshold dependency requires the drive allele to have an introduction frequency threshold, below which the drive would be actively removed from the population (Leftwich *et al.* 2018). Therefore, drive dispersal could theoretically be limited if low migration prevents the drive from exceeding its threshold in the new population. Private allele targeting involves sequences that are present only in the target population (or at least at sufficiently low frequencies in other populations, depending on the type of drive; Sudweeks *et al.* 2019).

The **Killer-Rescue (K-R)** drive consists of unlinked 'Killer' and 'Rescue' alleles (Webster *et al.* 2020). Offspring

---

Box 26.3: Self-limiting drive variants

The **daisy drive** is a powerful self-limiting system, which consists of serially dependent but unlinked genetic elements (Fig. 26.4) (Dhole *et al.* 2018; Noble *et al.* 2019). Constructs in the 'daisy chain' employ homing to drive the enhanced inheritance of the next element in the chain. However, the construct at the base of the chain follows patterns of normal Mendelian inheritance. Gradual erosion of the base construct due to fitness costs results in the sequential loss of dependent genetic elements in the chain over time, which may allow transient alteration of local wild populations without the threat of global spread.

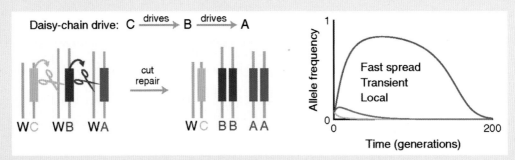

Fig. 26.4. Genomic constructs of a daisy chain system (left); and potential dynamics of these respective constructs in a population (right). These population dynamics are likely similar to other variations of self-limiting drive systems. Adapted from (Noble *et al.* 2019). Licensed under CC-BY-4.0: https://creativecommons.org/licenses/by/4.0/legalcode

Box 26.4: Geographic and population confinement

Intrinsically **confined drives** come in several varieties. One example is the Toxin-Antidote Recessive Embryo (TARE) drive, a type of CRISPR system that aims to disrupt a wildtype gene and generate recessive lethal 'toxic' alleles (Champer, Lee *et al.* 2020). Individuals carrying the TARE drive construct can 'rescue' essential gene function through the expression of a recoded version of the target gene, utilising the target gene's native promoter element. Successful in *Drosophila* (Champer, Lee *et al.* 2020), the system has potential application in other organisms where disrupted haplosufficient genes produce recessive lethal phenotypes. However, the TARE system itself is limited to population modification, rather than population suppression, and would require more difficult targeting of a haplolethal gene if population suppression is the goal (Champer, Kim *et al.* 2020). Several other examples of confined drives also exist such as RNAi-based toxin-antidote drives (Chen *et al.* 2007; Reeves *et al.* 2014) and species-specific incompatibilities (Maselko *et al.* 2020).

Table 26.1.   Summary of estimated benefits and challenges of implementing species-specific toxins, Trojan female technique and gene drives for vertebrate pest management.

Technology	Benefits	Challenges
Species-specific toxins	• Does not produce a genetically modified organism (GMO) • Relatively immediate effect on target population • Bait development and production timeline likely faster than TFT or gene drive	• Confirmation of species-specific activity (primary and secondary poisoning risk to species hard to verify) • mRNA stability in gastrointestinal (GI) tract and environmental exposure • GI uptake and delivery to site of action • Prevent immune response to foreign molecules in both target and non-target individuals • Bait avoidance behaviour resulting from sub-lethal bait sampling
Trojan female technique	• Non-GMO if mutation pre-exists and can be selectively bred into target species • Reproductively isolated effects (unless hybridisation occurs)	• Seeding individuals likely inbred (may require genetic engineering to increase genetic diversity among TFT carriers – requiring socio-political license) • Delayed effect on population (compared to toxin application) • Molecular and behavioural resistance
Gene drives	• Can be self-sustaining • Design flexibility for drive type, target, and level of confinement • Primary effects contained within target, reproductively connected species	• Requires release of genetically engineered organisms into a shared environment (requires socio-cultural license) • Delayed effect on population (compared to toxin application) • Molecular and behavioural resistance • Differences in international GMO regulation (migratory risk of self-perpetuating GMO organisms) • Potential for gene drive organisms to themselves become an invasive 'species' (see section 'Biological control')

lethality is observed where K alleles are inherited without R alleles. If the K allele is present at high frequency in a population, an artificial selection pressure is created, increasing the relative fitness of the R allele and any linked **cargo genes** in a push-pull dynamic. The K allele is expected to quickly be lost due to its high fitness cost unless the R allele fixates. The technique has been empirically successful in laboratory experiments with *Drosophila melanogaster*, where an initial 2:1 engineered to wild-type release ratio produced R allele frequencies exceeding 98% after 9 generations (Webster *et al.* 2020). The lethality of the K-R system can also be engineered to be dependent on environmental conditions (e.g. absence of tetracycline supplementation in feed; Webster *et al.* 2020), which provides a method to control lethality during the production of individuals for release.

Tethered drives aim to attain high levels of localised population suppression or modification with cargos that carry a high fitness cost (Dhole *et al.* 2019). These goals are difficult with threshold-dependent systems that are more sensitive to high fitness costs compared to strong homing-based drives. To overcome this, the tethered system consists of a homing construct (either a suppression drive or a drive with a costly cargo) that lacks Cas9 or another essential element of a gene drive and is therefore 'tethered' to a confined drive that provides the missing element.

Private alleles, genetic variants unique to a population, could be targeted to limit gene drive dispersal to the specific population where these alleles are found (Esvelt *et al.* 2014). However, it is likely this scenario would be restricted to isolated island populations, where genetic drift has acted on a small founding population, contributing to the fixation of particular alleles. Extending on the concept of private alleles, the locally fixed alleles (LFA) approach allows alleles to exist in other populations below thresholds of fixation (Sudweeks *et al.* 2019), limiting gene drive effects in adjacent non-target populations. The LFA approach has potential in island populations of mice that contribute to island biodiversity loss (Spatz *et al.* 2017) and demonstrate unique patterns of variation in female fertility genes compared with mainland populations (Oh *et al.* 2021).

Synthetic gene drives have so far been successful in laboratory populations of insects but have been more challenging to implement in mammals. The importance of controlling nuclease expression is also highlighted in the results from the first experiment to produce a substantial inheritance bias in mice (Grunwald *et al.* 2019). As a proof of concept, a coat-colour modifier (CMG) gene underwent germline conversion, resulting in up to 79% of eggs with the CMG on both chromosomes. This demonstrated that germline transmission had worked, albeit at a substantially lower efficiency than would be needed for an effective suppression drive. Further, although successful cleavage occurred in the male germline, HDR with the drive construct was not observed, indicating that further understanding and optimisation of germline conversion is required to maximise rodent gene drive transmission feasibility and efficiency in both sexes (Grunwald *et al.* 2019). Such fine-scale control will also mitigate cleavage outside the target meiotic window (i.e. maternally deposited Cas9) that is likely to produce undesirable modifications at the target and non-target sites (Chapman *et al.* 2017), compromising the fitness of gene drive carriers and ultimately preventing gene drive transmission (Beaghton *et al.* 2019; Oberhofer *et al.* 2019).

ADDRESSING ADDITIONAL BARRIERS TO RESEARCH AND DEVELOPMENT

In addition to the technical challenges associated with the development of the technology described previously (see section 'Pest management using genetic techniques'), there are also ecological, financial and socio-cultural considerations. These require varying levels of effort across research phases (Table 26.2).

Managing ecological outcomes

An important component of designing pest control systems targeting groups of species is determining the wider implications at an ecological level (Hayes *et al.* 2018). Interspecies relationships in multi-trophic invaded ecosystems already present a challenge for population management strategies that target single species as the potential for both competitive and predatory release of species runs the risk of producing a larger overall ecological impact (Tompkins and Veltman 2006; Ruscoe *et al.* 2011). For example, where species interactions occur between stoats, rats, mice and possums (Fig. 26.5), removing the rat population will likely result in increased stoat predation on native biodiversity as a result of reduced primary prey abundance (Tompkins and Veltman 2006).

These interaction effects are likely to be exacerbated by technology that can rapidly reduce a population, or target a single species (e.g. species-specific toxins, TFT and gene drives), particularly when applied to species with short generation times and high reproductive capacity. Laboratory and contained field trials, alongside multispecies modelling will be critical for predicting overall long-term population dynamics of the technology in each species (Hayes *et al.* 2018). Results will be valuable for exploring the feasibility of coordinating the management of multiple invasive

Table 26.2.   Summary of relative effort required for selected barriers in each phase of research and development.

Stakeholder engagement includes socio-cultural and political engagement. Number of stars indicate relative effort (1 = minimal relative effort; 5 = maximum relative effort). Progression through various phases of research and development for gene drive organisms is discussed by Hayes *et al.* (2018).

	Phase 1	Phase 2	Phase 3	Implementation
Successful outcome	Identification of promising technology with preliminary data in model species	Selected technology demonstrates functionality in laboratory tests using target species	Small-scale field trials using animals from the target population suggests functionality in wild populations with limited consequences	Management objectives (population control or eradication) are achieved
Financial cost and resource requirement	✷ ✷	✷ ✷ ✷	✷ ✷ ✷ ✷	✷ ✷ ✷ ✷ ✷
Stakeholder engagement	✷ ✷ ✷	✷ ✷ ✷	✷ ✷ ✷	✷ ✷ ✷
Technical challenges	✷ ✷ ✷ ✷	✷ ✷ ✷ ✷ ✷	✷ ✷ ✷	✷

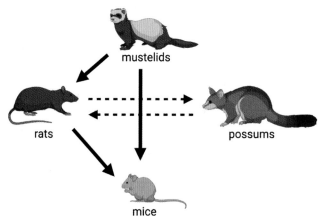

Fig. 26.5. Species interactions between mustelids (stoats and ferrets), rats, mice, and possums. Thick lines show predator-prey relationships; and dashed lines show competitive relationships for resources. Adapted from Tompkins and Veltman 2006 and created with BioRender.com.

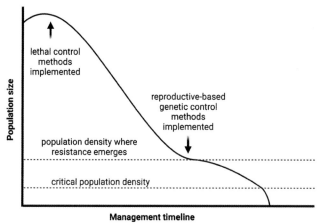

Fig. 26.6. Theoretical pest eradication scenario using a combination of technology. Improved variations of traditional technology (traps and toxins) and species-specific toxins are initially used to reduce target population size to a threshold where either 1) significant resistance to the technology emerges or; 2) genetic technology with limited dispersal capability could be implemented effectively. At this threshold, lethal control measures cease, and genetic technology like gene drives and Trojan female technique that target survival or fertility could be strategically used to reduce the remaining population, including those with evolved resistance to the initial traps and toxins. Widespread population sampling would allow monitoring of the dynamics of the technology, including dispersal rate and the emergence of genomic resistance. As the population declines to the critical population threshold, Allee effects and inbreeding depression are experienced, leading to the eradication of the target population.

species using safer and more effective variations of existing and new technology (Fig. 26.6). Additionally, genomic analysis of related, non-target species should also be conducted to investigate the potential for lateral transfer of intrinsic genetic technology (e.g. gene drives) via hybridisation events that may lead to the unintended suppression of non-target populations (Oye *et al.* 2014) or evolution of resistance (Box 26.2).

Traditional pest control methods still have a critical role to play in population suppression and eradication management plans, particularly where there is need for rapid implementation in settings where threats to non-target populations must be minimised, such as in high-density urban settings. As they are developed and implemented, species-specific toxins may join these traditional methods, but as with other traditional approaches will remain vulnerable to the evolution of behavioural and physiological resistance (see section 'Emerging challenges in pest management'). Genetic technologies like TFT and gene drives that leverage species reproductive behaviour may then be implemented to 'mop up' residual and resistant individuals – a similar recommendation given for the implementation of contraceptive techniques (Wimpenny *et al.* 2021). Implementing genetic control in smaller, genetically isolated populations may reduce the opportunity for both the evolution of resistance and migration to non-target populations. Additionally, genetic systems with lower invasion thresholds may be implemented more efficiently (see section 'Gene drive techniques'). As the population declines to the critical population density, **Allee effects** and inbreeding depression prevent further successful reproductive events in the target population and may accelerate population control and eradication efforts (O'Grady *et al.* 2006; Boukal and Berec 2009; Gemmell *et al.* 2013).

Financial cost and resource requirements

Research, development, and implementation of new pest control methods is dependent on commitment to large, long-term economic investment. The cost and resource requirements for laboratory trials, small-scale field trials, stakeholder engagement, data generation, analysis and storage (e.g. large population genomic datasets) are likely to increase as development progresses (Table 26.2). This is particularly true for non-model species that are not yet well genetically characterised and have a limited invasive geographical range. Additionally, species with a relatively low reproductive capacity and longer generation time (e.g. brushtail possums in NZ) will increase the relative research cost and resource requirements for genetic technology like gene drive and TFT approaches. Further, laboratory and small-scale field trials must be carefully designed to be representative of real-world impacts, considering differences in implementation and effects between captive laboratory populations and wild populations due to local behavioural adaptation or other indirect ecological effects (Tompkins and Veltman 2006; Russell *et al.* 2009; Mazza *et al.* 2020). For these reasons, it is important that funding agencies assess long-term priorities and develop institutional and public policy that provides long-term investment assurance to researchers and stakeholders to pursue building local and international capacity and capability. The high cost associated with the development of new technology also means it is imperative that research strikes a balance in conducting effective research while also being efficient. The development of long-term project plans with regular review points, and integrated processes that ensure they remain responsive to adopting promising new avenues of research and are aware of those that are exhausted, is critical to success.

Socio-cultural considerations

Successful research, development, and implementation of genetically engineered technology into a shared environment requires significant consideration from a multitude of social, cultural, economic, and legal dimensions (Dearden et al. 2018; Brossard et al. 2019; Kohl et al. 2019). The diversity of perspectives and interpretations held among stakeholders makes social engagement potentially the most challenging research component to navigate, and requires strong collaboration with social science, philosophy, politics and ethics researchers (Jones et al. 2019; MacDonald et al. 2020). Researchers need to be committed to co-development, considering the priorities, knowledge, and expectations of stakeholders, while maintaining a clear line of sight to what is practically feasible from a technical point of view (Long et al. 2020). Effective stakeholder engagement takes time and will change as the research progresses. For example, initial community co-development discussions may evolve to include community participation through population sample collection if the technology is to be implemented. Stakeholders are investors from the outset of a project, so it is important to respect this by opening a bi-directional dialogue early in the research trajectory, regularly discuss potential risks and benefits as research progresses, and seek repeated agreement when proposing a new research direction, or moving into a new phase of research or development (Taitingfong 2019; Jarvis et al. 2020).

Local communities and Indigenous peoples in the regions where the technology might be implemented are a critical stakeholder group. In the context of considering the possible application of genetically modified technologies and potentially even gene drives in New Zealand, cultural partnership is paramount owing to the unique political context that is outlined in Te Tiriti o Waitangi/The Treaty of Waitangi – a founding legal agreement between a number of Māori (Indigenous people of NZ) chiefs and representatives of the British Crown (Everett-Hincks and Henaghan 2019; Palmer et al. 2021). Genetic pest control technology is of particular interest to Māori as invasive species are a continuous threat to culturally significant biodiversity (Palmer et al. 2021) and the current use of toxins for control cause concern among some Māori (Warburton et al. 2021). Equally so, there are concerns with modifying the pattern of inheritance and releasing these modified lineages onto ancestral land, which is directly relevant to whakapapa (Māori concept of genealogy) (Hudson et al. 2019). Strong commitment to co-development, recognising Māori knowledge, needs and aspirations will empower Māori and research partners to safely research and develop new technology, while enhancing bicultural benefit (Rayne et al. 2020; Palmer et al. 2021).

National authorities and ethics committees will also be required to oversee proposed research to ensure that the appropriate regulatory processes are in place, for best practices and community rights (Carballar-Lejarazu and James 2017). As regulatory processes and policies are still developing, researchers should regularly present results and analyses to regulatory agencies to receive direction on risk evaluation (Long et al. 2020). There remains no international legal framework to regulate the development of self-perpetuating technology like gene drives (Esvelt and Gemmell 2017; Reynolds 2021). Researchers therefore need to exercise diligence, remain open to international expert advice on responsible science and hold each other accountable (Long et al. 2020). Despite the implementation of genetic technologies in vertebrate species beyond mice, rats and a few other species remaining a distant goal, their diverse complexity provides a novel opportunity to develop resilient and inclusive review, engagement, consultation, and accountability frameworks that will be useful in evaluating a diverse range of new biotechnology (Brossard et al. 2019; Hudson et al. 2019; Jones et al. 2019; Taitingfong 2019).

Considerations for new researchers and practitioners

There are several important considerations for researchers entering, and indeed continuing to conduct research in the field of genetic pest control. One of the key points is to consider where the investigated technology or method might be used. Different countries or regions may have significant variations in ecological, socio-cultural, and economic environments. Considering that genetic engineering remains a publicly controversial topic in some regions, it will likely also be politically charged. It is therefore strongly advisable to build multi-disciplinary teams, from both existing and new relationships, and seek out community representatives who understand the potential end-user environment. Regular advice and strong collaboration with experts in humanities, policy, and philosophy will also provide your teams with the latest understanding of progress and considerations on the socio-cultural landscape. This will be important to support effective communication and manage expectations with invested parties.

Research trends are known to go in cycles. For example, the Trojan female technique (TFT) gained attention in 2010. However, the idea relied on finding naturally occurring mutations because precision mitochondrial genome editing was unavailable (Teem *et al.* 2020). Unable to easily introduce or engineer the TFT method into vertebrate pest populations, attention and investment was diverted to the more promising gene editing technologies and species-specific toxins (Dearden *et al.* 2018). Recent advances in mitochondrial editing mean that developing the TFT method is once again a possibility (Mok *et al.* 2020). While no one wants to switch research directions too often, the TFT example illustrates the importance of researchers being strategic and ready to adapt as the research and technology evolves. As one research trajectory becomes limited, being decisive and moving to a new piece of research, while maintaining capacity and interest in the older idea in the interim may well enable future opportunities.

CONCLUSION

In an era of significant biodiversity crisis and global ecological change, widespread public engagement, investment, and research is urgently required to identify avenues that may yield new invasive species management tools. Here, we have reviewed concerns associated with current management tools and describe three genetic techniques that have potential for managing invasive species – species-specific toxins, Trojan female technique, and gene drives. We also highlight the emerging challenges that need to be addressed in the research and development phases, to prevent long-term issues, design complications, and unintended ecological consequences.

DISCUSSION TOPICS

1. What are some possible unintended consequences of releasing TFT or GDO that have been developed to suppress an invasive species population? (Hayes *et al.* 2018).

2. The development and use of various pest control technologies has several levels of consideration (e.g. development, delivery and maintenance costs; animal ethics; food security; international trade policies; socio-cultural licence; and human/environmental health (i.e. contamination or long-term ecological impact)). How would you prioritise these values in the development of new biotechnology (e.g. gene drives)? In what situation might the order of values change? (Long *et al.* 2020).

3. If you were to simulate TFT or gene drives in a contained laboratory environment, what factors might you need to manipulate to produce an environment that reflects a target wild population? (*Hints*: mortality by predation, disease, or starvation; habitat-dependent population density; genetic background; seasonal breeding; lifespan; mate selection; genetic drift) (Mazza *et al.* 2020; Feit *et al.* 2021).

4. Gene drives can be used for modification and suppression and have various degrees of efficiency, confinement, and self-limiting capacity. What sorts of gene drives might be most useful and acceptable in different realistic scenarios? Come up with a variety of different scenarios and propose for each why a particular type of gene drive is suitable for them (Bier 2021).

ACKNOWLEDGEMENTS

A.A. and A.C.C. are supported by Predator Free 2050 Ltd Capability Funding; A.C.C. is funded by a University of Otago writing bursary; N.J.G. is supported by the AgResearch Leading Thinkers Chair, the University of Otago, and funding from Predator Free 2050 Ltd and Genomics Aotearoa.

REFERENCES

Adams AL, Recio MR, Robertson BC, Dickinson KJ, Van Heezik Y (2014) Understanding home range behaviour and resource selection of invasive common brushtail possums (*Trichosurus vulpecula*) in urban environments. *Biological Invasions* **16**(9), 1791–1804. doi:10.1007/s10530-013-0627-4

Allen BL (2019) Para-aminopropiophenone (PAPP) in canid pest ejectors (CPEs) kills wild dogs and European red foxes quickly and humanely. *Environmental Science and Pollution Research* **26**(14), 14494–14501. doi:10.1007/S11356-019-04818-7

Allen ML (2021) Prospects for using RNAi as control for ants. *Frontiers in Agronomy* **3**, 20. doi:10.3389/FAGRO.2021.591539

Allsop SE, Dundas SJ, Adams PJ, Kreplins TL, Bateman PW, *et al.* (2017) Reduced efficacy of baiting programs for invasive species: some mechanisms and management implications. *Pacific Conservation Biology* **23**(3), 240–257. doi:10.1071/PC17006

Alphey L, Benedict M, Bellini R, Clark GG, Dame DA, *et al.* (2010) Sterile-insect methods for control of mosquito-borne diseases: an analysis. *Vector Borne and Zoonotic Diseases* **10**(3), 295–311. doi:10.1089/vbz.2009.0014

Alterio N, Moller H, Brown K (1999) Trappability and densities of stoats (*Mustela erminea*) and ship rats (*Rattus rattus*) in a South Island *Nothofagus* forest, New Zealand. *New Zealand Journal of Ecology* **23**(1), 95–100.

Anderson DP, McMurtrie P, Edge KA, Baxter PW, Byrom AE (2016) Inferential and forward projection modeling to evaluate options for controlling invasive mammals on islands. *Ecological Applications* **26**(8), 2546–2557.

Bale JS, Van Lenteren JC, Bigler F (2008) Biological control and sustainable food production. *Philosophical Transactions of the Royal Society B: Biological Sciences* **363**(1492), 761–776.

Barker GM, Addison PJ (2006) Early impact of endoparasitoid *Microctonus hyperodae* (Hymenoptera: Braconidae) after its establishment in *Listronotus bonariensis* (Coleoptera: Curculionidae) populations of northern New Zealand pastures. *Journal of Economic Entomology* **99**(2), 273–287.

Barlow ND (1994) Predicting the effect of a novel vertebrate bio-control agent: a model for viral-vectored immunocontraception of New Zealand possums. *Journal of Applied Ecology* **31**(3), 454–462. doi:10.2307/2404442

Barratt BIP, Ferguson CM, Bixley AS, Crook KE, Barton DM, *et al.* (2007) Field parasitism of nontarget weevil species (Coleoptera: Curculionidae) by the introduced biological control agent *Microctonus aethiopoides* Loan (Hymenoptera: Braconidae) over an altitude gradient. *Environmental Entomology* **36**(4), 826–839. doi:10.1093/ee/36.4.826

Barratt BIP, Moran VC, Bigler F, Van Lenteren JC (2018) The status of biological control and recommendations for improving uptake for the future. *BioControl* **63**(1), 155–167.

Barrett LG, Legros M, Kumaran N, Glassop D, Raghu S, *et al.* (2019) Gene drives in plants: opportunities and challenges for weed control and engineered resilience. *Proceedings of the Royal Society B* **286**(1911). doi:10.1098/RSPB.2019.1515

Barrett RDH, Schluter D (2008) Adaptation from standing genetic variation. *Trends in Ecology & Evolution* **23**(1), 38–44. doi:10.1016/J.TREE.2007.09.008

Beaghton AK, Hammond A, Nolan T, Crisanti A, Burt A (2019) Gene drive for population genetic control: non-functional resistance and parental effects. *Proceedings of the Royal Society B* **286**(1914), 20191586. doi:10.1098/rspb.2019.1586

Berry O, Algar D, Angus J, Hamilton N, Hilmer S, *et al.* (2012) Genetic tagging reveals a significant impact of poison baiting on an invasive species. *Journal of Wildlife Management* **76**(4), 729–739. doi:10.1002/jwmg.295

Beveridge AE, Daniel MJ (1966) A field trial of a new rat poison, compound S-6999, on brown rats. *Proceedings of the New Zealand Ecological Society* **13**(13), 40–43.

Bier E (2021) Gene drives gaining speed. *Nature Reviews Genetics* pp. 1–18. doi:10.1038/s41576-021-00386-0

Blackie HM, MacKay JW, Allen WJ, Smith DH, Barrett B, *et al.* (2014) Innovative developments for long-term mammalian pest control. *Pest Management Science* **70**(3), 345–351. doi:10.1002/ps.3627

Boukal DS, Berec L (2009) Modelling mate-finding Allee effects and populations dynamics, with applications in pest control. *Population Ecology* **51**(3), 445–458. doi:10.1007/S10144-009-0154-4/FIGURES/8

Boyle M, Hone J, Schwanz LE, Georges A (2014) Under what conditions do climate-driven sex ratios enhance versus diminish population persistence? *Ecology and Evolution* **4**(23), 4522. doi:10.1002/ECE3.1316

Brossard D, Belluck P, Gould F, Wirz CD (2019) Promises and perils of gene drives: Navigating the communication of complex, post-normal science. *Proceedings of the National Academy of Sciences* **116**(16), 7692–7697. doi:10.1073/pnas.1805874115

Caltagirone LE (1981) Landmark examples in classical biological control. *Annual Review of Entomology* **26**(1), 213–232. doi:10.1146/annurev.en.26.010181.001241

Campbell KJ, Beek J, Eason CT, Glen AS, Godwin J, *et al.* (2015) The next generation of rodent eradications: Innovative technologies and tools to improve species specificity and increase their feasibility on islands. *Biological Conservation* **185**, 47–58. doi:10.1016/j.biocon.2014.10.016

Carballar-Lejarazu R, James AA (2017) Population modification of Anopheline species to control malaria transmission. *Pathogens and Global Health* **111**(8), 424–435. doi:10.1080/20477724.2018.1427192

Carter A, Barr S, Bond C, Paske G, Peters D, *et al.* (2016) Controlling sympatric pest mammal populations in New Zealand with self-resetting, toxicant-free traps: A promising tool for invasive species management. *Biological Invasions* **18**(6), 1723–1736.

Champer J, Liu J, Oh SY, Reeves R, Luthra A, *et al.* (2018) Reducing resistance allele formation in CRISPR gene drive. *Proceedings of the National Academy of Sciences* **115**(21), 5522–5527. doi:10.1073/pnas.1720354115

Champer J, Lee E, Yang E, Liu C, Clark AG, *et al.* (2020) A toxin-antidote CRISPR gene drive system for regional population modification. *Nature Communications* **11**(1), 1082. doi:10.1038/s41467-020-14960-3

Champer J, Kim IK, Champer SE, Clark AG, Messer PW (2020) Performance analysis of novel toxin-antidote CRISPR gene drive systems. *BMC Biology* **18**(1), 1–17. doi:10.1186/S12915-020-0761-2

Champer SE, Oh SY, Liu C, Wen Z, Clark AG, *et al.* (2020) Computational and experimental performance of CRISPR homing gene drive strategies with multiplexed gRNAs. *Science Advances* **6**(10), eaaz0525. doi:10.1126/sciadv.aaz0525

Chapman JE, Gillum D, Kiani S (2017) Approaches to reduce CRISPR off-target effects for safer genome editing. *Applied Biosafety* **22**(1), 7–13. doi:10.1177/1535676017694148

Charlesworth D, Barton NH, Charlesworth B (2017) The sources of adaptive variation. *Proceedings. Biological Sciences* **284**(1855). doi:10.1098/RSPB.2016.2864

Chen C-H, Huang H, Ward CM, Su JT, Schaeffer LV, *et al.* (2007) A synthetic maternal-effect selfish genetic element drives population replacement in Drosophila. *Science* **316**(5824), 597–600. doi:10.1126/science.ll32067

Choi H, Conole D, Atkinson DJ, Laita O, Jay-Smith M, *et al.* (2016) Fatty acid-derived pro-toxicants of the rat selective toxicant norbormide. *Chemistry & Biodiversity* **13**(6), 762–775. doi:10.1002/cbdv.201500241

Cock MJW, Murphy ST, Kairo MT, Thompson E, Murphy RJ, *et al.* (2016) Trends in the classical biological control of insect pests by insects: an update of the BIOCAT database. *BioControl* **61**(4), 349–363. doi:10.1007/s10526-016-9726-3

Cooke BD (1983) Changes in the age-structure and size of populations of wild rabbits in South Australia, following the introduction of European rabbit fleas, *Spilopsyllus cuniculi* (Dale), as vectors of myxomatosis. *Australian Wildlife Research* **10**, 105–125.

Cooke BD, Fenner F (2002) Rabbit haemorrhagic disease and the biological control of wild rabbits, *Oryctolagus cuniculus*, in Australia and New Zealand. *Wildlife Research* **29**(6), 689–706. doi:10.1071/WR02010

Cooper DW, Larsen E (2006) Immunocontraception of mammalian wildlife: Ecological and immunogenetic issues. *Reproduction* **132**(6), 821–828. doi:10.1530/REP-06-0037

Cowan PE (1992) The eradication of introduced Australian brushtail possums, *Trichosurus vulpecula*, from Kapiti Island, a New Zealand nature reserve. *Biological Conservation* **61**(3), 217–226. doi:10.1016/0006-3207(92)91119-D

Cowan PE (1996) Possum biocontrol: prospects for fertility regulation. *Reproduction, Fertility and Development* **8**(4), 655–60.

Davies J, Davies D (2010) Origins and evolution of antibiotic resistance. *Microbiology and Molecular Biology Reviews* **74**(3), 417. doi:10.1128/MMBR.00016-10

Dearden PK, Gemmell NJ, Mercier OR, Lester PJ, Scott MJ, *et al.* (2018) The potential for the use of gene drives for pest control in New Zealand: a perspective. *Journal of the Royal Society of New Zealand* **48**(4), 225–244. doi:10.1080/03036758.2017.1385030

Dhole S, Vella MR, Lloyd AL, Gould F (2018) Invasion and migration of spatially self-limiting gene drives: A comparative analysis. *Evolutionary Applications* **11**(5), 794–808. doi:10.1111/eva.12583

Dhole S, Lloyd AL, Gould F (2019) Tethered homing gene drives: A new design for spatially restricted population replacement and suppression. *Evolutionary Applications* **12**(8), 1688–1702. doi:10.1111/eva.12827

DiCarlo JE, Chavez A, Dietz SL, Esvelt KM, Church GM (2015) Safeguarding CRISPR-Cas9 gene drives in yeast. *Nature Biotechnology* **33**(12), 1250–1255. doi:10.1038/nbt.3412

Duckworth JA, Buddle BM, Scobie S (1998) Fertility of brushtail possums (*Trichosurus vulpecula*) immunised against sperm. *Journal of Reproductive Immunology* **37**(2), 125–138. doi:10.1016/S0165-0378(97)00076-4

Eason C, Miller A, Ogilvie S, Fairweather A (2011) An updated review of the toxicology and ecotoxicology of sodium fluoroacetate (1080) in relation to its use as a pest control tool in New Zealand. *New Zealand Journal of Ecology* **35**, 1–20. doi:10.2307/24060627

Eason CT, Frampton CM, Henderson R, Thomas MD, Morgan DR (1993) Sodium monofluoroacetate and alternative toxins for possum control. *New Zealand Journal of Zoology* **20**(4), 329–334. doi:10.1080/03014223.1993.10420354

Eason CT, Murphy EC, Hix S, Macmorran DB (2010) Development of a new humane toxin for predator control in New Zealand. *Integrative Zoology* **5**(1), 31–36. doi:10.1111/j.1749-4877.2010.00183.x

Eason CT, Miller A, MacMorran DB, Murphy EC (2014) Toxicology and ecotoxicology of para-aminopropiophenone (PAPP) – a new predator control tool for stoats and feral cats in New Zealand. *New Zealand Journal of Ecology* **38**(2), 177–188.

Eason CT, Shapiro L, Ogilvie S, King C, Clout M (2017) Trends in the development of mammalian pest control technology in New Zealand. *New Zealand Journal of Zoology* **44**(4), 267–304. doi:10.1080/03014223.2017.1337645

Eason CT, Ross J, Miller A (2013) Secondary poisoning risks from 1080-poisoned carcasses and risk of trophic transfer-a review. *New Zealand Journal of Zoology* **40**(3), 217–225. doi:10.1080/03014223.2012.740488

Emami-Khoyi A, Parbhu SP, Ross JG, Murphy EC, Bothwell J, *et al.* (2020) De novo transcriptome assembly and annotation of liver and brain tissues of common brushtail possums (*Trichosurus vulpecula*) in New Zealand: Transcriptome diversity after decades of population control. *Genes* **11**(4), 436. doi:10.3390/GENES11040436

Esvelt KM, Smidler AL, Catteruccia F, Church GM (2014) Concerning RNA-guided gene drives for the alteration of wild populations. *eLife* **3**(1), e03401.

Esvelt KM, Gemmell NJ (2017) Conservation demands safe gene drive. *PLoS Biology* **15**(11), e2003850. doi:10.1371/journal.pbio.2003850

Everett-Hincks J, Henaghan M (2019) Gene editing in Aotearoa – legal considerations for policy makers. *Victoria University of Wellington Law Review* **50**(3), 515.

Fayrer-Hosken RA, Grobler D, Van Altena JJ, Bertschinger HJ, Kirkpatrick JF (2000) Immunocontraception of African elephants. *Nature* **407**(6801), 149–149. doi:10.1038/35025136

Feit B, Blüthgen N, Daouti E, Straub C, Traugott M, *et al.* (2021) Landscape complexity promotes resilience of biological pest control to climate change. *Proceedings of the Royal Society B* **288**(1951). doi:10.1098/RSPB.2021.0547

Fisher P, Campbell KJ, Howald GR, Warburton B (2019) Anticoagulant rodenticides, islands, and animal welfare accountancy. *Animals* **9**(11). doi:10.3390/ANI9110919

Franz G, Robinson AS (2011) Molecular technologies to improve the effectiveness of the sterile insect technique. *Genetica* **139**(1), 1–5. doi:10.1007/s10709-010-9543-z

Gemmell NJ, Jalilzadeh A, Didham RK, Soboleva T, Tompkins DM (2013) The Trojan female technique: a novel, effective and humane approach for pest population control. *Proceedings of the Royal Society B: Biological Sciences* **280**(1773), 20132549. doi:10.1098/rspb.2013.2549

Gerard PJ, Wilson DJ, Eden TM (2011) Field release, establishment and initial dispersal of Irish *Microtonus aethiopoides* in *Sitona lepidus* populations in northern New Zealand pastures. *BioControl* **56**(6), 861–870.

Goldson S, Bourdôt GW, Brockerhoff EG, Byrom AE, Clout MN, *et al.* (2015) New Zealand pest management: Current and future challenges. *Journal of the Royal Society of New Zealand* **45**(1), 31–58. doi:10.1080/03036758.2014.1000343

Gonçalves A, Kolokotronis SO, Wharton D (2010) Modeling the eradication of invasive mammals using the sterile male technique. *Biological Invasions* **12**(4), 751–759. doi:10.1007/s10530-009-9477-5

Green W, Rohan M (2012) Opposition to aerial 1080 poisoning for control of invasive mammals in New Zealand: Risk perceptions and agency responses. *Journal of the Royal Society of New Zealand* **42**(3), 185–213. doi:10.1080/03036758.2011.556130

Gronwald M, Russell JC (2021) Measuring rat relative abundance using camera traps and digital strike counters for Goodnature

A24 self-resetting traps. *New Zealand Journal of Ecology* **45**(1), 3430. doi:10.20417/nzjecol.45.7

Grunwald HA, Gantz VM, Poplawski G, Xu XR, Bier E, *et al.* (2019) Super-Mendelian inheritance mediated by CRISPR–Cas9 in the female mouse germline. *Nature* **566**(7742), 105–109. doi:10.1038/s41586-019-0875-2

Hajek AE, Hurley BP, Kenis M, Garnas JR, Bush SJ, *et al.* (2016) Exotic biological control agents: A solution or contribution to arthropod invasions? *Biological Invasions* **18**(4), 953–969.

Hammond A, Karlsson X, Morianou I, Kyrou K, Beaghton A, *et al.* (2021) Regulating the expression of gene drives is key to increasing their invasive potential and the mitigation of resistance. *PLOS Genetics* **17**(1), e1009321. doi:10.1371/JOURNAL.PGEN.1009321

Hammond AM, Kyrou K, Bruttini M, North A, Galizi R, *et al.* (2017) The creation and selection of mutations resistant to a gene drive over multiple generations in the malaria mosquito. *PLoS Genetics* **13**(10), e1007039. doi:10.1371/journal.pgen.1007039

Hardy CM, Hinds LA, Kerr PJ, Lloyd ML, Redwood AJ, *et al.* (2006) Biological control of vertebrate pests using virally vectored immunocontraception. *Journal of Reproductive Immunology* **71**(2), 102–111. doi:10.1016/j.jri.2006.04.006

Hartung T, Rovida C (2009) Chemical regulators have overreached. *Nature* **460**(7259), 1080–1081. doi:10.1038/4601080a

Hawkins NJ, Bass C, Dixon A, Neve P (2019) The evolutionary origins of pesticide resistance. *Biological Reviews* **94**(1), 135–155. doi:10.1111/BRV.12440

Hayes KR, Hosack GR, Dana GV, Foster SD, Ford JH, *et al.* (2018) Identifying and detecting potentially adverse ecological outcomes associated with the release of gene-drive modified organisms. *Journal of Responsible Innovation* **5**, S139–S158. doi:10.1080/23299460.2017.1415585

Heath G, Childs D, Docker MF, McCauley DW, Whyard S (2014) RNA interference technology to control pest sea lampreys – a proof-of-concept. *PLoS One* **9**(2), e88387. doi:10.1371/JOURNAL.PONE.0088387

Hemingway J, Ranson H (2003) Insecticide resistance in insect vectors of human disease. *Annual Review of Entomology* **45**, 371–391. doi:10.1146/ANNUREV.ENTO.45.1.371

Holman L (2019) Evolutionary simulations of Z-linked suppression gene drives. *Proceedings of the Royal Society B* **286**(1912). doi:10.1098/RSPB.2019.1070

Horak KE (2020) RNAi: Applications in vertebrate pest management. *Trends in Biotechnology* **38**(11), 1200–1202. doi:10.1016/J.TIBTECH.2020.05.001

Howarth FG (1991) Environmental impacts of classical biological control. *Annual Review of Entomology* **36**(1), 485–509. doi:10.1146/annurev.en.36.010191.002413

Hudson M, Mead AT, Chagné D, Roskruge N, Morrison S, *et al.* (2019) Indigenous perspectives and gene editing in Aotearoa New Zealand. *Frontiers in Bioengineering and Biotechnology* **7**, 70. doi:10.3389/fbioe.2019.00070

Innes J, Kelly D, Overton JM, Gillies C (2010) Predation and other factors currently limiting New Zealand forest birds. *New Zealand Journal of Ecology* **34**(1), 86–114.

Ishizuka M, Tanikawa T, Tanaka KD, Heewon M, Okajima F, *et al.* (2008) Pesticide resistance in wild mammals – Mechanisms of anticoagulant resistance in wild rodents. *The Journal of Toxicological Sciences* **33**(3), 283–291. doi:10.2131/JTS.33.283

Jarvis RM, Borrelle SB, Forsdick NJ, Pérez-Hämmerle KV, Dubois NS, *et al.* (2020) Navigating spaces between conservation research and practice: Are we making progress? *Ecological Solutions and Evidence* **1**(2), e12028. doi:10.1002/2688-8319.12028

Johnston M, Algar D, O'Donoghue M, Morris J, Buckmaster T, *et al.* (2020) Efficacy and welfare assessment of an encapsulated para-aminopropiophenone (PAPP) formulation as a bait-delivered toxicant for feral cats (*Felis catus*). *Wildlife Research* **47**(8), 686. doi:10.1071/WR19171

Jolly SE (1993) Biological control of possums. *New Zealand Journal of Zoology* **204**(20), 335–339. doi:10.1080/03014223.1993.10420355

Jones MS, Delborne JA, Elsensohn J, Mitchell PD, Brown ZS (2019) Does the U.S. public support using gene drives in agriculture? And what do they want to know? *Science Advances* **5**(9), eaau8462.

King CM, Edgar RL (1977) Techniques for trapping and tracking stoats (*Mustela erminea*); a review, and a new system. *New Zealand Journal of Zoology* **4**(2), 193–212.

Kohl PA, Brossard D, Scheufele DA, Xenos MA (2019) Public views about gene editing wildlife for conservation. *Conservation Biology* **33**(6), 1286–1295. doi:10.1111/cobi.13310

Kyrou K, Hammond AM, Galizi R, Kranjc N, Burt A, *et al.* (2018) A CRISPR–Cas9 gene drive targeting doublesex causes complete population suppression in caged *Anopheles gambiae* mosquitoes. *Nature Biotechnology* **36**(11), 1062–1066. doi:10.1038/nbt.4245

Latham ADM, Latham MC, Cieraad E, Tompkins DM, Warburton B (2015) Climate change turns up the heat on vertebrate pest control. *Biological Invasions* **17**(10), 2821–2829. doi:10.1007/s10530-015-0931-2

Latham ADM, Warburton B, Byrom AE, Pech RP (2017) The ecology and management of mammal invasions in forests. *Biological Invasions* **19**(11), 3121–3139.

Leftwich PT, Edgington MP, Harvey-Samuel T, Carabajal Paladino LZ, Norman VC, *et al.* (2018) Recent advances in threshold-dependent gene drives for mosquitoes. *Biochemical Society Transactions*. Portland Press Ltd, 1203–1212. doi:10.1042/BST20180076

Leung K, Ras E, Ferguson KB, Ariëns S, Babendreier D, *et al.* (2020) Next-generation biological control: The need for integrating genetics and genomics. *Biological Reviews* **95**(6), 1838–1854. doi:10.1111/brv.12641

Littin K, Mellor DJ, Warburton B, Eason CT (2004) Animal welfare and ethical issues relevant to the humane control of vertebrate pests. *New Zealand Veterinary Journal* **52**(1), 1–10. doi:10.1080/00480169.2004.36384

Llewelyn J, Schwarzkopf L, Phillips BL, Shine R (2014) After the crash: How do predators adjust following the invasion of a novel toxic prey type? *Austral Ecology* **39**(2), 190–197. doi:10.1111/AEC.12058

Long KC, Alphey L, Annas GJ, Bloss CS, Campbell KJ, *et al.* (2020) Core commitments for field trials of gene drive organisms. *Science* **370**(6523), 1417 LP–1419. doi:10.1126/science.abd1908

Ma X, Hopkins B, Gao X, Feng Z, Wang D (2019) Specific toxicity in six rodent species from China of a new modified norbormide. *New Zealand Journal of Zoology* **46**(4), 275–284. doi:10.1080/03014223.2018.1540996

MacDonald EA, Balanovic J, Edwards ED, Abrahamse W, Frame B, *et al.* (2020) Public opinion towards gene drive as a pest control approach for biodiversity conservation and the association of underlying worldviews. *Environmental Communication* **14**(7), 904–918. doi:10.1080/17524032.2019.1702568

Magris M, Wignall AE, Herberstein ME (2015) The sterile male technique: irradiation negatively affects male fertility but not male courtship. *Journal of Insect Physiology* **75**, 85–90. doi:10.1016/J.JINSPHYS.2015.02.014

Maselko M, Feltman N, Upadhyay A, Hayward A, Das S, *et al.* (2020) Engineering multiple species-like genetic incompatibilities in insects. *Nature Communications* **11**(1), 1–7. doi:10.1038/s41467-020-18348-1

Mazza V, Dammhahn M, Lösche E, Eccard JA (2020) Small mammals in the big city: Behavioural adjustments of non-commensal rodents to urban environments. *Global Change Biology* **26**(11), 6326–6337. doi:10.1111/gcb.15304

McFarlane GR, Whitelaw CBA, Lillico SG (2018) CRISPR-based gene drives for pest control. *Trends in Biotechnology* **36**(2), 130–133. doi:10.1016/j.tibtech.2017.10.001

McGee CF, McGilloway DA, Buckle AP (2020) Anticoagulant rodenticides and resistance development in rodent pest species – A comprehensive review. *Journal of Stored Products Research* **88**, 101688. doi:10.1016/J.JSPR.2020.101688

Meenken D, Booth LH (1997) The risk to dogs of poisoning from sodium monofluoroacetate (1080) residues in possum (*Trichosurus vulpecula*). *New Zealand Journal of Agricultural Research* **40**(4), 573–576. doi:10.1080/00288233.1997.9513280

Messer PW, Petrov DA (2013) Population genomics of rapid adaptation by soft selective sweeps. *Trends in Ecology & Evolution* **28**(11), 659–669. doi:10.1016/J.TREE.2013.08.003

Messing RH, Wright MG (2006) Biological control of invasive species: solution or pollution? *Frontiers in Ecology and the Environment* **4**(3), 132–140.

Miller LA, Johns BE, Killian GJ (2000) Immunocontraception of white-tailed deer using native and recombinant zona pellucida vaccines. *Animal Reproduction Science* **63**(3–4), 187–195. doi:10.1016/S0378-4320(00)00177-9

Min J, Smidler AL, Najjar D, Esvelt KM (2018) Harnessing gene drive. *Journal of Responsible Innovation* **5**(sup1), S40–S65. doi:10.1080/23299460.2017.1415586

Mok BY, de Moraes MH, Zeng J, Bosch DE, Kotrys AV, *et al.* (2020) A bacterial cytidine deaminase toxin enables CRISPR-free mitochondrial base editing. *Nature* **583**(7817), 631–637. doi:10.1038/s41586-020-2477-4

Moro D, Byrne M, Kennedy M, Campbell S, Tizard M (2018) Identifying knowledge gaps for gene drive research to control invasive animal species: the next CRISPR step. *Global Ecology and Conservation* **13**, e00363. doi:10.1016/j.gecco.2017.e00363

Nakada K, Sato A, Yoshida K, Morita T, Tanaka H, *et al.* (2006) Mitochondria-related male infertility. *Proceedings of the National Academy of Sciences of the United States of America* **103**(41), 15148–15153. doi:10.1073/pnas.0604641103

Noble C, Min J, Olejarz J, Buchthal J, Chavez A, *et al.* (2019) Daisy-chain gene drives for the alteration of local populations. *Proceedings of the National Academy of Sciences* **116**(17), 8275–8282. doi:10.1073/pnas.1716358116

O'Grady JJ, Brook BW, Reed DH, Ballou JD, Tonkyn DW, *et al.* (2006) Realistic levels of inbreeding depression strongly affect extinction risk in wild populations. *Biological Conservation* **133**(1), 42–51. doi:10.1016/J.BIOCON.2006.05.016

Oberhofer G, Ivy T, Hay BA (2019) Cleave and Rescue, a novel selfish genetic element and general strategy for gene drive. *Proceedings of the National Academy of Sciences* **116**(13), 6250–6259. doi:10.1073/PNAS.1816928116

Ogilvie SC, Thomas MD, Morriss GA, Morgan DR, Eason CT (2010) Investigation of sodium monofluoroacetate (1080) bait shyness in wild brushtail possum (*Trichosurus vulpecula*) populations. *International Journal of Pest Management* **46**(1), 77–80. doi:10.1080/096708700227615

Oh KP, Shiels AB, Shiels L, Blondel DV, Campbell KJ, *et al.* (2021) Population genomics of invasive rodents on islands: Genetic consequences of colonization and prospects for localized synthetic gene drive. *Evolutionary Applications* **14**, 1421–1435. doi:10.1111/eva.13210

Oye KA, Esvelt K, Appleton E, Catteruccia F, Church G, *et al.* (2014) Biotechnology. Regulating gene drives. *Science* **345**(6197), 626–628. doi:10.1126/science.1254287

Palmer S, Dearden PK, Mercier OR, King-Hunt A, Lester PJ (2021) Gene drive and RNAi technologies: A bio-cultural review of next-generation tools for pest wasp management in New Zealand. *Journal of the Royal Society of New Zealand* **52**, 508–525. doi:10.1080/03036758.2021.1985531

Paul D, Sanap G, Shenoy S, Kalyane D, Kalia K, *et al.* (2021) Artificial intelligence in drug discovery and development. *Drug Discovery Today* **26**(1), 80. doi:10.1016/J.DRUDIS.2020.10.010

Pejchar L, Mooney HA (2009) Invasive species, ecosystem services and human well-being. *Trends in Ecology & Evolution* **24**(9), 497–504. doi:10.1016/J.TREE.2009.03.016

Pérez Santín, E, Rodríguez Solana R, González García M, García Suárez MD, Blanco Díaz GD, *et al.* (2021) Toxicity prediction based on artificial intelligence: A multidisciplinary overview. *Wiley Interdisciplinary Reviews: Computational Molecular Science* **11**(5), e1516. doi:10.1002/WCMS.1516

Polkinghorne I, Hamerli D, Cowan P, Duckworth J (2005) Plant-based immunocontraceptive control of wildlife – 'potentials, limitations, and possums'. *Vaccine* **23**(15), 1847–1850. doi:10.1016/J.VACCINE.2004.11.016

Preston CR, Flores CC, Engels WR (2006) Differential usage of alternative pathways of double-strand break repair in *Drosophila*. *Genetics* **172**(2), 1055–1068. doi:10.1534/genetics.105.050138

Price TAR, Windbichler N, Unckless RL, Sutter A, Runge JN, *et al.* (2020) Resistance to natural and synthetic gene drive systems. *Journal of Evolutionary Biology* **33**(10), 1345–1360. doi:10.1111/JEB.13693

Prowse TAA, Adikusuma F, Cassey P, Thomas P, Ross JV (2019) A Y-chromosome shredding gene drive for controlling pest vertebrate populations. *eLife* **8**, e41873. doi:10.7554/eLife.41873

Rayne A, Byrnes G, Collier-Robinson L, Hollows J, McIntosh A, *et al.* (2020) Centring Indigenous knowledge systems to re-imagine conservation translocations. *People and Nature* **2**(3), 512–526. doi:10.1002/PAN3.10126

Reeves RG, Bryk J, Altrock PM, Denton JA, Reed FA (2014) First steps towards underdominant genetic transformation of insect populations. *PLoS One* **9**(5), e97557. doi:10.1371/JOURNAL.PONE.0097557

Rennison D, Laita O, Conole D, Jay-Smith M, Knauf J, *et al.* (2013) Prodrugs of N-dicarboximide derivatives of the rat selective toxicant norbormide. *Bioorganic & Medicinal Chemistry* **21**(18), 5886–5899. doi:10.1016/J.BMC.2013.06.071

Reynolds JL (2021) Engineering biological diversity: The international governance of synthetic biology, gene drives, and de-extinction for conservation. *Current Opinion in Environmental Sustainability* **49**, 1–6. doi:10.1016/J.COSUST.2020.10.001

Rost S, Pelz HJ, Menzel S, MacNicoll AD, León V, *et al.* (2009) Novel mutations in the VKORC1 gene of wild rats and mice – a response to 50 years of selection pressure by warfarin? *BMC Genetics* **10**(1), 1–9. doi:10.1186/1471-2156-10-4

Roszkowski AP, Nause BR, Michael EH, Jacobs L (1965) The pharmacological properties of norbormide, a selective rat toxicant. *Journal of Pharmacology and Experimental Therapeutics* **149**(2), 288–299.

Ruscoe WA, Ramsey DS, Pech RP, Sweetapple PJ, Yockney I, *et al.* (2011) Unexpected consequences of control: Competitive vs. predator release in a four-species assemblage of invasive mammals. *Ecology Letters* **14**(10), 1035–1042. doi:10.1111/J.1461-0248.2011.01673.X

Russell JC, Beaven BM, MacKay JW, Towns DR, Clout MN (2008) Testing island biosecurity systems for invasive rats. *Wildlife Research* **35**(3), 215–221. doi:10.1071/WR07032

Russell JC, Lecomte V, Dumont Y, Le Corre M (2009) Intraguild predation and mesopredator release effect on long-lived prey. *Ecological Modelling* **220**(8), 1098–1104. doi:10.1016/j.ecolmodel.2009.01.017

Russell JC, Broome KG (2016) Fifty years of rodent eradications in New Zealand: Another decade of advances. *New Zealand Journal of Ecology* **40**(2), 197–204.

Scott MJ, Concha C, Welch JB, Phillips PL, Skoda SR (2017) Review of research advances in the screwworm eradication program over the past 25 years. *Entomologia Experimentalis et Applicata* **164**(3), 226–236. doi:10.1111/eea.12607

Shanmuganathan T, Pallister J, Doody S, McCallum H, Robinson T, *et al.* (2010) Biological control of the cane toad in Australia: A review. *Animal Conservation* **13**(s1), 16–23. doi:10.1111/j.1469-1795.2009.00319.x

Soares AO, Borges I, Borges PA, Labrie G, Lucas E (2007) *Harmonia axyridis*: What will stop the invader? *BioControl* **53**(1), 127–145. doi:10.1007/S10526-007-9141-X

Song Y, Endepols S, Klemann N, Richter D, Matuschka FR, *et al.* (2011) Adaptive introgression of anticoagulant rodent poison resistance by hybridization between old world mice. *Current Biology* **21**(15), 1296–1301. doi:10.1016/J.CUB.2011.06.043

Spatz DR, Zilliacus KM, Holmes ND, Butchart SH, Genovesi P, *et al.* (2017) Globally threatened vertebrates on islands with invasive species. *Science Advances* **3**(10), e1603080. doi:10.1126/sciadv.1603080

Sudweeks J, Hollingsworth B, Blondel DV, Campbell KJ, Dhole S, *et al.* (2019) Locally fixed alleles: A method to localize gene drive to island populations. *Scientific Reports* **9**(1), 1–10. doi:10.1038/s41598-019-51994-0

Taitingfong RI (2019) Islands as laboratories: Indigenous knowledge and gene drives in the Pacific. *Human Biology* **91**(3), 179. doi:10.13110/humanbiology.91.3.01

Teem JL, Alphey L, Descamps S, Edgington MP, Edwards O, *et al.* (2020) Genetic biocontrol for invasive species. *Frontiers in Bioengineering and Biotechnology* **8**, 452. doi:10.3389/fbioe.2020.00452

Tomasetto F, Tylianakis JM, Reale M, Wratten S, Goldson SL (2017) Intensified agriculture favors evolved resistance to biological control. *Proceedings of the National Academy of Sciences* **114**(15), 3885–3890.

Tompkins DM, Byrom AE, Pech RP (2013) Predicted responses of invasive mammal communities to climate-related changes in mast frequency in forest ecosystems. *Ecological Applications* **23**(5), 1075–1085. doi:10.1890/12-0915.1

Tompkins DM, Veltman CJ (2006) Unexpected consequences of vertebrate pest control: predictions from a four-species community model. *Ecological Applications : A Publication of the Ecological Society of America* **16**(3), 1050–61.

Towns DR, West CJ, Broome KG (2012) Purposes, outcomes and challenges of eradicating invasive mammals from New Zealand islands: An historical perspective. *Wildlife Research* **40**(2), 94–107. doi:10.1071/WR12064

Turner A, Kirkpatrick JF (2002) Effects of immunocontraception on population, longevity and body condition in wild mares (*Equus caballus*). *Reproduction (Cambridge, England) Supplement* **60**, 187–195.

Twigg LE, Martin GR, Lowe TJ (2002) Evidence of pesticide resistance in medium-sized mammalian pests: A case study with 1080 poison and Australian rabbits. *Journal of Applied Ecology* **39**, 549–560.

Tyndale-Biscoe C (1994) Virus-vectored immunocontraception of feral mammals. *Reproduction, Fertility and Development* **6**(3), 281–287. doi:10.1071/RD9940281

Ujvari B, Oakwood M, Madsen T (2013) Queensland northern quolls are not immune to cane toad toxin. *Wildlife Research* **40**(3), 228–231. doi:10.1071/WR13011

Unckless RL, Clark AG, Messer PW (2017) Evolution of resistance against CRISPR/Cas9 gene drive. *Genetics* **205**(2), 827–841. doi:10.1534/genetics.116.197285

van Eeden LM, Dickman CR, Ritchie EG, Newsome TM (2017) Shifting public values and what they mean for increasing democracy in wildlife management decisions. *Biodiversity and Conservation* **26**(11), 2759–2763. doi:10.1007/S10531-017-1378-9

Van Lenteren JC, Drost YC, Van Roermund HJ, Posthuma-Doodeman CJ (1997) Aphelinid parasitoids as sustainable biological control agents in greenhouses. *Journal of Applied Entomology* **121**(1–5), 473–485.

Warburton B, Eason C, Fisher P, Hancox N, Hopkins B, *et al.* (2021) Alternatives for mammal pest control in New Zealand in the context of concerns about 1080 toxicant (sodium fluoroacetate). *New Zealand Journal of Zoology* **49**, 79–121. doi:10.1080/03014223.2021.1977345

Warburton B, Cowan P, Shepherd J (2009) *How many possums are now in New Zealand following control and how many would there be without it?* Landcare Research Contract Report LC0910.

Landcare Research, Lincoln, New Zealand. doi:10.7931/rz39-d050

Warburton B, Gormley AM (2015) Optimising the application of multiple-capture traps for invasive species management using spatial simulation. *PLoS one*. Edited by D.A. Lightfoot, **10**(3), e0120373. doi:10.1371/journal.pone.0120373

Webster JP, Brunton CFA, Macdonald DW (1994) Effect of *Toxoplasma gondii* upon neophobic behaviour in wild brown rats, *Rattus norvegicus*. *Parasitology* **109**(1), 37–43. doi:10.1017/S003118200007774X

Webster SH, Vella MR, Scott MJ (2020) Development and testing of a novel killer–rescue self-limiting gene drive system in *Drosophila melanogaster*. *Proceedings of the Royal Society B* **287**(1925). doi:10.1098/RSPB.2019.2994

Wilkinson R, Fitzgerald G (2006) *Public Attitudes Toward Possum Fertility Control and Genetic Engineering in New Zealand*. Manaaki Whenua Press, New Zealand.

Wimpenny C, Hinds LA, Herbert CA, Wilson M, Coulson G (2021) Fertility control for managing macropods – Current approaches and future prospects. *Ecological Management & Restoration* **22**(S1), 147–156. doi:10.1111/EMR.12461

Wolff JN, Tompkins DM, Gemmell NJ, Dowling DK *et al.* (2016) Mitonuclear interactions, mtDNA-mediated thermal plasticity, and implications for the Trojan Female Technique for pest control. *Scientific Reports* **6**(1), 1–7. doi:10.1038/srep30016

Wolff JN, Gemmell NJ, Tompkins DM, Dowling DK (2017) Introduction of a male-harming mitochondrial haplotype via 'Trojan Females' achieves population suppression in fruit flies. *eLife* 6. doi:10.7554/eLife.23551

Wright J (2017) *Annual Report on the aerial use of 1080*. Environmental Protection Authority, New Zealand.

Wu B, Luo L, Gao XJ (2016) Cas9-triggered chain ablation of cas9 as a gene drive brake. *Nature Biotechnology* **34**(2), 137–138. doi:10.1038/nbt.3444

Xu XRS, Bulger EA, Gantz VM, Klanseck C, Heimler SR, *et al.* (2020) Active genetic neutralizing elements for halting or deleting gene drives. *Molecular Cell* **80**(2), 246–262.e4. doi:10.1016/J.MOLCEL.2020.09.003

Yan Y, Finnigan GC (2018) Development of a multi-locus CRISPR gene drive system in budding yeast. *Scientific Reports* **8**(1), 17277. doi:10.1038/s41598-018-34909-3

27 Perspective – The 'E' in RD&E and the application of genomics for environmental and biosecurity risk management

Geoff Grossel, Australian Government Department of Agriculture, Fisheries & Forestry, Canberra, Australia

The application of genomics for environmental and biosecurity risk management offers sensitive, efficient, and accurate detection, diagnostic, surveillance, and monitoring capability. The Australian Government has made significant investments in genomics research ranging from blue-sky through to contracted research meeting end-user specifications. In some instances, this has resulted in immediate benefits to environmental and biosecurity management, but not always. Here, I want to provide my personal perspective on what are the ingredients of a successful research partnership. It is an imprecise science, but my aim is to encourage emerging applied researchers to realise that to make a difference (i.e. create impact), their work must not only be great science, but it should be built on clear understandings of the needs of end-users. The most effective way to achieve this is through collegiate collaboration throughout the 'Research, Development and Extension' (RD&E) process, or what I like to call the 'Research to Market Pathway'.

The biggest challenge to achieving impact and a return-on-investment is not a lack of innovation or quality research, but rather that there is not enough emphasis on the 'E' in RD&E process. While it is by no means expected that all research should or could result in an end-to-end business solution, in my opinion the return-on-investment in the environment and biosecurity sectors is often lower than it is in big money disciplines such as human genomics and medicine. Why is it so, and how can we remedy it?

The key to success for a researcher is simple: get involved with the funder and end-user from the very beginning of the proposal and design stage. Most research funders conduct RD&E *in-series* (i.e. as separate projects one after the other), this can have the effect of creating a perception of an us and them situation that effectively keeps funders and end-users at arm's length from researchers. Researchers are typically encouraged to focus on publications, but these may have a different focus to the needs of government and industry involved in applying the science to specific problems. Bridging the gap between the knowledge presented in academic literature and the needs of end users requires an extra effort. Successful applied researchers achieve results for their clients by engaging in 1) a collaborative, collegiate relationship; 2) a client-focused design process; and 3) a shared vision with your funder/end-user team. This means R, D, & E is operating *in-parallel* (i.e. at the same time) instead of *in-series*.

Whenever I think about new emerging innovations and promising genomics research projects, I immediately start thinking of the bigger application picture. What follows is a brief list of considerations for running RD&E *in-parallel*:

- *Knowing research priorities and business needs*: Have early and ongoing conversations with a variety of people throughout the ecosystem in which your research may have an application. When working *in-parallel* across the RD&E pathway the folks you need to talk to may be outside of your research domain. Many will be found inside funding entities, sitting on government committees, and on the boards of public or privately owned related industries. Approach them for open ended conversations about their work and the challenges they face. Don't focus too much on your own research interests, engage, ask questions, and listen. Seek recommendations for others who you might talk to. In time, and with enough conversations, themes will emerge that you can use to inform your research planning. You will be surprised at how happy people are to talk about their work and what are the blockers to them achieving maximum success. Many leaders in research seem to have similar traits; they are happy to talk, they build their networks, and they collaborate. So, don't be afraid to go straight to leading experts. As a by-product you will have created a network of colleagues to whom you can return in the future for advice and *vice-versa*.

- *What can research deliver?* In biosecurity, there are many technologies focused on the question of detection, including image capture and analysis, X-ray, robots, drones, diagnostics, gas sensors, sniffer dogs, etc. Genomics has many properties that make it an attractive investment. For example, it can be more sensitive, specific, accurate, rapid, cheaper, determine provenance and be complementary to other competing technologies. But caution is required! We tend to gravitate toward the latest shiny gadget. This presents a huge business risk when promising long-term investments are abandoned in search of the next big thing. You need to apply due diligence and be honest with yourself and your funders about what your research approach can reasonably deliver and how well it meets needs. Over-promising will be personally unsatisfying for you and reduce the chances you will be funded in the future. Knowing the commercial maturity of the technology and your strategic partner/s is one of the most fundamental considerations for mitigating business risk that is often overlooked. Bespoke genomics technology doesn't scale very well and has few of the service and support networks required for the extension and application to the needs of industry and government. A business intelligence analysis and an estimate of your return-on-investment are key factors to include in early discussions with end users.

- *Implementation and operationalisation*, aka the 'E' in RD&E: This is the business-end of the process for the

application of genomics. Academic researchers generally have limited business analyst and project management skills, so becoming an applied researcher involves working closely (*in-parallel*) with end-users and clients. I'm not saying we should all rush out and do an MBA, but basic project management skills and some entrepreneurial passion can go a long way and at a minimum allow all team members to be able to communicate in the same language.

- *Public/private partnerships – strength in collaboration*: Business partnership planning was once considered an unnecessary skill for scientists, but for applied scientists it is necessary. On the job upskilling on legal, intellectual property, contracts and other partnering arrangements isn't pretty or much fun but is now a highly sought-after skill. I can't stress enough the importance of diverse, collaborative, collegiate win-win partnerships between research and private/public stakeholders for *in-parallel* RD&E programs.

- *Data and analytics solutions*: IT solutions that are accessible, secure, integrated, and scalable are critical and essential for the successful application of genomics research. Genomics researchers maintaining skill sets in bioinformatics and diversifying to other IT systems that enable applications of genomics is important. Skill development in app development, QR code implementation, image capture systems and laboratory reporting and management systems enhance genomic and bioinformatic skill sets enormously. Understanding the IT solutions environment and early *in-parallel* engagement with IT development stakeholders are central to client-focused design process.

- *Strategic forecasting*: Keep up with the rapid pace of innovation and change in genomics. Are we reviewing and continually improving? Are we reviewing and appropriately investing in the newest shiny technology? Are we reviewing and factoring in redundancy of legacy systems? Are you staying at the cutting edge in your field? Are you upskilling your project and financial management capabilities? Are you expanding and cultivating your collegiate networks?

Research is only part of the RD&E journey when it comes to the application of genomics research. If you aspire to be an applied scientist, you need to be involved with the bigger picture, collaborate with all stakeholders, be collegiate, be entrepreneurial, less isolated, and *think big*.

Glossary

A20: Tumor necrosis factor α-induced protein 3.

ABBA-BABA: Test to detect deviation from a strictly bifurcating evolutionary history, often interpreted as a test for introgression; also called D-statistics.

Adaptive genetic variation: Genes, loci or genomic regions that are under natural selection and have a direct effect on fitness. Used to identify local adaptations and assess evolutionary potential and adaptive capacity.

Additive genetic variation: The proportion of the genetic variation in a population that responds to natural selection.

Allee effect: Density dependent changes to population growth rate or individual fitness that result from low population density. Examples include inability to find a mate, or reduced protection from predation when not in a group.

Alpha diversity: The biological diversity found at a local level, or in a single sample. Generally, the smallest unit of measured diversity in hierarchical systems for biological sampling.

Ancestry tract: Haplotype composed of genetic variants originating from the same lineage. Introgressed tracts refer to ancestry tracts originating from a foreign lineage.

Ancient DNA (aDNA): A term commonly used to refer to DNA extracted from any specimen that is not fresh, contemporary, or stored for the express purpose of DNA analysis. Often this refers to subfossil material, but increasingly includes museum and herbarium specimens.

Aneuploidy: A chromosomal condition resulting from either an excess or deficit of a chromosome or chromosomes so that the chromosome number is not an exact multiple of the typical haploid set in the species.

Animal midden: Piles of excrement that animals periodically return to and build up. Often used as a territorial marker. Rodent middens can also include edible plants, insects and vertebrate remains, as well as sticks and pebbles, cemented together by urine which hardens and preserves the midden as a paleontological record.

Anthropocene: The proposed current epoch defined by human impact on global ecosystems.

Artificial Intelligence: Capability of a computer to mimic cognitive functions, such as learning and problem solving, to learn from big-data, and make decisions.

Ascertainment bias: Genetic markers ascertained within a specific spatial range or period of time may present a bias if used outside the original spatial range or time because the markers are subject to various demographic and evolutionary processes which may result in different allele frequencies across space.

ASV (Amplified Sequence Variant): A sequence variant found in the pool of sequenced PCR amplified in eDNA studies.

Barcode: A region of DNA with low to no *intra*specific variation but with enough *inter*specific variation to distinguish species (i.e. variation that is unique between species). These regions are often flanked by highly conserved regions.

Baseline: A fixed point of reference that is used for the purpose of comparison; in ecology, this typically refers to a specific time point in the past (usually prior to a disturbance event).

Beta diversity: The extent of taxonomic compositional change between communities.

Beta (β) value: The proportion of CpG sites in DNA from a given tissue that are methylated, ranging from 0 for completely unmethylated to 1, completely methylated.

Biological age: The spectrum of biological states between the earliest stage of life and death. Various measures of this have been proposed, which are of interest when a specified measure of biological age does not consistently correspond with chronological age.

BLAST (Biological Local Alignment Search Tool): A program for searching nucleic acid databases for sequence similarity with a query sequence.

Capture-mark-recapture (CMR): Models are widely used to estimate animal population size. A sample of animals is collected and marked so that when they are sampled again, the ratio of previously marked to unmarked animals can be calculated and used to estimate detection success and population size.

Cargo genes: Genes that are linked to **selfish genetic elements**.

Cas9: CRISPR associated protein 9.

Chromatin: Complex formed by the DNA molecule and histone proteins to pack the DNA in eukaryotic cells. The basic structural unit of the chromatin is the nucleosome which consists of 147 nucleotides of DNA wrapped around a multiprotein core made up of two copies of each of the four histones: H2A H2B, H3, and H4.

Chromatin accessibility: The degree of physical compaction of the chromatin and its accessibility to macromolecules in the nucleus. Epigenetic marks such as histones and DNA methylation can physically change the accessibility of the chromatin, affecting which genes are transcribed.

Chronogram: A phylogenetic tree where branch lengths represent the amount of time since divergence.

Chronological age: Time elapsed since a defined moment in early life, generally birth or hatching in vertebrates.

Clock CpGs/clock-type sites: CpG sites that consistently become hypermethylated or hypomethylated with age. Also called aDMPs (age-related DNA methylation positions).

Cloning: A molecular technique where fragments of DNA are recombined into a vector and introduced into a microorganism such as bacteria, where it is replicated by the host's cellular machinery as the bacteria reproduces. When plated out, individual populations of bacteria contain a unique recombinant molecule. In this way, different fragments of DNA could be partitioned out of a mixture for Sanger sequencing. Prior to NGS, this was a necessary step in shotgun sequencing.

Close-kin mark-recapture (CKMR): An analytical method used to estimate demographic parameters such as abundance and dispersal distance, based on the identification of related individuals (kin) within a population sample. Kin are typically identified through molecular analysis.

Coalescent: The point at which the ancestry of two alleles converges (coalesces) at a common ancestral sequence in the past.

Cohort: Group of individuals that share a common birth year or other time unit.

Connectance: The number of observed interactions out of all possible interactions between interacting species. Plant-pollinator networks tend to have low connectance values, suggesting that there are more specialist species than commonly thought, which may indicate a higher number of species at risk of extinction.

Coprolite: Fossilised faeces.

CpG island: A region of CpG sites generally found around the promoter and first exon of vertebrate genes with a much higher density of CpGs than the genomic average.

CpG site: A cytosine-phosphate-guanosine site is a 5′CG 3′ DNA sequence. The CpG term distinguishes this sequence along one strand (and its antiparallel reverse complement) from a CG base pair across strands.

CRISPR: Clustered regularly interspaced short palindromic repeats. Prokaryotic DNA derived from bacteriophages used in anti-viral immune response that has been adapted for gene editing technology.

Crossover event: The exchange of genetic material between two homologous chromosomes during meiosis.

Deep learning: A subset of machine learning and artificial intelligence, in which multilayered neural networks learn from large data volumes, without requiring feature extraction.

De-extinction: The concept of resurrecting an extinct species, artificially producing a likeness of an extinct species, or restoring lost genetic diversity through genetic intervention including cloning, gene-editing or selective breeding.

Demultiplexing: The bioinformatic process of dividing the results of HTS output files into smaller files based on their sequence characteristics. The identifying sequences are most often index sequences artificially added to different subsets of the library to associate them with a particular sample, population, etc.

Denoising: Identification and removal of nucleotide variants that are erroneous in DNA sequencing data. Denoising methods have to balance the identification of true errors with the retention of true sequence variants.

Derived allele: An allele that is not the ancestral allele that was present in the common ancestor of two species.

DNA barcode: A specific DNA sequence used to identify a species.

DNA methylation: The addition of a methyl group to a DNA molecule.

Effective population size (N_e): The size of the theoretically ideal population that would experience the same amount of genetic drift as the observed population.

Elastic net regression: A linear algorithm that can determine the minimum number of predictors required to determine an outcome. Highly suited to datasets with a high number of predictors and low sample size.

Endemism: A measure of species diversity measuring the geographic restriction of the taxa in a region. A taxon is endemic if it is restricted to an area.

epiGBS: Genotyping by sequencing with bisulfite treatment.

Epigenetic clock: A combination of specific CpG sites, where levels of DNA methylation in a tissue are measured to estimate the biological age of members of a species.

Epigenetic imprinting: Epigenetic modification of the DNA in a parent-of-origin-dependent manner that leads to the activation/expression of one copy of the gene and the repression/silencing of the other copy.

Epigenetic memory: Ability to retain epigenetic alterations in the absence of the signal that generated them. When epigenetic alterations are passed to progeny this transgenerational inheritance provides a 'memory' of the environment of previous generations.

Epigenetic reprogramming: Genome-wide erasure and remodelling of epigenetic modifications during germline differentiation.

Epigenome: The entire suite of epigenetic molecules found in one cell type and physiological state, or the aggregation of cell epigenomes as an individual's epigenome. The epigenome is frequently erroneously used to mean the 'methylome' which is the DNA methylation sub-component of the epigenome.

Evolutionarily significant unit (ESU): A reciprocally monophyletic group of organisms considered distinct for the purposes of conservation. This means that all individuals within the evolutionary significant unit have a common ancestor that is not shared by individuals outside the group. An evolutionary significant unit may be a species, or a group below the species level such a race, subspecies or genetic lineage.

Evolutionary distinctiveness: A measure of how evolutionarily unique a taxon is, calculated using a phylogeny.

Evolutionary rescue: A process in which declining populations avoid extinction through genetic adaptations that improve fitness and increase population growth.

False-negative: In eDNA metabarcoding, a false-negative refers to the non-detection (through PCR or sequencing) of a taxon, despite its existence in the DNA template. This can arise from primer biases or a complete primer mismatch, laboratory processing issues, insufficient sequencing depth, an obscured DNA signal and contamination.

False-positive: In eDNA metabarcoding, a false-positive refers to the PCR or sequencing detection of a taxon that does not exist on the DNA template. This can arise from PCR and/or sequencing error, and contamination.

Fitness: Comparative ability for organisms to survive and reproduce and thus contribute to the subsequent generation.

Forward primer: A PCR primer with a sequence that is the same as part of the sense target sequence, which binds to the anti-sense strand.

Functional diversity: A metric using the range of species traits present in a region to measure the variety of species' niches and functions in the region's biodiversity.

Gametes: Specialised reproductive cells that carry half on an individual's genetic material.

Gamma diversity: The overall biological diversity found in a landscape, or in a biological survey of an area. Generally the highest level of measured diversity in a hierarchical system for studying biodiversity.

GBIF: Global Biodiversity Information Facility.

Genetic drift: Random changes in allele frequencies in a population between generations due to random sampling individuals that become parents and binomial sampling of alleles during meiosis.

Genetic rescue: Conservation management or natural processes that increase the fitness of a small population suffering from inbreeding depression by encouraging gene flow or hybridisation with another population or subspecies to restore genetic diversity.

Genome: The complete genetic information of an organism, encoded as DNA. The genome includes genes, i.e. DNA that encodes proteins, as well as non-coding DNA.

Genome assembly: The process of reconstructing a genome from a number of DNA sequences.

Genomic erosion: A process in which the limited population size, and therefore gene pool, of a threatened species leads to loss of genetic diversity, which can lower a species' ability to adapt to changing environments, and increase the number of expressed harmful recessive genes, further reducing the species survival prospects.

Genomic vulnerability: The magnitude of genomic change (shift in allele frequency) a population will need to undergo to track modelled changes in genotype-environment associations under future climate change scenarios.

Haplotype: The combination of alleles at loci that are found in close proximity on a single chromosome, or organelle genome.

Hardy–Weinberg equilibrium (HWE): In an ideal population at HWE (i.e. a population of infinite population size and not under the influence of any evolutionary force such as genetic drift, gene flow, mutation, natural or sexual selection), allele and genotype frequencies are constant over generations and thus predictable. HWE is the classical benchmark in population genetics, which is particularly interested in explaining deviations from this equilibrium.

Heterogamety: Sex chromosome complement contains one of each chromosome (i.e. XY and ZW).

Heterozygosity: Having different alleles (forms) at a particular genetic sequence (locus).

High-throughput sequencing (HTS): A generic term to describe any nucleic acid sequencing platform that determines the sequence of pools of DNA sequences at one time.

Homing: Germline process used by selfish genetic elements (e.g. engineered gene drives) to copy their sequence onto chromosomes that do not contain them.

Homogametic: Sex chromosome complement contains two of the same chromosomes (i.e. XX and ZZ).

Homozygosity: Having identical alleles (forms) of a particular genetic sequence.

Homozygous mutation load: The decrease in fitness caused by homozygosity of recessive or partially recessive deleterious alleles.

Hypermethylation: Relative increase in proportion of methylated CpGs at a site, region or over a whole genome.

Hypomethylation: Relative decrease in proportion of methylated CpGs at a site, region or over a whole genome.

Identical by descent (IBD): Regions of the genome that are copies of the same region derived from a common ancestor.

Identity-by-descent tract: A continuous segment over which two haplotypes are identical by descent.

Inbreeding depression: The relative reduction in fitness of progeny from matings between related individuals compared with progeny from unrelated individuals.

Inbreeding load: The reduction in fitness of inbred individuals compared to noninbred individuals.

Invasive species: Organisms that spread and maintain themselves independent of human assistance following introduction to a new environment beyond their native ecological range.

Isothermal amplification: A single temperature process used to amplify a nucleic acid (e.g. LAMP).

Keystone species: A species that plays such an important role that the survival of other species, and thus the stability of an ecosystem, relies on its survival.

K-mer: A short nucleotide sequence of k bases.

Life history: The pattern of survival and reproduction, along with the traits that directly affect survival and the timing or amount of reproduction.

Lineage: A single line of descent within a phylogenetic tree. This can be a clade such as a family or genus, but is also commonly used to represent a line of descent below the species level.

Linkage disequilibrium (LD): The nonrandom association of alleles at different loci within a population resulting from loci being on the same chromosome. Loci are said to be in linkage disequilibrium when the frequency of association of their different alleles is higher or lower than what would be expected if the loci were associated randomly.

Longitudinal (age) **study:** Research that follows individuals through time.

Loss of function (LOF) mutation: A mutation in a protein coding sequence that destroys the function of the protein. Such large effect mutations are almost always recessive, and therefore they affect the phenotype only when homozygous.

Machine learning: A subset of artificial intelligence that uses a series of algorithms to analyse large volumes of data, identify subtle patterns, and make informed decisions based on those patterns. Performance improves with exposure to more data over time.

Mb: One million base pairs.

Metabarcoding: The use of a specific gene sequences to identify multiple taxa within a complex environmental sample (e.g. eDNA).

Methylome: All of the DNA methylation information contained in one organism or cell. This is analogous to a 'genome' but the methylome varies among cell types and with physiological state. This means that the total methylome of an individual is an aggregate of all the cell methylomes in the animal that themselves change with time, cellular identity and cell physiology.

Microsatellite: A series of two or more repeating nucleotides in a section of a genome. The number of repeating nucleotides varies among individuals and are used as a genetic marker.

Minor allele frequency: The population frequency of the second most common allele at a SNP locus.

Missense mutations: A mutation in which a nucleotide change results in a codon that codes for a different amino acid. It is a type of non-synonymous substitution.

Modularity: Modules are well-connected groups of species that have a significantly higher number of within-group connections than to species in other groups. The degree of modularity in a network can reflect factors such as habitat partitioning and selection pressure. For example, plant-pollinator networks with more than 150 species tend exhibit high levels of modularity.

Mutation load: The decrease in fitness caused by the accumulation of deleterious alleles introduced by mutation.

Nestedness: The degree in which a module is interacting within a larger module. Networks with high degrees of nestedness have been found to be more robust to disturbance.

Neutral genetic variation: Genes, loci or genomic regions that have no (or very limited) effect on fitness and are therefore selectively neutral. Used to study population structure, gene flow, dispersal, demographic history, inbreeding and relatedness.

Next generation sequencing (NGS): The first name given to high-throughput parallel sequencing systems (HTS), originally used to market 454 pyrosequencing technology. This term is often used interchangeably with HTS.

Non-recombining region: The region on a sex chromosome that does not undergo genetic crossover during meiosis.

Organelle: A cellular substructure including the mitochondria and the chloroplast (in plants). Organelles generally have their own, small circular genome and are present in high copy numbers within cells, in contrast to the nuclear genome which has two copies per cell in diploids, is typically larger, and composed of linear chromosomes.

OTU (operational taxonomic unit): A group of similar sequences that are used as a proxy for a species or higher-level taxonomic unit. In general, the sequences are approximately as similar to each other as clusters of sequences found in a DNA metabarcode in one species, but other taxonomic levels can be used.

Outbreeding depression: The reduction in fitness of hybrids compared with the parental types.

Palaeognath: A comparatively small clade sister to all other living birds (neognaths) that contains extant and extinct flightless ratites (ostriches, rheas, moa, emus, cassowaries, elephant birds, and kiwis), as well as the volant South American tinamous.

Pangenome: The collection of the entire genomic variation within a species. A pangenome is built from collective whole-genome sequences of multiple individuals.

Pedigree inbreeding coefficient (F_p): The expected increase in homozygosity of inbred individuals relative to the founders of the pedigree based upon pedigree analysis. F_p is also the expected decrease in heterozygosity throughout the genome of inbred individuals.

Phased genome: A genome sequence in which the haplotypes are identified as being on either the maternal or paternal chromosomes.

Phenotype: An organism's observable traits, the product of the environment, gene expression, and an interaction between the two.

Phred quality scores: A measure of the probability that a nucleotide has been accurately determined in a DNA sequence. The score is on a logarithmic scale with a score of 10 indicating a 1 in 10 chance that the base has been called incorrectly, a score of 30 indicating a 1 in 1000 chance, 40 indicating 1 in 10 000, etc.

Phylogenetic: The study of evolutionary relationships among taxa.

Phylogenetic diversity (PD): A metric combining phylogenetic and distribution data to measure the amount of the tree of life,

as represented by branch lengths, that is represented in a region's biodiversity.

Phylogenetic endemism (PE): A metric combining phylogenetic diversity and endemism to measure the amount of geographically restricted evolutionary diversity in a region.

Phylogram: A phylogenetic tree where branch length represents the amount of molecular substitutions or character changes since divergence.

Polymerase chain reaction (PCR): a molecular technique used to make copies of targeted regions of DNA.

Prebiotic: A biological substrate that provides nutrition that preferentially supports one or more microbial species.

Primer biases: During the annealing step of a PCR (45–65°C), primers will form hydrogen bonds with single-stranded template DNA. The most stable hydrogen bonds, which endure a temperature increase in the next 'extension' step, are formed when the primer matches the target sequence perfectly. Fragments with template-primer mismatches can still form hydrogen bonds and endure the extension step (depending on the number of mismatches and the location); however, they are typically amplified at a lower rate than template/primers with strong hydrogen bonds. The existence of mismatches can therefore induce preferential PCR amplification, i.e. 'primer bias', which affects downstream sequencing depth and abundance metrics.

Probability of identity: The statistical power of a set of genetic markers' ability to correctly identify individuals from a pool of samples.

Probiotic: Microorganisms that are added to a biological community to alter its composition.

Reciprocally monophyletic: A monophyletic group of organisms includes all descendants of a recent common ancestor. When two monophyletic sister clades no longer admix, they are reciprocally monophyletic.

Reduced-representation genome sequencing: A suite of approaches that sequence restriction enzyme digested DNA in order to provide genome-wide information associated with restriction cleavage sites (e.g. Genotyping-by-Sequencing, GBS; Restriction Site Associated DNA sequencing, RAD-seq; Diversity Arrays Technology sequencing, DArT-seq).

Reference genome: A DNA sequence database for a species which is assembled from the genome sequence of one or more individuals. DNA sequences from other individuals are often aligned to a reference genomes in order to compare the genetic composition of individuals, populations, and species.

Refugium (plural: refugia): An area where a population or taxa can survive during unfavourable conditions in the surrounding region.

Reverse primer: A PCR primer with a sequence that is in the same sense as the antisense strand of the target DNA sequence, and binds to the sense strand during the PCR.

RNA: Ribonucleic acid; a single stranded nucleic acid that is less stable than DNA and contains the base uracil (U) instead of thymine (T). Messenger RNA (mRNA) is transcribed from DNA by cellular machinery, and is then translated into protein. RNA is the main constituent of ribosomes (rRNA; translate mRNA to protein), and transfer RNAs (tRNA; carry amino acids, the building blocks of proteins).

RNAseq: Ribonucleic acid (RNA) Sequencing.

Runs of homozygosity (ROH): Genomic regions where an individual has DNA sequences on homologous chromosomes that are IBD because of inbreeding. F_{ROH} is the observed increase in homozygosity of individuals over their entire genome based upon summing ROH regions.

Sanger sequencing: A method for sequencing DNA by synthesis and resolution of multiple fragments that each end in a dideoxy-terminated base corresponding to a base in the template sequence.

SCR: Spatial capture-recapture refers to a subset of the capture-recapture models that explicitly include space, by incorporating where animals were detected, directly in the analysis.

Selfish genetic elements: Genetic sequences that bias their transmission.

Semelparous: Breeds once then dies.

Sequencing depth: The number of sequence reads that are obtained for an HTS library. This correlates with degree to which the diversity in a sequencing library is analysed.

Sequencing library: The pool of DNA fragments that is prepared for HTS analysis.

Sex chromosomes: Inherited chromosome pair that determines sex by the action of the sex determining gene or genes that they contain.

Sex determination: The process by which the bipotential gonads are directed to develop as either testes or ovaries.

Sex differentiation: The process by which the bipotential gonads morphological change to become either testes or ovaries.

Sex identification: Classifying an individual as male or female, either on the basis of their sexual phenotype or the sex chromosome complement.

Single nucleotide polymorphism (SNP): A nucleotide site (base pair) in a DNA sequence that is polymorphic in a population and can be used as a marker to assess genetic variation within and among populations.

Species distribution models: Correlative or mechanistic (process-based) approaches used to predict the distribution of species or suitable habitat across geographic space and time based on their associations with environmental conditions. Also known as ecological niche, bioclimatic, climate-envelope or habitat suitability models.

Substitution: A type of mutation in which one nucleotide is replaced by a different nucleotide.

Synbiotics: A combination of probiotics and prebiotics.

Taxonomic resolution: The ability to distinguish closely related taxa based on a chosen barcode. Taxonomic resolution is dependent on the mutational rate of the chosen barcode for the taxonomic group you are interested in.

Thiatic: Kin relationship between niece/nephew and aunt/uncle.

True breeding value: Actual phenotypic value (derived from the sum of the contribution of each allele to that phenotypic trait, i.e. additive genetic variance) of the progeny generated by a given progenitor measured as a deviation of the progeny from the average phenotypic value of a reference population.

Unlinked markers: Markers that are inherited independently either because they are on different chromosomes or because they far apart on the same chromosome.

Vicariance: The geographical separation of a population into two new populations, typically by a physical barrier such as a mountain range, river, or continental shifts.

Voucher specimen: A sample permanently archived in a publicly accessible biorepository that allows for future verification, replication, or extension of a scientific experiment.

Whole genome sequencing (WGS): An approach using high-throughput sequencing to determine the (nearly) complete DNA sequence of the genome of an organism.

Whole transcriptome sequencing: An approach using high-throughput sequencing to determine the sequence of all RNA transcripts (transcriptome) and quantify the amount of RNA in the sample. Also known as RNA sequencing (RNAseq).

Index